MW00574524

STATISTICS

A TOOL FOR THE SOCIAL SCIENCES

STATISTICS

A TOOL FOR THE SOCIAL SCIENCES

R. LYMAN OTT
Marion Merrell Dow

CYNTHIA REXROAT
Memphis State University

RICHARD LARSON
Clemson University

WILLIAM MENDENHALL
University of Florida

Duxbury Press
An Imprint of Wadsworth Publishing Company
Belmont, California

Duxbury Press
An Imprint of Wadsworth Publishing Company
A division of Wadsworth, Inc.

Assistant Editor: Marcia Cole
Production Editor: Chris Crochetière
Manufacturing Coordinator: Marcia Locke
Interior/Cover Designer: Chris Crochetière
Typesetter: APS
Printer/Binder: Arcata Graphics/Halliday
Cover Printer: Henry N. Sawyer Co., Inc.
Cover image from an original acrylic and pastel painting, "Acanthus" (1986),
by Sharon Shepherd

✪ This book is printed on recycled, acid-free paper.

Printed in the United States of America.

5 6 7 8 9 — 96

Library of Congress Cataloging-in-Publication Data

Statistics : a tool for the social sciences / Lyman Ott... #et al.].
  p.   cm.
  Rev. ed. of: Statistics / Lyman Ott. 4th ed. c1987.
  Includes index.
  ISBN 0-534-92931-1
  1. Social sciences—Statistical methods. 2. Statistics. I. Ott,
Lyman. II. Ott, Lyman. Statistics.
HA29.086   1991
519.5′.243—dc20
                                              91-18113
                                              CIP

CONTENTS

CHAPTER 1   **WHAT IS STATISTICS?   1**

1.1   Introduction   2
1.2   Why Study Statistics?   2
1.3   Research in the Social Sciences   3
1.4   How Do Social Researchers Use Statistics?   5
1.5   Descriptive and Inferential Statistics   6
1.6   Introduction to Calculators and Computers   12
1.7   Calculators   12
1.8   Computers and Statistical Software   13
1.9   A Note to the Student   14
        Summary   15
        Key Words   15
        Supplementary Exercises for Chapter 1   16

CHAPTER 2   **MEASUREMENT   18**

2.1   Introduction   19
2.2   Constants and Variables   19
2.3   Scales of Measurement for Qualitative and Quantitative Variables   23
2.4   Examples of Social Data   28
2.5   Comparisons of Variables Employing Ratios, Proportions, Percentages, and Rates   31
2.6   Are the Measurements Rounded?   39
2.7   Validity and Reliability   42
        Summary   44
        Key Words   45
        Key Formulas   46
        Supplementary Exercises for Chapter 2   46

GRAPHICAL TECHNIQUES FOR DESCRIBING DATA
CHAPTER 3 FROM A SINGLE VARIABLE 50

3.1 Introduction 51
3.2 Organizing Qualitative Data 52
3.3 Graphing Categorical Data: The Pie Chart 54
3.4 Graphing Qualitative Data: The Bar Graph 57
3.5 Graphing Qualitative Data: The Statistical Map (Optional) 59
3.6 Organizing Quantitative Data 65
3.7 Graphing Quantitative Data: The Histogram 71
3.8 Comments About Histograms 76
3.9 Displaying Quantitative Data: The Stem-and-Leaf Plot (Optional) 80
3.10 Graphing Quantitative Data: The Frequency Polygon (Optional) 83
3.11 Cumulative Relation Frequency Polygons (Optional) 85
3.12 Different Shapes of Frequency Polygons (Optional) 87
3.13 Additional Graphing Techniques: The Time Trend (Optional) 88
3.14 Graphical Distortions 92
Summary 95
Key Words 96
Supplementary Exercises for Chapter 3 97

NUMERICAL TECHNIQUES FOR DESCRIBING DATA
CHAPTER 4 FROM A SINGLE SAMPLE 108

4.1 Introduction 109
4.2 A Measure of Central Tendency: The Mode 110
4.3 A Measure of Central Tendency: The Median 113
4.4 A Measure of Central Tendency: The Mean 117
4.5 Coding to Determine $\bar{X}$ for Grouped Data (Optional) 123
4.6 A Measure of Location: Percentile Ranks 126
4.7 Data Variation 129
4.8 A Measure of Variability for Qualitative Data: The Index of Qualitative Variation (Optional) 130
4.9 A Measure of Variability for Quantitative Data: The Range 133
4.10 A Measure of Variability for Quantitative Data: The Variance 136
4.11 Coding to Determine s for Grouped Data (Optional) 143
4.12 How to Guess the Standard Deviation of Sample Data 146
4.13 The Box Plot 148
Summary 154
Key Words 155
Key Formulas 156
Supplementary Exercises for Chapter 4 156

CHAPTER 5
PROBABILITY, INFERENCES, AND SAMPLING DISTRIBUTIONS IN THE SOCIAL SCIENCES 166

handwritten: Z-scores & Probability → Type I error

5.1   Introduction   167
5.2   What Is Probability?   168
5.3   Finding the Probability of an Outcome   170
5.4   Variables: Discrete and Continuous   171
5.5   Probability Distributions for Discrete Variables   172
5.6   A Useful Discrete Variable: The Binomial   175
5.7   Probability Distributions for Continuous Variables   185
5.8   A Useful Continuous Variable: The Normal Probability Distribution   188
5.9   Tabulated Areas Under the Normal Curve   189
5.10 Normal Approximation to the Binomial   197
5.11 Random Sampling   201
5.12 The Sampling Distribution for $\bar{X}$ 204
      Summary   208
      Key Words   209
      Key Formulas   210
      Supplementary Exercises for Chapter 5   210

CHAPTER 6
CONCEPTS OF ESTIMATION: THE ONE-SAMPLE CASE 216

handwritten: Estimating pop mean w/ an interval (1 sample)

6.1   Introduction   217
6.2   Estimation of a Population Mean   219
6.3   Estimation of the Binomial Parameter p 228
6.4   Choosing the Sample Size for Estimating a Population Mean or Proportion   231
      Summary   235
      Key Words   236
      Key Formulas   236
      Supplementary Exercises for Chapter 6   237

CHAPTER 7
STATISTICAL TESTS OF HYPOTHESES: THE ONE-SAMPLE CASE 240

handwritten: Sig Tests (1 sample)

handwritten: Comparing our mean w/ some hypothetical mean

7.1   Introduction   241
7.2   A Statistical Test of a Hypothesis   241
7.3   How Good Is Our Decision?   245
7.4   A Statistical Test About a Population Mean   247
7.5   How to Select the Research and Null Hypotheses   254

7.6 z-Scores and the Choice of α 256
7.7   A Statistical Test About a Binomial Parameter   259
7.8   Level of Significance of a Statistical Test   263
7.9   Small-Sample Test for a Population Mean   266
7.10   One-Sample Goodness-of-Fit Test: The Chi-Square Test   274
       Summary   281
       Key Words   283
       Key Formulas   284
       Supplementary Exercises for Chapter 7   284

→ Always a 2-tailed   → 1/2 tailed

ESTIMATION AND STATISTICAL TESTS
CHAPTER 8   OF TWO SAMPLES   289

8.1   Introduction   290
8.2   The Sampling Distribution of the Difference Between Two Sample
       Statistics   291
8.3   Comparison of Two Population Means: Large-Sample Results   295
8.4   Comparison of Two Population Means: Small-Sample Results   302
8.5   Another Two-Sample Test: The Mann-Whitney U-Test   309
8.6   Comparison of Two Binomial Parameters   315
8.7   The Paired t-Test   321
       Summary   325
       Key Words   326
       Key Formulas   326
       Supplementary Exercises for Chapter 8   328

CHAPTER 9   CROSS-CLASSIFICATION OF DATA   336

9.1   Introduction   337
9.2   Cross-Classification Data: Percentage Comparisons   337
9.3   The Chi-Square Test of Independence   346
9.4   Fisher's Exact Test   358
9.5   The McNemar Test   362
       Summary   364
       Key Words   365
       Key Formulas   366
       Supplementary Exercises for Chapter 9   366

CHAPTER 10   **MEASURES OF ASSOCIATION: NOMINAL AND ORDINAL DATA   374**

10.1   Introduction   375
10.2   Nominal Measures of Association: The Contingency Coefficient and Cramer's V 375
10.3   Proportional Reduction in Error for Measures of Association   380
10.4   A PRE Nominal Measure of Association: Lambda   385
10.5   A PRE Ordinal Measure of Association: Gamma   389
10.6   Another PRE Ordinal Measure of Association: Spearman's Rho   400
10.7   Measure of Association for a 2×2 Table: Yule's Q 405
        Summary   411
        Key Words   411
        Key Formulas   412
        Supplementary Exercises for Chapter 10   413

CHAPTER 11   **CONTINGENCY ANALYSIS: MULTIVARIATE EXTENSIONS   419**

11.1   Introduction   420
11.2   Controlling for the Effect of a Third Variable with Only Two Categories   420
11.3   Replication   424
11.4   Spuriousness   426
11.5   Interpretation   429
11.6   Specification (Interaction)   434
11.7   Controlling for the Effect of a Third Variable for Nominal Variables with Three or More Categories   439
11.8   Controlling for the Effect of a Third Variable for Variables Measured on an Ordinal Scale   448
        Summary   454
        Key Words   454
        Key Formulas   455
        Supplementary Exercises for Chapter 11   455

CHAPTER 12   **BIVARIATE REGRESSION AND CORRELATION   463**

12.1   Introduction   464
12.2   The Scatter Diagram   464
12.3   Method of Least Squares   470
12.4   The Coefficient of Determination r^2 475

12.5   The Pearson Product-Moment Correlation Coefficient r 479
12.6   A Test of Significance for r 484
12.7   Interpretations of r 487
12.8   Some Assumptions Underlying Bivariate Regression and Correlation   489
       Summary   494
       Key Words   495
       Key Formulas   496
       Supplementary Exercises for Chapter 12   497

CHAPTER 13   # REGRESSION AND CORRELATION: MULTIVARIATE EXTENSIONS   503

13.1   Introduction   504
13.2   Method of Least Squares for Multiple Regression   504
13.3   Interpretations of Multiple Regression Estimates   509
13.4   Measuring the Strength of Associations in Multiple Regression   512
13.5   Determining the Relative Importance of the Independent Variables in Multiple Regression   514
13.6   Coefficient of Determination R^2 517
13.7   Applying the Assumptions of Regression and Correlation   520
13.8   Outcomes for a Bivariate Relationship when Controlling for a Third Variable   524
13.9   The Problem of Multicollinearity in Multiple Regression   529
       Summary   534
       Key Words   535
       Key Formulas   535
       Supplementary Exercises for Chapter 13   536

CHAPTER 14   # DIFFERENCES AMONG MORE THAN TWO POPULATION MEANS   547

14.1   Introduction   548
14.2   The Logic Behind an Analysis of Variance   548
14.3   A Test of a Hypothesis About More Than Two Population Means   550
14.4   Kruskal-Wallis One-Way Analysis of Variance by Rank   558
       Summary   562
       Key Words   563
       Key Formulas   563
       Supplementary Exercises for Chapter 14   564

APPENDIX   567

Index to Useful Mathematical Notation and Algebraic Topics   568
Table 1   Normal Curve Areas   569
Table 2   Percentage Points of the t Distribution   570
Table 3   Percentage Points of the Chi-square Distribution   571
Table 4   Percentage Points of the F Distribution, $a = .05$ 573
Table 5   Percentage Points of the F Distribution, $a = .01$ 575
Table 6   Random Numbers   577
Table 7   Database A   578
Table 8   Database B   584
Table 9   Database C   586
Table 10   Database D   592

REFERENCES   595

ANSWER SECTION   599

INDEX   629

PREFACE

This fifth edition of *Statistics*: *A Tool for the Social Sciences* contains several new features that we think make the book more appealing to students and, at the same time, more relevant to the social sciences. We have also added another sociologist as co-author; her area of expertise involves the interpretation of multivariate outcomes.

IMPORTANT FEATURES OF THE FIFTH EDITION

- A new chapter has been added to present multivariate extensions of contingency tables. Chapter 11 emphasizes using contingency table analyses to understand the relationship between two variables while controlling for a third.
- A new chapter has been added to expand the discussion of regression and correlation to multivariate situations. Chapter 13 focuses on applying regression and correlation methods to relationships between two variables when controlling for a third variable.
- As with the previous edition, computer applications are used to illustrate some of the analyses. Instructors using the previous edition have indicated that many different statistical software packages are being used in the classroom, so this edition of our text has deemphasized specific software. Emphasis is placed on interpreting the output for computer-generated analyses, not on actually doing the analyses using computer software.
- Numerous examples of specific research have been incorporated into the body of the text.
- Current research findings are used in exercises as a framework against which hypothetical findings are evaluated.
- The number of exercises has been increased by about 15%.
- Additional databases and exercises from these databases have been included.
- The glossary of key words at the end of each chapter has been expanded.
- Numerous smaller changes have been made, in response to suggestions from reviewers and users.

AN OVERVIEW OF THE FIFTH EDITION

The fifth edition of *Statistics: A Tool for the Social Sciences* is a modern introductory statistics test that has been developed specifically for the social sciences. The modern features of the text include exploratory data analysis techniques (such as stem-and-leaf plots and box plots); a brief exposure to computers and statistical software packages (such as SPSS^x and Minitab); an equal emphasis on the two major divisions of statistics — descriptive statistics and inferential statistics; and a new treatment of multivariate extension of contingency analysis, as well as regression and correlation. The focus of the multivariate extensions provides the student with an appreciation of *statistics as a tool* and the need for theory to guide research. In these features, our text differs from the other social science statistics books currently available.

As with previous editions, there is little emphasis on mathematics, particularly probability theory. The mathematical background required for the course is quite elementary, requiring only an understanding of the use of basic mathematical formulas.

This fifth edition includes examples and exercises that involve contemporary issues. They are designed to stimulate and motivate students. We have provided carefully worked-out examples based on data that deal with individuals, groups, organizations, and societies—the whole gamut of social reality. These examples and exercises aim at strengthening the user's fluency with the statistical techniques needed in social research.

Key features of our text include its organization, its continuity, its focus on the theory underpinning research, and the emphasis on showing the relevance of statistics to social research. Data description and statistical inference are split into two clearly identified categories. We include the standard treatment of descriptive statistics—so essential for the presentation and interpretation of social data—as well as thorough but elementary introduction to the concepts of statistical inference. Boxed definitions, clearly distinguishable formulas and important rules, and boldface terms and key points are devices that aid the presentation of material and make the book easy for the student to use.

Continuity is maintained by relating each topic to one of the two objectives of statistics — description and inference — as well as to preceding chapters and sections. Chapter introductions and summaries also help establish continuity. The statistical concepts are applied to practical problems as provided by worked-out examples in the body of the text, many of which have been taken from social science literature; a large number of practical exercises at the end of sections and chapters; and four major databases, from which additional exercises are drawn. The databases are so ample that the instructor can develop many additional exercises. These databases are available from the publisher on a data disk.

ORGANIZATION OF THE TEXT

The text can be divided into two portions: one aimed at data description (Chapters 2, 3, 4, 5, 10, and 11), and the other concerned with statistical inference (Chapters 6, 7, 8, 9, 12, 13, and 14). These two major topics, data description and statistical inference, are closely related. One must know how to describe data in order to make an inference about a population based on sample data. Thus chapters dealing with data description usually precede those concerned with statistical inference.

ACKNOWLEDGMENTS

We wish to acknowledge the many helpful comments from users of our four previous editions. We also thank colleagues who provided detailed critiques of former editions, as well as the manuscript of this edition. In particular, thanks are expressed to:

Dr. Dargan Frierson, Jr.
University of North Carolina–
Wilmington

Prof. Ann Marie Kazyaka
Temple University

Prof. Charles D. Kincaid
University of Florida

Prof. Patricia Murphy
University of New Hampshire

Dr. Raymond K. Neff
Case Western Reserve University

Prof. Paul Nelson
Kansas State University

Prof. Marco Orru
University of South Florida

Prof. Lawrence Rosen
Temple University

Dr. Steven Stack
Wayne State University

A special note of gratitude is extended to our editor, Michael Payne, and our production editor, Chris Crochetière.

Thanks are also due to A. Hald, the Biometrika Trustees, the Chemical Rubber Company, and F. J. Massey, Jr., for permission to reprint tables. Last, but not least, we acknowledge the patience and encouragement of our families.

R. Lyman Ott
Richard F. Larson
Cynthia A. Rexroat
William Mendenhall

CHAPTER 1

WHAT IS STATISTICS?

GENERAL OBJECTIVES

Statistics is an indispensable tool for social sciences. This chapter shows you the importance of statistics, regardless of your major. Emphasis is placed on the ways social researchers use statistics and the general role of research in the social sciences.

SPECIFIC OBJECTIVES

1. To explain what statistics is and why you should study it.
2. To show you how understanding and prediction, two goals of the social sciences, require objectivity in research. Specific steps are presented to help you ensure objectivity.
3. To show how social researchers use statistics in everyday operations. Statistics can be used to characterize groups, organizations, and societies as well as to make comparisons among them.
4. To introduce the concepts of descriptive statistics and inferential statistics.
5. To introduce you briefly to two very important tools: electronic, hand-held calculators and microcomputers, both of which are used in statistical analyses.

1.1   INTRODUCTION

The word *statistics* has a dual meaning for social researchers. First, it refers to numbers such as drug addiction rates, abortion rates, gross national product information, per capita income, and so on. Second, it refers to a field of study. The former usage is the one that is most familiar, but the latter usage will be frequently employed in this text.

Since statistics (the field of study) involves numbers, an understanding of it requires a basic knowledge of mathematics. But the ideas behind statistics — what it is attempting to do and how we go about it — are reasonable, easily explained, and readily comprehensible. The purpose of our text is to answer these questions: What is statistics? How does it work? How do social researchers use it? Are some statistical techniques more useful than others to social researchers? In general, we seek to provide you with an understanding of the basic concepts of statistics and to show how statistics can be of use to you. We will do this while keeping in mind that you are primarily interested in application — statistics as a tool — rather than in the mathematics of the discipline.

1.2   WHY STUDY STATISTICS?

There are two principal reasons for learning statistics. First, we are all exposed to statistics: manufacturers' claims for products, the results of consumer and political polls, and the findings of social research. Many of these results involve inferences based on sampling. Some of the inferences are valid; others are invalid. Some are based on samples of adequate size; others are not. Yet the published results bear the ring of truth. Some people say that statistics can be made to support almost anything. Others say it is easy to lie with statistics. Both statements are true. It is easy to misuse statistics to distort the truth, purposely or unwittingly, when presenting the results of sampling to the uninformed. Thus one reason for studying statistics is that you need to know how to evaluate published data, when to believe them, when to be skeptical, and when to reject them.

A second reason for learning statistics is that it may be essential in your career. As a major in one of the social sciences, your job may require that you interpret the results of sampling (surveys or experimentation), employ statistical methods of analysis to make inferences, describe the characteristics of a group or organization, interpret statistical information, or write a report based on statistical analyses. For example, you may be asked to estimate, on the basis of a sampling of hospital records, the proportion of hospital patients whose bills are "forgiven." Or you might wish to compare the rates of bill forgiveness for two hospitals. Do the different rates in the two samples really imply a difference in the forgiveness rates for the two hospitals, or is the observed difference due simply to random variation in the records from day to day? Or you might wish to estimate the frequency of reincarceration of criminals, grouped according to social class, based on a random sample of 200 criminals who have completed a rehabilitation program.

Although we are primarily interested in the role of statistics in the social sciences, statistics is used in almost all areas of science, business, and industry. Statistics is essential to the social, biological, and physical sciences because all scientists make use of observations of natural phenomena, through sample surveys or experimentation, to gather facts, test hypotheses, and develop theories. In business, sample data are used to forecast sales and profit. Sample data are used in engineering and manufacturing to monitor product quality. Also, sampling of accounts is a new and useful tool for accountants who are conducting audits.

1.3   RESEARCH IN THE SOCIAL SCIENCES

The various social sciences differ in many ways, and so do their practitioners — anthropologists, economists, political scientists, psychologists, and sociologists. One way in which the practitioners differ is the emphasis they place on different aspects of the social world around them. Sociologists, for example, usually focus on human groups, organizations, and modern societies; political scientists emphasize forms of government and political philosophies; and anthropologists highlight preliterate and primitive peoples. Economists study the production and distribution of goods and services, whereas psychologists examine perception, memory, and learning. However, most social scientists share certain common broad interests. They are interested in *understanding* human social life, and they endeavor to develop knowledge about it so that they can make *predictions*.

Human social life is complex, and each of us is caught up in a shared social existence. To study human social life, we must acquire the ability to view it objectively. That is, we must learn to view human social life and all of its manifestations as they are, not as we might want them to be. *Objectivity* in the social sciences is often difficult, but not impossible, to achieve. It is difficult because each of us is a part, in some way, of the social reality we want to understand. And knowledge of that social reality can influence us, our relatives, and our community.

Understanding requires that we conceptualize and measure, to some extent, what we want to understand. It might be divorce, home mortgages, religious beliefs, or dating and courtship behavior. We usually begin with a question or series of questions about some aspect of our social world. We decide what we want to study and when, where, and how we want to collect the relevant information. In short, research is essential to achieve any sort of valid understanding, and the research must be undertaken with as much objectivity as possible.

A social researcher interested, for example, in dating and courtship will want to collect facts, analyze those facts, and classify them systematically. Ultimately, the social researcher will want to describe dating and courtship, show that changes have taken place in the patterns of dating and courtship over time, and probably explore the factors that might explain various patterns.

Two important questions appear, one at the beginning and one at the end of the research process: What are the important variables that must be studied? What is a satisfactory explanation? We attempt to answer these two questions by examining the current body of information. We review whatever published research there is, and we talk to experts in the field. We make firsthand observations.

Understanding, as a phenomenon, is difficult to explain. Fundamentally, we have understanding when we have facts that seem to make sense and can be related to some theoretical framework. From the facts and theory, we can develop some general explanatory statements. These statements, in our present example, should tell us much about dating and courtship.

Understanding leads to prediction. For example, if we really understand the changes that have taken place in behavior expectations, attitudes about dating and courtship, available alternatives, and how these changes are viewed by young people, we should be able to predict dating and courtship patterns with a fair degree of accuracy. The more knowledge we acquire, the more factors we study, the more conditions we specify, and the more communities we examine, the more accurate our predictions should be.

When one social researcher publishes information about a dating and courtship trend, others are led to check out that trend in the same locality and then in other localities. If the trend holds up in future studies, the confidence we have in that trend increases. Over time, other factors are studied, and new tests are made. The process continues because it is always possible that the early trend in dating and courtship was misinterpreted. In this light, we should always keep in mind that the findings of the social sciences are tentative. They may be modified or revised, depending on additional information. When do social researchers think their knowledge is adequate? The critical test is prediction. Have we learned enough about dating and courtship to predict the results of the next study before the results are in?

Thus understanding and prediction depend on research, and data collection is one phase of the research process. We usually begin a study by sketching out a research design or blueprint that identifies the variables we will measure and specifies the procedures we will follow in collecting and analyzing information.

Social scientists who engage in research follow some research design. If the design is good and the researcher follows it closely, answers should be obtained for the important questions. The design itself will indicate the limits of the investigation.

Let us examine briefly the general format underlying much of social research. We usually start with a hypothesis or an educated guess about the existence of some trend, pattern, or relationship. The hypothesis names the variables of interest. We then identify the population to be studied and the kind of data-gathering instruments we will use. We might, for example, develop an interview guide or construct a mail questionnaire. Data are then collected. We might have a stack of questionnaires, police records, census returns, or medical reports.

Classification, the next step, requires some form of quantification. The data must be organized in some fashion so as to reveal any trends, patterns, or relationships.

After classification, we analyze the data. Here, statistics — the primary content of this text — comes into play. Depending on the data, we will make appropriate calculations that will be used to summarize information or to allow us to make generalizations.

Thus statistics as a tool is not an isolated topic. It is an integral part of each of the social sciences. Although it is especially critical to data analysis, it permeates much of research design and data collection. Without it, research would be almost impossible, and conveying research information would be extremely difficult. Now let us look closely at how social researchers use statistics.

1.4   HOW DO SOCIAL RESEARCHERS USE STATISTICS?

As social researchers, we use statistics in several ways. First, we might be concerned with studying and analyzing the structure, social behavior patterns, and interactions of groups, organizations, and societies. Since the data set amassed to study a particular problem frequently is large and contains many facts, we seek means for organizing and summarizing the data to facilitate examination. A discussion of different methods for organizing and summarizing data falls under the broad category of descriptive statistics.

Second, we might be concerned with methodology and statistical inference. For this situation, much consulting and research time could be devoted to sampling decisions (how much data to acquire and how to acquire it) and to inference decisions (how to make the inferences). The acquisition of sample data, sample surveys, and experiments yields information and costs money. For example, a sample of 1000 voters should give more information about voter preferences in an upcoming election than a sample of 500. However, by varying the survey or experimental procedure — how we select the data and how many observations we take from each source — we can vary the cost, quality and quantity of information in the experiment. Rather simple modifications in the selection of data can sometimes reduce the cost of the sample to $\frac{1}{100}$ or less of the cost of conventional sampling procedures. Knowledge of statistics and statistical techniques can help us make these sampling decisions.

The method of inference for a given sample survey or experimental design will involve either a prediction or a decision about some characteristic of the population or universe of interest. Methods of inference in the social sciences, as in other disciplines, vary: Some are good, some are bad, and some seem to be best for most occasions. It is up to us to select the appropriate method for a given situation.

The preceding discussion points to the most important contribution of statistics to the social sciences. In addition to facilitating data description, **the major contribution of statistics is in the evaluation of the quality or "goodness" of an inference.** Anyone can devise a method of inference. However, it is often quite difficult to say how good the inference is. For example, if we sample records of 50 criminals who have undergone a rehabilitation program and estimate that 30% of all criminals who participate in such a program will be returned to prison, we would like to know how far this estimate lies from the true percentage. Is the error 5%, 10%, or 30%? Similarly, in reaching a decision about a characteristic of a population or universe based on sample data, we should be aware of the probability of drawing an incorrect conclusion.

To summarize, first, we use statistics to summarize data. Second, we use statistics to help design surveys and experiments that minimize the cost of obtaining a specified quantity of information. Third, we seek the best method of inference for a given sampling situation. Finally, as social researchers, we use statistics to measure the goodness of an inference.

1.5   DESCRIPTIVE AND INFERENTIAL STATISTICS

Statistics, though a separate discipline in one sense, is often taught as part of some other discipline such as sociology, economics, or political science. Because this text is for students in the social sciences, we will approach statistics from a social science perspective. In so doing we must consider two branches of statistics, descriptive statistics and inferential statistics. Both are important for applications in social research.

What is *descriptive statistics*? Let us explain the idea with examples. We are often confronted with a mass of data that needs to be described. We might have specific bits of information, such as the total family income for each student in a university with 25,000 students. If we wish to describe the total family income for each student at the university, the listing of 25,000 family incomes would be cumbersome indeed. Descriptive statistics can provide us with graphical and numerical techniques for describing concisely the total family income for the students of the university. These same descriptive techniques could also be used to describe such things as the drug use of the residents of New York State, the occupational status of young adults in Chicago, the religious beliefs of the residents of Seattle, or the preschool preparation of first-graders currently attending Lincoln Grade School.

Descriptive statistics can also be used to compare two characteristics measured on every person in a group, to compare groups using the same characteristic, and to compare a group and a standard. For example, we might wish to examine the relationship between IQ and grade point average for students at a university. Similarly, we might wish to examine the socioeconomic backgrounds of husbands and wives at the time of their marriage. A study of descriptive statistics will enable us to make these comparisons. In every instance it is assumed that we have information on each subject or object and that we wish to describe one or more characteristics of a group or to make comparisons between groups.

Finally, descriptive statistics plays an important role in preliminary data analysis — that is, analysis prior to the use of inferential statistics. We are beginning to see a renewed interest in descriptive statistics and a new label applied to it — *exploratory data analysis*. Much can be learned from exploratory data analysis, and the various descriptive techniques covered in this text can be meaningfully used in this context.

What is *inferential statistics*? Again, let us answer the question by considering a few examples. Suppose we wish to estimate the proportion of 50,000 migrant workers in a particular state who have completed six years or more of public school education. Suppose further that a fairly complete list of these workers is available from state records for worker's accident compensation. How could we obtain public school information for those migrant workers listed on the state records? One way would be to locate and interview each of the 50,000 migrant workers, but this method would be costly and time-consuming. It also would probably be impossible to contact every single worker. An easier and more efficient approach would be to *sample* randomly, say, 1000 workers from the list of all migrant workers and to contact each of these persons individually. It is obviously easier to locate 1000 workers than 50,000. We could then use the proportion of workers in the sample who have six or more years of education to estimate the proportion of all migrant workers in the state who possess the same characteristic. We will show in later chapters that the sample proportion will be quite close to the proportion for all migrant workers in the state with six or more years of public school education. In addition, and perhaps more importantly, we can determine how much this estimate will differ from the actual proportion of all migrant workers with six or more years of public schooling.

A second example is related to predicting election results and collecting information from Gallup polls, Harris polls, and other public opinion surveys. The use of survey techniques for predicting the outcome of an election began during the 1936 campaign, when the Roper, Gallup, and Crossley polls accurately predicted the outcome of the presidential election. Because of the widespread use of survey techniques in elections today, we are all somewhat familiar with this application of inferential statistics.

Another interesting poll was conducted during that same 1936 campaign. The Gallup organization applied inferential statistics to the results of a survey to predict the outcome of a much larger *Literary Digest* poll and then published the results of their survey before the *Literary Digest* results were released. This was done by sending the survey to 3000 of the subscribers who were participating in the *Digest* poll and by using the information obtained from the 3000 persons sampled to predict the results of the entire *Digest* poll. Gallup not only predicted the results of the *Digest* survey to within 1 percentage point before it was released, but also indicated why the *Digest* poll would predict the wrong outcome to the election.

The *Digest* poll was substantially in error because the people it surveyed were clearly not representative of all the voters. *Digest* interviewees consisted of new automobile owners and telephone subscribers. Because 1936 was a depression year, these two groups were hardly representative of that large segment of the voting populace who had marginal incomes or were out of work.

Public opinion polls and election surveys at the local, state, and national levels are very much a part of our lives; hardly a day goes by without the results of some survey being reported on television, on radio, or in the newspaper. How can these pollsters presume to know the opinions of more than 100 million adult Americans in a national opinion survey? They certainly cannot reach their conclusions by contacting every person in the United States. Rather, they sample the opinions of a small number of adults to estimate the reaction of all adult Americans.

Gallup polls conducted on national issues make use of personal interviews with approximately 5 people in each of 362 sampling areas throughout the country, for a total of approximately 1500 people. As you might expect, the accuracy of the prediction depends on how representative the sampling areas are and how well the 5 individual opinions within an area reflect the consensus for the entire area. The selection process begins by sorting the many different voting districts within the United States into seven broad categories related to population size. Then sampling areas are selected from these categories. Every ten years, when the U.S. Census Bureau releases new population information, the assignment of voting districts to the categories is updated, and a new set of 362 sampling areas is chosen. The amazing result of this survey process is that the proportion in the sample who hold a particular opinion matches very closely the proportion of people holding that opinion in the complete population from which the sample was drawn. Some people may find this assertion difficult to believe; convincing supportive evidence will be supplied in subsequent chapters.

As a third example of inferential statistics, suppose that the board of education for a large metropolitan area wishes to estimate the average number of children in families living in the city in order to plan for a reorganization of school districts. The board could do this by interviewing every family in the city, but this method has some obvious disadvantages. Not only would it be very costly to conduct so many interviews, but also the survey would be incomplete and subject to inaccuracies, because some families would not be home when the interviewers made their visits. A second way, which employs the concepts of inferential statistics, is to select a random sample of 400 families from the city and interview each family. Since only a few families would not be at home, these families could be revisited until they were interviewed. It would then be possible to estimate the average number of children in a family for the entire city by calculating the average for the sample of 400 families. This method of determining the average number of children per family is much less costly than surveying an entire city — and it is very accurate.

Let us now try to identify from these examples the characteristics common to all inferential statistical problems. **First, each example involved making an observation or measurement that could not be predicted with certainty in advance.** Indeed, results of repeated observations are likely to vary in an unpredictable (random) manner. For example, we cannot say in advance whether a particular migrant worker selected from the state list has attended public school for six or more years, or whether a randomly selected voter will vote for the Democratic presidential candidate. Similarly, we cannot say in advance how many children the Smith family has.

Second, each example involved sampling. A sample of migrant workers was selected from the state list, a sample of people was taken from the entire voting population of the United States, and a sample of 400 families was obtained from the total number of families in the city.

Third, although this is not obvious, each example involved the collection of data or measurements, one measurement corresponding to each element of the sample. We realize that observations on the elements of the sample may be quantitative (as when we record age, income, or IQ) or qualitative (as when we record sex, political party affiliation, or marital status). However, even these qualitative observations can be viewed as measurements if we assign a number to each qualitative category. For example, when a migrant worker is interviewed, we can assign a score to the result: $X = 1$ if he or she has had as many as six years of education, and $X = 0$ if he or she has not. The total number of migrant workers with at least six years of education in the sample is the sum of these measurements. Similarly, measurements (such as 0s and 1s) are obtained when we sample voter intentions; the sampling of the number of children in the 400 households yields 400 measurements, one for each family.

Finally, each example exhibited a common objective. That is, the purpose of sampling is to obtain information from a subset of the population of interest in order to make an inference about the entire population. For the estimation problem concerning migrant workers, the population of interest is the large set of 1s and 0s corresponding to those workers who have and those who have not had at least six years of education. Similarly, the population for the voter problem would be the set of 1s and 0s corresponding to the 100 million or more voters in the United States. Voters would be assigned a 1 if they intended to vote for the Democratic candidate and a 0 if not. The objective of sampling is to estimate the proportion of eligible voters who favor the Democratic presidential candidate — that is, the proportion of 1s in the population. The population associated with the household survey is the number of children per household recorded for all families in the city. The objective is to estimate the average number of children per family in the city. In other words, researchers wish to make an inference about the families of the city based on information contained in the sample of 400 families.

FOUR CHARACTERISTICS COMMON TO INFERENTIAL STATISTICS PROBLEMS

1. random observations   **3.** numerical data
2. sampling   **4.** common inferential objective

Note again that a population or universe is a collection of measurements or scores, not a collection of people (which is the usual connotation of the term). Note also that populations may exist in fact or be imaginary. The populations for the three examples we have discussed exist, even though we do not actually possess the complete collection of 1s and 0s corresponding to the two educational categories for migrant workers, the entire set of voters favoring or opposing the Democratic candidate, or the number of children in each family. In contrast, if we sample the pulse rates of a set of hypertensive patients who are administered a drug product, the population of pulse rates measured on all hypertensive patients who could be administered the drug product in the future is referred to as an imaginary population. Figure 1.1 illustrates the relationship between the population and a sample.

FIGURE 1.1

Relationship between the population and a sample

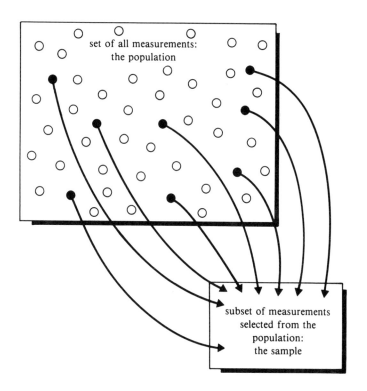

The following are the definitions of the basic concepts of statistics we have discussed so far.

DEFINITION 1.1 | A **population** or **universe** is the set representing all measurements of interest to the researcher.

DEFINITION 1.2	A **sample** is a subset of measurements selected from the population of interest.

DEFINITION 1.3	A **statistic** is a numerical descriptive measure computed from a sample.

DEFINITION 1.4	**Descriptive statistics** is a branch of statistics concerned with numerical and graphical techniques for describing one or more characteristics of a group and for comparing characteristics between groups.

DEFINITION 1.5	**Inferential statistics** is a branch of statistics concerned with the acquisition of data, with sampling, and with making inferences about a population based on the data.

DEFINITION 1.6	The **objective of inferential statistics** is to make an inference about a population based on the information contained in a sample.

1.6   INTRODUCTION TO CALCULATORS AND COMPUTERS

Before we begin any formal development of the subject matter of statistics, we should also mention two very important tools of the trade: electronic, hand-held calculators and, more importantly, computers. As the lay connotation of statistics implies, the field of statistics involves data. We will be summarizing data and using data to make inferences in the form of estimates, predictions, and decisions. The better we are able to perform the calculations required in summarizing data and in drawing inferences from data, the more time we can spend actually understanding them — that is, understanding the summarizations and inferences made from the data.

1.7   CALCULATORS

A calculator can be very helpful to a student taking a first course in statistics. It can be useful in doing standard arithmetic operations such as addition, subtraction, multiplication, and division, as well as for squaring numbers and taking square roots. Many hand-held calculators can also take logarithms, compute two statistical quantities presented in Chapter 4 (a mean $\bar{X}$ and a standard deviation s), and do simple programming. We will not recommend a specific brand of calculator for your course; if you do not have one, perhaps your professor can refer you to a store that carries inexpensive, high-quality calculators suitable for a beginning course in statistics. The calculator should be able to do at least the following: add, subtract, multiply, divide, calculate squares and square roots, and save the sum of a sequence of numbers.

1.8   COMPUTERS AND STATISTICAL SOFTWARE

The availability and accessibility of computers and the development of computer **software** (programs or program systems developed for computers) that is relatively easy to use have greatly affected the field of statistics. The calculations for large data sets can become complex and time-consuming when using a hand-held calculator. A computer can be of tremendous help in making such calculations, even for a student in an introductory course. Specific programs or more general software systems can perform statistical calculations and analyses almost instantaneously after the data are entered into the computer. Also, it is not necessary to know computer programming to use most statistical software for planned analyses.

Because of space limitations and the fact that there are so many fine statistical packages, this text will not cover any specific package or packages for microcomputers. If your instructor uses a statistical package, he or she will have the necessary instructions. The major **statistical software systems** include BMDP, Minitab, SAS, and SPSS^X. Each of these has a user's manual that gives detailed instructions for entering data and performing the desired calculations and analyses. Other systems developed specifically for unsophisticated users provide program "prompts" at a computer terminal to lead you through a desired analysis.

Now let us give a few general observations about computers and their use in statistics for the social sciences. First, if used properly, computers can be a tremendous aid, especially for processing large data sets requiring repetitive calculations — such as the four data sets at the end of this text. Such repetitive calculations are often called *number-crunching* operations. However, computers are mindless beasts; they can do only what they have been told (programmed) to do, no matter how absurd the results may turn out to be.

Second, the acronym *GIGO* (Garbage In, Garbage Out) suggests another problem area. Inferences made from data, whether based on analyses done by hand or by a computer, are only as good as the data upon which they are based. If we have erroneous data or apply the wrong procedures (analyses), the conclusions we draw will probably be wrong.

Third, there is a general misconception that computers always provide numerically accurate results. Although the major software systems have been thoroughly tested, we should still review the computer calculations, just to be sure that they make sense. Do not believe everything that is on neatly printed computer output. Computers are *not* a substitute for thinking; the user must still formulate the problem and interpret the computer output correctly. To analyze data properly, sound judgment and an understanding of statistical concepts are necessary.

Finally, neither computers nor statistical procedures are a substitute for a good research design that is based on relevant literature and contains testable hypotheses. In addition, the variables of interest must be measured before hypotheses can be tested. A thorough understanding of the research data, the data collection process, and the statistical output are all necessary to make sense of the findings.

1.9   A NOTE TO THE STUDENT

We think with words and concepts. Thus statistics, like any language, requires the memorization of new terms and ideas. Commit to memory as many definitions and concepts as possible. Focus on the broader aspects of statistics. What is statistics? How does it work? What are some of the more important applications? To assist you, reread this chapter from time to time, so that the details do not obscure the broader significance of statistics as a tool for the social sciences.

As you read through the text, refer occasionally to this chapter and review the objective of statistics, its specific role in social research, and the characteristics of a statistical problem. Each of the following chapters is directed, in some way, toward answering the questions posed here. Each is essential to completing the overall picture of the role of statistics in the social sciences.

In the Appendix you will find several tables. Appendix Tables 7, 8, 9, and 10 contain databases—sets of data. You will use these databases in some of the exercises, and we will refer to them throughout the text. You might find it worthwhile to familiarize yourself with these databases.

Appendix Table 7 — Database A — is based on two samples, consisting of 100 college students in Oklahoma and 100 college students in California. These students were asked questions about their views regarding the seriousness of certain criminal and political acts. Appendix Table 8 — Database B — contains demographic and political data for 60 different nations. These data are based on the most recent government and United Nations sources for birth rates, death rates, life expectancies, and degrees of urbanization.

Database B also contains a measure of each nation's level of technology. This measure, developed by W. Parker Frisbie and Clifford J. Clark of the University of Texas (1982), has been modified for our use. Appendix Table 9 — Database C — reports the basic data from a clinical trial involving 100 patients. Each patient exhibited signs of depression and was given medication throughout the study. Finally, Appendix Table 10 — Database D — provides official information from a sample of 30 states. For each state, Database D contains the "official" abortion rate, percentage of births to unmarried mothers, forcible rape rate, murder rate, population density, level of poverty, and suicide rate.

SUMMARY

As social researchers, we are concerned with both descriptive and inferential statistics. Descriptive statistical techniques are employed to describe one or more characteristics of a group or to compare groups when we have data on all objects of interest. In contrast, inferential statistical techniques are used when we possess only a sample of data and wish to make an inference about the universe or population from which it was selected.

This chapter has also given a brief introduction to two very important tools of the trade: electronic calculators and computers. Clearly, computers will dominate in the future, and numerous statistical software packages have been developed. Each package usually provides all the instructions you will need to use it. Your instructor will guide you in this matter. Because understanding statistics is so critical, your instructor may choose to limit your involvement with computers. This text has been explicitly designed to be used either with or without computer access.

KEY WORDS

Descriptive statistics A branch of statistics concerned with numerical and graphical techniques for describing one or more characteristics of a group and comparing characteristics between groups.

Inferential statistics A branch of statistics concerned with the acquisition of data, with sampling, and with the use of the data in making inferences about a population.

Objective of inferential statistics To make an inference about a population based on the information contained in a sample.

Population   The set representing all measurements of interest to the researcher.

Sample   A subset of measurements selected from the population of interest.

Software   Programs or program systems already developed and available for computer users.

Statistical software systems   Software programs such as BMDP, Minitab, SAS, and SPSS^X.

Statistic   Numerical, descriptive measure computed from a sample.

Universe   The set representing all measurements of interest to the researcher. Used interchangeably with the term *population*.

SUPPLEMENTARY EXERCISES FOR CHAPTER 1

1. What is statistics?

2. Distinguish between descriptive statistics and inferential statistics.

3. What is a population?

4. What is a sample?

5. Write a brief essay stating in your own words *why* social researchers must understand statistics. Could you make a similar argument for most people living in an industrial society?

6. Scan the business or financial section of a newspaper and identify applications of descriptive statistics.

7. Refer to recent issues of a professional journal suggested to you by your instructor and find several articles in which data are summarized. Indicate whether descriptive or inferential statistical techniques are used by the author(s).

8. Refer to the articles of Exercise 7. In each case identify the population and the sample employing inferential statistical techniques.

9. What are some of the special problems that confront the social researcher in achieving objectivity in research?

10. Discuss the relationship between *understanding* and *prediction*.

11. Discuss the advantages of using computers in statistics for calculation and analysis.

12. A hand-held calculator should be able to perform certain functions in order to be useful in a statistics course. Name the functions you think it must be able to perform.

13. Describe the relationship between the sample and the population when doing social science research.

14. Social scientists generally accept the following maxim: The major contribution of statistics is in the evaluation of the quality or "goodness" of an inference. What is the meaning of this maxim?

15. The *Literary Digest* poll of 1936 failed to project the winner of the 1936 presidential campaign. What were some of the problems with the 1936 *Literary Digest* poll? What steps could have been taken to increase substantially the likelihood of correctly predicting the eventual winner?

CHAPTER 2

MEASUREMENT

GENERAL OBJECTIVES

Most people believe that human social behavior is so complex and elusive that attempts to measure or quantify it are meaningless or impossible. This chapter introduces you to the fundamental concepts of measurement in such a way that the measurement of human social behavior is understandable. It also introduces two important ideas: validity and reliability. Without them the social sciences would be nothing more than speculation based on personal bias, and measurement would be meaningless.

SPECIFIC OBJECTIVES

1. To define what a constant is, what a variable is, how quantitative variables differ from qualitative ones, and what the difference is between discrete and continuous variables.
2. To help you examine the nature of measurement itself, pointing out the different scales of measurements: nominal, ordinal, interval, and ratio.
3. To explore ratios, proportions, percentages, and the rounding of measurements or scores.
4. To provide an overview of two very important ideas: reliability and validity.

2.1   INTRODUCTION

Social researchers are interested in developing new knowledge and testing old ideas about human social life. In this process specific hypotheses are often generated from theory to guide our research. As we stated in Chapter 1, we develop or select a research design that identifies the variables we will measure and that specifies the procedures we will follow in collecting and analyzing information relative to our hypotheses.

As we also stated in Chapter 1, statistics is concerned with two types of research problems: data description (including exploratory data analysis) and the making of inferences about a population or universe based on information contained in a sample. Implicit in this statement is the fact that we can actually measure the various social, political, and economic variables of interest, no matter how complex and abstract they might be.

For example, it is possible to classify people according to racial categories or to measure birth rates, family incomes, or total national product. It is more difficult to measure the social status of a person, the technological development of a society, or the religiosity of a group. Consequently, before discussing data description and statistical inference, we must consider the types of measurements required in studying social, political, and economic phenomena.

2.2   CONSTANTS AND VARIABLES

Inferential statistics is basically concerned with using information in a sample to make inferences about a population. Suppose, for example, that we plan to conduct a study to determine the cost of obtaining a marriage license at a county courthouse. To do this we inquire about the license fee. Note here that it would take only one observation (the result of one inquiry) to ascertain the cost of a license, because the marriage fee is constant over a given period of time. Different observations by different researchers would yield the same fee.

DEFINITION 2.1	When observations on the same phenomenon do not change in successive trials, the phenomenon is called a **constant**.

Consider the following extension of the previous example. We plan to obtain a sample of marriage fees charged by counties in a state and then use this information to estimate the average fee for the entire state. Each of ten researchers is assigned to contact a different county to obtain the stated marriage fee. Although all counties perform essentially the same function, not all ten researchers will observe the same fee.

DEFINITION 2.2	When observations on the same phenomenon can vary from trial to trial, the phenomenon is called a **variable**.

We have seen that the marriage license fee charged in a particular county courthouse is a constant (at a given time), whereas the county marriage license fee in a state is a variable, because it may vary from county to county.

We are concerned primarily with the observation of variables. Summarizing and condensing data would be quite simple for observations made on constants. When the observations vary, however, statistics can be a valuable tool in describing the data and formulating techniques for making inferences.

Variables can be categorized into two broad classes: quantitative and qualitative variables.

DEFINITION 2.3	A **quantitative variable** is a variable whose observations vary in magnitude from trial to trial.

Examples of quantitative variables include the following:

family income	suicide rate
prison capacity	religiosity
crude birth rate	degree of technology
divorce-to-marriage ratio	cost of living

Quantitative variables can be further classified as one of two types: discrete or continuous.

DEFINITION 2.4	When observations on a quantitative variable can assume only a countable number of values, the variable is called a **discrete variable**.

Typical examples of discrete variables include the following:

- number of inmates in each state prison
- number of immigrants from a particular country
- number of banks in a state

- annual number of deaths due to lung cancer
- daily number of industrial accidents due to inadequate safety precautions

Note that for each of these examples, we are able to count the number of values that the variable can assume.

DEFINITION 2.5	When observations on a quantitative variable can assume any one of the countless number of values in a line interval, the variable is called a **continuous variable**.

For example, the average amount of electricity consumed per household per month in Rochester, New York, can assume any of infinitely many values. During a particular month the average might be 90.5 kilowatt-hours, 105.126, 118.77789, and so on. Another example of a continuous quantitative variable is the age of United States senators when they take the oath of office. Certainly a senator could assume every possible gradation of age between the regulatory lower limit of 30 years and the upper limits of life. Other typical continuous variables are marriage rates, crime rates, and length of life of persons receiving Medicare. From a practical standpoint, most continuous variables are measured as if they were discrete. For example, weight is a continuous variable, but in determining someone's weight we might count by ounces or grams for an infant and by pounds or kilograms for an adult. In spite of this, it is still important to distinguish between discrete and continuous variables; we will find that when making a statistical inference, certain methods are appropriate for discrete variables, others for continuous variables.

Not all variables encountered in social research are quantitative. For example, occupation differs from one person to another, but the variable "occupation" cannot be quantified. We can attach a number (called a "score") to a person, assigning a 1 if the person is a carpenter, a 2 if a plumber, and so on (or some other procedure), but this number would only be for identification.

DEFINITION 2.6	A **qualitative variable** is a variable whose observations vary in kind but not in degree.

Sex, prison status, religious affiliation, marital status, political party affiliation, voter registration, and employment status all are examples of qualitative variables. Note that none of these qualitative variables can be arranged in order of magnitude. One political party affiliation cannot be considered "greater" or "more" than another affiliation. Quantitative variables, on the other hand, can be ranked by order of magnitude.

In our discussion of qualitative and quantitative variables, we have assumed that we are able to measure the variable of interest. However, not all variables can be measured with the same sophistication or scale. We will consider the different scales of measurement in the next section.

EXERCISES

1. Sex discrimination or sexism is prevalent in our society. In doing research, would this variable be more likely to be treated in a quantitative or qualitative manner? Explain your answer.

2. In the following list of social concepts, indicate those that, in your judgment, refer to quantitative variables. Explain your choices.

   infant mortality rate   extent of urbanization

   type of economy   social institutions

   caste systems   marriage forms

3. Of the terms listed in Exercise 2, list those that refer to qualitative variables.

4. Are there some variables in Exercise 2 that could be treated as both qualitative and quantitative? Which ones? Explain your answers.

5. Infants die one at a time, yet we consider infant mortality rate to be a continuous variable. Explain this apparent inconsistency.

6. Categorize each of the following variables as qualitative or quantitative:

   penal codes   assessed valuation of homes

   voter concern   income tax bracket

   political parties   occupation

   campaign contributions

7. Of the items listed in Exercise 6, which of the quantitative variables are discrete? Which are continuous?

2.3   SCALES OF MEASUREMENT FOR QUALITATIVE AND QUANTITATIVE VARIABLES

Measurement is closely related to quantification. Most social researchers distinguish between quantification by categorization (for nominal data) and quantification by measurement (for ordinal, interval, and ratio data). We also recognize this distinction and will use these four scales of measurement throughout this text.

The four scales vary in the degree to which they quantify a variable. They are called nominal, ordinal, interval, and ratio scales. Because ordinal scales represent the lowest level of measurement, they are often categorized and treated as quantification based on categorization, just as nominal data are.

As we will see, a particular type of variable can be measured on one or perhaps more than one scale, but no single scale is dominant in the social sciences. Because statistical techniques and procedures have been developed for use with particular scales of measurement, it is essential that you understand the scales and be able to determine which is most appropriate to use with the variable (or variables) that you wish to measure.

| DEFINITION 2.7 | A **nominal scale** categorizes qualitative objects by name. These categories are called *levels* of the scale and are assigned identifying symbols such as numbers or letters. |

All qualitative variables are measured on a nominal scale. For example, the qualitative variable "prisoner status" could be divided into four levels —"fish" or new prisoner, "resident" or regular inmate, "trustee" or prisoner who has freedom of movement throughout the facility, and "solitary confinement"—so that all observations on potential prisoners could be measured or categorized as one of these levels. Sometimes nominal scales are labeled with numbers. For identification, we could assign the number 1 to a fish, 2 to a resident, 3 to a trustee, and 4 to an individual in solitary confinement. You must remember, however, that we have used numbers to indicate levels on a nominal scale for the qualitative variable "prisoner status," but we cannot assign an order of magnitude to the various levels. We could just as reasonably have assigned letters to the categories.

| DEFINITION 2.8 | An **ordinal scale** incorporates the features of a nominal scale and the additional feature that observations can be ordered or ranked by degree. |

For example, a crude prestige ranking of occupations, such as the one shown in Table 2.1, would serve as an ordinal scale. Although we can rank observations on an ordinal scale from low to high, we cannot assign a distance between the ranks. (On an ordinal scale, a rank denotes the level of the variable.) Hence we have no way of determining the distance between levels of prestige for the occupations in Table 2.1.

TABLE 2.1

Prestige ranking of occupations

Occupation	Rank
professional	1
white-collar worker	2
blue-collar worker	3

Other examples of variables often measured on an ordinal scale are degree of alienation, social class status, and intelligence. Any variable that can be measured on an ordinal scale (where levels can be ranked) can also be measured on a nominal scale (where levels are not ranked). The three levels of occupational prestige in Table 2.1 (professional, white-collar, and blue-collar), therefore, would also serve as a nominal scale. Ordinal data are often used in a categorical manner; that is, categories are developed, and the categories are ordered by magnitude. Because of the frequency with which ordinal data are grouped into categories, both nominal and ordinal data are called *categorical data*.

| DEFINITION 2.9 | An **interval scale** incorporates all features of an ordinal (and hence nominal) scale and the additional feature that distances between levels on the scale can be specified. |

IQ tests provide an example of an interval scale. Suppose that all sixth-grade students in eight different elementary schools are administered the same IQ test. If the average score for each school is as shown in Table 2.2, not only can we rank the average IQs from lowest to highest, but we can also state exact distances, measured in score units on the IQ test, between the schools. Based on the average IQ score, school G seems to resemble school F more than school H does. Other quantitative variables that can be measured by interval-level scales are social variables in which the intervals appear to be of equal width because of the techniques of measurement used. Examples include anomie, group morale, social attitudes, and social distance.

TABLE 2.2

Average IQ results

School	IQ
A	150
B	128
C	126
D	125
E	122
F	120
G	110
H	75

One undesirable feature of the interval scale is that the origin on the scale is undetermined; that is, we do not know where zero is located. For example, an IQ test score of 0 does not correspond to zero intelligence. In fact, we do not know the exact intelligence level implied by a test score of 0.

Not knowing where the origin is located on a scale means that we cannot form valid ratios of observations. For example, using the data in Table 2.2, we might be tempted to form the ratio

$$\frac{\text{IQ school A}}{\text{IQ school H}} = \frac{150}{75} = 2$$

This result, however, does not permit us to say that sixth-grade students in school A are twice as intelligent on the average as their counterparts in school H. If a meaningful zero point can be defined for an interval scale, the scale becomes a ratio scale.

DEFINITION 2.10 | A **ratio scale** incorporates all the features of an interval (and hence nominal and ordinal) scale and the additional feature that ratios can be formed with levels of the scale.

Typical examples of social variables measured on ratio scales are suicide rates, income, and rates of population change. For example, in measuring the population change of various states, we can determine the projected percentage change between 1990 and 2010. Table 2.3 contains the projected change for ten states.

State	% Change
Arizona	+41.8
Florida	+36.8
California	+28.2
Texas	+25.8
Colorado	+19.3
South Carolina	+18.5
Alabama	+10.2
Vermont	+8.2
New York	+2.1
Pennsylvania	−5.9

Source: U.S. Bureau of the Census, *Statistical Abstract of the United States*.

As with IQ averages for schools, we can rank the states according to the projected percentage change. We can also specify the exact difference in projected change between any pair of states. The projected rate of change in South Carolina, for example, is more like that of Colorado than that of Arizona or Pennsylvania. A projected change of 0% has meaning, even though it is unlikely that any state will exhibit such a pattern. Since we can define a zero point, ratios between levels or projected + and − changes have meaning. For example, we can form the ratio

$$\frac{\text{projected population change in Arizona}}{\text{projected population change in Alabama}} = \frac{41.8}{10.2} = 4.1$$

This result shows that the projected change between 1990 and 2010 is over 4 times greater for Arizona than Alabama.

To summarize, there are four scales of measurement of variables: nominal, ordinal, interval, and ratio. Since no one scale of measurement dominates the social sciences, you should be familiar with all four.

SUMMARY OF MEASUREMENT SCALES

Nominal scale Levels are identified by name only.

Ordinal scale Levels can be identified by name and ordered (ranked) according to their relative magnitudes.

Interval scale   Levels can be ranked, and distances between levels of the scale can be determined.
Ratio scale   Distances can be determined between levels, and there is a meaningful zero point for the scale.

Note that qualitative variables are always measured on a nominal scale. Ordinal, interval, and ratio scales are appropriate for quantitative variables, but they vary in the degree to which they express the magnitude of the variable levels. An ordinal scale is the least informative, because it simply shows the ranks for levels of the scale. An interval scale defines a distance between two measurements or scores, but the location of the origin (zero) of the scale is unknown. The most informative quantitative scale, the ratio scale, possesses a known origin and is constructed so that ratios of measurements are truly meaningful. **We see, therefore, that the four scales differ in their ability to quantify data. Nominal scales allow for no quantitative interpretation, while ratio scales possess the most quantitative sophistication.**

TABLE 2.4	Scale for Which Statistical Technique Was Developed	Scale of Measurement			
Applicability of statistical techniques to different scales of measurement		Nominal	Ordinal	Interval	Ratio
	nominal	yes	+	+	+
	ordinal	—	yes	+	+
	interval	—	—	yes	+
	ratio	—	—	—	yes

+ = permissible to use technique for data in this scale, but there is a loss of information
− = not permissible to use techique for data in this scale

Certain statistical techniques have been developed for each measurement scale, but we do have some flexibility in their use. Table 2.4 summarizes which statistical techniques are appropriate for a particular scale of measurement.

For example, ratio data can be employed as interval data, so statistical techniques appropriate for measurement on an interval scale can also be used for variables measured on a ratio scale. Similarly, statistical techniques developed for ordinal data can be used for interval and ratio data. Techniques for nominal data can be employed for any of the other three kinds of data, but some information in the data will be lost. More discussion about the techniques for each scale will be presented in succeeding chapters as we develop statistical procedures. As we study these procedures, we should keep Table 2.4 at our fingertips to remind us of the applicability of various techniques. We turn now to some examples of data that we might collect in a study.

2.4   EXAMPLES OF SOCIAL DATA

The results of Section 2.3 are illustrated in the next four examples. Note that Example 2.3 could have more than one solution.

EXAMPLE 2.1   Welfare recipients in Atlanta were surveyed and categorized on the basis of marital status, using the classifications given in Table 2.5. Identify the scale used in measuring the data in the table.

TABLE 2.5

Classification of marital status

single	widowed
married	other
divorced	

SOLUTION   The levels of the qualitative variable "marital status" differ in name only and cannot be ranked. Hence the data are measured on a nominal scale.

EXAMPLE 2.2   Administrative officials at many universities require parents of students who are applying for financial aid to file financial reports. If a particular university required parents to check one of the income categories listed in Table 2.6, determine the scale of the measurements collected.

TABLE 2.6

Categories of gross annual income

far below average	above average
below average	far above average
average	

SOLUTION   Since we can assign a rank to these levels of income categories but cannot
                  determine the exact distance between these levels, the appropriate scale is
                  the ordinal scale.

<table>
<tr><td></td><td colspan="2">EXAMPLE 2.3</td><td>The Neal and Seeman Powerlessness Scale was administered to five groups of
college students. Each student responded to the seven-item point scale. The
results — the average for each group—are listed in Table 2.7. Determine the
scale used in measuring these data.</td></tr>
</table>

TABLE 2.7		
Average powerlessness	4.5	1.3
score for five groups	3.2	2.8
	4.4	

SOLUTION   We can define a distance between two scores, but the location of the origin is
                  unknown. For example, a score of 0 on the Neal-Seeman social scale does not
                  correspond to a true zero measure of powerlessness. In fact, we do not know
                  what a Neal-Seeman score of 0 implies. Hence the scale is an interval scale.
                      Some sociologists would argue that although the average powerlessness
                  scores are measurements, we cannot really determine a distance between the
                  levels of the scale. These scientists would consider the Neal and Seeman
                  Powerlessness Scale to be an ordinal scale.

                      Example 2.3 illustrates that caution must be exercised when determining
                  the scale of measurement. Not all people will agree with your categorization
                  of a scale. The important point is that you understand why a scale has been
                  classified into a particular category and where there might be some disagree-
                  ment with your reasoning.

EXAMPLE 2.4   The Federal Bureau of Investigation maintains records of forcible rapes per
                  100,000 inhabitants for all standard metropolitan statistical areas (SMSAs) in
                  the United States. The forcible rape rates for a sample of eight metropolitan
                  areas are shown in Table 2.8. Determine the scale of the measurement
                  appropriate for the forcible rape rate.

TABLE 2.8

Forcible rape rates (per 100,000 people)

SMSA	Rate
Atlanta	60.9
Dallas	72.4
Denver	42.9
Detroit	62.6
Los Angeles	45.9
Milwaukee	33.3
San Diego	33.0
Washington, DC	29.3

Source: U.S. Department of Justice, *Uniform Crime Reports for the United States.*

SOLUTION

The appropriate scale for the data of Table 2.8 is the ratio scale, because the distances are defined between different forcible rape rates and because there is a meaningful zero point on the scale. Consequently, a forcible rape rate of 0 would indicate that no forcible rapes had been reported in that SMSA (a rather unlikely result). Since we can define a zero point, meaningful ratios of measurement can also be formed. For example, the forcible rape rate for Dallas is 2.47 times the rate for Washington, DC:

$$\frac{72.4}{29.3} = 2.47$$

It is interesting to note that we can easily convert the ratio scale of Example 2.4 into a scale of lesser quantitative sophistication. For example, we could categorize forcible rape rates for SMSAs using the classifications given in Table 2.9. For measuring data collected according to the categories of the table, we would use the ordinal scale, because we can rank the levels of the variable "forcible rape rate classification" from low to high.

TABLE 2.9

Forcible rape rate classifications per 100,000 people

low (rates less than 40)

medium (rates between 40 and 60)

high (rates greater than 60)

Now that we can distinguish among the four scales of measurement, we will consider several methods that are useful for comparing variables.

EXERCISES

8. One measure of fertility is the crude birth rate—that is, live births per 1000 people. Is the crude birth rate measured on a nominal, ordinal, interval, or ratio scale? Explain your answer.

9. Give an example (other than one mentioned in the text) of a nominal scale currently used in the social sciences.

10. A researcher first ranked the faculties at three universities according to national prestige, then according to actual scholarly productivity. The two rankings of the three universities (denoted as A, B, and C) are given in the accompanying table. Given this level of data, can a researcher *meaningfully* add the ranks (i.e., 2 for university A, 5 for B, and 5 for C) and conclude that universities B and C are equal universities? Comment.

EXERCISE 10

Faculty ranking for three universities

National Prestige		Scholarly Productivity	
1	A	1	A
2	B	2	C
3	C	3	B

11. What are the advantages in measuring social phenomena by a ratio scale as opposed to an interval scale?

12. Using the average IQ scores in Table 2.2, suggest categories for treating the data at the interval level and then at the nominal level. Indicate which schools would be placed in the various categories.

13. Search the literature in your library for any of the following variables. Try to locate examples where infant mortality, for example, is treated at the ordinal level and then at the ratio level.

infant mortality   aggression

alienation   industrialism

group morale   popularity

2.5 COMPARISONS OF VARIABLES EMPLOYING RATIOS, PROPORTIONS, PERCENTAGES, AND RATES

Among the many types of data that you will encounter in the social science literature, ratios, proportions, percentages, and rates are used for comparing two numbers in a set or comparing two sets of measurements. For example, we may be interested in comparing the consumer price index for this month with that for last month. Labor unions are interested in comparing their members' salaries to the national average for all related industries. Similarly, a high school senior contemplating a particular college might be interested in comparing the number of females to the number of males attending the college.

Comparisons can be made in two ways. We can subtract one score from the other score, or we can divide one score by the other. **Subtraction provides us with an absolute measure of the difference between two quantities and can be applied to data measured on either an interval or a ratio scale. The quotient of two numbers provides a relative comparison and can be applied only to data measured on a ratio scale.** Absolute measures of comparisons will be considered later. At this point we will introduce several relative measures for comparing two measurements. Except for rates, the choice of using ratios, proportions, or percentages depends on the preference of the user.

Attendance figures for a state university at the end of the spring quarters of 1980 and 1990 showed the breakdown given in Table 2.10. A potential student concerned about the campus social life might wish to compare the number of males to the number of females. Note that the variables "number of males" and "number of females" are both discrete variables measured on a ratio scale. For the spring semester of 1990 the *ratio* of the number of males to the number of females on the state university campus was, from Table 2.10,

$$\text{male-to-female ratio} = \frac{\text{number of males}}{\text{number of females}} = \frac{16,000}{15,000} = 1.07$$

TABLE 2.10

Enrollments by sex for
spring 1980 and 1990
at a state university

Sex	1980	1990
male	11,100	16,000
female	8,000	15,000
Total	19,100	31,000

That is, there were 1.07 males to every female on campus or, equivalently, 107 males to every 100 females. Similarly, during the spring semester of 1980, the male-to-female ratio was

$$\frac{11,100}{8,000} = 1.39$$

That is, there were 1.39 males for every female.

The preceding discussion leads us to the following definition.

DEFINITION 2.11	If there are n_A elements in set A and n_B elements in set B, the quantity n_A/n_B is called the **ratio** of the number of elements in A to the number of elements in set B. Similarly, n_B/n_A is the ratio of the number of elements in set B to the number in set A. (*Note*: Elements cannot belong in both sets. They must be either in set A or set B.)

Ratios are used extensively to compare the number of elements in one set to the number in a second set. We illustrate this idea in the next example.

EXAMPLE 2.5	Voter registration lists in a particular county precinct listed the following numbers of Democrats and Republicans:

| Democrats | 200 |
| Republicans | 240 |

Compute the ratio of the number of Democrats to Republicans in the precinct.

SOLUTION   The Democrat-to-Republican ratio is given by

$$\frac{\text{number of registered Democrats}}{\text{number of registered Republicans}} = \frac{200}{240} = .83$$

Thus there is .83 registered Democrat for every Republican registered in the precinct.

We are not always interested in comparing two numbers by using a ratio. Sometimes a *proportion* provides a useful comparison. A proportion is really a special kind of ratio, where the denominator is the total number in sets A and B. For example, using the data in Table 2.10, the proportion of males at a state university in the spring of 1990 was

$$\text{proportion of males} = \frac{\text{number of males}}{\text{total number of students}} = \frac{16,000}{31,000} = .52$$

That is, .52 of the campus student body was composed of males. Similarly, the proportion of females for the spring of 1990 was

$$\text{proportion of females} = \frac{\text{number of females}}{\text{total number of students}} = \frac{15,000}{31,000} = .48$$

DEFINITION 2.12 | If there are n_A elements in set A and n_B in set B, the **proportion** of the total number of elements $n_A + n_B$ that are in set A is

$$\frac{\text{number in set A}}{\text{total number in sets A and B}} = \frac{n_A}{n_A + n_B}$$

Similarly, the proportion in set B is

$$\frac{n_B}{n_A + n_B}$$

(*Note*: There are only two sets. Elements cannot belong to both sets. They must be either in set A or in set B.)

EXAMPLE 2.6   Using the data from Example 2.5, compute the proportion of Democrats and the proportion of Republicans registered in the precinct.

SOLUTION   Recall that there were 200 registered Democrats and 240 registered Republicans. Hence the proportion of Democrats is

$$\text{proportion of Democrats} = \frac{200}{200 + 240} = .45$$

Similarly, the proportion of Republicans is $240/440 = .55$.

Some people dislike working with fractions and decimals: they prefer *percentages*.

DEFINITION 2.13 | If there are n_A elements in set A and n_B elements in set B, the **percentage** of the total elements in set A is the proportion in set A multiplied by 100. That is,

$$\text{percentage in set A} = (\text{proportion in set A})(100)$$

$$= \frac{n_A}{n_A + n_B}(100)$$

Similarly,

$$\text{percentage in set B} = (\text{proportion in set B})(100)$$

$$= \frac{n_B}{n_A + n_B}(100)$$

(*Note*: Elements cannot belong in both sets. They must be either in set A or in set B.)

| EXAMPLE 2.7 | Compute the percentage of registered Democrats and registered Republicans, using the data in Example 2.5. |

SOLUTION | In Example 2.6 we computed the proportions of Democrats and Republicans as .45 and .55, respectively. So the percentage of Democrats is

$$.45 \times 100 = 45\%$$

and the percentage of Republicans is

$$.55 \times 100 = 55\%$$

The final method of comparison that utilizes the ratio of two measurements concerns *rates*. Common examples include birth rates, death rates, murder rates, and divorce rates. What are rates and what do they measure?

| DEFINITION 2.14 | The **rate of occurrence** of a particular outcome is found by dividing the actual number of occurrences by the number of possible times the outcome could have occurred.

$$\text{rate} = \frac{\text{number of actual occurrences}}{\text{number of possible occurrences}}$$

We illustrate the use of rates in the next example.

| EXAMPLE 2.8 | Table 2.11 shows the population and murder data for each of ten SMSAs. Determine the murder and nonnegligent manslaughter rates for each of the ten SMSAs listed in Table 2.11. |

SOLUTION | Utilizing Definition 2.14 and Table 2.11, we have the murder rates shown in Table 2.12.

TABLE 2.11

Number of murders
and nonnegligent
manslaughters in ten
SMSAs

SMSA	Population	Number
Albany, NY	849,920	27
Albuquerque, NM	489,181	60
Birmingham, AL	926,839	146
Charleston, SC	512,409	44
Milwaukee, WI	1,404,042	88
New Orleans, LA	1,308,848	262
Reno, NV	244,219	19
Syracuse, NY	650,125	19
Tacoma, WA	554,833	58
Wichita, KA	447,117	18

Source: U.S. Department of Justice, *Uniform Crime Reports for the United States.*

TABLE 2.12

Murder rates for ten
SMSAs

SMSA	Rate
Albany, NY	$\frac{27}{849,920} = .000032$
Albuquerque, NM	$\frac{60}{489,181} = .000123$
Birmingham, AL	$\frac{146}{926,839} = .000158$
Charleston, SC	$\frac{44}{512,409} = .000086$
Milwaukee, WI	$\frac{88}{1,404,042} = .000063$
New Orleans, LA	$\frac{262}{1,308,848} = .000200$
Reno, NV	$\frac{19}{244,219} = .000078$
Syracuse, NY	$\frac{19}{650,125} = .000029$
Tacoma, WA	$\frac{58}{554,833} = .000106$
Wichita, KA	$\frac{18}{447,117} = .000040$

Quite often rates are multiplied by a larger number, such as 100,000, to give the number of occurrences per 100,000 possible occurrences. This makes the rate easier to read and less subject to misinterpretation. Thus the rates for Example 2.8 could be multiplied by 100,000 to give the number of murders and nonnegligent manslaughters per 100,000 people. These rates are listed in Table 2.13.

TABLE 2.13

Murder rates (per 100,000 people) for ten SMSAs

SMSA	Rate
Albany, NY	3.2
Albuquerque, NM	12.3
Birmingham, AL	15.8
Charleston, SC	8.6
Milwaukee, WI	6.3
New Orleans, LA	20.0
Reno, NV	7.8
Syracuse, NY	2.9
Tacoma, WA	10.6
Wichita, KA	4.0

In this section we have considered comparisons of measurements by using the quotients of numbers. Ratios, proportions, percentages, and rates provide ways for comparing two measurements. Although we did not emphasize this point, most of the examples given to illustrate these procedures used measurements made at a fixed time. For example, we compared the number of males to the number of females enrolled at a state university in the spring of 1990 as well as the proportion of males in 1980 and 1990. Similarly, we compared the proportion (and percentage) of registered Democrats and Republicans for a specified precinct.

We now turn to an evaluation of the precision of the data we measure. Just how precise are they?

EXERCISES

14. State how a proportion differs from a percentage.

15. State how a rate differs from a ratio.

16. A state university has 400 students on full-time athletic scholarships. Of this total, 275 are males and 125 are females. What is the ratio of male athletic scholarships to female scholarships?

17. Refer to Exercise 16 and calculate the percentage of scholarships held by females.

18. Refer to Exercise 16 and calculate the percentage of scholarships held by males.

19. Use the data in the accompanying table to answer the following questions:
    a. What is the proportion of upper-middle-class males to all males?
    b. What is the ratio of all males to all females?
    c. What is the percentage of lower-middle-class males and females in the total group?

EXERCISE 19

Social class back-
ground of 107 interior
designers

Class	Males	Females	Total
upper	20	23	43
upper-middle	18	16	34
middle	5	10	15
lower-middle	4	7	11
lower	1	3	4
Total	48	59	107

20. Refer to Exercise 19.
    a. If 2 males of the 48 died during the study, what would be the crude death rate for males?
    b. If 6 females moved to other states during the study, what would be the geographical mobility rate for females?
    c. Would the data be easier to understand if the numbers were converted to percentages? Comment.

21. Margaret Eichler (1975) reported results of a study of the relationship between power and sexual fear in certain primitive societies. Suppose you replicate her study and report your research effort below. Use your data to answer the following questions.
    a. For those societies in which male genital mutilation is present, what is the ratio of kinship groups classified as patrilineal to those classified as matrilineal?
    b. What proportion of primitive societies in which male genital mutilation is present are classified as patrilineal?
    c. What percentage of primitive societies in which male genital mutilation is absent are classified as matrilineal?

EXERCISE 21

Classification of 200
primitive societies

| Male Genital Mutilation | Kinship Group | |
	Patrilineal	Matrilineal
present	52	11
absent	69	68

2.6   ARE THE MEASUREMENTS ROUNDED?

There is a difference between the actual value of a variable that we wish to measure and the value recorded by our measuring instrument. Because of the limitations of measuring equipment and the inexactness of human measurers, many observations will be imprecise. Weights of people are recorded to the nearest pound or kilogram; distances between adjacent cities are recorded to the nearest mile or kilometer; amounts of gasoline are recorded to the nearest tenth of a gallon or liter. We have actually *rounded* the true weights, miles, and gallons. There are, then, two sets of data: the true measurements, which we rarely can obtain, and the actual observed measurements, called the rounded observations. The difference between the true and the rounded measurements is called the **rounding error** and is a function of the rounding procedure. The precision of any measurement will be affected by the rounding procedure.

GENERAL ROUNDING PROCEDURE

1. Specify the rounding unit. We could round measurements to the nearest integer (or whole number), nearest 100, nearest 1000, nearest tenth, nearest thousandth, and so on.
2. Round each measurement to the nearest rounding unit.
3. If the actual observation lies at the midpoint of a rounding unit, round toward the nearest even unit.

We illustrate the rounding procedure in the next example.

EXAMPLE 2.9   A political scientist examined voting records in eight states. The data shown in Table 2.14 represent the percentage of eligible voters who actually cast ballots in the 1988 presidential election. Round these numbers to the nearest percentage point.

TABLE 2.14

Eligible voters casting
ballots in the 1988
presidential election

State	% Voting	State	% Voting
Alabama	50.2	Georgia	38.8
California	47.4	Hawaii	32.1
Connecticut	57.9	Minnesota	66.4
Florida	44.7	Washington	54.5

Source: U.S. Bureau of the Census, Statistical Abstract of the United States.

SOLUTION

The rounding unit for this example is 1%, which means that we must round measurements up or down to the nearest percentage point. No problem arises for Alabama, California, Connecticut, Florida, Georgia, Hawaii, or Minnesota, because 50.2 rounds down to 50, 47.4 rounds down to 47, 57.9 rounds up to 58, 44.7 rounds up to 45, 38.8 rounds up to 39, 32.1 rounds down to 32, and 66.4 rounds down to 66. However, for Washington, the observation falls at the midpoint of a rounding unit, so we apply the additional rule of rounding toward the nearest even unit. Therefore, rounding to the nearest even percentage point, 54.5 becomes 54.

EXAMPLE 2.10   Round the effective tax rates given in Table 2.15 to the nearest whole number.

TABLE 2.15

Effective tax rate (per
$1000) on residential
property for some U.S.
cities, by region

South	Rate	North	Rate	West	Rate
Atlanta, GA	15.0	Boston, MA	10.8	Anchorage, AK	14.8
Baltimore, MD	26.4	Chicago, IL	15.5	Billings, MT	13.0
Birmingham, AL	7.0	Cleveland, OH	21.0	Boise City, ID	19.3
Columbia, SC	11.3	Detroit, MI	41.0	Denver, CO	9.4
Houston, TX	15.3	Indianapolis, IN	15.7	Honolulu, HA	5.9
Jacksonville, FL	19.7	Milwaukee, WI	36.9	Las Vegas, NV	8.8
Little Rock, AR	10.2	New York, NY	11.3	Los Angeles, CA	6.4
Memphis, TN	17.7	Newark, NJ	32.0	Phoenix, AZ	6.8
New Orleans, LA	13.9	Philadelphia, PA	23.8	St. Louis, MO	11.6
Washington, DC	11.5	Portland, ME	15.7	Seattle, WA	12.4

Source: U.S. Bureau of the Census, Statistical Abstract of the United States.

SOLUTION

The rounding unit for the tax rate is 1, so we round up or down, depending on the actual rate. The results are shown in Table 2.16.

TABLE 2.16

Rounded rates of
Table 2.15

South	North	West
15	11	15
26	16	13
7	21	19
11	41	9
15	16	6
20	37	9
10	11	6
18	32	7
14	24	12
12	16	12

As mentioned previously, to determine the precision of our measurements, we must know the rounding procedure. If we observed the rounded numbers 81, 60, 70, and 17 and knew that the actual numbers had been rounded to the nearest ones unit, we could try to reconstruct the actual measurements. Although this is not entirely possible, we can construct limits, called **true limits**, that encompass the actual measurements. These true limits are presented in Table 2.17 for the rounded data of Example 2.9. **Note that we form the upper true limit by adding one-half of a rounding unit to the rounded measurement. Similarly, the lower true limit is formed by subtracting one-half of a rounding unit from the rounded measurement.**

TABLE 2.17

Reconstructing true
limits for measure-
ments rounded to the
nearest ones unit

Rounded Measurement	True Limits of Actual Measurements
32	31.5–32.5
39	38.5–39.5
45	44.5–45.5
47	46.5–47.5
50	49.5–50.5
54	53.5–54.5
58	57.5–58.5
66	65.5–66.5

Several additional comments should be made regarding rounding and the precision or quality of our measurements. First, the more rounding we use, the less precision we have. But the key to the entire process is to know the limitations of the rounding procedure. If we know the rounding unit, we can determine the true limits for the measurements. These limits determine the precision of the rounded data. Second, when calculations are performed, it is often wise to round only *after* all calculations have been performed. This procedure reduces the rounding errors.

Our discussion of rounding has focused on one procedure, rounding to the nearest even unit. Even though most data in the social sciences are rounded to the nearest even unit, such a procedure is arbitrary and far from universal. Western societies round age down to the last whole number; Japanese round age up to the next whole number. An American infant is not 1 year old until it has reached its 12th month of life. The infant then remains at age 1 until its 24th month. On the other hand, a Japanese infant is 1 year old at birth and becomes 2 years old after only 12 months.

EXERCISES

22. The data shown are the number of voters in city precincts favoring a political candidate. Round each figure to the nearest tens.

742,   675,   1281,   98,   637,   435,   790,   1285

23. Can discrete data be rounded? Explain your answer with reference to an example of your choice.

24. If an American female youngster states that she is 11 years old, what are the true limits of her age?

25. Round the following numbers to the nearest tenth:

.05,   .67,   1.20,   1.646,   139.85,   17.35

26. Round the following numbers to the nearest hundred:

52,   34,   7861,   4.3,   156,   122.92

27. Use the data of Table 2.15 and round the property tax rates for the South to the nearest ten.

2.7   VALIDITY AND RELIABILITY

In Chapter 1 we discussed the two branches of statistics and indicated that in addition to facilitating data description, the most important contribution of statistics to the social sciences is in measuring the goodness or quality of an inference. Although we have not yet discussed statistical inference in detail, the terms *goodness* and *quality* used in this context relate to evaluating the probability of making an incorrect decision about the population of interest.

Two other important issues, *validity* and *reliability*, must be considered when deciding on the variable or variables of interest for a survey or experimental setting. Do the variables measure what they are intended to measure (**validity**)? Are the measurements obtained from the variables of interest stable (**reliability**)?

For example, in a study designed to compare the attitudes of college students and older adults toward sexual permissiveness, a questionnaire was developed. A sample of older adults was obtained, and personal interviews were conducted with each individual in the sample. A similar sample of college students was obtained, with interviews executed in the same manner. Now, regardless of whether we are using descriptive statistics or inferential statistics for making comparisons of the two groups, we must be certain that our instrument, the questionnaire, is measuring attitudes toward sexual permissiveness. That is, can we distinguish between different attitudes toward sexual permissiveness using the questionnaire developed? Are the measurements we obtain valid?

Several techniques are often used to check validity. First, we can examine the data collection instrument for *face validity*; that is, are the items or questions appropriately worded and adequately focused on the variables of interest? Second, we can check the measurements obtained for a group of individuals whose attitudes toward sexual permissiveness are known. Third, we can have experts in the field evaluate the instrument.

Sometimes we can improve the validity of a study by using a different research technique. For example, an interview guide might be more useful than a mail questionnaire. Many older adults have difficulty in responding to sensitive issues related to sex, even when filling out an anonymous questionnaire. But many researchers are able to establish good rapport with some of the interviewees and can help them overcome their reluctance to answer sensitive questions.

The reliability of data obtained from a questionnaire is also an issue of concern. With reliability we are concerned with consistency; that is, does the instrument produce the same results when employed on two or more separate occasions with the same sample? As with validity, several techniques are available to test for reliability. The *test-retest* procedure is the most frequently used technique. As the name implies, the instrument is administered at least twice to the same sample. If the instrument is reliable, the results from the various administrations will be very similar.

Successful research requires that our findings be both valid and reliable.

An instrument might give us reliable information, yet the information could lack validity. For example, we could ask individuals how much they earn. They could consistently give us the same figure, but some respondents might tell us how much salary they make, and others their total income from trusts, investments, gifts, and salary.

Questions related to the validity and reliability of data are not always easily answered. However, they must be considered when a social scientist embarks on a research project or attempts to understand reports of research findings by other scientists. We will not have time to go into more detail in this text, since these topics are usually dealt with at length in courses related to sample survey design, questionnaire construction, and research methodology. We will proceed on the assumption that the validity and reliability of the variables of interest have been considered.

SUMMARY

Social, economic, and political variables can be of two types, quantitative and qualitative. A quantitative variable is one whose observations vary in magnitude from trial to trial. All other variables are qualitative. Quantitative variables can be subdivided into two groups: discrete, which can assume a countable number of values, and continuous.

Measurement of a variable, quantitative or qualitative, can be more difficult than it sounds. The first step is the selection of an appropriate scale of measurement: nominal, ordinal, interval, or ratio. If a variable lends itself to measurement on a ratio scale, it can also be measured by use of any of the less sophisticated scales: interval, ordinal, or nominal. The scales decrease in level of quantitative sophistication from the ratio scale to the nominal scale. Any variable that can be measured on one scale can also be measured on any less sophisticated scale. Qualitative data, not being at all quantitative, can be measured only on a nominal scale.

Statistical techniques appropriate for data generated by the four scales of measurement have overlapping utility. Techniques appropriate for one scale of measurement will apply also to data collected from a more sophisticated scale. In particular, techniques appropriate for a nominal scale can be employed for any type of data.

Ratios, proportions, percentages, and rates are methods for comparing variables. The precision of recorded measurements depends both on the measuring instrument used and on whether the measurements are rounded. We distinguished between the actual and rounded values of a variable and noted the rules employed in rounding data to acquire manageable numbers. Similarly, we noted the loss of precision and utilized true limits as a measure of data precision. Finally, we discussed the validity and reliability of a measuring process.

KEY WORDS

Constant   A phenomenon whose observations do not change in successive trials.

Continuous variable   A quantitative variable whose observations can assume any one of the countless number of values in a line interval.

Discrete variable   A quantitative variable whose observations can assume only a countable number of values.

Interval scale   A scale that incorporates all of the features of an ordinal scale and the additional feature that distances between levels on the scale can be specified.

Nominal scale   A scale that categorizes qualitative objects by name.

Ordinal scale   A scale that incorporates the features of a nominal scale and the additional feature that observations can be ordered or ranked by degree.

Percentage   A proportion multiplied by 100.

Proportion   The number of elements in a set possessing a specific characteristic divided by the total number of elements in the set.

Qualitative variable   A variable whose observations vary in kind but not in degree.

Quantitative variable   A variable whose observations vary in magnitude from trial to trial.

Rate of occurrence   The number of actual occurrences divided by the number of possible occurrences. It is usually expressed per 100, 1000, or 100,000.

Ratio   The number of elements in one set divided by the number of elements in another set.

Ratio scale   A scale that incorporates all the features of interval scales and the additional feature that ratios can be formed with levels of the scale.

Reliability   The stability of a score or measurement. Repeated observations of the same phenomenon should be consistent.

True limits   Limits for rounded measurements that encompass the actual measurements. True limits for a rounded measurement are formed by adding or subtracting one-half a rounding unit from the rounded measurement.

Validity   A variable has validity if it measures what it is intended to measure.

Variable   A phenomenon whose observations vary from trial to trial.

KEY FORMULAS

If there are n_A elements in set A and n_B elements in set B, then

Ratio of A to B $\dfrac{n_A}{n_B}$

Ratio of B to A $\dfrac{n_B}{n_A}$

Proportion in A $\dfrac{n_A}{n_A + n_B}$

Proportion in B $\dfrac{n_B}{n_A + n_B}$

Percentage in A $\dfrac{n_A}{n_A + n_B}(100)$

Percentage in B $\dfrac{n_B}{n_A + n_B}(100)$

SUPPLEMENTARY EXERCISES FOR CHAPTER 2

28. List ten variables of particular interest to social researchers.
    a. Which of these ten variables are quantitative? With which scale — ordinal, interval, or ratio — are they most often measured?
    b. Which of these ten variables are qualitative? Explain your answer.

29. Distinguish between quantitative and qualitative variables. Does this distinction lie in the mind of the researcher or in the *real* nature of social phenomena? Explain your answer.

30. Distinguish between continuous and discrete variables. Give examples of four continuous and four discrete variables not mentioned in the text.

31. Given the following social concepts, specify the most informative scale of measurement (nominal, ordinal, interval, or ratio) appropriate for the phenomenon in question. In each instance, explain your answer.

    population of Sacramento   sex
    alienation   employment status
    religiosity   social status
    religious affiliation   primitive tribes
    suicide rate

32. In society A there are 14,000 men and 16,000 women.
  a. What is the ratio of men to women?
  b. What is the ratio of women to men?
  c. What is the proportion of men in the society?
  d. What is the proportion of women in the society?

33. Society A, using the latest fertility technology, dramatically increases the number of boy babies and dramatically reduces the number of girl babies born each year for ten years. After a decade there are 17,000 males and 13,000 females.
  a. What is the ratio of males to females?
  b. What is the ratio of females to males?
  c. What is the proportion of males in the society?
  d. What is the proportion of females in the society?

34. A small, preliterate society has a total population of 1200. Four natives die from flesh wounds. What is the rate of deaths from flesh wounds?

35. The accompanying scores are the percentages of eligible voters registered in each of a sample of 20 SMSAs. Round each to the nearest percentage point and then to the nearest 10%.

80.2	72.9	60.0	68.3	84.8
49.7	75.1	70.6	50.5	72.8
65.3	73.0	80.7	69.6	56.1
67.4	63.3	74.7	64.1	81.8

36. Give the true limits for the 20 numbers listed in Exercise 35.

37. Give an example, other than one from the text, in which a social researcher would be interested in using ratios rather than frequency counts. Explain your selection.

38. Using the data in Table 2.13, round the murder rates to the nearest ones unit.

39. Give the true limits for the rounded rates in Exercise 38.

40. Why might a researcher prefer to use percentages instead of proportions? Explain your answer.

41. Why might a researcher prefer to use rates instead of ratios? Explain your answer.

42. Convert the forcible rape rates per 100,000 in Table 2.8 to rates per 1000 people. Which rate is easier to understand? Comment.

43. Round the rates in Table 2.8 to the nearest tens unit.

44. Round the rates in Table 2.8 to the nearest hundred. Give the true limits for each rounded rate.

45. Using the rates per 1000 people in Exercise 42, give the true limits for each rounded rate.

46. Using Database A, Appendix Table 7, and focusing on the background information for 200 university students, answer the following:
   a. What is the ratio of Catholics to Protestants?
   b. What proportion of all students are social science majors?
   c. What are the true limits of each student's age (numbered 001 through 015 inclusive)?

47. Using Database B, Appendix Table 8, round the infant mortality rates to the nearest tens unit for the first 20 nations (Algeria through Ireland). List the true limits for each of these rounded rates.

48. Using Database C, Appendix Table 9, indicate the level of measurement actually used for each of the following variables:

   a. age
   b. marital status
   c. coffee/tea consumption
   d. tobacco consumption
   e. alcohol consumption
   f. previous treatment for emotional problems
   g. hospitalization
   h. psychiatric treatment

49. Using Database A, Appendix Table 7, indicate which of the nine variables (crimes, college, sex, age, marital status, religion, race, income, and major) are qualitative? Explain your choices.

50. Using Database D, Appendix Table 10, indicate which of the seven variables (abortions, births to unmarried women, forcible rapes, murders, population density, poverty, and suicide) are discrete? Explain your choices. (Note: examine the way in which each variable was measured.)

51. Using Database D, Appendix Table 10, round the 30 suicide rates to the nearest percentage point and then answer the following questions:
   a. What is the ratio of states with suicide rates of 12 and higher to those of 11 and below?
   b. What is the proportion of states with suicide rates of 15 or more?
   c. What is the proportion of states with suicide rates of 12 or more?

52. Using Database D, Appendix Table 10, round the population density figures for the 30 states to the nearest tens and then answer the following questions:
   a. What is the proportion of states that have a population density of 100 or less?
   b. What is the proportion of states that have a population density of 60 or less?
   c. What is the proportion of states that have a population density of 200 or more?

53. Using Database D, Appendix Table 10, note that all of the entries in the table are expressed in terms of tenths, except for population density.

Should a researcher round all of the other numbers to the nearest whole number, or should population density be recalculated to the nearest tenth? Explain your position.

54. Review Database D, Appendix Table 10. Note that each abortion figure is per 1000 women age 15–44, births to unmarried women is in percentage points, forcible rape is per 100,000 people, murder is per 100,000 people, population density is in persons per square mile, poverty is measured in terms of percentage of people below the government's established income level, and suicide is based on the number of deaths from suicide per 100,000 deaths. Do these different bases make the data more difficult to interpret? How would you measure each of the variables if you had the opportunity to measure them any way you wished?

CHAPTER 3

GRAPHICAL TECHNIQUES FOR DESCRIBING DATA FROM A SINGLE VARIABLE

GENERAL OBJECTIVES

Social researchers often forget that they must communicate effectively with the general public, which is basically distrustful of attempts to measure human behavior and generally not prepared to handle statistical terms and symbols. Graphs, charts, and tables can help in this process and sometimes eliminate the need for more technical expressions.

This chapter introduces you to graphical techniques that describe data from one variable. You will learn which graphical techniques are most meaningful, depending on the kind of data available.

SPECIFIC OBJECTIVES

1. To show you the need to condense data and present them in summary form; to stress the fact that "A picture is worth a thousand words."
2. To share with you two guidelines for organizing qualitative data: the principle of exclusiveness and the principle of inclusiveness.
3. To introduce and illustrate the use of the pie chart, bar graph, and statistical map.
4. To share with you the guidelines used to organize quantitative data: criteria for selecting class intervals, apparent and real class limits, uniform interval widths, and relative frequency.
5. To introduce the histogram, stem-and-leaf plot, and frequency polygon.
6. To introduce and illustrate the use of time trends.
7. To highlight different shapes of frequency distributions and graphical distortions.
8. To give examples of computer output that illustrate the use of some of these graphical techniques.

3.1   INTRODUCTION

We often need to share the results of our studies with a lay audience — that is, with people not familiar with the complexities of social research. In this chapter we will examine a variety of graphical techniques used to share information simply and intelligently with a lay audience. These techniques include the construction of a pie chart, bar graph, statistical map, stem-and-leaf plot, histogram, polygon, and frequency distribution. We will also examine the guidelines that social researchers use to organize qualitative and quantitative data.

Before we can share our research results, we must describe the various measurements. As we stated in Chapter 1, social researchers use statistical techniques to make inferences about a population or universe based on information contained in a sample. Since the population or universe is usually a large mass of data or set of measurements, and since these data are by their very nature disorganized and varied, it is necessary to find some means of condensing and describing them. After we complete the description, we will be able to talk about a population, and, in the case of a sample, to state an inference about the population.

We are especially interested in studying ways to describe data or a set of measurements because we need to condense information from our research and present it in summary form. For example, the abortion figures for all counties in the United States in a given year must be described in condensed form before they are published. The data collected by the Bureau of the Census are a second example of data that require condensation and description prior to publication. Although census, social, economic, and political data may ultimately be employed to make projections about the future, simple description of these large quantities of data is necessary to make them available immediately for public use as indicators of the quality of life in a society.

The process of description is difficult. Suppose we ask you to describe the person sitting next to you so precisely that a stranger could select the individual from a group of others having similar physical characteristics. It is not an easy task. Fingerprints, voiceprints, and photographs, which are all pictorial, are the most precise ways of human identification. The description of a set of measurements is also a difficult task, but like the description of a person, it can be accomplished most easily by using graphical or pictorial techniques. We agree with the old maxim, "A picture is worth a thousand words."

Pictorial description is as old as the history of humankind. Cave drawings convey scattered bits of information about the life of prehistoric peoples. Similarly, vast quantities of knowledge about the life and culture of the Babylonians, Egyptians, Greeks, and Romans are brought to life by means of drawings and sculpture. Thus art has been used to convey a picture of various life-styles, history, and culture in all ages. Not surprisingly, pictures are of value in describing social data.

Social data are described in two ways, graphically and numerically. Graphical techniques are presented primarily in this chapter. Numerical techniques will follow in Chapter 4. The graphical methods in this chapter fall into two categories: those most suitable for categorical variables, including nominal and ordinal categorical data — the pie chart, bar graph, and statistical map — and those appropriate for quantitative variables, especially interval and ratio data — the frequency histogram, stem-and-leaf plot, and frequency polygon. An additional graphical representation — the time trend — is suitable for showing change over time for both qualitative and quantitative variables. Examples of each technique will be given, so that you can see how these descriptive tools can be applied to real-life situations.

3.2   ORGANIZING QUALITATIVE DATA

Social researchers are frequently required to organize and condense large quantities of data for public distribution. For example, data collected by the Bureau of the Census must be carefully condensed and packaged so that the general public can readily understand them. Similarly, social, economic, and political data that measure the health and welfare of a nation must be summarized before they are made available for public consumption.

In this section we will be concerned with the organization of data collected from qualitative variables. Two principles will guide us in grouping or categorizing these data.

PRINCIPLE OF EXCLUSIVENESS
No observation is classified into more than one category.

PRINCIPLE OF INCLUSIVENESS
Every observation is classified into a category.

In organizing a set of data, we require that enough categories be included so that every observation can be classified. At the same time, we require that the extent of classification be so precise that no observation can be logically placed into more than one category. The categories listed in Table 3.1

TABLE 3.1	**What Is Your Religious Affiliation?**	
Categories of religious affiliation	Catholic	other
	Jewish	no affiliation
	Protestant	no response

illustrate the principles of exclusiveness and inclusiveness. Note that every person interviewed can be placed into one of the six categories, and no one could respond with an answer that falls into more than one category. Data organized according to these guidelines are clear and unambiguous.

Now that you are somewhat familiar with the principles of exclusiveness and inclusiveness, let us examine a set of categories that illustrates how *not* to collect data (see Table 3.2). The problem here is that there are too many overlapping categories. Such categories as "poverty," "lack of jobs," "poor housing," and "too much welfare" may all be indicators of the same problem. Although the questionnaire asks respondents to choose one of the categories, the respondents may become confused by the multiple entries available for the same response. Similarly, the categories "criminal elements," "failure of public officials," and "police brutality" may again focus on the same general cause for the riots.

TABLE 3.2	**Which of the Following Do You Think Is the Most Important Cause of the Disorders?**	
Perceived causes of the Detroit race riots	black nationalism	poor housing
	poverty	too much welfare
	criminal elements	police brutality
	lack of jobs	don't know
	failure of public officials	other
	powerlessness	not ascertained

Being aware of these general principles for organizing qualitative variables, you can evaluate the organization of survey and study results published in newspapers, magazines, and professional journals. Are the results organized in such a way that we can draw some valid conclusions?

Now that you can organize data on a qualitative variable according to the principles of exclusiveness and inclusiveness, we will proceed to the graphical description of qualitative data.

EXERCISES

1. Table 3.2 contains the perceived causes of a racial disorder. Use these causes as the basis for developing your own set of mutually exclusive and inclusive categories.

2. In response to the question "What is your religious affiliation?", a researcher developed six categories. Evaluate these categories in terms of the principles of exclusiveness and inclusiveness:

Roman Catholic	Protestant
Episcopal	Jewish
Lutheran	none

3. Evaluate the following five classifications for "race," using the principles of exclusiveness and inclusiveness:

Hindu	Negroid
Moslem	other
Caucasoid	

4. Evaluate the following 11 classifications for "major in college," using the principles of exclusiveness and inclusiveness:

political science	physics
anthropology	chemistry
social sciences	other
sociology	none
history	not ascertained
physical sciences	

3.3 GRAPHING CATEGORICAL DATA: THE PIE CHART

Constructing a **pie chart** is one of the most common graphical procedures for describing a set of measurements. Traditionally, pie charts have been used with categorical data — either nominal or ordinal data. Essentially, the pie chart partitions a set of measurements into a few categories, much as you might slice a pie. The pie chart is best suited for displaying the percentage of the total assigned to each category.

The data in Table 3.3 shows the pattern of immigration of over 12.5 million migrants to the United States during a recent 27-year period. The U.S. Census Bureau reports that these immigrants came from Europe, Asia,

TABLE 3.3

Region of origin for re-
cent immigrants to the
United States

Region of Origin	Number	Percentage
Europe	2,550,200	20.3
Asia	4,245,800	33.8
North America	4,556,100	36.3
South America	823,900	6.6
Africa and others	370,400	3.0

Source: U.S. Bureau of the Census, *Statistical Abstract of the United States.*

North America (other than the United States), South America, or Africa and other areas. On the basis of official records, all immigrants were classified according to their region of origin.

Although you can scan the data in Table 3.3, the results are more easily interpreted by using a pie chart. From Figure 3.1 we can make certain inferences about recent patterns of migration. For example, the largest number of immigrants (approximately 36%) came from other countries in North America, followed by Asia (34%).

FIGURE 3.1

Pie chart for the data
of Table 3.3

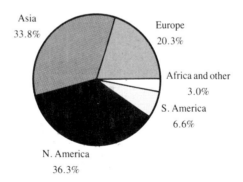

The pie chart of Figure 3.1 is constructed by apportioning the 360° of the circle according to the percentage in each regional category. Thus

$$\frac{36.3(360°)}{100} = 130.68°$$

would be assigned to North America. Similarly, we would assign

$$\frac{20.3(360°)}{100} = 73.08°$$

to those who migrated from Europe to the United States. The remainder of the pie is divided proportionally among the other three categories.

FIGURE 3.2

Percentage distribution
of United States popu-
lation age 25 and over,
by educational level
and race

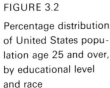

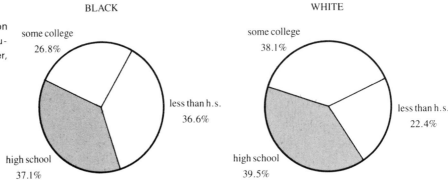

FIGURE 3.2

Percentage distribution
of United States popu-
lation age 25 and over,
by educational level
and race

Source: U.S. Bureau of the Census, *Statistical Abstract of the United States*

The two pie charts of Figure 3.2 display the percentage distribution of the
United States population age 25 years and over in terms of educational levels.
Each segment of the circle corresponds to the specific population of blacks
(or whites) with some college, a high school diploma, and less than a high
school education.

FIGURE 3.3

Percentage distribution
of drug-related com-
plaints, by ethnic
background

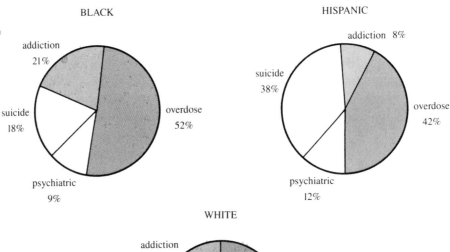

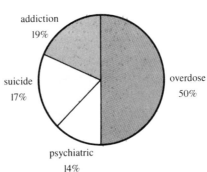

Other examples of pie charts can be found throughout the social science literature. For example, Figure 3.3 displays the percentage distribution for four drug-related complaints at emergency wards in three large metropolitan areas for white, black, and Hispanic patients, per 100 patient records for each ethnic group. Note that the overdose category was the most frequent complaint for emergency-room admission in all three ethnic groups.

GUIDELINES FOR CONSTRUCTING PIE CHARTS

1. Try to organize the data into a few categories (seven or fewer). Too many categories make the pie chart difficult to interpret.
2. When possible, display the pieces of the pie chart in either ascending or descending order of magnitude.
3. Use pie charts for displaying the percentage (rather than the number) of measurements in each category, since these charts are easier to interpret that way.

Note that pie charts are appropriate for data measured on a nominal scale and hence can be used for any data measured on an ordinal, interval, or ratio scale.

3.4   GRAPHING QUALITATIVE DATA: THE BAR GRAPH

The **bar graph** provides a second way to display qualitative data in graphical form. Figure 3.4 is a bar graph that gives the estimated membership of the principal religions in the United States.

A bar graph is relatively easy to construct and interpret using the following guidelines.

GUIDELINES FOR CONSTRUCTING BAR GRAPHS

1. Frequencies are labeled along the vertical axis (ordinate) of the chart; categories of the qualitative variable are labeled along the horizontal axis (abscissa).
2. To avoid distorting the graph, the vertical scale (for frequencies) should start at zero.

3. Rectangles are then constructed over each category, with the height of the rectangle equal to the number of observations in the category.
4. For clarity, a space is left between each category on the horizontal axis.

FIGURE 3.4

Estimated membership of the principal religions in the United States

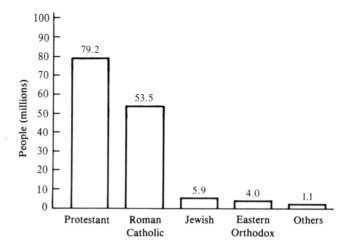

Source: U.S. Department of Commerce, Bureau of the Census

FIGURE 3.5

Percentage of arrests for possession of illegal drugs, by sex

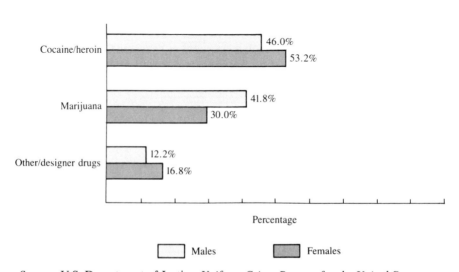

Source: U.S. Department of Justice, *Uniform Crime Reports for the United States*

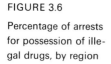

FIGURE 3.6

Percentage of arrests for possession of illegal drugs, by region

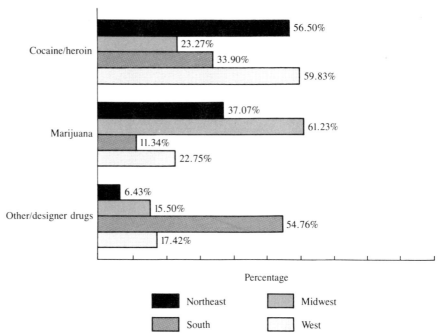

Source: U.S. Department of Justice, *Uniform Crime Reports for the United States*

When bar graphs are displayed horizontally, the roles of the two axes are reversed. This change is illustrated in Figure 3.5, which displays estimates of arrests for the possession of illegal drugs, by sex. The data come from the Federal Bureau of Investigation (FBI) and are grouped into three categories: cocaine or heroin, marijuana, and others (including designer drugs).

Bar charts or graphs can be used for numerous variables. The bar chart in Figure 3.6 offers a comparison of the percentages of arrests for drug possession, both by type and by region of the country in which the arrests took place.

3.5 GRAPHING QUALITATIVE DATA: THE STATISTICAL MAP (OPTIONAL)

A third form for graphically describing qualitative data is the **statistical map**. These maps are extremely useful for displaying geographical variation in such variables as income, sex ratios, marriage and divorce rates, crime rates, and election results.

FIGURE 3.7

Average daily room
charge for semiprivate
hospital room, by state

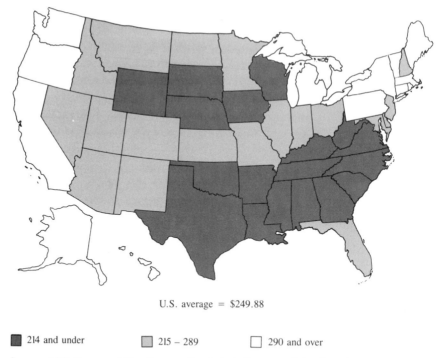

U.S. average = $249.88

■ 214 and under   ▨ 215 – 289   ☐ 290 and over

Source: U.S. Bureau of the Census, *Statistical Abstract of the United States*

Figure 3.7 presents a statistical map of the average daily room charge for
a semiprivate hospital room throughout the United States. As can be seen
from Figure 3.7, the guiding principle of the statistical map is to depict
graphically different classifications of a variable by different shadings. The
major problem in constructing these maps is choosing the units to be shaded.
When we wish to display geographical variation over the entire United
States, individual states provide a convenient unit. Similarly, city blocks or
voting precincts would provide convenient units for a statistical map of a city.

GUIDELINES FOR CONSTRUCTING STATISTICAL MAPS

1. Select area units that are large enough to be easily distinguishable,
   yet relevant to the study.
2. Use a color (or shading) code, with a separate shading for each
   category. To make a map easy to read, keep the number of
   categories small — say, five or fewer.

Figure 3.8 presents a geographical breakdown by state of the projected percentage of the population in the year 2000 that will be black.

In Sections 3.2 through 3.4 we discussed ways to organize data collected from qualitative variables and present them graphically. Although these procedures are basically designed for qualitative data, they can also be used for quantitative data. Other procedures, however, often provide more meaningful ways to organize and graph data from quantitative variables. We turn to these procedures in the next section.

FIGURE 3.8

Projected percentage of population in the year 2000 that will be black, by state

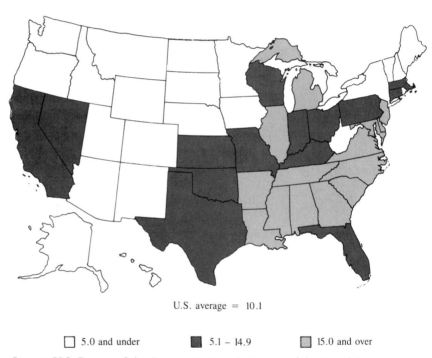

U.S. average = 10.1

☐ 5.0 and under   ■ 5.1 – 14.9   ▨ 15.0 and over

Source: U.S. Bureau of the Census, *Statistical Abstract of the United States*

EXERCISES

5. What is a pie chart, and why is the number of categories usually limited to seven?

6. How does a bar graph differ from a statistical map? When might you use a statistical map rather than a bar graph?

7. We can expect employment to increase in the major occupational categories in the state of Ohio between 1990 and 2000. Construct a pie chart for the anticipated increases, by category, which are as follows:

   - clerical workers, 18.9%
   - craft and kindred workers, 11.8%
   - laborers, 6.6%
   - managers, 7.9%
   - operatives, 15.2%
   - professionals and technical workers, 16.3%
   - salespeople, 6.1%
   - service workers, 17.2%

8. Using the data from the table on the number of workers in greater Cincinnati who work for the largest foreign investors, construct a bar graph.

Exercise 8

Number of greater Cincinnati workers employed by five of the largest foreign investors

Major Foreign Investors	Number of Workers
Great Britain	6500
Ireland	138
Japan	1200
Netherlands	200
West Germany	1450

9. Using the data in the accompanying table, construct a pie chart for the quality of housing for lower-middle-class blacks.

EXERCISE 9

Housing quality of blacks in Chicago, by socioeconomic status

| Status | Quality | | | |
	Sound	Unsound	Dilapidated	Total
upper	13	0	0	13
upper-middle	9	1	1	11
middle	37	3	6	46
lower-middle	36	38	34	108
lower	36	39	52	127
Total	131	81	93	305

10. Using the data in the accompanying table, construct a pie chart for the Asian population by racial-ethnic grouping.

EXERCISE 10

Nine racial-ethnic populations in the United States

Asian Racial-Ethnic Grouping	Number (thousands)	Percentage
Chinese	812	24.61
Filipino	782	23.70
Indian	387	11.73
Japanese	716	21.70
Korean	357	10.82
Vietnamese	245	7.43
Total	3299	99.99*

Pacific Islander Racial-Ethnic Grouping	Number (thousands)	Percentage
Hawaiian	172	70.78
Guamanian	31	12.76
Samoan	40	16.46
Total	243	100.00

Source: U.S. Bureau of the Census, *Statistical Abstract of the United States*
* Total does not equal 100.0% due to rounding.

11. Using the data in Exercise 9, construct a pie chart for quality of housing for lower-class blacks.

12. Using the data in Exercise 9, construct a pie chart for quality of housing for all blacks.

13. Using the data in Exercise 10, construct a pie chart for the Pacific Islander population by racial-ethnic grouping.

14. Using the data in Exercise 9, construct a bar graph for unsound housing by socioeconomic status.

15. Using the data in Exercise 10, construct a bar graph for the Asian population by racial-ethnic grouping.

16. Using the data in Exercise 10, construct a bar graph for the Pacific Islander population by racial-ethnic grouping.

17. Using the data in the accompanying table, construct a statistical map showing the distribution of death rates due to cancer, by state. Use four densities of shading (174 and below, 175–199, 200–219, and 220 and over).

EXERCISE 17

Death rates due to
cancer, by state and
region

Area	Rate
Northeast	220.1
Maine	226.7
New Hampshire	200.3
Vermont	197.0
Massachusetts	224.2
Rhode Island	239.1
Connecticut	214.5
Middle Atlantic	224.2
New York	216.0
New Jersey	224.2
Pennsylvania	236.5
East North Central	200.5
Ohio	211.7
Indiana	202.5
Illinois	199.3
Michigan	189.6
Wisconsin	196.7
West North Central	198.3
Minnesota	182.1
Iowa	205.6
Missouri	213.7
North Dakota	177.3
South Dakota	203.2
Nebraska	196.9
Kansas	190.8
South Atlantic	205.1
Delaware	210.7
Maryland	202.2
Virginia	186.9
West Virginia	224.8

Area	Rate
North Carolina	183.1
South Carolina	171.0
Georgia	168.6
Florida	249.4
East South Central	198.7
Kentucky	202.8
Tennessee	197.7
Alabama	201.9
Mississippi	190.0
West South Central	164.3
Arkansas	214.1
Louisiana	179.1
Oklahoma	193.2
Texas	147.5
Mountains	149.3
Montana	179.1
Idaho	158.8
Wyoming	127.2
Colorado	133.4
New Mexico	140.7
Arizona	177.7
Utah	98.4
Nevada	183.7
Pacific	172.0
Washington	177.2
Oregon	194.7
California	172.1
Alaska	83.1
Hawaii	133.2

Source: U.S. Bureau of the Census, *Statistical Abstract of the United States.*

18. Repeat Exercise 17 by constructing a statistical map showing the distribution of death rates due to cancer, by region. Use the same four densities of shading. Compare the two statistical maps. Write a paragraph or two, noting the differences between the two maps and how these differences might lead to different conclusions.

3.6 ORGANIZING QUANTITATIVE DATA

Quantitative data — specifically, data measured on interval or ratio scales — are categorized similarly to qualitative variables. The only difference is that the categories for qualitative variables are assigned a nominal (or verbal) label, whereas the categories for quantitative variables are intervals measured on an interval or ratio scale. In statistical language these intervals are called **class intervals.**

The selection of classes for a quantitative variable should conform to the principles of exclusiveness and inclusiveness described in Section 3.2. The intervals cannot overlap, and they must be inclusive, so that every measurement falls into an interval. The following guideline expresses these two requirements in one sentence.

GUIDELINE FOR SELECTING CLASS INTERVALS
Choose the intervals so that every measurement or score falls in one and only one interval. The intervals will then conform to the principles of exclusiveness and inclusiveness.

Additional criteria for selecting class intervals, chosen for convenience and ease of data interpretation, are the following.

ADDITIONAL CRITERIA FOR SELECTING CLASS INTERVALS
1. Choose the intervals so that no gaps appear between them.
2. Choose the intervals so that they have a common width, called the *class width.*

The reason for the latter two criteria will become apparent when we discuss graphical techniques for describing quantitative data. Now let us consider the mechanics for meeting the criteria that we have just given.

It is easy to construct class intervals that do not overlap, are contiguous (have no gaps), and have equal width. However, a point of confusion often arises about the **class limits** or endpoints of the intervals. This is because intervals are sometimes constructed in such a way that a measurement can fall directly on the point dividing two intervals. To which interval is the score then assigned? Suppose that a researcher has categorized data on a quantitative variable, the ratio of the number of children to the number of bedrooms for each household in an urban area. The following intervals were used: 0 to 1, 2 to 3, 4 to 5, 6 to 7, and so on. The **apparent class limits** for these data are then 0 to 1, 2 to 3, 4 to 5, 6 to 7, and so on. But the **real class limits** are: $-.5$ to 1.5, 1.5 to 3.5, 3.5 to 5.5, 5.5 to 7.5, and so on. Note that we would not know whether to assign the ratio 1.5 to the first or to the second interval. However, using the rounding procedures of Section 2.6, we would round to the nearest even unit. Hence 1.5 would be rounded to 2. Similarly, if we observed the measurement 5.5, we would round to 6. Let us now illustrate how we organize quantitative data.

Samples of 30 cities were selected, one sample from each region, to obtain information on violent crime rates. These rates are presented for each of the 90 cities in Table 3.4. We note from the table that the crime rates lie between 189 and 1020, but it is still difficult to describe how the 90 measurements are distributed along this interval. If we had only 5 or 6 crime rates, there would not be much of a problem, but we have 90 rates. Are most of the individual cities near 189, near 1020, or evenly distributed along the interval of measurement? To answer the question, we will construct a table giving the frequency distribution for the 90 observed violent crime rates.

The **range** of a set of scores is defined to be the difference between the largest and smallest scores. For our data set the largest score is 1020, the smallest score is 189, and the range is $1020 - 189 = 831$. To construct a table giving the frequency distribution of a set of scores, we divide the interval 189 to 1020 into an arbitrary number of class intervals.

If the number of scores is small, we do not bother to graph them. If the number of scores is large, we adopt a sufficient number of class intervals to provide a detailed picture of the data. As a rule of thumb, we advise using between 10 and 20 intervals for a large set of scores.

The class intervals should be of uniform width. To determine an appropriate class width, divide the range by the number of intervals that seem appropriate for the number of scores we wish to describe. Round the resulting number to a convenient interval width. This number is the class width or interval size, usually symbolized by the letter i. Suppose we decide to use approximately 15 intervals for the data in Table 3.4. Then the range divided by 15 is $831/15 = 55.4$, so an appropriate interval width is 55.

Having determined an appropriate class width, choose the first interval so that it includes the smallest observation. A convention frequently followed is to choose the lower apparent limit of the first interval to be either 0 or an

	South	Rate	North	Rate	West	Rate
TABLE 3.4	**South**	**Rate**	**North**	**Rate**	**West**	**Rate**
Violent crime rates for 90 SMSAs selected from the South, North, and West	Albany, GA	876	Allentown, PA	189	Abilene, TX	570
	Anderson, SC	578	Battle Creek, MI	661	Albuquerque, NM	928
	Anniston, AL	718	Benton Harbor, MI	877	Anchorage, AK	516
	Athens, GA	388	Bridgeport, CT	563	Bakersfield, CA	885
	Augusta, GA	562	Buffalo, NY	647	Brownsville, TX	751
	Baton Rouge, LA	971	Canton, OH	447	Denver, CO	561
	Charleston, SC	698	Cincinnati, OH	336	Fresno, CA	1020
	Charlottesville VA	298	Cleveland, OH	526	Galveston, TX	592
	Chattanooga, TN	673	Columbus, OH	624	Houston, TX	814
	Columbus, GA	537	Dayton, OH	605	Kansas City, MO	843
	Dothan, AL	642	Des Moines, IA	496	Lawton, OK	466
	Florence, SC	856	Dubuque, IA	296	Lubbock, TX	498
	Fort Smith, AR	376	Gary, IN	628	Merced, CA	562
	Gadsden, AL	508	Grand Rapids, MI	481	Modesto, CA	739
	Greensboro, NC	529	Janesville, WI	224	Oklahoma City, OK	562
	Hickory, NC	393	Kalamazoo, MI	868	Reno, NV	817
	Knoxville, TN	354	Lima, OH	804	Sacramento, CA	690
	Lake Charles, LA	735	Madison, WI	210	St. Louis, MO	720
	Little Rock, AR	811	Milwaukee, WI	421	Salinas, CA	758
	Macon, GA	504	Minneapolis, MN	435	San Diego, CA	731
	Monroe, LA	807	Nassau, NY	291	Santa Ana, CA	480
	Nashville, TN	719	New Britain, CT	393	Seattle, WA	559
	Norfolk, VA	464	Philadelphia, PA	605	Sioux City, IA	505
	Raleigh, NC	410	Pittsburgh, PA	341	Stockton, CA	703
	Richmond, VA	491	Portland, ME	352	Tacoma, WA	809
	Savannah, GA	557	Racine, WI	374	Tucson, AZ	706
	Shreveport, LA	771	Reading, PA	267	Victoria, TX	631
	Washington, DC	685	Saginaw, MI	684	Waco, TX	626
	Wilmington, DE	448	Syracuse, NY	685	Wichita Falls, TX	639
	Wilmington, NC	571	Worcester, MA	460	Yakima, WA	585

Source: U.S. Department of Justice, *Uniform Crime Reports for the United States.*
Note: Rates represent the number of violent crimes (murder, forcible rape, robbery, and aggravated assault) per 100,000 inhabitants, rounded to the nearest whole number.

integral multiple of the interval width. Such a procedure ensures uniformity in the construction of tables and graphs. It is also important to choose class intervals so that no observation falls on a point of division between two class intervals. This eliminates any ambiguity in placing observations into intervals.

For the violent crime rate example, the smallest observation is 189, and the interval width is 55. Since the interval width is 55, potential candidates for the lower apparent limit are 0, 55, 110, 165, and so forth. If we choose 0 as the lower apparent limit, we have the following limits:

Apparent Class Limits	Real Class Limits
0– 54	−0.5– 54.5
55–109	54.5–109.5
110–164	109.5–164.5
165–219	164.5–219.5

Although the real class limits are nonoverlapping, contiguous, and of equal width (55), the first interval does not include the smallest score. Choosing 165 as the lower apparent limit for the first interval, we obtain the apparent and real class limits that follow. Note that the first interval now includes 189, the smallest score.

Apparent Class Limits	Real Class Limits
165– 219	164.5– 219.5
220– 274	219.5– 274.5
275– 329	274.5– 329.5
330– 384	329.5– 384.5
385– 439	384.5– 439.5
440– 494	439.5– 494.5
495– 549	494.5– 549.5
550– 604	549.5– 604.5
605– 659	604.5– 659.5
660– 714	659.5– 714.5
715– 769	714.5– 769.5
770– 824	769.5– 824.5
825– 879	824.5– 879.5
880– 934	879.5– 934.5
935– 989	934.5– 989.5
990–1044	989.5–1044.5

These are the class limits we will use for our example. As often happens, however, given the actual distribution of scores, we end up with 14 or 16 class intervals instead of the 15 we had intended. In our current example, we end up with 16 intervals. In succeeding sections we will use real rather than apparent class limits exclusively. You can easily obtain real class limits if you are given the apparent class limits.

The class intervals formed by the real class limits for our example were selected according to the following principles.

PRINCIPLES FOR SELECTING CLASS INTERVALS

1. Decide on the number of intervals necessary to describe the measurements or scores — usually, approximately 15 intervals will do.
2. Divide the range of the scores by the number of intervals. Round to a convenient unit. This gives the class interval width.
3. Locate the first interval so that it includes the smallest score. The lower apparent limit of the first interval should be an integral multiple of the interval width or be zero.
4. If a score falls on a real class limit, use the rounding procedures of Chapter 2 to assign the score to a class interval.

Having specified the class intervals, we will now consider how the measurements or scores are distributed into the classes. Examine each of the 90 observations in Table 3.4 and keep a tally of the number falling in each of the 16 class intervals. The number falling into a given class is called the **class frequency**. The total of the class frequencies is called the **sample size** and is denoted by n; for our example, $n = 90$. The tallies and class frequencies for our example are shown for each class in Table 3.5. The table portrays the **frequency distribution** of the $n = 90$ violent crime rates.

The **relative frequency** for a class interval is defined to be the frequency of the class divided by the sample size. If we let f_i denote the frequency of class j, then the relative frequency for class j is defined as shown in the box.

| DEFINITION 3.1 | Let class j have frequency f_j and assume there are n items in the sample. Then the **relative frequency for class j** is f_j/n. |

For example, the relative frequency for the ninth class interval, with real limits 604.5 to 659.5, can be found as follows. The sample size is $n = 90$, and

TABLE 3.5

Frequency distribution
for the data of Table
3.4

Class j	Class Interval	Tally	Class Frequency	Relative Frequency
1	164.5– 219.5	//	2	.022
2	219.5– 274.5	//	2	.022
3	274.5– 329.5	////	4	.044
4	329.5– 384.5	𝍸𝍸 /	6	.067
5	384.5– 439.5	𝍸𝍸 /	6	.067
6	439.5– 494.5	𝍸𝍸 ///	8	.089
7	494.5– 549.5	𝍸𝍸 ////	9	.100
8	549.5– 604.5	𝍸𝍸 𝍸𝍸 //	12	.133
9	604.5– 659.5	𝍸𝍸 ////	9	.100
10	659.5– 714.5	𝍸𝍸 ///	8	.089
11	714.5– 769.5	𝍸𝍸 ///	8	.089
12	769.5– 824.5	𝍸𝍸 //	7	.078
13	824.5– 879.5	𝍸𝍸	5	.056
14	879.5– 934.5	//	2	.022
15	934.5– 989.5	/	1	.011
16	989.5–1044.5	/	1	.011
Total			90	1.000

the frequency for the ninth interval is $f_9 = 9$. Hence

$$\text{relative frequency for class } 9 = \frac{9}{90} = .100$$

One final comment should be made about constructing a frequency distribution for a set of scores. Following the steps outlined above does not guarantee that the class intervals and frequencies will adequately reflect the original data. The following check can be performed if there are not too many sample scores. Compute the quantity fX (frequency times class midpoint) for each class, and add these products across classes. If the frequency table adequately reflects the data, this sum will be close to the sum of the original scores. If the sum of the fX quantities is not close to the sum of the original scores, we have probably used too few class intervals. Decrease the class width and construct another table. Further discussion of this idea will follow a worked example in Section 4.4.

Having discussed the organization of data for a quantitative variable, we will now consider graphical techniques for describing the data.

3.7   GRAPHING QUANTITATIVE DATA: THE HISTOGRAM

Social data from a frequency distribution are, by tradition, likely to be displayed as a graph called a **histogram** (or *frequency histogram*). In creating the histogram, we mark the real class limits along the horizontal axis and the frequencies along the vertical axis. Rectangles are then constructed over each class interval, with the height of the rectangle equal to the class frequency. The frequency histogram for the data in Table 3.5 is given in Figure 3.9.

Sometimes the results of a frequency table are presented graphically by using a **relative frequency histogram**. Both relative frequency histograms and frequency histograms are useful graphic tools for describing the distribution of data measured on an interval or ratio scale. The only difference from the frequency histogram in the relative frequency histogram is that the vertical axis is scaled for relative frequency rather than frequency. Using the relative frequency histogram, it is easier to locate the fraction or percentage of scores lying in a given interval. The relative frequency histogram for Table 3.5 is presented in Figure 3.10. Very little distinction is made between these two histograms, since they become the same figure if drawn to the same scale. We often call either one simply a histogram.

Whenever possible, histograms for social data are constructed so that the height of the vertical axis is approximately two-thirds to three-fourths the length of the horizontal axis. This avoids graphical distortions caused by stretching or shrinking the vertical axis to accentuate or mask any change.

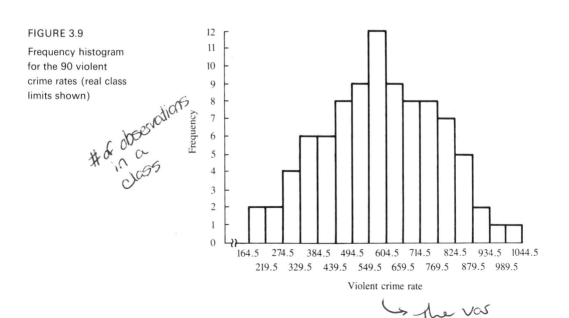

FIGURE 3.9

Frequency histogram for the 90 violent crime rates (real class limits shown)

Violent crime rate

FIGURE 3.10

Relative frequency
histogram for the 90
violent crime rates
(real class limits
shown)

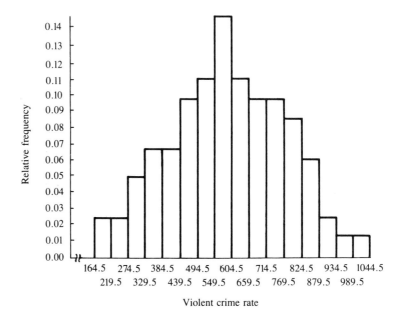

FIGURE 3.11

Histogram for $n = 300$
violent crime rates
(real class limits
shown)

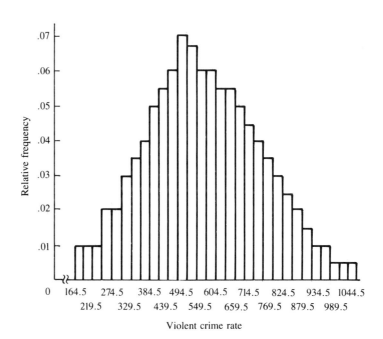

Histograms for large sets of data frequently appear to be almost smooth curves. A histogram describing the set of violent crime rates from a sample of 300 cities is shown in Figure 3.11. We have intentionally employed more intervals than usual, to show that the relative frequency histogram begins to approach a smooth curve when both the number of measurements and the number of class intervals are increased.

EXERCISES

19. Compute the relative frequency for each class interval for Colombian males only, using the data in the accompanying table.

EXERCISE 19

Age at first heterosexual (coital) experience among Colombians

Age	Number of Males	Number of Females
8–9	1	0
10–11	5	0
12–13	42	16
14–15	68	77
16–17	64	74
18–19	72	70
20–21	29	32
22–23	13	28
24–25	13	12
26–27	2	3
28–29	0	5
30–31	2	2
Total	311	319

Source: David M. Monsees, "Study of First Heterosexual Experience" (unpublished paper); by permission.

20. Compute the relative frequency for each class interval for females only, using the data in Exercise 19.

21. Based on the frequency distribution in the accompanying table, what is the class interval width? Also give the real class limits.

EXERCISE 21

Average daily tempera-
ture for 67 cities

Temperature	Frequency
39–41	3
42–44	2
45–47	8
48–50	10
51–53	9
54–56	10
57–59	8
60–62	7
63–65	3
66–68	3
69–71	2
72–74	0
75–77	2
Total	67

22. Based on the frequency distribution contained in the accompanying table, what is the class interval width? Construct a relative histogram for these data.

EXERCISE 22

Index of presence of
psychiatric symptoms
in residents of South
County

Index Score	Frequency	*relative Freq*	Percentage	*Cumulative relative Freq*
0–2	130	.074	7.9	.074
3–5	302	.184	18.4	.263
6–8	462	.281	28.1	.544
9–11	365	.222	22.2	.766
12–14	232		14.1	
15–17	88		5.3	
18–20	41		2.5	
21–23	12		.7	
24–26	8		.5	
27–29	3		.2	
30–32	2		.1	
Total	1645		100.0	

Source: George J. Warheit, *Southern Mental Health Needs and Services Project*, NIMH 15900-05 (unpublished data); by permission.

23. Use the accompanying frequency table for the student survey.
   a. Identify the real class limits.
   b. Construct a frequency histogram for the number of students by the size of the college.

EXERCISE 23

Number of students
surveyed by size of
college or university

Size of School	Number of Students
0–2,499	94
2,500–4,999	268
5,000–7,499	154
7,500–9,999	72
10,000–12,499	206
12,500–14,999	147
15,000–17,499	465
17,500–19,999	333
20,000–22,499	150
22,500–24,999	162
Total	2051

Source: Asoke Basu, Norman R. Jackman,
and Richard G. Ames, "Attitudes and
Opinions About Colleges and Universities"
(unpublished paper); by permission.

24. Compute the relative frequencies for the average daily semiprivate room
charges shown in the accompanying table.

EXERCISE 24

Average daily charges
for a semiprivate room
at a U.S. hospital, by
state

Expenditure (dollars)	Number of States
371–385	1
356–370	1
341–355	1
326–340	3
311–325	1
296–325	4
281–295	1
266–280	4
251–265	3
236–250	7
221–235	2
206–220	5
191–205	7
176–190	4
161–175	3

Source: U.S. Bureau of the Census, *Statistical
Abstract of the United States*

25. Set up a frequency histogram for the data in the accompanying table on heroin addicts in two suburban high schools.

EXERCISE 25

Number of persons
whose first heroin use
is in a given year

Year	Number of Addicts
1965	3
1966	15
1967	12
1968	9
1969	11
1970	8
1971	6
1972	8
1973	1
1974	3
Total	76

Source: David B. Graeven, *The Study of a Heroin Epidemic*, NIDA RO-1-DA-00940 (unpublished data); by permission.

3.8   COMMENTS ABOUT HISTOGRAMS

The relative frequency histogram is the graph of primary interest in statistical inference. We now present some pertinent comments about its interpretation and relevance to inference.

First, it is important to note that **the fraction of the total number of scores falling in an interval is equal to the ratio of the area under the histogram over the interval to the total area under the histogram.** For example, the fraction of the 90 violent crime rates (of Table 3.5) less than 549 is $\frac{37}{90}$. You will note in Figure 3.12 that $\frac{37}{90}$ of the total area (shaded) under the relative frequency histogram lies to the left of 549.5.

The second pertinent point in interpreting the frequency histogram is that **if a single observation is selected at random from the set of all scores, the probability that it lies in a particular interval is equal to the fraction of the total number of measurements falling in that interval** (the relative frequency for that interval). For example, if 90 cards were labeled with the respective rates in Table 3.4 and then shuffled, the probability of choosing a crime rate between

FIGURE 3.12

Relative frequency
histogram showing
fraction of rates below
549.5 (real class limits
shown)

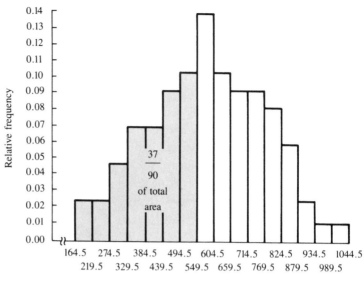

164.5 and 549.5 would be $\frac{37}{90}$, because 37 of the 90 rates fall in this interval. From Figure 3.12 we note that the area under the frequency histogram over the interval 164.5 to 549.5 (shaded) is equal to $\frac{37}{90}$ of the total area. Similarly, the probability of choosing a crime rate between 384.5 and 549.5 is $\frac{23}{90}$ (see Figure 3.13).

FIGURE 3.13

Relative frequency
histogram showing
fraction of rates in the
interval 384.5 to 549.5
(real class limits
shown)

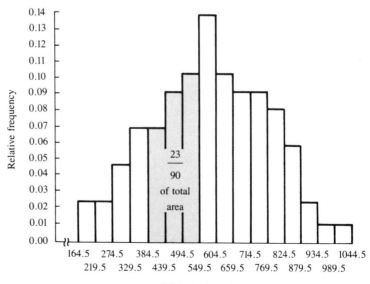

The third important point is that **although we can construct a frequency histogram for any set of numerical values in a sample or a population, our objective is to describe or make inferences about a population**. Although we will seldom have all the scores for the population in question and hence will not be able to construct the frequency histogram physically, we can imagine that one could be constructed and that it would possess an outline similar to that obtained for a sample. Since populations usually contain a large number of scores, the number of classes can be made large enough that the population frequency histogram becomes almost a smooth curve.

As the number of scores in a sample increases, we can select smaller class intervals. The resulting histogram will be more regular and approach being a smooth curve. Figure 3.14 shows three frequency histograms for crime rates. The first is a histogram for a sample of $n = 90$ scores, the second for a sample of $n = 300$ scores, and the third for the entire population. Note that the scale of the relative frequency (ordinate) will change from one figure to another. Second, observe that it may be necessary to change the endpoints of the class intervals (as has been done in Figures 3.14a and 3.14b) so that no score falls on the boundary between two classes.

The frequency histogram is an excellent way to characterize a population of scores. The area under the frequency histogram for the population tells us the proportion of the total number of scores in the population falling in given

FIGURE 3.14

Relative frequency histograms for two samples and population of recorded violent crime rate for U.S. cities (real class limits shown)

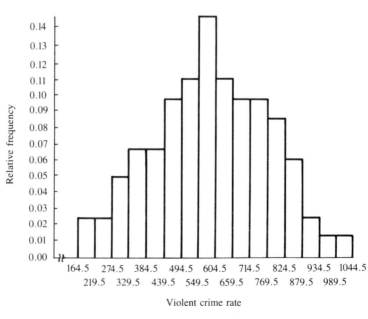

(a) Sample, $n = 90$

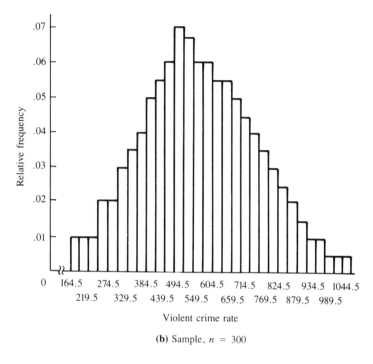

(b) Sample, $n = 300$

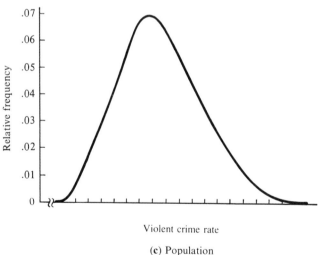

(c) Population

intervals. We can also see from the frequency histogram for the population what the largest and the smallest scores might be. However, the histogram, like other graphical techniques, does have one major shortcoming. This shortcoming becomes obvious when we try to use a sample histogram to make an inference about a population histogram. It is difficult to measure the similarity (or dissimilarity) between two histograms. Consequently, in Chapter 4, we will discuss other ways of using the sample data to make inferences about the population from which the sample is drawn.

EXERCISES

26. Using the data in Exercise 19, plot the distribution of age at first heterosexual experience for Colombian males, in the form of a frequency histogram.

27. Repeat Exercise 26 for Colombian females.

28. Use a frequency histogram to describe graphically the annual average daily mean temperature for the data in Exercise 21.

29. If the data in Exercise 22 on the index of the presence of psychiatric symptoms were plotted in a frequency histogram and then in a relative frequency histogram, would the two figures be identical? Comment.

30. Using the data in Exercise 23, construct a relative frequency histogram.

31. If you were to plot the data in Exercise 24 in the form of a histogram, would you use 370.5 to 385.5 or 371 to 385 as your first interval on the horizontal axis? Comment.

3.9   DISPLAYING QUANTITATIVE DATA: THE STEM-AND-LEAF PLOT (OPTIONAL)

The emergence of exploratory data analysis (EDA) has resulted in renewed interest in the use of descriptive statistics to understand social data. One graphical technique of EDA that has become quite popular is the *stem-and-leaf-plot.*

The **stem-and-leaf plot** is a clever, simple device to construct a histogram-like picture of a frequency distribution. It allows us to use the information contained in a frequency distribution to show the range of scores, any concentrations of scores, the shape of the distribution, any specific values or scores that are not represented, and any stray or extreme scores.

The stem-and-leaf plot does *not* follow the principles for selecting class intervals given in Section 3.6. It has its own, unique set of organizational principles, and we will follow them only when dealing with the stem-and-leaf plot and the box plot (to be covered in Section 4.13). We will use the data shown in Table 3.4 to illustrate how to construct a stem-and-leaf plot.

FIGURE 3.15	1 89
	2 98 96 24 10 91 67
Stem-and-leaf plot for	3 88 76 93 54 36 93 41 52 74
violent crime rates of	4 64 10 91 48 47 96 81 21 35 60 66 98 80
Table 3.4	5 78 62 37 08 29 04 57 71 63 26 70 16 61 92 62 62 59 05 85
	6 98 73 42 85 61 47 24 05 28 05 84 85 90 31 26 39
	7 18 35 19 71 51 39 20 58 31 03 06
	8 76 56 11 07 77 68 04 85 14 43 17 09
	9 71 28
	10 20

The original scores of Table 3.4 are either three- or four-digit numbers. For three-digit numbers, we will use the first, or *leading*, digit of scores as the *stem* (see Figure 3.15) and the *trailing* digits as the *leaf.* When we have four-digit numbers, we will use the first two digits as the stem. For example, the violent crime rate in St. Louis is 720. The leading digit is 7, and the trailing digits are 20. In the case of Fresno, the leading digits are 10 and the trailing digits are 20. If our data consisted of six-digit numbers, such as 104,328, we might use the first two digits as stem numbers, use the second two digits as leaf numbers, and ignore the last two digits.

The smallest rate in the data on violent crime is 189, and the largest is 1020. We will display the values in a stem-and-leaf plot as shown in Figure 3.15. The leading digit (stem of a score) determines the row in which a score is placed. The trailing digits for a score are then written in that row. In this way each score is recorded in the stem-and-leaf plot.

We can see that each stem defines a class interval, and the limits of each interval are the largest and smallest possible scores for the class. The values represented by each leaf must be between the lower and upper limits of the interval.

The diagram can be made a bit neater by ordering the data within a row from lowest to highest, but this process is time-consuming if done by hand. Such ordering is shown in Figure 3.16 for the data of Table 3.4. The result is that a stem-and-leaf plot is a graph that looks much like a histogram turned sideways (compare Figures 3.9 and 3.15). The advantage of such a graph over the histogram is that it reflects not only frequencies, concentration(s) of scores, and the shape of the distribution, but also the actual scores. From the scores, we can determine whether there are any values not represented and whether there are stray or extreme values.

FIGURE 3.16

Stem-and-leaf plot of
Table 3.4 and Figure
3.15

1	89
2	10 24 67 91 96 98
3	36 41 52 54 74 76 88 93 93
4	10 21 35 47 48 60 64 66 80 81 91 96 98
5	04 05 08 16 26 29 37 57 59 61 62 62 62 63 70 71 78 85 92
6	05 05 24 26 28 31 39 42 47 61 73 84 85 85 90 98
7	03 06 18 19 20 31 35 39 51 58 71
8	04 07 09 11 14 17 43 56 68 76 77 85
9	28 71
10	20

In summary, to display a mass of data in the stem-and-leaf plot format:

1. Split each score or value into two sets of digits. The first or leading set of digits is the term, and the second or trailing set of digits is the leaf.
2. List all possible stem digits from lowest to highest.
3. For each score in the mass of data, write down the leaf numbers on the line with the appropriate stem number.
4. If the display looks too cramped and narrow, stretch the display by using two lines per stem; for example, place leaf digits 0, 1, 2, 3, and 4 on the first line of the stem and leaf digits 5, 6, 7, 8, and 9 on the second line.
5. If too many trailing digits are present, such as in a six- or seven-digit score, drop the rightmost trailing digit(s) to maximize the clarity of the display.

The rules for developing a stem-and-leaf plot are different than the rules for establishing class intervals for the traditional frequency distribution and the rules for other procedures that we will consider later. Class intervals for stem-and-leaf plots are, then, in a sense atypical.

EXERCISES

32. Use the data in Exercise 17 to construct a stem-and-leaf plot. First, round the data to the nearest unit, thus using only the first three digits.
33. Construct a stem-and-leaf plot for the newspaper circulation data in the accompanying table (newspapers sold per 100 people).

EXERCISE 33

Number of newspapers
sold (per 100 people),
by state

Alabama	18	Missouri	25
Alaska	24	Montana	23
Arizona	21	Nebraska	29
Arkansas	23	Nevada	26
California	23	New Hampshire	20
Colorado	29	New Jersey	22
Connecticut	27	New Mexico	21
Delaware	22	New York	43
D.C.	140	North Carolina	22
Florida	25	North Dakota	28
Georgia	18	Ohio	25
Hawaii	22	Oklahoma	23
Idaho	20	Oregon	24
Illinois	23	Pennsylvania	26
Indiana	28	Rhode Island	30
Iowa	26	South Carolina	19
Kansas	22	South Dakota	24
Kentucky	18	Tennessee	20
Louisiana	18	Texas	21
Maine	24	Utah	17
Maryland	15	Vermont	23
Massachusetts	36	Virginia	42
Michigan	27	Washington	25
Minnesota	22	West Virginia	23
Mississippi	15	Wisconsin	24
		Wyoming	20

Source: U.S. Bureau of the Census, *Statistical Abstract of the United States.*

34. Refer to Exercise 33. Because there are only five stem numbers, construct another stem-and-leaf plot, but this time stretch the display by using two lines per stem, with leaf digits 0, 1, 2, 3, and 4 on the first line and 5, 6, 7, 8, and 9 on the second.

3.10   GRAPHING QUANTITATIVE DATA: THE FREQUENCY POLYGON (OPTIONAL)

The **frequency polygon** is an alternate way to graph the results of a frequency distribution. The frequency polygon gives an impression of continuity and shows a gradual change from class to class. As with histograms, the frequency polygon is used with interval or ratio scale data. The vertical axis (or ordinate) is labeled with frequencies, and the real class limits are marked on the horizontal axis (or abscissa). The frequency associated with each class is indicated by placing a dot over the midpoint of a class interval, with the height of the dot equal to the class frequency. The dots are then joined by straight lines. The frequency polygon for the violent crime rate data of Table 3.5 is presented in Figure 3.17. You will note that the polygon begins at the lower real limit of the first class interval and ends at the upper real limit of the last class interval. Again, to avoid distortions produced by different scales on the axes, we attempt to hold the height of the vertical axis to approximately two-thirds to three-fourths the length of the horizontal axis.

FIGURE 3.17

Frequency polygon for the violent crime rates of 90 sampled cities (real class limits shown)

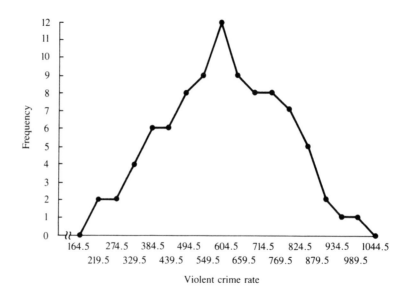

EXERCISES

35. Plot the data in Exercise 21 in the form of a frequency polygon.

36. Use both sets of data contained in Exercise 19 to plot a frequency polygon, first for the males and then for the females. Plot the two polygons on the same graph and interpret the results.

37. Do frequency polygons have the same probabilistic interpretation as relative frequency histograms?

38. Plot the data in Exercise 22 in the form of a frequency polygon.

39. Plot the data in Exercise 23 in the form of a frequency polygon.

40. Plot the data in Exercise 24 in the form of a frequency polygon.

41. Plot the data in Exercise 25 in the form of a relative frequency polygon.

3.11 CUMULATIVE RELATIVE FREQUENCY POLYGONS (OPTIONAL)

Social researchers are often interested in the proportion of measurements less than or equal to some specific value. For example, they might be interested in the fraction of the SMSAs with violent crime rates less than or equal to 384.5. This quantity, called the **cumulative relative frequency** at 384.5, is the sum of the relative frequencies for all classes up to and including class 4 — that is, the class with an upper real limit equal to 384.5.

DEFINITION 3.2 | The **cumulative relative frequency for class** j is equal to the sum of the relative frequencies for all classes up to and including the jth class.

For the crime rate data, the cumulative relative frequency at the fourth class is as follows:

$$\text{cumulative relative frequency at class } 4 = .022 + .022 + .044 + .067$$
$$= .155$$

In a similar way we can obtain the cumulative relative frequencies for all classes. These are shown in Table 3.6 for the data of Table 3.5.

The cumulative relative frequencies can be graphically displayed by using a **cumulative relative frequency polygon**, which is constructed like the frequency polygon of Section 3.10. The vertical axis is labeled "Cumulative relative frequency" rather than "Frequency," however. The cumulative relative frequency associated with each class is indicated by a dot placed over the upper endpoint of the class interval, with the height of the dot equal to the class cumulative relative frequency. The dots are then joined by straight lines. The cumulative relative frequency polygon for the data of Table 3.6 is shown in Figure 3.18.

TABLE 3.6

Cumulative relative
frequencies for the
data in Table 3.5

Class j	Class Interval	Relative Frequency	Cumulative Relative Frequency
1	164.5– 219.5	.022	.022
2	219.5– 274.5	.022	.044
3	274.5– 329.5	.044	.088
4	329.5– 384.5	.067	.155
5	384.5– 439.5	.067	.222
6	439.5– 494.5	.089	.311
7	494.5– 549.5	.100	.411
8	549.5– 604.5	.133	.544
9	604.5– 659.5	.100	.644
10	659.5– 714.5	.089	.733
11	714.5– 769.5	.089	.822
12	769.5– 824.5	.078	.900
13	824.5– 879.5	.056	.956
14	879.5– 934.5	.022	.978
15	934.5– 989.5	.011	.989
16	989.5–1044.5	.011	1.000

FIGURE 3.18

Cumulative relative
frequency polygon for
the data of Table 3.6
(real class limits
shown)

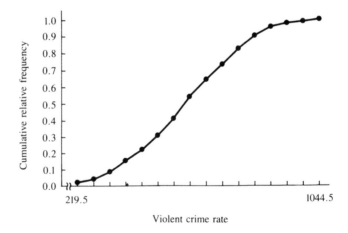

EXERCISES

42. Set up a cumulative relative frequency column for the data for Colombian
males in Exercise 19.

43. Set up a cumulative relative frequency column for the data for females in Exercise 19. Plot the cumulative relative frequency distribution.

44. When might a cumulative relative frequency polygon be more useful than a relative frequency polygon? Comment.

45. Set up a cumulative relative frequency column for the data in Exercise 22.

46. Construct a cumulative relative frequency column for the data in Exercise 23.

47. Set up a cumulative relative frequency column for the data in Exercise 24.

48. Construct a cumulative relative frequency polygon for the data of Exercise 25.

3.12   DIFFERENT SHAPES OF FREQUENCY POLYGONS (OPTIONAL)

In Sections 3.6 through 3.11 we studied procedures for organizing quantitative data and presented the construction of the frequency distribution as a graphical technique for describing data. We will now describe briefly the typical shapes of these histograms.

The most common shape for a frequency distribution is the bell-shaped (or normal) curve, pictured in Figure 3.19a. Although we will discuss the normal curve in greater detail in Chapters 4 and 5, it is important to note that the normal curve is the most important frequency distribution that we will encounter in this text. This is because so many populations of real data, collected in many areas of the social sciences, possess nearly normal frequency distributions. For example, social variables, such as the average hourly wage of construction workers by county, average Social Security payments to retirees by area of residence, and the length of patient confinement in hospitals, may possess frequency distributions that are approximately bell shaped.

Two other curves, the J-shaped and U-shaped curves, are indicated in Figures 3.19b and 3.19c, respectively. Although less common than the bell-shaped normal curve, these two curves are not rare. Almost any behavior that is governed by an enforced social norm has a J-shaped frequency distribution. Typical examples include the number of people (frequency) who commit incestuous acts, kill people, or hijack planes during a particular year.

FIGURE 3.19

Typical shapes for frequency distributions

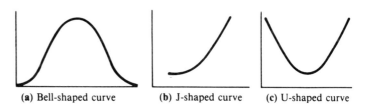

(a) Bell-shaped curve   (b) J-shaped curve   (c) U-shaped curve

The horizontal axis of the J-shaped curve shows values of X, the number of incestuous acts, persons killed, or hijackings, and the vertical axis shows the frequency.

Examples of variables with U-shaped distributions include the number of people who use physician services $X = 0, 1, 2, \ldots$ times per year. This curve will vary as a function of the social class and age of the people. Similarly, looking only at all patients seeking a medical service, you obtain a U-shaped curve if you plot frequency (number of patients) as a function of the age of the patients.

3.13   ADDITIONAL GRAPHING TECHNIQUES: THE TIME TREND (OPTIONAL)

Social researchers are often interested in showing how certain variables change over time. They might be interested in changes in attitudes toward various racial and ethnic groups, or changes in the rate of savings in the United States, or changes in the crime rates of various cities. A **time trend** (also referred to as a **trend line**) is a graphical display of the numerical values of a quantitative or qualitative variable at various points in time. The variable's value at each timepoint is indicated by a dot, and the dots are connected by a straight line to form the trend line. Plotting a time trend involves two variables: time (a quantitative variable) and the variable of interest (either qualitative or quantitative). Figure 3.20 is a time trend

FIGURE 3.20

Percentage of childless women age 30 to 34, 1970–1986

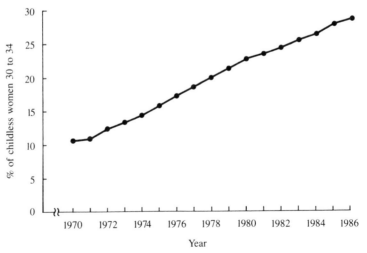

Source: National Center for Health Statistics, *Vital Statistics of the United States.*

showing the percentage of white women age 30 to 34 who have not had any children. This trend is presented from 1970 to 1986.

Usually, timepoints are labeled chronologically across the horizontal axis (abscissa), and the numerical values (frequencies, percentages, rates, etc.) of the variable of interest are labeled along the vertical axis (ordinate). Time can be measured in days, months, years, or any other unit of time. As a rule of thumb, a trend line should consist of no fewer than 4 or 5 timepoints. Many more timepoints than this are desirable, however, in order to give a more complete picture of changes in a variable over time.

How the social researcher measures time frequently depends on the time intervals at which data are available. For example, the U.S. Census Bureau reports average family income only on a yearly basis. When information about a variable of interest is available in different units of time, the social researcher must decide which units are most appropriate for the research. In an election year, a political scientist would most likely examine weekly or monthly changes in candidate preferences among registered voters. On the other hand, a sociologist interested in trends in premarital sex would probably look at yearly changes in rates of premarital coitus.

Hypothetical time trends that show the Dow Jones industrial average (an average of stock price increases and decreases per day of trading on Wall Street) appear in Figures 3.21 and 3.22. Figure 3.21 is a hypothetical example of how this information is presented on the ABC Nightly News, and Figure 3.22 represents the way the information is presented on the PBS Nightly Business Report.

If we have merely a passing interest in how the stock market is doing, we can probably get the information we want from the ABC Nightly News. It reports the daily average for several days in a row (Figure 3.21). If we own

FIGURE 3.21

Hypothetical Dow Jones averages, by day, for a week in June

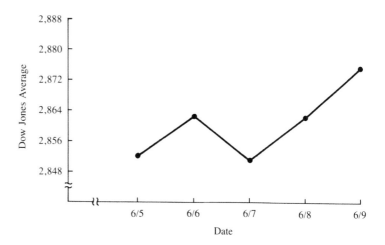

FIGURE 3.22

Hypothetical Dow
Jones averages
(hourly) for June 9

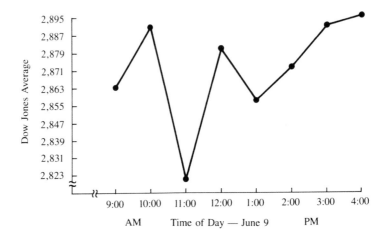

stock, however, we may be more interested in hourly trends of each day that
stocks are traded (Figure 3.22).

Time trends can be constructed for quantitative variables. However, as in
the case of the stem-and-leaf plot, the construction of a time trend for a
quantitative variable does *not* follow the principles for selecting class
intervals given in Section 3.6. To represent changes pictorially in a quantitative variable, the actual values of the variable at each timepoint are plotted.

Many times a social researcher wishes to compare trends in a variable for
two or more groups at the same time. Figure 3.23 reports the values of two
ratios from 1976 to 1988: the ratio of the median family income of blacks to

FIGURE 3.23

Ratio of black and
Hispanic median fa-
mily income to white
median family income,
1976–1988

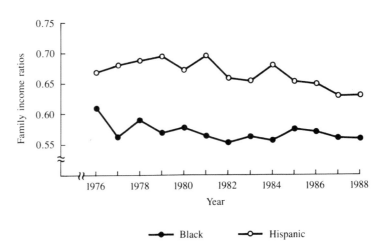

Source: U.S. Bureau of the Census, *Statistical Abstract of the United
States*.

the median family income of whites, and the ratio of the median family income of Hispanics to the median family income of whites. (Remember from Chapter 2 that a ratio is a quantitative level of measurement.)

Median family income represents the income amount that divides family incomes into two groups — the top half and the bottom half. In 1987 the median family income for blacks was $18,098, meaning that one-half of all black families had incomes above $18,098 and one-half had incomes below $18,098. The median, one of several measures of central tendency, is discussed more fully in Chapter 4.

Figure 3.23 shows that the ratio of black and Hispanic to white family income fluctuated between 1976 and 1988, but the overall trend in both ratios indicates that they declined over this time. A social researcher would interpret these trends to mean that the income of black and Hispanic families generally declined relative to the income of white families.

Sometimes information is not available in equal time intervals. For example, polling organizations such as Gallup or the National Opinion Research Center do not necessarily ask the American public the same questions about their attitudes or behavior on a yearly basis. Sometimes there will be a gap of more than two years before a question is asked again.

When information is not available in equal time intervals, the interval width between timepoints (the horizontal axis) must reflect this fact. If, for example, a social researcher is plotting values of a variable for 1985, 1986, 1987, and 1990, the interval width between 1987 and 1990 on the horizontal

FIGURE 3.24

Church attendance of U.S. Protestants and Catholics in a typical week, 1954–1988

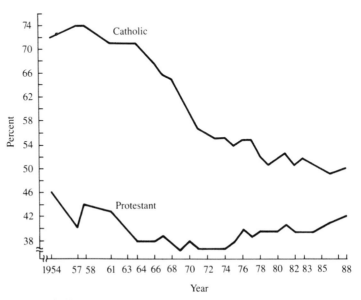

Source: Gallup.

axis should be three times the width of that between the other years. If these interval widths were spaced evenly, the resulting trend line could be seriously misleading. Other examples of graphic distortion are discussed in Section 3.14.

Figure 3.24 presents the trend in church attendance among United States Catholics from 1958 to 1988. As can be seen, the width of the intervals between timepoints reflects the fact that Catholics and Protestants were not asked about their church attendance every year.

3.14   GRAPHICAL DISTORTIONS

Pictures provide an excellent way to distort the truth. We have all seen physical fitness ads that feature perfect male and female specimens of health. Will these fitness programs really cause such delightful, drastic changes in us? Similarly, a mail order catalog sketch of a product is frequently more attractive than the real thing. Yet we take this type of lying for granted, and we submit to these minifrauds with much less distress than perhaps we should. Statistical pictures are histograms, frequency polygons, pie charts, and bar graphs. These types of drawings or displays of numerical results are more difficult to combine with sketches of lovely females or handsome males and hence are secure from the most common form of graphic distortion. However, one can shrink or stretch axes to imply the desired results, because of our intuitive associations of shallow and steep slopes with small and large increases, respectively.

For example, suppose that the number of near-fatal collisions between aircraft per month at a major airport is recorded as 13, 14, 14, 15, and 15 for January though May. If we want this growth to appear small (perhaps we represent the Civil Aeronautics Board), we will show the results using the frequency polygon of Figure 3.25. The increase is discernible, but it does not appear to be very great. If we want the increases to appear great (perhaps we belong to a citizens' safety group), look at the graph of the same data in Figure 3.26. The vertical axis is stretched and does not include zero. Note the impression of a substantial rise indicated by the steep slope.

Another way to decrease or increase a slope is to stretch or shrink the horizontal axis. Of course, we are sometimes limited in the amount of shrink or stretch we can apply and still achieve a picture that appears reasonable to the viewer. For example, you could not shrink or stretch the horizontal axes of Figures 3.25 and 3.26 very much because of the limited number of data points ($n = 5$).

Shrinking or stretching axes to increase the slopes in bar graphs, histograms, frequency polygons, or other figures usually catches the hasty

FIGURE 3.25

Number of near-fatal
collisions per month

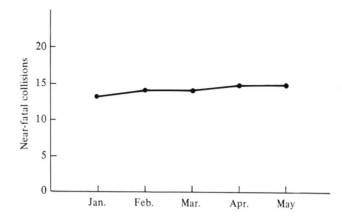

FIGURE 3.26

Number of near-fatal
collisions per month

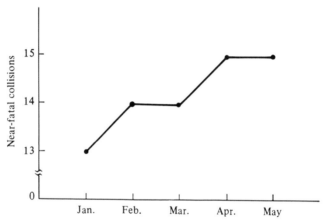

reader unaware; the distortions are apparent only if you look closely at the axes. **The important point, however, is that whether increasing or decreasing trends are judged to be large or small depends on the importance to the observer of the actual change, not on the slopes shown in graphical representations.** In other words, a graph itself has no inherent meaning; it is the observer's judgment or interpretation of the graph that gives meaning to the trends. For example, assume that the United States unemployment rate increases .2% over a one-month period. Some economists may interpret this as a sizable increase in unemployment, but other economists might consider the increase unimportant to the economy.

EXERCISES

49. What is a time trend, and why should the number of timepoints be sufficiently large?

50. In what ways can graphical distortion occur?

51. Using the data in the accompanying table, construct a time trend showing white support for a black presidential candidate.

EXERCISE 51

White support for a black presidential candidate

Year	Percent Willing to Vote for a Qualified Black Nominated by Their Own Political Party
1980	81
1981	81
1982	83
1983	86
1984	85
1985	83
1986	83
1987	82
1988	81
1989	81

52. Using data from the table in Exercise 51, construct a time trend for even years of the data (e.g., 1980, 1982, etc.).

53. Compare the trend lines you obtained in Exercises 51 and 52.

54. Using the data from the table below, construct a time trend showing the percentage of all families with children headed by single women.

EXERCISE 54

Percentage of all families with children headed by single women

Year	Percentage of All Families Headed by Single Women
1960	5.3
1965	6.6
1970	9.1
1975	13.4
1980	16.7
1985	20.0
1990*	27.1

Source: U.S. Bureau of the Census, *Statistical Abstract of the United States.*
* Estimate.

55. Using data from the table in Exercise 54, construct a time trend in which the timepoints along the horizontal axis are evenly spaced.

56. Compare the time trends you obtained in Exercises 54 and 55. Discuss how a time trend can be misleading if the interval width between timepoints does not correspond to the actual length of time between data observation points.

57. Using the data in the accompanying table, construct a graph of the price of tomatoes per pound for the months shown.

EXERCISE 57

Price of tomatoes per
pound, by month

Month	Price of Tomatoes per Pound
August	$.55
September	$.75
October	$.80
November	$1.25
December	$1.35

58. Using the data in Exercise 57, change the length of the vertical axis so that the increase in the price of tomatoes appears to be much smaller.

59. Using the data in Exercise 57, change the length of the vertical axis so that the increase in the price of tomatoes appears to be much greater.

SUMMARY

We learn how to describe a set of scores for two reasons. First, one of the uses of statistics in social research is to make inferences about a population based on information contained in a sample. Since populations are sets of measurements, existing or imaginary, we need some method for talking about the population or, equivalently, for describing a set of measurements. The second reason is the need for condensing and describing large quantities of social data that are collected annually by various government agencies, or even every ten years by the Bureau of the Census.

Data can be described either graphically or numerically. Graphical techniques such as the pie chart, the bar chart, histograms, stem-and-leaf plots, and frequency polygons are presented in this chapter. Numerical descriptive measures are discussed in Chapter 4.

Note the role of data description in statistical inference. You cannot make an inference about anything unless you are able to describe the object of interest. Graphical descriptions of sample data are similar to corresponding figures for the population from which the sample was drawn, but this type of inference possesses limitations that will be made apparent in Chapter 4. The sole purpose of this chapter is data description.

KEY WORDS

Bar graph   A graph describing qualitative data in which noncontiguous bars are constructed. Each bar represents a category of the variable. The height of each bar equals the number of observations in the category.

Class frequency   Number of observations falling into a class interval of a frequency distribution.

Class intervals   Intervals that define the categories of a frequency distribution.

Class limits   Endpoints of a class interval of a frequency distribution.

Cumulative relative frequency for a class   The sum of the relative frequencies for all classes up to and including that class.

Cumulative relative frequency polygon   A graph that builds on a frequency polygon in which the vertical axis represents the cumulative relative frequency. The cumulative relative frequency associated with each class interval is indicated by a dot placed over the upper endpoint of the class interval.

Frequency distribution   A way of organizing quantitative data in which interval or ratio data are grouped according to class intervals. The frequency or count is shown for each class interval.

Frequency polygon   A graph for describing quantitative data in a frequency distribution. The frequency for a class is indicated by a dot over the midpoint of the interval. The dots are connected by straight lines to form the polygon.

Histogram   A traditional graph of quantitative data in a frequency distribution. Adjacent columns or rectangles are constructed over each class interval, with the height of each rectangle equal to the class frequency. Also called a *frequency histogram.*

Pie chart   One of the most common graphs for describing qualitative data, in which a circle is partitioned into a few sections. The size of each section is proportional to the percentage of cases represented by the section.

Principle of exclusiveness   No observation is classified into more than one category.

Principle of inclusiveness   Every observation is classified into a category.

Range   The difference between the largest and smallest measurements of a set.

Real class limits   Interval endpoints for grouped data that form nonoverlapping, contiguous classes of equal width.

Relative frequency for a class   The proportion of the measurements of a frequency distribution falling into a class.

Relative frequency histogram   Same as a histogram, except the height of each rectangle over a class interval is now scaled for relative frequency rather than frequency.

Sample size   The total of the class frequencies.

Statistical map   A graph for describing data (often qualitative data) in which categories of the variable are displayed on a map so as to reveal geographical variation.

Stem-and-leaf plot   A graph for describing quantitative data in which a histogram-like picture of a frequency distribution is constructed. The plot reveals all scores, and the scores are ordered from smallest to largest.

Trend line   A graph for describing changes in the value of a qualitative or quantitative variable over time. The variable's value at each timepoint is indicated by a dot, and dots are connected by a straight line to form the trend line.

SUPPLEMENTARY EXERCISES FOR CHAPTER 3

60. A researcher asked a group of high school dropouts their reasons for leaving school. Their responses are summarized in the accompanying table. Evaluate the organization of responses by the principles of exclusiveness and inclusiveness.

EXERCISE 60

Percentage of high school dropouts and accompanying reasons

Reason	Percentage
dissatisfied with school	31
needed income to help support family	29
joined the armed forces	13
arrested and placed in a detention home	11
do not know	9
gave no reason	5
other	2

61. Construct a pie chart for the estimated membership of the principal religions in the United States. See Figure 3.4 (Suggestion: Combine "Eastern Orthodox" and "Others.")

62. Using the data in Table 3.3, construct a bar graph.

63. Find an example of a statistical map used in the social science literature.

64. Use the data in Table 3.4 to construct a frequency distribution in which the interval width is 80; that is, $i = 80$.

65. Compute the relative frequencies for the data in Exercise 64.

66. Construct a frequency histogram for the data in Exercise 64.

67. Construct a frequency polygon for the data in Exercise 64.

68. Construct a bar graph using the unemployment data shown in the accompanying table.

EXERCISE 68

Rate of unemployment in the civilian labor force

Year	Rate of Unemployment
1950	5.3
1955	4.4
1960	5.5
1965	4.5
1970	4.9
1975	8.5
1980	7.6
1985	7.2
1990*	5.6

Source: U.S. Bureau of the Census, *Statistical Abstract of the United States.*
* Estimate.

69. Refer to the data in Exercise 17, dealing with death rates due to cancer. First, round to the nearest whole number; second, construct a frequency distribution with a lower apparent limit of 83 and a class interval width of 13; finally, construct a cumulative relative frequency polygon for the death rate due to cancer.

70. George Warheit and his colleagues surveyed the presence of depressive symptoms in South County. Construct a relative frequency polygon for their data, shown in the accompanying table.

EXERCISE 70

Presence of depressive symptoms in South County

Index Score	f	Percentage
0–4	83	5.0
5–9	350	21.3
10–14	352	21.4
15–19	330	20.1
20–24	214	13.0
25–29	146	8.9
30–34	81	4.9
35–39	44	2.7
40–44	27	1.6
45–49	9	.5
50–54	6	.4
55–59	2	.1
60–64	1	.1
Total	1645	100.0

Source: George J. Warheit, *Southern Mental Health Needs and Services*, NIMJ 15900–05 (unpublished data); by permission.

71. Construct a cumulative relative frequency polygon for the data in Exercise 70.

72. Construct a relative frequency polygon for the data in Exercise 17. Let $i = 10$.

73. The accompanying table gives the age at inauguration and at death for 35 presidents.

a. Construct a frequency table for the age-at-inauguration data. Let the interval width be 4; that is, $i = 4$, with an apparent lower limit for the distribution of 42.

b. Construct a frequency histogram for the data.

EXERCISE 73

Ages at inauguration
and death for 35 U.S.
presidents

President	Age at Inauguration	Death
Washington	57	67
J. Adams	61	90
Jefferson	57	83
Madison	57	85
Monroe	58	73
J. Q. Adams	57	80
Jackson	61	78
Van Buren	54	79
W. H. Harrison	68	68
Tyler	51	71
Polk	49	53
Taylor	64	65
Fillmore	50	74
Pierce	48	64
Buchanan	65	77
Lincoln	52	56
A. Johnson	56	66
Grant	46	63
Hayes	54	70
Garfield	49	49
Arthur	50	56
Cleveland	47	71
B. Harrison	55	67
McKinley	54	58
T. Roosevelt	42	60
Taft	51	72
Wilson	56	67
Harding	55	57
Coolidge	51	69
Hoover	54	90
F. Roosevelt	51	63
Truman	60	88
Eisenhower	62	78
Kennedy	43	46
L. Johnson	55	64

74. Refer to Exercise 73. Use the accompanying computer-generated frequency histogram and stem-and-leaf diagram to describe the data. Compare this output to your calculations for Exercise 73.

```
MTB > histogram 'AGE';
SUBC> increment 4;
SUBC> start 43.5.

Histogram of AGE   N = 35

Midpoint    Count
  43.50        2   **
  47.50        5   *****
  51.50        7   *******
  55.50       13   *************
  59.50        4   ****
  63.50        3   ***
  67.50        1   *

MTB > stem leaf 'AGE';
SUBC> increment 3.

Stem-and-leaf of AGE        N  = 35
Leaf Unit = 1.0


    2      4 23
    7      4 67899
  (11)     5 00111124444
   17      5 5556677778
    7      6 01124
    2      6 58
```

75. Use the accompanying table on percentage change in teachers' salaries for one year, by state.
   a. Compute the relative frequencies.
   b. Construct a frequency histogram.
   c. Construct a frequency polygon.

EXERCISE 75

Percentage change in
teachers' salaries for
one year, by state

% Change	f
-2	1
-1	0
0	0
$+1$	4
2	3
3	3
4	2
5	5
6	8

continued

% Change	f
7	9
8	6
9	2
10	4
11	2
12	0
13	1
Total	50

Source: U.S. Department of Commerce, Bureau of the Census.

76. Use the accompanying table on infant mortality rate, by state.
  a. Compute the relative frequencies.
  b. Construct a frequency histogram.
  c. Construct a frequency polygon.

EXERCISE 76

Infant mortality rate (deaths per 1000 live births), by state

Rate	f
7.0– 7.4	3
7.5– 7.9	2
8.0– 8.4	2
8.5– 8.9	2
9.0– 9.4	7
9.5– 9.9	4
10.0–10.4	7
10.5–10.9	4
11.0–11.4	9
11.5–11.9	2
12.0–12.4	1
12.5–12.9	2
13.0–13.4	2
13.5–13.9	3
Total	50

Source: U.S. Bureau of the Census, *Statistical Abstract of the United States.*

77. Use the data in the accompanying table on average percentage increase in personal income in one year, by state.
  a. Compute the relative frequencies.
  b. Construct a frequency histogram.
  c. Construct a frequency polygon.

EXERCISE 77

Average percentage increase in personal income for one year, by state

% Increase	f
0	1
1	0
2	0
3	1
4	0
5	2
6	3
7	6
8	13
9	10
10	9
11	2
12	2
13	1
Total	50

Source: U.S. Bureau of the Census, *Statistical Abstract of the United States.*

78. Use the data in the accompanying table on per capita outlay in federal dollars, by state.
  a. Compute the relative frequencies.
  b. Construct a frequency histogram.
  c. Construct a frequency polygon.

EXERCISE 78

Per capita outlay in federal dollars, by state

Dollars	f
2000–2199	1
2200–2399	7
2400–2599	9
2600–2799	6
2800–2999	9

continued

Dollars	f
3000–3199	6
3200–3399	2
3400–3599	2
3600–3799	1
3800–3999	0
4000–4199	3
4200–4399	3
4400–4599	0
4600–4799	1
Total	50

Source: U.S. Bureau of the Census, *Statistical Abstract of the United States.*

79. The accompanying table shows the projected percentage change in population between 1985 and 2000, by state.
   a. Compute the relative frequencies.
   b. Construct a frequency histogram.
   c. Construct a frequency polygon.

EXERCISE 79

Projected percentage increase in population between 1985 and 2000, by state

% Change	f
−5– −1	2
0– 4	11
5– 9	10
10– 14	5
15– 19	8
20– 24	6
25– 29	3
30– 34	2
35– 39	2
40– 44	0
45– 49	1
Total	50

Source: U.S. Bureau of the Census, *Statistical Abstract of the United States.*

80. Using Database A, Appendix Table 7, and focusing on the number of acts judged to be serious crimes, construct a frequency distribution. Set the interval width equal to 1; that is, $i = 1$.

81. Construct a frequency histogram for the data in Exercise 80.

82. Construct a frequency polygon for the data in Exercise 80.

83. Construct a cumulative relative frequency polygon for the data in Exercise 80.

84. Construct a stem-and-leaf plot for the data in Exercise 80. Stretch the display by using two lines per stem, so that leaf digits 0, 1, 2, 3, and 4 appear on the first line and leaf digits 5, 6, 7, 8, and 9 on the second.

85. Using Database A, Appendix Table 7, and focusing on religious preference, construct a pie chart.

86. Using Database B, Appendix Table 8, and focusing on the level-of-technology measurement for all 60 nations, construct a frequency distribution. Set the interval width equal to 6; that is, $i = 6$.

87. Construct a frequency histogram for the data in Exercise 86.

88. Construct a frequency polygon for the data in Exercise 86.

89. Construct a cumulative relative frequency polygon for the data in Exercise 86.

90. Using Database C, Appendix Table 9, construct separate stem-and-leaf plots for the HAM-D anxiety scores for the four treatment groups.

91. Using Database C, Appendix Table 9, construct separate stem-and-leaf plots for the HAM-D retardation, sleep disturbance, and total scores for the four treatment groups.

92. Based on your plots in Exercises 90 and 91, do the four treatment groups look comparable at the end of the study? Why might they be different?

93. Refer to Database C, Appendix Table 9. Suggest some graphical technique for comparing the data on the daily consumption of tobacco for the four treatment groups prior to their receiving the assigned medication.

94. Refer to Exercise 93. Do the same for the history of alcohol use prior to medication.

95. A frequency histogram and stem-and-leaf plot are shown in computer output form for the violent crime data of Table 3.4. Describe the data and compare the computer output to the hand-generated display done for these data earlier in the chapter.

```
MTB > histogram 'RATE';
SUBC> increment 55;
SUBC> start 192.5.

Histogram of RATE   N = 90

Midpoint    Count
  192.5       2     **
  247.5       2     **
  302.5       3     ***
  357.5       6     ******        continued
```

```
        412.5     6   ******
        467.5     8   ********
        522.5     9   *********
        577.5    12   ************
        632.5     9   *********
        687.5     9   *********
        742.5     8   ********
        797.5     7   *******
        852.5     5   *****
        907.5     2   **
        962.5     1   *
       1017.5     1   *

   MTB > stem leaf 'RATE';
   SUBC> increment 100.

   Stem-and-leaf of RATE        N  = 90
   Leaf Unit = 10


        1      1  8
        7      2  126999
       16      3  345577899
       29      4  1234466688999
      (19)     5  0001223556666677789
       42      6  0022233446788899
       26      7  00112333557
       15      8  000111456778
        3      9  27
        1     10  2
```

96. Using Database D, Appendix Table 10, perform the following operations.
   a. Round the rates of forcible rape for the 30 states to the nearest whole unit. Construct a pie chart in terms of three categories: 25 and below; 26 to 40; and 41 and above.
   b. Use the same information and construct a bar graph.
   c. Use the same information and construct a statistical map of the United States. Develop three densities of shadings. Describe any regional or area patterns that are apparent.

97. Using Database D, Appendix Table 10, construct a frequency distribution for population density. Use seven categories, but follow the other rules in establishing a frequency distribution.

98. Refer to Exercise 97. Complete the following:
   a. Compute the relative frequencies for the data.
   b. Construct a frequency histogram for the data.
   c. Construct a frequency polygon for the data.
   d. Construct a bar graph using seven categories.

99. Using Database B, Appendix Table 8, perform the following operations:
   a. Construct a frequency distribution for the infant mortality rates for all 60 nations. Use seven categories, but follow the other rules in establishing a frequency distribution.
   b. Compute the relative frequencies for the data.
   c. Construct a frequency histogram for the data.

    d. Construct a frequency polygon for the data.

    e. Construct a bar graph using seven categories.

100. Using Database B, Appendix Table 8, perform the following operations.

    a. Construct a frequency distribution for the per capita GNP in U.S. dollars for all 60 nations. Use seven categories, but follow the other rules in establishing a frequency distribution.

    b. Compute the relative frequencies for the data.

    c. Construct a frequency histogram for the data.

    d. Construct a frequency polygon for the data.

    e. Construct a bar graph using seven categories.

101. Using Database B, Appendix Table 8, perform the following operations.

    a. Construct a frequency distribution for the life expectancies for all 60 nations. Use five categories, but follow the other rules in establishing a frequency distribution.

    b. Compute the relative frequencies for the data.

    c. Construct a frequency histogram for the data.

    d. Construct a frequency polygon for the data.

    e. Construct a bar graph using five categories.

    f. Construct a pie chart using five categories.

102. Repeat Exercise 101 using 10 categories. Compare your results with those from Exercise 100. Comment on the appropriateness of using 5 categories as against using 10.

CHAPTER 4

NUMERICAL TECHNIQUES FOR DESCRIBING DATA FROM A SINGLE SAMPLE

GENERAL OBJECTIVES

Social researchers are often interested in a single variable from one sample. This chapter presents numerical techniques for describing and summarizing such data. It includes several of the more commonly known and used numerical techniques that compactly describe such a set of data. These techniques are useful, whether the intended audience consists of social scientists or lay people.

SPECIFIC OBJECTIVES

1. To explain the differences among three measures of central tendency: mode, median, and mean. Along with percentile ranks, these measures emphasize location.
2. To show how to compute these measures of location without the use of hand calculators or more advanced computer software.
3. To demonstrate what you need to know about the spread or distribution of scores in addition to some measure of location.
4. To illustrate and measure variability among qualitative data.
5. To show how to measure the variability for quantitative data and to illustrate the various measures: range, variance, and standard deviation.
6. To give examples of computer output where measure of location and variability have been computed.

4.1   INTRODUCTION

When preparing a written report based on social research, we frequently use some of the graphical techniques presented in Chapter 3. Those techniques are very easily understood by a lay audience. However, we are often called upon to handle such large quantities of data, involving so many variables, that we need to employ other techniques to summarize and describe our findings in a more concise manner. If we had, for example, 50 sets of data and employed graphical techniques, we would probably have at least 50 different histograms, frequency polygons, pie charts, or the like. These would make for a lengthy report.

In this chapter we will introduce you to numerical descriptive measures that allow us to use only one, two, or three numbers to describe a complex set of data. If we had 50 different sets of data, we could probably summarize and describe them adequately in a one- or two-page report. Numerical descriptive measures are also important because they can often be used in more advanced analyses, whereas the graphical techniques are usually end products.

Although graphical techniques were covered in Chapter 3, we will end this chapter with a consideration of the *box plot*. It is also a type of graph, but it requires several of the numerical techniques that precede our discussion of it in this chapter.

Social researchers use numbers to convey a mental image of physical objects or conditions. For example, most of us understand the meaning attached to the expression 98.6° when used to describe body temperature or .38 or .45 when used to describe a handgun. In the latter case, we have no difficulty in creating a mental picture of a handgun. So it is with statistics. Although satisfied by the ability of a frequency distribution to describe a set of scores, we often seek one, two, or more numbers, called *numerical descriptive measures*, to create a mental picture of the frequency distribution for a set of data.

We have two good reasons for using numerical as well as graphical techniques for data description. First, we frequently wish to discuss sets of measurements, populations, and large sets of social, economic, political, or census data, and it is inconvenient to carry frequency histograms about in one's pocket. It would be much easier if we could create a picture of the frequency distribution in the minds of our listeners by using one or two descriptive numbers. Second, the frequency distribution is an excellent method for characterizing a sample, but it has some limitations when used to make inferences. The irregular frequency histogram of the sample will be similar to the corresponding distribution for the population, but how similar?

How do we measure the goodness of our inference? How do we measure the degree of dissimilarity between the two figures?

The frequency histogram based on a sample can be used to make an inference about the shape of the population frequency distribution, but there is no satisfactory method for saying how good the inference is. In contrast, numerical descriptive measures of the population can be *estimated* by using the sample measurements, and we can say, with a measured degree of confidence, how close the estimate will be to the population descriptive measure. Population numerical descriptive measures will frequently be the target of our inferences (that is, we will estimate or make decisions about them). Thus we give them a special name.

DEFINITION 4.1   Numerical descriptive measures computed from a sample are called **statistics**.

DEFINITION 4.2   Numerical descriptive measures of a population are called **parameters**.

The two most important types of parameters are those that locate the center and those that describe the spread of the distribution. They are called *measures of central tendency* and *measures of variability*, respectively. We will show that two numbers, one locating the center of a distribution and one the spread, do provide a very good description of the frequency distribution for a set of scores. As you might suspect, we will frequently use a descriptive measure of the sample to estimate the value of the corresponding parameter of the population or universe.

Measures of central tendency and their definitions, interpretations, and applications will be presented in Sections 4.2 through 4.6. Measures of variability and their calculation and interpretation occupy most of the remainder of the chapter. This chapter will provide especially important touches to the description of a set of scores — the first step in our study of statistical inference. We will use these descriptive measures in later chapters to state inferences about populations based on sample measurements.

4.2   A MEASURE OF CENTRAL TENDENCY: THE MODE

The first measure of central tendency we will discuss is the mode of a distribution of measurements. (Keep in mind that scores and values are types of measurements.)

| DEFINITION 4.3 | The **mode** of a set of scores or measurements is the measurement that occurs with greatest frequency. |

The mode is the least common of the three measures of central tendency (mode, median, and mean) considered in this text, but is very useful in business for identifying those products or product sizes in greatest demand. A shirt or dress manufacturer is interested in the sizes most frequently purchased. Frequent reference is also made to the mode of a set of measurements in advertising campaigns. We often hear that more housewives prefer Brand W than any other laundry detergent, or that more doctors smoke Lungs cigarettes than any other brand. Social surveys sometimes refer to the mode of a set of measurements, such as the most frequently observed number of children per family in a suburban demographic study. The mode is employed where it is important to locate the measurement that occurs most frequently in a set. Also, the mode, unlike any other measure of central tendency that we will discuss, can be used for nominal data.

| EXAMPLE 4.1 | A research team analyzed divorce rates in 25 states. The number of divorces was determined for each state and converted to a rate. Each rate (per 1000 population) was then rounded to the nearest integer. These data are given in Table 4.1. Determine the modal divorce rate. |

TABLE 4.1

Divorce rates in 25 states

5	6	9	5	9
7	7	6	9	6
6	5	5	7	6
5	9	8	6	6
6	6	5	5	8

SOLUTION

First, let us arrange the measurements in order, ranging from the smallest to the largest:

5, 5, 5, 5, 5, 5, 5, 6, 6, 6, 6, 6, 6, 6, 6, 6, 7, 7, 7, 8, 8, 9, 9, 9, 9

From these data we see that the modal divorce rate per state is 6.

Sometimes a set of scores has more than one mode. We can label these sets of scores (or, correspondingly, the frequency distributions of these sets of scores) as bimodal, trimodal, and so on. An extension of this situation occurs when all observations appear the same number of times. In this case the mode gives no information in locating the center of the distribution, and we say that the frequency distribution possesses no mode.

Identifying the mode for the data of Example 4.1 was quite easy, because we were dealing with the actual scores. However, some difficulties arise when we try to compute the mode for data grouped in a frequency table (often referred to as **grouped data**). Consider the following example: Three samples of 30 SMSAs were drawn to obtain information on violent crime rates. The crime rate for each SMSA was recorded in Table 3.4. Recall that we organized the data to obtain a single frequency distribution of these (reproduced here in Table 4.2). The question is, How do we find the mode for this set of data?

| DEFINITION 4.4 | The **mode** for data arranged in a frequency table (grouped data) is defined to be the midpoint of the class interval with the highest frequency. |

TABLE 4.2

Frequency distribution for the 90 violent crime rates

Real Class Interval	Apparent Class Limits*	Frequency	Relative Frequency
164.5– 219.5	165– 219	2	.022
219.5– 274.5	220– 274	2	.022
274.5– 329.5	275– 329	4	.044
329.5– 384.5	330– 384	6	.067
384.5– 439.5	385– 439	6	.067
439.5– 494.5	440– 494	8	.089
494.5– 549.5	495– 549	9	.100
549.5– 604.5	550– 604	12	.133
604.5– 659.5	605– 659	9	.100
659.5– 714.5	660– 714	8	.089
714.5– 769.5	715– 769	8	.089
769.5– 824.5	770– 824	7	.078
824.5– 879.5	825– 879	5	.056
879.5– 934.5	880– 934	2	.022
934.5– 989.5	935– 989	1	.011
989.5–1044.5	990–1044	1	.011

Source: U.S. Bureau of the Census, *Statistical Abstract of the United States.*

* Class intervals for social data are usually presented with apparent limits, as shown. The real class limits are shown in the column on the extreme left.

| EXAMPLE 4.2 | Compute the mode for the data in Table 4.2. |

SOLUTION One class interval has the highest frequency (12). If two intervals both had 12, we would have a bimodal distribution. That is not the case. Our mode is given by the midpoint of the eighth class interval. Since the interval width is 55, we find the mode by adding 27.5 (or $\frac{1}{2}$ of 55) to the lower endpoint of the class interval. Thus the mode is

$$\text{mode} = 549.5 + 27.5 = 577$$

EXERCISES

1. The accompanying data represent the percentage of eligible voters in a sample of 10 voting districts.

   63,   56,   32,   48,   48,   45,   45,   45,   39,   41

   Find the mode.

2. The accompanying data represent a sample of 10 scores on a social sensitivity scale (the higher the score, the greater the sensitivity to the needs of others).

   7,   4,   4,   5,   6,   0,   3,   8,   2,   10

   Find the mode.

3. Find the mode for the data in Exercise 70, Chapter 3.
4. Find the mode for the data in Exercise 75, Chapter 3.
5. Find the mode for the data in Exercise 23, Chapter 3.

4.3   A MEASURE OF CENTRAL TENDENCY: THE MEDIAN

The median is also a measure of central tendency. It is computed in the same way for either a sample or a population. The following definitions refer to ungrouped data.

| DEFINITION 4.5 | The **median** for an odd number of scores is the middle score when the scores are arranged in increasing order. |

DEFINITION 4.6 | The **median** for an even number of scores is the average of the two middle observations when the scores are arranged in increasing order.

Note that the median is a number chosen so that half the scores lie below it, half above. Thus, if the median wage of a government employee is $5.70 per hour, it means that 50% of all government employees make less than $5.70 per hour, and 50% make more. The median is a very popular measure of central tendency for describing social data. Newspaper reports and magazines frequently refer to the median wage increase won by unions, the median age of persons receiving Social Security benefits, the median income of families in the United States, and the gap between the median income for men and for women.

EXAMPLE 4.3 | Find the median of these seven test scores: 95, 86, 78, 90, 62, 73, and 89.

SOLUTION   We must first arrange the scores in increasing order:

$$62, \quad 73, \quad 78, \quad 86, \quad 89, \quad 90, \quad 95$$

Since we have an odd number (7) of measurements, the median is the middle score; that is,

$$\text{median} = 86$$

EXAMPLE 4.4 | Suppose that 3 more students out of a class of 30 took the test of Example 4.3 and scored 73, 75, and 91. Find the median for the combined 10 test scores.

SOLUTION   Since we have an even number of observations, the sample median is the average of the two middle scores when the scores are arranged in numerical order. Arranging the scores in increasing order, we have

$$62, \quad 73, \quad 73, \quad 75, \quad 78, \quad 86, \quad 89, \quad 90, \quad 91, \quad 95$$

The two midpoint test scores are 78 and 86; hence the median is

$$\text{median} = \frac{78 + 86}{2} = 82$$

As with the mode, we have to adjust our procedure for computing the median for grouped data. This is because the exact values of the scores are lost when they have been grouped. Hence, although we may know that the middle observation occurs in a particular class, we may not know exactly where to locate the median within the interval.

If almost half of the observations have been counted before you come to the interval containing the median, you would be inclined to locate the median toward the lower portion of the interval that contains the median (median interval). On the other hand, if the interval up to and including the median interval contains exactly 50% of the scores, you would be inclined to move the median to the upper end of the interval that contains the median. The definition of the median for grouped data makes this type of adjustment.

| DEFINITION 4.7 | The **median** for data arranged in a frequency table (grouped data) is given by

$$M_{\mathrm{d}} = L + \frac{i}{f_m}\,(50\% \text{ of } n - cf_b)$$

where

M_d = median

L = lower real limit of the class interval that includes the median

n = total frequency

cf_b = sum of the frequencies (cumulative frequency) for all class intervals *below* the interval that includes the median

f_m = frequency of the class interval that includes the median

i = interval width

EXAMPLE 4.5   Compute the median for the violent crime rate data of Table 4.2.

SOLUTION   We must first determine L, n, cf_b, f_m, and i. Recall that we sampled 90 SMSAs; therefore $n = 90$. The interval width is $i = 55$. To determine the interval that contains the median, we begin to sum the relative frequencies from the lowest interval until the cumulative relative frequency exceeds .50.

Backtracking, we then determine the interval whose relative frequency makes the cumulative relative frequency exceed .50. This interval contains the median. For our data, the frequencies, cumulative frequencies, and the cumulative relative frequencies are as listed in Table 4.3. The cumulative relative frequency through interval 7 is .411, and through interval 8 it is .544. Thus interval 8 contains the median, and

$$L = 549.5$$

The frequency for class interval 8 is $f_m = 12$, and the cumulative frequency for intervals below interval 8 is $cf_b = 37$. The median for the grouped data is then

$$M_d = L + \frac{i}{f_m} (50\% \text{ of } n - cf_b) = 549.5 + \frac{55}{12}(45 - 37)$$

$$= 549.5 + 36.67 = 586.17$$

Sometimes students make the mistake of computing 50% of the quantity $(n - cf_b)$ in the formula for M_d. Rather, as the formula indicates, we compute 50% of n and then subtract cf_b.

TABLE 4.3

Frequencies for violent crime rate data of Table 4.2

Real Class Interval	Frequency	Relative Frequency	Cumulative Relative Frequency
164.5– 219.5	2	.022	.022
219.5– 274.5	2	.022	.044
274.5– 329.5	4	.044	.088
329.5– 384.5	6	.067	.155
384.5– 439.5	6	.067	.222
439.5– 494.5	8	.089	.311
494.5– 549.5	9	.100	.411
549.5– 604.5	12	.133	.544
604.5– 659.5	9	.100	.644
659.5– 714.5	8	.089	.733
714.5– 769.5	8	.089	.822
769.5– 824.5	7	.078	.900
824.5– 879.5	5	.056	.956
879.5– 934.5	2	.022	.978
934.5– 989.5	1	.011	.989
989.5–1044.5	1	.011	1.000

You might ask whether the median for a data set and the median for the same data set grouped in a frequency table would be the same value. In most cases they would not be identical, since the median for grouped data is only an approximation to the median for the actual data. The difference between the values for grouped and ungrouped data is a consequence of the class intervals chosen for grouping the data. So, if we have a choice, we use the median for the data set ungrouped.

EXERCISES

6. Find the median for the data in Exercise 1.

7. Find the median for the data in Exercise 2.

8. Find the median for the data in Exercise 70, Chapter 3.

9. Find the median for the data in Exercise 75, Chapter 3.

10. Find the median for the data in Exercise 25, Chapter 3.

11. Find the median for the data in Exercise 19, Chapter 3.

12. Find the median for the data in Exercise 20, Chapter 3.

13. Find the median for the data in Exercise 21, Chapter 3.

4.4   A MEASURE OF CENTRAL TENDENCY: THE MEAN

The most widely used measure of central tendency is the arithmetic mean of a set of scores.

DEFINITION 4.8

The **arithmetic mean** for a set of scores or measurements is the sum of the scores divided by the number of scores in the set.

The arithmetic mean, often called the *mean* or *average*, is employed in all fields of science and business. Thus we commonly see phrases such as the mean income for persons living in an urban area, the mean tensile strength of a cable, the mean velocity of the first stage of a missile, the mean increase in the cost-of-living index over the past six months, and the mean closing price of a group of stocks (such as the Dow Jones average of 30 industrials).

EXAMPLE 4.6

Several researchers developed an index to measure the living desirability of seven communities. Find the mean for the seven index scores.

95,   86,   78,   90,   62,   73,   89

SOLUTION

$$\text{mean} = \frac{\text{sum of scores}}{n}$$

$$= \frac{95 + 86 + 78 + 90 + 62 + 73 + 89}{7} = 81.86$$

The mean for the sample and for the population are defined the same way, since both are based on sets of scores, but we will use separate symbols for each. Although we will seldom actually calculate the universe or population mean, we will estimate or make decisions about it based on the sample mean. Thus it is important to draw a distinction between the two quantities. We will use the symbol $\bar{X}$("X bar") to denote the mean of a sample and μ (the Greek letter mu) to denote the mean of a population or universe.

$\bar{X}$ is the **sample mean.**

μ is the **population** or **universe mean.**

It is convenient to introduce at this point some notation that we will use in the computational formulas encountered in this and later chapters. First, let the letter X represent the measurement or score we are observing. If we refer specifically to a sample, X represents any measurement in the set. It may also be convenient to use a subscript to denote a particular score in the set. If we consider the seven measurements from Example 4.6,

$$95, \quad 86, \quad 78, \quad 90, \quad 62, \quad 73, \quad 89$$

we could let X_1 denote the first observation. Thus $X_1 = 95$. In the same manner we could let $X_2 = 86$, $X_3 = 78, \dots, X_7 = 89$.

To indicate a sum, we use the Greek symbol Σ (sigma). Thus ΣX indicates the sum of the scores that are denoted by the symbol X. In Example 4.6

$$\Sigma X = X_1 + X_2 + X_3 + X_4 + X_5 + X_6 + X_7$$
$$= 95 + 86 + \cdots + 89 = 573$$

If we have a sample of n scores that we denote by $X_1, X_2, \dots, X_n$, the sample mean is given by

$$\bar{X} = \frac{\Sigma X}{n} = \frac{X_1 + X_2 + \cdots + X_n}{n}$$

EXAMPLE 4.7

Compute the mean violent crime rate for the original sample of 90 cities (see Table 3.4).

SOLUTION

The sample of 90 crime rates can be labeled $X_1, X_2, \ldots, X_{90}$. Hence

$$\bar{X} = \frac{X_1 + X_2 + \cdots + X_{90}}{90}$$

$$= \frac{876 + 578 + \cdots + 585}{90} = \frac{52{,}986}{90} = 588.7$$

The formula for computing the mean of a set of scores is slightly altered when the data are grouped. Since we cannot reconstruct the actual scores before grouping, we represent all values in a given class interval by the midpoint of the interval. If we set X equal to the midpoint of a class interval, then the product fX denotes the sum of all scores in that interval. For example, if $X = 5$ is a class midpoint and the class contains $f = 10$ scores, then we could approximate the class sum as 10 times 5 and denote the sum of the scores in the class as $fX = 10(5) = 50$. Similarly, ΣfX represents the sum of all scores accumulated over all classes.

DEFINITION 4.9

Let X be the midpoint of a class interval with class frequency f. Then the **mean** for data arranged in a frequency table (grouped data) is

$$\bar{X} = \frac{\Sigma fX}{n}$$

EXAMPLE 4.8

Compute the sample mean for the grouped data of Table 4.2.

SOLUTION

The appropriate class intervals, midpoints, and frequencies are listed in Table 4.4. Using the formula given in Definition 4.9, we have

$$\bar{X} = \frac{\Sigma fX}{n} = \frac{52{,}810}{90} = 586.8$$

TABLE 4.4

Violent crime rate data
for Example 4.8

Class Interval	Real Class Interval	Midpoint X	Frequency	fX
1	164.5– 219.5	192	2	384
2	219.5– 274.5	247	2	494
3	274.5– 329.5	302	4	1,208
4	329.5– 384.5	357	6	2,142
5	384.5– 439.5	412	6	2,472
6	439.5– 494.5	467	8	3,736
7	494.5– 549.5	522	9	4,698
8	549.5– 604.5	577	12	6,924
9	604.5– 659.5	632	9	5,688
10	659.5– 714.5	687	8	5,496
11	714.5– 769.5	742	8	5,936
12	769.5– 824.5	797	7	5,579
13	824.5– 879.5	852	5	4,260
14	879.5– 934.5	907	2	1,814
15	934.5– 989.5	962	1	962
16	989.5–1044.5	1017	1	1,017
Total			90	52,810

If we had grouped our data into intervals 54 or 56 units wide, the midpoints
would have contained decimals. By using odd whole numbers, we avoided
decimals in the table.

Note that the mean computed for the grouped data (Example 4.8) differs
from that computed from the actual measurements (Example 4.7). This
difference is due to the method by which the data were grouped. **The sample
mean for grouped data is only an approximation to the sample mean for the
actual observations**. Also, recall that in Section 3.6 we indicated that ΣfX
should be close to the sum of the original scores (ΣX) if the frequency table is
to reflect the scores adequately. In the example we have been discussing,
$\Sigma fX = 52,810$, and $\Sigma X = 52,986$. These two values can be considered to be
close, since the grouped mean (586.8) is a very good approximation to the
actual mean (588.7). Whenever we have the original scores and desire to
construct a frequency table, compute ΣfX for the table to check whether the
frequency table adequately reflects the data.

Having discussed three measures of central tendency — the mode, median, and mean — we might wonder which quantity to use in describing a set
of scores. The answer depends on the application. As we will see in later

chapters, the sample mean is the most important measure of central tendency for statistical inference, particularly in estimation and testing hypotheses about social phenomena. As noted earlier, the mode is used when we wish to know the most frequently observed value of X. It tends to be a measure of popularity and provides a measure of central tendency for qualitative data where the mean and median are not applicable. In some situations the median provides more descriptive information about the center of a distribution. For example, suppose we are interested in describing the distribution of ages for bridegrooms in a particular city over a given year. It would be easy to sample the marriage licenses on file with a justice of the peace. We would undoubtedly find many grooms who were in their late teens or early twenties,

FIGURE 4.1

Relationship among the mean μ, median M_d, and mode M_o.

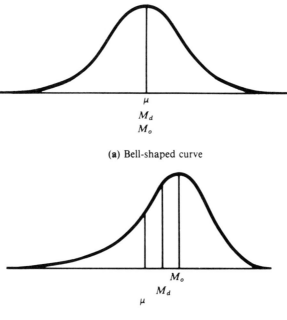

(a) Bell-shaped curve

(b) Distribution skewed to the left

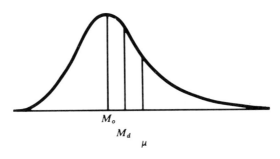

(c) Distribution skewed to the right

but some grooms would be much older. The median, which reflects the midpoint of the sample, would therefore be a better indicator of the ages of bridegrooms, because the mean age would be inflated by the much older grooms.

In a normal bell-shaped curve, the values of the mean, mode, and median are identical (see Figure 4.1a). If the distribution is skewed to the left (negative skew), the mean μ is the smallest value of the three, and the mode is the largest (see Figure 4.1b). When the distribution is skewed to the right (positive skew), μ is the largest value of the three, and the mode is the smallest (see Figure 4.1c). In each case the median is the most central value, and for this reason the median is a widely used measure of location of the center of a distribution.

A summary of the characteristics of the three measures of central tendency discussed in this chapter follows.

MAJOR CHARACTERISTICS OF EACH MEASURE OF CENTRAL TENDENCY

Mode

1. The mode is the most frequent or probable measurement or score in a distribution.
2. There can be more than one mode per distribution of scores.
3. The mode is not influenced by extreme scores.
4. Modes of subsets cannot be combined to determine the mode of the whole set.
5. The mode can be calculated when the ends of the distribution are open, provided that it does not fall in an open-ended interval.
6. The mode's value can change if the data are organized into different categories.
7. The mode is applicable to both qualitative and quantitative data.

Median

1. The median is the central value, with 50% of the scores larger than it and 50% smaller.
2. There is only one median per distribution.
3. The median is not influenced by extreme values.
4. Medians of subsets cannot be combined to determine the median of the whole set.
5. The median can be calculated when the ends of the distribution are open, provided that it does not fall in an open-ended interval.

6. The median's value is rather stable even when data are organized into different categories.
7. The median is applicable to quantitative data only.

Mean

1. The mean is the sum of all scores divided by the number of scores.
2. There is only one mean per distribution.
3. The mean is influenced by extreme scores; therefore it may not be very representative of the distribution.
4. Means of subsets, when weighted, can be combined to determine the mean of the whole set.
5. The mean cannot be calculated when the ends of the distribution are open.
6. The mean is applicable to interval and ratio data only.

4.5 CODING TO DETERMINE $\bar{X}$ FOR GROUPED DATA (OPTIONAL)

Data are frequently coded to simplify the calculation of $\bar{X}$, especially when computing the sample mean for a frequency table with large interval midpoints and when calculators are not available. Although the calculation of $\bar{X}$ for the data in Example 4.8 was not too difficult, the computations would have been much easier using class midpoints of 8, 7, 6, … rather than 1138, 1069, 1000, …. The coding is accomplished using the following steps.

STEPS FOR SIMPLIFYING THE CALCULATION OF $\bar{X}$ FOR GROUPED DATA

1. Inspect the frequency table and select the class interval you think is likely to contain the mean.
2. Let m denote the midpoint of this interval. (*Note:* The selection of m is not critical; just choose a class interval near the middle of the distribution.)
3. Subtract the value of m from each interval midpoint.
4. Compute the coded class interval midpoints X_c as $(X - m)/i$, where i is the interval width.

5. Using the coded midpoints X_c (rather than X), compute a sample mean $\bar{X}_c$. Note:

$$\bar{X}_c = \frac{\Sigma fX_c}{n}$$

6. The sample mean for the original (uncoded) data in the frequency table is

$$\bar{X} = i\bar{X}_c + m$$

We illustrate these coding steps in the next example, for the data of Table 4.2.

EXAMPLE 4.9

Use the coding steps just described to compute the mean $\bar{X}$ for the grouped data of Table 4.2.

SOLUTION

Suppose we think that the mean will lie in the eighth class interval. Then $m = 577$. Steps 2 through 4 of the coding procedure are illustrated in columns 4 and 5 of Table 4.5. Having selected $m = 577$, we subtract m from each class midpoint (column four). In column 5 of Table 4.5, we compute the coded midpoints by using the formula

$$X_c = \frac{X - 577}{55}$$

or simply by dividing the entries in column 4 by $i = 55$, the interval width.

We now use the coded midpoints X_c as we would the original midpoints to compute a sample mean. The formula for the mean of the coded units is

$$\bar{X}_c = \frac{\Sigma fX_c}{n}$$

Note how easy it is to form the products fX_c in column 6. Then, with the sum of entries in column 6 equal to 16, the sample mean for the coded units is

$$\bar{X} = \frac{\Sigma fX_c}{n} = \frac{16}{90} = .178$$

The mean for the measurements in the original (uncoded) units is

$$\bar{X} = i\bar{X}_c + m = 55(.178) + 577 = 586.79$$

which is identical (except for a slight rounding error) to the answer we obtained in Example 4.8.

TABLE 4.5	Real	Midpoint			$X_c = \dfrac{X - m}{i}$	
Computation of $\bar{X}$ using coded midpoints	Class Interval	X	f	$X - m$		fX_c
	164.5– 219.5	192	2	−385	−7	−14
	219.5– 274.5	247	2	−330	−6	−12
	274.5– 329.5	302	4	−275	−5	−20
	329.5– 384.5	357	6	−220	−4	−24
	384.5– 439.5	412	6	−165	−3	−18
	439.5– 494.5	467	8	−110	−2	−16
	494.5– 549.5	522	9	−55	−1	−9
	549.5– 604.5	577	12	0	0	0
	604.5– 659.5	632	9	55	1	9
	659.5– 714.5	687	8	110	2	16
	714.5– 769.5	742	8	165	3	24
	769.5– 824.5	797	7	220	4	28
	824.5– 879.5	852	5	275	5	25
	879.5– 934.5	907	2	330	6	12
	934.5– 989.5	962	1	385	7	7
	989.5–1044.5	1017	1	440	8	8
	Total		90			16

Although you might feel that the additional steps required in coding do not really simplify things, the actual calculations required can easily be done by hand after coding to obtain much smaller midpoints. If we always have access to an electronic calculator or a computer, this might not seem to be a problem. However, sometimes the mere fact that the numbers are smaller and simpler to manipulate makes the coding worthwhile, regardless of whether we use a calculator or not.

Having considered the major measures of central tendency in previous sections, we will present a more general measure of location in the next section.

EXERCISES

14. Find the mean for the data in Exercise 1.

15. Find the mean for the data in Exercise 2.

16. Find the mean for the data in Exercise 24, Chapter 3. Use the uncoded formula.

17. Repeat Exercise 16, but use the coded formula with m equal to the midpoint of the interval 206–220.

18. Repeat Exercise 16, but use the coded formula with m equal to the midpoint of the interval 281–295. Are your answers to Exercises 16, 17, and 18 the same? If not, check your calculations.

19. Find the mean for the data on males in Exercise 19, Chapter 3. Use the coded formula with m equal to the midpoint of the interval 18 to 19.

20. Find the mean for the data on females in Exercise 19, Chapter 3.

21. Find the mean for the data in Exercise 21, Chapter 3. Use the coded formula with m equal to the midpoint of the interval 51–53.

22. Find the mean for the data in Exercise 21, but use the coded formula with m equal to the midpoint of the interval 57–59.

23. Find the mean for the data in Exercise 24, Chapter 3. Use the coded formula with m equal to the midpoint of the interval 161–175.

24. The length of survival (in years) after discovery of a rare type of cancer was recorded for each of six cancer patients. The data are as follows:

$$1.7, \quad 3.2, \quad 2.1, \quad 4.6, \quad 1.4, \quad 2.8$$

Calculate the mean survival for this sample of six patients.

4.6   A MEASURE OF LOCATION: PERCENTILE RANKS

Percentile ranks express the fraction or percentage of scores above or below specified values and hence are used to locate an observation in relation to other observations. Percentiles are the scores themselves; the definition follows.

DEFINITION 4.10   Let $X_1, X_2, \ldots, X_n$ be a set of n scores arranged in increasing order. The **Pth percentile** is the value of X such that P percent of the scores are less than that value of X and $(100 - P)$ percent are greater.

For example, the 80th percentile of a large set of scores on a variable X corresponds to the value X such that 80% of the values or scores fall below it and 20% lie above it (see Figure 4.2). Note that the 50th percentile of a set of scores is the median and that all measurements of central tendency are measures of location because they locate the center of a distribution of scores.

Percentile ranks are frequently used to describe the results of achievement tests and the final ranking of a person in comparison to the rest of the

FIGURE 4.2

80th percentile rank

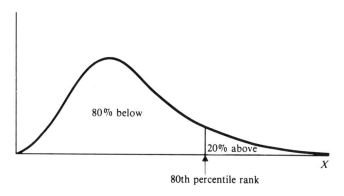

people taking an examination. Phrases such as "John S. scored at the 90th percentile on the Scholastic Aptitude Test this year" or "Susie J. scored at the 85th percentile on a national speed-reading examination for fourth graders" locate a person in relation to the others who took the same examination.

Special names are given to the 25th and 75th percentiles of a set of scores.

DEFINITION 4.11 | The **lower quartile** of a large set of data is defined to be the 25th percentile. Twenty-five percent of the scores fall below the lower quartile and 75 percent above (see Figure 4.3).

DEFINITION 4.12 | The **upper quartile** of a large set of data is defined to be the 75th percentile. Seventy-five percent of the scores fall below the upper quartile and 25 percent above (see Figure 4.3).

Having learned how to compute the median, you will find that percentiles are easy to compute. After all, the median is the 50th percentile.

FIGURE 4.3

Lower quartile, median, and upper quartile

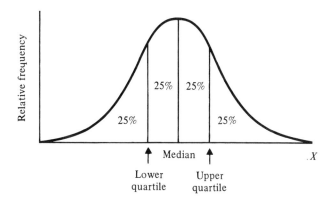

COMPUTING PERCENTILES

The Pth percentile is found by using the formula

$$P_p = L + \frac{i}{f_p}(P\% \text{ of } n - cf_b)$$

where

P_p = percentile

L = lower real limit of the class interval that includes the percentile we wish to find

n = total frequency

cf_b = sum of the frequencies (cumulative frequency) for all class intervals *below* the interval that includes the percentile of interest

f_p = frequency of the class interval that includes the percentile of interest

In working with percentiles, we are given the percentile rank of an individual and attempt to determine the individual's score. Suppose we were asked to use the crime rate data of Table 4.3 to determine the 40th percentile. To determine the 40th percentile, we must locate the interval for which the cumulative relative frequency exceeds .40. This interval contains the 40th percentile. For the data of Table 4.3, the seventh interval contains the 40th percentile. Thus $L = 494.5$. Then, referring to Table 4.3, we see that

$$n = 90 \qquad f_{40} = 9$$
$$cf_b = 28 \qquad i = 55$$

Substituting these values into the formula, we have

$$P_{40} = L + \frac{i}{f_p}(40\% \text{ of } n - cf_b)$$

$$= 494.5 + \frac{55}{9}(36 - 28) = 543.39$$

EXERCISES

25. Compute the 60th percentile for the data of Exercise 23, Chapter 3.

26. Refer to Exercise 25. Use the same data to compute the 90th percentile.

27. Use the data from Exercise 24, Chapter 3, to determine the 25th percentile.

28. Use the data from Exercise 24, Chapter 3, to determine the 75th percentile.

29. Refer to Exercise 28. Use the same data to compute the 50th percentile. Compare that value to the mode and mean for the same set of data.

30. Use the data from Exercise 22, Chapter 3, to compute the 75th percentile.

31. Use the data from Exercise 22, Chapter 3, to compute the 50th percentile. Compare that value with both the mode and the mean.

32. Refer to Table 4.3. Compute the 25th percentile.

33. Using the data from Exercise 32, compute the 60th percentile.

34. Using the data from Exercise 32, compute the 75th percentile.

4.7   DATA VARIATION

The three measures of central tendency — the mean, median, and mode — locate the center of a distribution of data, but they tell us nothing about the spread or variation of the scores. The importance of data variation is exemplified by a story that a friend of ours, a law professor, tells frequently in our presence. Gathering a group of listeners about her and casting a mischievous glance in our direction, she asks, "Have you ever heard the story about the statistician who could not swim and drowned in a river with an average depth of 3 feet?" Although we admit to some discomfort every time we hear the joke, it does stress the importance of describing data variation. The mean (or any other measure of central tendency) tells only part of the story — only partially describes a distribution of scores.

The law professor's joke illustrates the importance of describing data variation or spread. A machine manufacturing size 9 shoes on the average would not be considered satisfactory if the actual sizes varied from $8\frac{3}{8}$ to $9\frac{1}{2}$. A machine producing 1-inch nails on the average would not be satisfactory if the actual lengths varied from $\frac{1}{2}$ to $1\frac{1}{2}$ inches. Indeed, variation of product quality is probably of far greater importance to a manufacturer than measures of central tendency.

Keep in mind that the objective of numerical description is to obtain a set of measures (one or more) that will create a mental reconstruction of the frequency distribution of the data we wish to describe. A measure of central tendency locates only the center of the distribution. The previous examples amply illustrate the need for numerical measures of data variation or spread.

Five numerical descriptive measures of data variation are described in this chapter: the index of qualitative variation, the range, the interquartile range, the variance, and the standard deviation. The percentile ranks of Section 4.6 constitute a sixth, because they provide information on data variability as well as location. Each measure has certain advantages and disadvantages, and some tend to be favored over others in the various fields of science. We begin by describing the index of qualitative variation.

4.8   A MEASURE OF VARIABILITY FOR QUALITATIVE DATA: THE INDEX OF QUALITATIVE VARIATION (OPTIONAL)

We noted previously that a qualitative variable can vary in kind or quality from trial to trial. Just how variable are these observations? Since we cannot compute actual numerical differences between observations, we count the number of observations that differ in quality. We will illustrate a common method for counting the number of observations that differ.

A sample of 20 faculty members was selected to determine the sex and age of preschool children eligible for a university-supported nursery school for three-year-olds. Faculty members were asked to state the sex of their eligible children. Possible results are listed in Table 4.6.

TABLE 4.6

Possible results for sex classification of three-year-olds

(a)		(b)	
Sex	**Frequency**	**Sex**	**Frequency**
male	20	male	19
female	0	female	1

(c)		(d)	
Sex	**Frequency**	**Sex**	**Frequency**
male	18	male	10
female	2	female	10

In Table 4.6a, all 20 of the three-year-olds are boys; hence there is no variability in the qualitative variable "sex," and the number of observations that differ in quality is zero. In contrast, the results in Table 4.6b indicate that 19 are males and 1 is female. Since each of the 19 boys is of a different sex than the 1 girl, there are 19 observations that differ in quality. Similarly, for the outcome of 18 boys and 2 girls, each of the 18 boys differs in sex from each of the 2 girls; hence there are $18 \times 2 = 36$ observations that differ in sex. By the same reasoning, if the outcome were as listed in Table 4.6d, 10 boys and 10 girls, each of the 10 boys differs in sex from each of the 10 girls, making $10 \times 10 = 100$ observations that differ in the qualitative variable "sex."

The counting scheme that we have just illustrated is by no means restricted to a qualitative variable at two levels. For example, if the previous survey was conducted to determine the sex and age of preschool children eligible for a university nursery school for three- and four-year-olds, typical results might appear as in Table 4.7.

TABLE 4.7

Sex and age of children eligible for a preschool nursery

(a)			(b)	
Classification	**Frequency**		**Classification**	**Frequency**
female			*female*	
three-year-olds	10		three-year-olds	4
four-year-olds	5		four-year-olds	2
male			*male*	
three-year-olds	5		three-year-olds	7
four-year-olds	0		four-year-olds	7

Each of the 10 three-year-old girls in Table 4.7a is of a different sex-age classification than each of 5 four-year-old girls. There are thus $10 \times 5 = 50$ observations that differ. In the same way, the 10 three-year-old girls are of a different sex-age classification than the 5 three-year-old boys, which makes $10 \times 5 = 50$ more observations that differ in the sex-age classification. Finally, the 5 four-year-old girls and the 5 three-year-old boys make $5 \times 5 = 25$ more observations of a different sex-age classification. According to our counting scheme, the total number of observations in Table 4.7a that differ in their sex-age classification is then

$$50 + 50 + 25 = 125$$

In general, the total number of differences for a set of observations is determined by first multiplying each frequency by every other frequency (this would produce one product for every pair of frequencies) and then summing these products.

EXAMPLE 4.10   Determine the total number of differences for the data listed in Table 4.7b.

SOLUTION   The frequencies for the classifications are given as 4, 2, 7, and 7. Hence to find the total number of differences given, we first multiply each frequency by the other classification frequencies as follows:

$$4 \times 2 = 8$$
$$4 \times 7 = 28$$
$$4 \times 7 = 28$$
$$2 \times 7 = 14$$
$$2 \times 7 = 14$$
$$7 \times 7 = 49$$

Note now that each frequency is multiplied by every other frequency. The total number of observed differences is then the sum of these products:

$$8 + 28 + 28 + 14 + 14 + 49 = 141$$

The total number of observed differences is not to be confused with the maximum number of possible differences. The latter quantity is the largest possible value for the total number of observed differences. Although proof is omitted, this maximum number is given in the following theorem.

THEOREM 4.1

The maximum number of possible differences for n observations on a qualitative variable with l levels is

$$\frac{n^2(l-1)}{2l}$$

We can now express the total number of observed differences as a percentage of the maximum number of possible differences. This quantity is called the *index of qualitative variation* (IQV).

DEFINITION 4.13

The **index of qualitative variation** is the total number of observed differences expressed as a percentage of the maximum number of possible differences:

$$IQV = \frac{\text{total number of observed differences}}{\text{maximum number of possible differences}} \times 100$$

EXAMPLE 4.11

Compute the IQV for the data of Table 4.7b.

SOLUTION

Recall that in Example 4.10 we computed the total number of observed differences to be 141. The maximum number of possible differences can be found from Theorem 4.1 with $n = 20$ and l, the number of classifications, equal to 4:

$$\text{maximum number of possible differences} = \frac{(20)^2(3)}{2(4)} = 150$$

Hence the index of qualitative variation is

$$IQV = \frac{141}{150} \times 100 = 94\%$$

If the IQV is 0%, there is perfect homogeneity in our sample; if the IQV is 100%, there is perfect heterogeneity in our sample with respect to the qualitative characteristics being considered.

The IQV is *the* measure of data variation for qualitative variables used in the social sciences. Since many of our variables are either interval or ratio level, we will omit further discussion and proceed to the important topic of variation for quantitative variables.

EXERCISES

35. For a group of 4 Catholics, 3 Jews, and 9 Protestants, calculate the IQV. Interpret.

36. For the six Asian racial-ethnic groups shown in Exercise 10, Chapter 3, calculate the IQV. Interpret.

37. For the three Pacific islander racial-ethnic groups shown in Exercise 10, Chapter 3, calculate the IQV. Interpret.

38. If a group of students is composed of 3 men and 7 women; 1 Catholic, 1 Jew, and 8 Protestants; and 4 whites and 6 blacks, is it possible to represent this diversity by means of a single IQV? Explain your answer.

4.9   A MEASURE OF VARIABILITY FOR QUANTITATIVE DATA: THE RANGE

The simplest measure of data variation is the range.

DEFINITION 4.14	The **range** of a set of scores for ungrouped data is the difference between the largest and the smallest scores.

DEFINITION 4.15	If data are grouped in classes, the **range** is the difference between the upper real limit of the highest class and the lower real limit of the lowest class.

The range is employed extensively as a measure of variability in summaries of data that are made available to the general public. We might read that the range of salaries for social scientists with the rank of assistant professor is $4000, the range in temperature in Miami throughout the year is 50 °F, and the range in personal property taxes for a given state is $600. The range is also widely used to describe variation in the quality of an industrial product when small samples are selected periodically from an operating production line. For small samples the range is about as good as any other measure of variation.

EXAMPLE 4.12

Find the range for the 90 measurements of violent crime rates summarized in Table 4.2.

SOLUTION

The range for grouped data is the difference between the upper real limit of the highest class and the lower real limit of the lowest class. Hence the range equals $1044.5 - 164.5 = 880$. Note that if we use the ungrouped measurements given in Table 3.4, the range is $1020 - 189 = 831$.

Although simple to define and calculate, the range is not always satisfactory as a measure of variability. The two distributions of scores shown in Figure 4.4 have the same range (6), but it is apparent that the data for the two distributions differ greatly in variation. The data for Figure 4.4a are much less variable than those for Figure 4.4b. Figure 4.4a has most of its scores very close to the mean; Figure 4.4b has the scores spread more evenly throughout the range.

FIGURE 4.4

Two distributions with the same range

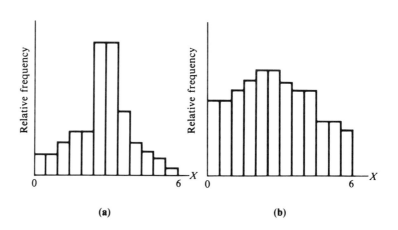

(a)   (b)

A sample range is extremely variable, because any change in the extreme observations alters its value. This instability is reduced by considering certain intermediate ranges — in particular, the interquartile range.

DEFINITION 4.16 | The **interquartile range** (IQR) of a set of scores is defined to be the difference between the upper and lower quartiles (see Figure 4.5).

Although the median, the interquartile range, and the range of a set of scores provide fairly good descriptions of a set of data, we still require three measures to create a mental image of the frequency distribution. Since a single number is easier to interpret, we seek a more sensitive measure to describe the variation of a set of measurements.

FIGURE 4.5

Interquartile range

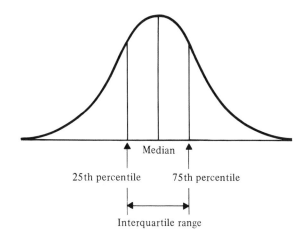

EXERCISES

39. Using the data in Exercise 19, Chapter 3, calculate the interquartile range for the age of males.

40. Repeat Exercise 39 for the interquartile range of the female ages.

41. Using the data in Table 4.2, calculate the interquartile range.

42. Find the range for the data in Exercise 23, Chapter 3. Now calculate the interquartile range for the same data.

4.10   A MEASURE OF VARIABILITY FOR QUANTITATIVE DATA: THE VARIANCE

The shortcoming of the range as a measure of variation is that it is insensitive to a pileup of data near the center of the distribution (see Figure 4.4). To overcome this problem, we use the *deviations*, or distances, of the data from their center. A data set with only a little variability among the scores will have most of the data located near the center of the distribution, as shown in Figure 4.4a. The distances of most of the scores from their center are small. More of the distances from the center of a more variable set would be larger (see Figure 4.4b).

To illustrate, suppose that we have five scores: $X_1 = 68$, $X_2 = 67$, $X_3 = 63$, $X_4 = 66$, and $X_5 = 61$, which represent the percentages of registered voters in five cities who voted at least once during the last year. These data are shown in the *dot diagram* of Figure 4.6. (Dot diagrams are used to depict very small sets of scores.) Each score is located by a dot above the horizontal axis of the diagram.

We use the mean

$$\bar{X} = \frac{\Sigma X}{n} = \frac{325}{5} = 65$$

to locate the center of the set. We construct horizontal lines in Figure 4.6 to represent the distances (deviations) of the measurements from their mean. Surely, the larger the deviations, the greater the variation among the scores. The deviations of the scores are computed by using the formula $X - \bar{X}$. The deviation of X_1 from the mean is

$$X_1 - \bar{X} = 68 - 65 = 3$$

The five scores and their deviations from the mean are shown in Table 4.8 (and in Figure 4.6).

FIGURE 4.6
Dot diagram

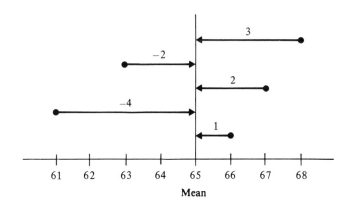

Mean

TABLE 4.8

Deviation of the five percentages from their mean

Score X	Deviation $X - \bar{X}$
68	3
67	2
66	1
63	-2
61	-4
$\Sigma X = 325$	$\Sigma(X - \bar{X}) = 0$

$$\bar{X} = \frac{\Sigma X}{n} = \frac{325}{5} = 65$$

Many different measures of variation could be constructed using the deviations of the scores from their mean. A first thought would be to use their arithmetic average, but this will always equal zero, as it does in Table 4.8. This is because the negative and positive deviations always balance one another. A second possibility is to use the sum of the squared deviations of the scores from their mean. Recall that the deviation of a score X from the sample mean $\bar{X}$ is expressed as $X - \bar{X}$. The square of a deviation is represented as $(X - \bar{X})^2$, and the sum of the squared deviations can be written as

$$\Sigma(X - \bar{X})^2$$

DEFINITION 4.17 | The **variance** of a set of n scores is defined to be the sum of the squared deviations of the scores about their mean, divided by $n - 1$:

$$\text{variance} = \frac{\Sigma(X - \bar{X})^2}{n - 1}$$

The variance is most frequently used as a measure of variability in technical and professional journals. Very seldom is the variance of a set of scores presented to the general public. We will soon show that the variance can be used to obtain a very practical and easily understood measure of data variation.

It is convenient to distinguish between the variance of a set of sample scores and the variance of a population. We will use the symbol s^2 to represent the sample variance, where

$$s^2 = \frac{\Sigma(X - \bar{X})^2}{n - 1}$$

The corresponding population variance will be denoted by σ^2 (σ is the lowercase Greek letter sigma). Sometimes researchers define the sample variance to be $\Sigma(X - \bar{X})^2/n$, and the population variance as $\sigma^2 = \Sigma(X - \bar{X})^2/N$ where N is the population size. However, since σ^2 is usually unknown, and since the quantity $\Sigma(X - \bar{X})^2/n$ tends to underestimate σ^2, whereas s^2 does not, we will use s^2 as the sample variance throughout this text.

---

s^2 is the **sample variance**, given by the formula

$$s^2 = \frac{\Sigma(X - \bar{X})^2}{n - 1}$$

σ^2 is the **population variance**.

EXAMPLE 4.13

Calculate the variance for the five percentages 68, 67, 66, 63, and 61 given in Table 4.8.

SOLUTION

From Table 4.8 we obtain the deviations $X - \bar{X}$. The squared deviations are shown in Table 4.9.

TABLE 4.9

Calculations for Example 4.13

$(X - \bar{X})^2$
9
4
1
4
16

The sample variance is

$$s^2 = \frac{\Sigma(X - \bar{X})^2}{n - 1} = \frac{9 + 4 + 1 + 4 + 16}{5 - 1} = \frac{34}{4} = 8.5$$

We can slightly modify our variance formula so we can apply it to grouped data. Recall that in computing the mean for grouped data (Section 4.4), we used the interval midpoint to represent each observation in the interval. We use this same procedure in calculating the variance for grouped data.

DEFINITION 4.18 | If X represents the midpoint of a class interval with frequency f and $\bar{X}$ denotes the mean for grouped data, the **variance** of a set of n grouped scores is defined to be

$$s^2 = \frac{\Sigma f(X - \bar{X})^2}{n - 1}$$

Examination of Definitions 4.17 and 4.18 indicates that the larger the variation or spread in a set of scores is, the larger the variance. We can compare variances of sets of scores to compare variability, but it is difficult to interpret the variance for a single set of scores. What can we say about the spread of a set of scores with a variance of 2.0? We will try to answer this question and provide you with a measure of variability that is useful not only for comparing sets of scores but also for describing a single set of scores.

DEFINITION 4.19 | The **standard deviation** of a set of scores is defined to be the positive square root of the variance.

The sample standard deviation will be denoted by s, and the corresponding population standard deviation by σ.

---

s is the **sample standard deviation**:

$$s = \sqrt{s^2}$$

σ is the **population standard deviation**:

$$\sigma = \sqrt{\sigma^2}$$

Many electronic desk calculators have a key to calculate the sample standard deviation s after data are entered. If you do not have access to such a calculator, you can rewrite the formulas for s^2 (and hence s) of Definitions 4.17 and 4.18 in a simpler computational form, as follows:

SHORTCUT FORMULAS FOR s^2, GROUPED AND UNGROUPED DATA

Ungrouped: $s^2 = \dfrac{1}{n-1}\left[\Sigma X^2 - \dfrac{(\Sigma X)^2}{n}\right]$

Grouped: $s^2 = \dfrac{1}{n-1}\left[\Sigma fX^2 - \dfrac{(\Sigma fX)^2}{n}\right]$

$s = \sqrt{s^2}$

EXAMPLE 4.14   Calculate the sample variance and standard deviation for the data of Table 4.8, using the shortcut formula for s^2.

SOLUTION   It is convenient to make a table of calculations when using the shortcut formula for s^2, as shown in Table 4.10. The totals for X and X^2 columns of Table 4.10, ΣX and ΣX^2, are needed in the formula for s^2. For $n = 5$ we have

$$s^2 = \frac{1}{n-1}\left[\Sigma X^2 - \frac{(\Sigma X)^2}{n}\right] = \frac{1}{4}\left[21{,}159 - \frac{(325)^2}{5}\right]$$

$$= \frac{1}{4}(21{,}159 - 21{,}125) = \frac{34}{4} = 8.5$$

TABLE 4.10

Calculations for s^2 for data of Table 4.8

	X	X^2
	68	4,624
	67	4,489
	66	4,356
	63	3,969
	61	3,721
Total	325	21,159

Note that this is identical to the result for Example 4.13, where we used the formula

$$s^2 = \frac{\Sigma(X - \bar{X})^2}{n-1}$$

The sample standard deviation is then

$$s = \sqrt{8.5} = 2.92$$

For the shortcut formula using grouped data, we multiply f by X and f by X^2 for each class. If we then add fX for each class and fX^2 for each class, we obtain ΣfX and ΣfX^2, respectively. These quantities are used to compute s^2 and will be illustrated in Section 4.11 for coded data.

We now state a rule that gives practical significance to the standard deviation of a set of scores. Particularly, it describes the spread (variation) of a set of scores by the percentage of scores that we might expect to find within certain distances from the mean. The rule applies to any mound-shaped frequency distributions (frequency histograms that pile up near the center). Because mound-shaped distributions of social data are common, the rule possesses wide applicability. It is called the *empirical rule*.

EMPIRICAL RULE

Given a frequency distribution that is mound shaped (see Figure 4.7a), the interval

$$\bar{X} - s \text{ to } \bar{X} + s \text{ contains approximately } 68\% \text{ of the scores}$$

$$\bar{X} - 2s \text{ to } \bar{X} + 2s \text{ contains approximately } 95\% \text{ of the scores}$$

$$\bar{X} - 3s \text{ to } \bar{X} + 3s \text{ contains approximately all of the scores}$$

The empirical rule as stated is approximate because it must apply to any mound-shaped distribution.

If a set of scores possesses a bell-shaped distribution, as shown in Figure 4.7b, the empirical rule can be restated more precisely as follows:

$$\bar{X} - s \text{ to } \bar{X} + s \text{ contains } 68.26\% \text{ of the scores}$$

$$\bar{X} - 2s \text{ to } \bar{X} + 2s \text{ contains } 95.44\% \text{ of the scores}$$

$$\bar{X} - 3s \text{ to } \bar{X} + 3s \text{ contains } 99.74\% \text{ of the scores}$$

An equivalent and perhaps more familiar restatement of the rule for a bell-shaped distribution is

$$\bar{X} - 1.96s \text{ to } \bar{X} + 1.96s \text{ contains } 95\% \text{ of the scores}$$

$$\bar{X} - 2.58s \text{ to } \bar{X} + 2.58s \text{ contains } 99\% \text{ of the scores}$$

We will study more about the bell-shaped (normal) distribution in Chapter 5.

FIGURE 4.7

Empirical rule and fre-
quency distributions

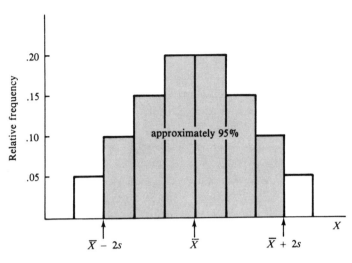

(a) Mound-shaped frequency distribution

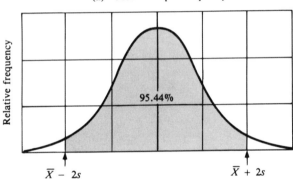

(b) Bell-shaped frequency distribution

EXAMPLE 4.15

A study was conducted to determine the average length of time it takes for an item to be completed on an assembly line operation. A sample of 50 items is timed. The mean and standard deviation (in hours) for the 50 measurements are $\bar{X} = 4.8$ and $s = .42$. If we assume that the measurements have a mound-shaped frequency histogram, describe the data using the empirical rule.

SOLUTION

The empirical rule tells us that approximately 68% of the scores lie in the interval $\bar{X} - s$ to $\bar{X} + s$ — that is, the interval from 4.38 to 5.22. The interval $\bar{X} - 2s$ to $\bar{X} + 2s$ (that is, the interval 3.96 to 5.64) contains approximately 95% of the scores. Approximately all of the scores are in the interval $\bar{X} - 3s$ to $\bar{X} + 3s$ — that is, the interval 3.54 to 6.06.

We have discussed four measures of variability for quantitative data in this chapter: the range, the interquartile range, the variance, and the standard deviation. Although each of these measures is useful in data description, **the variance and the standard deviation of a set of scores provide us with information that enables us to do the following:**

1. **Compare variability between sets of scores.**
2. **Interpret the variability of a single set of scores by using the empirical rule.** However, remember that the empirical rule applies only to data that form mound-shaped frequency distributions.

Because of these two characteristics, the standard deviation will be used almost exclusively to measure the variability of a single set of scores in the remainder of this text.

A final comment concerning the standard deviation should be made. Social researchers often like to compare the magnitude of the standard deviation of a set of scores to a particular baseline, such as $\bar{X}$. The next definition tells us how to do this.

DEFINITION 4.20 | The **coefficient of relative variation** (CRV) for the standard deviation is the standard deviation expressed as a percentage of the mean $\bar{X}$:

$$CRV = \frac{s}{\bar{X}} \times 100$$

To compare two different standard deviations quickly, the social researcher will sometimes compute the CRV for each and then discuss the difference between them. A standard deviation of 10 with $\bar{X} = 1000$ represents, relatively speaking, less variation than a standard deviation of 10 with $\bar{X} = 100$. The respective CRVs are 1 and 10. Compared with the means, the relative variation in the first sample is only $\frac{1}{10}$ the relative variation in the second.

4.11 CODING TO DETERMINE *s* FOR GROUPED DATA (OPTIONAL)

As with calculations for the mean, data arranged in the frequency table are sometimes coded to simplify our computations. The coding procedure makes use of Steps 1 through 4 explained in Section 4.5 for calculating $\bar{X}$. For convenience, all the steps are given next.

STEPS FOR SIMPLIFYING THE CALCULATION OF s FOR GROUPED DATA

1. Inspect the frequency table and select the class interval you think is likely to contain the mean.
2. Let m denote the midpoint of this interval.
3. Subtract m from each interval midpoint.
4. Compute the coded class interval midpoints X_c as $X_c = (X - m)/i$, where i is the interval width.
5. Using the coded midpoints X_c (rather than X), compute a sample variance and standard deviation. Use the formulas

$$s_c^2 = \frac{1}{n-1}\left[\Sigma f X_c^2 - \frac{(\Sigma f X_c)^2}{n}\right]$$

$$s_c = \sqrt{s_c^2}$$

6. The standard deviation for the original (uncoded) data in the frequency table is

$$s = i s_c$$

EXAMPLE 4.16

Using the data of Table 4.11, derived from Table 4.2, apply the coding principles just discussed to compute s^2, the sample variance for the grouped data on the violent crime rate.

SOLUTION

Substituting into the shortcut formula and using the coded units, we find

$$s_c^2 = \frac{1}{n-1}\left[\Sigma f X_c^2 - \frac{(\Sigma f X_c)^2}{n}\right]$$

$$= \frac{1}{89}\left[996 - \frac{(16)^2}{90}\right] = \frac{1}{89}(996 - 2.84) = 11.16$$

$$s_c = \sqrt{11.16} = 3.34$$

Then the standard deviation of the violent crime rate data in Table 4.2 is

$$s = i s_c = 55(3.34) = 183.70$$

This answer can be checked by computing s for these data without coding.

TABLE 4.11

Violent crime rate data
based on Table 4.2

Real Class Interval	Midpoint X	f	X_c	fX_c	fX_c^2
164.5– 219.5	192	2	-7	-14	98
219.5– 274.5	247	2	-6	-12	72
274.5– 329.5	302	4	-5	-20	100
329.5– 384.5	357	6	-4	-24	96
384.5– 439.5	412	6	-3	-18	54
439.5– 494.5	467	8	-2	-16	32
494.5– 549.5	522	9	-1	-9	9
549.5– 604.5	577	12	0	0	0
604.5– 659.5	632	9	1	9	9
659.5– 714.5	687	8	2	16	32
714.5– 769.5	742	8	3	24	72
769.5– 824.5	797	7	4	28	112
824.5– 879.5	852	5	5	25	125
879.5– 934.5	907	2	6	12	72
934.5– 989.5	962	1	7	7	49
989.5–1044.5	1017	1	8	8	64
Total		90		16	996

EXERCISES

43. Calculate the standard deviation of the IQ scores below:

150,   75,   128,   110,   126,   120,   125,   122

44. Compute the standard deviation of the ungrouped murder rates for the ten metropolitan areas below:

4,   7,   2,   9,   4,   21,   8,   2,   7,   7

45. Compute the standard deviation of the ungrouped data in Exercise 1.

46. Compute the standard deviation of the ungrouped data in Exercise 2.

47. Calculate the standard deviation of the data on males in Exercise 19, Chapter 3. Use the coded formula and set *m* equal to the midpoint of the interval 20–21.

48. Calculate the standard deviation of the data in Exercise 19, Chapter 3, for females only. Use the coded formula and set *m* equal to the midpoint of the interval 18–19.

49. Calculate the standard deviation of the data in Exercise 21, Chapter 3. Use the coded formula and set *m* equal to the midpoint of the interval 54–56.

50. Calculate the standard deviation of the data in Exercise 22, Chapter 3. Use the coded formula and set m equal to the midpoint of the interval 6–8.

51. Calculate the standard deviation of the data in Exercise 23, Chapter 3. Use the coded formula and set m equal to the midpoint of the interval 12,500–14,999.

52. Calculate the standard deviation of the data in Exercise 23, Chapter 3. Use the coded formula and set m equal to the midpoint of the interval 17,500–19,999.

53. Calculate the standard deviation of the data in Exercise 24, Chapter 3. Use the coded formula and set m equal to the midpoint of the interval 281–295.

54. Students in a college economics class were interested in examining price increases for a certain make of car over a specified period of time. To do this, they obtained price increases of $n = 24$ different models over a six-month period, as shown in the accompanying table.

EXERCISE 54

Price increases (dollars)

100	121	130	129
150	116	120	117
154	125	110	119
130	115	125	123
90	109	100	120
92	112	115	118

The sample mean and standard deviation for this set of measurements are as follows: $\bar{X} = \$118.33$ and $s = \$15.01$, respectively. Previous experience working with price increases indicates that we can assume that the set of 24 price increases is mound-shaped. Describe the variability of the sample by using the empirical rule.

55. Refer to Exercise 54. Calculate the coefficient of relative variation.

4.12   HOW TO GUESS THE STANDARD DEVIATION OF SAMPLE DATA

Many times sample data are presented without accompanying numerical descriptive measures such as the mean and standard deviation. Although the sample mean can be computed very easily, the calculations required for obtaining s (even with the shortcut formula of Section 4.10) can be difficult and time-consuming. **When we want to obtain a rough approximation to the actual sample standard deviation, without going through the tedious calcula-**

tions, we can use the following formula:

$$s \approx \frac{\text{range}}{4}$$

(read "s is approximately equal to the range divided by 4").

That development of this approximation is quite simple. For mound-shaped distributions, we learned that the interval $\bar{X} - 2s$ to $\bar{X} + 2s$ contains approximately 95% of the scores. Since this interval contains most of the scores, it can be used to approximate the range of the scores. The difference between the largest and smallest scores is approximately $(\bar{X} + 2s) - (\bar{X} - 2s) = 4s$. Since the range is approximately $4s$, the range divided by 4 gives an approximate value for s.

APPROXIMATION TO s USING THE RANGE

$$s \approx \frac{\text{range}}{4}$$

(*Note*: This approximation will work best for mound-shaped distributions.)

Another reason for using this approximation is to check our calculation of s when using the shortcut formula. Arithmetic mistakes in determining the standard deviation can easily occur, so we suggest using the range approximation as a check even when the calculation s is required.

EXAMPLE 4.17

Fifteen students with similar socioeconomic backgrounds were compared on an IQ test at the end of their freshman year. Their scores are presented in Table 4.12. Use the range of the observations to approximate s. Calculate s using the usual shortcut formula and compare this value with your approximate value.

TABLE 4.12

IQ scores

116	132	114	134	128
129	123	122	126	125
129	118	131	130	126

SOLUTION

We approximate the value of s using the range of the measurements divided by 4. From Table 4.12 we see that the range is $134 - 114 = 20$.

Our approximation is then

$$\text{approximate value of } s = \frac{\text{range}}{4} = \frac{20}{4} = 5.0$$

Using the shortcut formula to calculate the exact value of s, we need to compute ΣX^2 and ΣX:

$$\Sigma X^2 = (116)^2 + (129)^2 + \cdots + (126)^2 = 236{,}873$$
$$\Sigma X = 116 + 129 + \cdots + 126 = 1883$$

Hence

$$\Sigma X^2 - \frac{(\Sigma X)^2}{n} = 236{,}873 - \frac{(1883)^2}{15}$$
$$= 236{,}873 - 236{,}379.267 = 493.733$$

The sample variance s^2 is then

$$s^2 = \frac{493.733}{14} = 35.267$$

and the standard deviation is

$$s = \sqrt{35.267} = 5.94$$

Although the approximate value of s, 5.0, differs somewhat from the actual value, 5.94, it still provides a check on our calculations. For instance, we know that our calculation of 5.94 is at least reasonable. If we had computed s to be 59.4, it would certainly not agree with our check. We advise running this simple check everytime you compute a standard deviation.

EXERCISES

56. Since an approximate value of the standard deviation is the range divided by 4, check the standard deviation determined in Exercise 50.

57. Use the range approximation for s to check your calculations in Exercise 51.

4.13   THE BOX PLOT

Figure 4.8 is a stem-and-leaf plot of violent crime rates in the United States. The **box plot** is another graphical display that builds on the information displayed in a stem-and-leaf plot. As mentioned in Chapter 3, a stem-and-leaf

1	89
2	10 24 67 91 96 98
3	36 41 52 54 74 76 88 93 93
4	10 21 35 47 48 60 64 66 80 81 91 96 98
5	04 05 08 16 26 29 37 57 59 61 62 62 62 63 70 71 78 85 92
6	05 05 24 26 28 31 39 42 47 61 73 84 85 85 90 98
7	03 06 18 19 20 31 35 39 51 58 71
8	04 07 09 11 14 17 43 56 68 76 77 85
9	28 71
10	20

plot provides a graphical representation of a set of scores that can be used to examine the shape of the distribution, the range of scores, and the concentration of scores. The box plot is more concerned with the symmetry of the distribution and incorporates numerical measures of central tendency and location in order to study the variability of the scores and the concentration of scores in the tails of the distribution.

Before we show how to construct and interpret a box plot, it is necessary to introduce several new terms that are peculiar to the language of EDA. We are familiar with the definitions of the lower quartile, median, and upper quartile of a distribution, presented earlier in this chapter. The box plot uses the median and *hinges* of a distribution. Hinges are very similar to quartiles of a distribution, but because of the method by which they are computed for sample data, the lower and upper hinges of a distribution may differ very slightly from the lower and upper quartiles of a set of scores. Having said this and recognizing the slight distinction, we will compute hinges in this text but refer to them as the lower and upper quartiles of the sample data.

We can now illustrate a skeleton box plot with an example.

EXAMPLE 4.18

Use the data from the stem-and-leaf plot of Figure 4.8 for the $n = 90$ violent crime rates to construct a skeleton box plot.

SOLUTION

When the scores are ordered from lowest to highest, the median score and quartile scores are located as follows:

$$\text{median location} = \frac{n + 1}{2}$$

$$\text{quartile location} = \frac{\text{truncated median location} + 1}{2}$$

where the truncated median location is simply the median location with the decimal .5 omitted where present. For the distribution of $n = 90$ violent crime rates, we have

$$\text{median location} = \frac{90 + 1}{2} = 45.5$$

$$\text{truncated median location} = 45$$

and

$$\text{quartile location} = \frac{45 + 1}{2} = 23$$

Since the median location is the 45.5th score in the distribution, we average the 45th and 46th scores to compute the median. For these data the 45th score (counting from the lowest to the highest in Figure 4.8) is 571, and the 46th is 578; hence the median is

$$M = \frac{571 + 578}{2} = 574.5$$

Then, in order to find the lower and upper quartiles for this distribution of scores, we determine the 23rd score counting from the low side of the distribution and from the high side of the distribution, respectively. The 23rd lowest score and 23rd highest scores are 464 and 719;

$$\text{lower quartile, } Q_1 = 464$$

$$\text{upper quartile, } Q_3 = 719$$

These three descriptive measures and the smallest and largest values in a data set are used to construct a skeleton box plot (see Figure 4.9). The skeleton plot is constructed by drawing a box between the lower and upper quartiles, with a solid line drawn across the box to locate the median. A straight line is

FIGURE 4.9

Skeleton box plot for the data of Figure 4.8

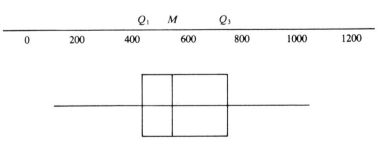

then drawn connecting the box to each of the extreme values. These straight lines are sometimes called *whiskers*, and the entire graph a *box-and-whiskers plot*.

With a quick glance at a skeleton box plot, it is easy to obtain an impression about the following characteristics:

1. lower and upper quartiles, Q_1 and Q_3
2. interquartile range (IQR), the distance between the lower and upper quartiles
3. most extreme (lowest and highest) values
4. symmetry or asymmetry of the distribution of scores

If we had been presented with Figure 4.9 without having seen the original data, we could have observed that

$$Q_1 \approx 450$$
$$Q_3 \approx 750$$
$$\text{IQR} \approx 750 - 450 = 300$$
$$M \approx 560$$

most extreme values: 170 and 1020

Also, because the median is closer to the lower quartile than the upper quartile and because the upper whisker is a little longer than the lower whisker, the distribution departs slightly from symmetry. To see that this conclusion is true, refer back to the stem-and-leaf plot for these data in Figure 4.8.

The skeleton box plot can be expanded to include more information about extreme values in the tails of the distribution. To do so, we need the following additional quantities:

$$\text{lower inner fence} = Q_1 - 1.5(\text{IQR})$$
$$\text{upper inner fence} = Q_3 + 1.5(\text{IQR})$$
$$\text{lower outer fence} = Q_1 - 3(\text{IQR})$$
$$\text{upper outer fence} = Q_3 + 3(\text{IQR})$$
$$\text{lower adjacent score} = \text{most extreme score in the interval}$$
$$\text{from } Q_1 \text{ to the lower inner fence}$$
$$\text{upper adjacent score} = \text{most extreme score in the interval}$$
$$\text{from } Q_3 \text{ to the upper inner fence}$$

Any score beyond an inner fence on either side is called a **mild outlier**; a score beyond an outer fence on either side is called an **extreme outlier**.

EXAMPLE 4.19   Compute the inner and outer fences for the data of Example 4.18.

SOLUTION   For these data we found the lower and upper quartiles to be 464 and 719 respectively; the IQR $= 719 - 464 = 255$. Then

$$\text{lower inner fence} = 464 - 1.5(255) = 81.5$$
$$\text{upper inner fence} = 719 + 1.5(255) = 1101.5$$
$$\text{lower outer fence} = 464 - 3(255) = -301$$
$$\text{upper outer fence} = 719 + 3(255) = 1484$$

Also from the stem-and-leaf plot we see that the lower and upper adjacent values are 189 and 1020.

We now have all the quantities necessary for constructing a box plot.

STEPS IN CONSTRUCTING A BOX PLOT
1. As with a skeleton box plot, mark off a box from the lower quartile to the upper quartile.
2. Draw a solid line across the box to locate the median.
3. Mark the location of the upper and lower adjacent values with an X.
4. Draw a dashed line between each quartile and its adjacent value.
5. Mark each extreme outlier with a special symbol (such as an *).

EXAMPLE 4.20   Construct a box plot for the data of Example 4.18.

SOLUTION   The box plot is shown in Figure 4.10.

FIGURE 4.10

The box plot for the data of Figure 4.8

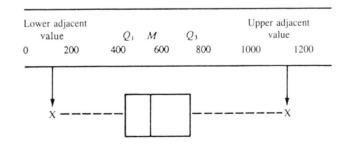

What information can be drawn from a box plot? First, the center of the distribution of scores is indicated by the median line in the box plot. Second, a measure of the variability of the scores is given by the interquartile range, the length of the box. Recall that the box is constructed between the lower and upper quartiles, so it contains the middle 50% of the scores in the distribution, with 25% on either side of the median line inside the box. Third, by examining the relative position of the median line, we can gauge the symmetry of the middle 50% of the scores. For example, if the median line is closer to the lower quartile than to the upper, there is a greater concentration of scores on the lower side of the median within the box than on the upper side; a symmetric distribution of scores would have the median line located in the center of the box. Fourth, additional information about skewness is obtained from the lengths of the whiskers; the longer one whisker is relative to the other one, the more skewness there is in the tail with the longer whisker. Fifth, a general assessment can be made about the presence of outliers by examining the number of scores classified as mild outliers and the number classified as extreme outliers. This comparison assists us in choosing appropriate methods for our statistical inferences.

EXERCISES

58. Using the data in Exercise 33, Chapter 3, present the number of newspapers sold per 100 people in a skeleton box plot.

59. Explain the skeleton box plot of Exercise 58 to include the following:
    a. lower inner fence
    b. upper inner fence
    c. lower outer fence
    d. upper outer fence

60. Refer to Exercise 58. Continue to expand the skeleton box plot to include the following:
    a. lower adjacent score
    b. upper adjacent score
    c. all mild outliers
    d. all extreme outliers

61. Construct a box plot using the data of Table 2.15. Then list each of the following values of the effective tax rate on residential property:
    a. lower inner fence
    b. upper inner fence
    c. lower outer fence
    d. upper outer fence

62. Refer to Exercise 61. For the box plot, list each of the following values:
 a. lower adjacent score
 b. upper adjacent score
 c. all mild outliers
 d. all extreme outliers

63. Output for a computer-generated box plot is shown here for the data of Example 4.20. Compare this output to the solution for Example 4.20. Are the results similar? What might cause the results to be slightly different?

EXERCISE 63   MTB > boxplot 'RATE'

```
                          ------------------
        ------------------I      +      I--------------------
                          ------------------
    --------+---------+---------+---------+---------+-------RATE
          300       450       600       750       900
```


SUMMARY

The research-oriented social scientist requires statistical tools to make a meaningful inference about a population based on information contained in a sample. Since making an inference implies description of the population or universe, we seek a way to describe a set of scores.

Graphical descriptive techniques, presented primarily in Chapter 3, are very effective for describing a set of measurements or scores, but they are unsatisfactory for statistical inference. The difficulty is that we can say that the sample frequency histogram will be similar to the population frequency distribution, but we have no way to measure the goodness of the inference. Equivalently, graphical descriptive techniques provide no way to measure the degree of difference between two irregularly shaped figures.

Numerical descriptive measures are numbers that create a mental image of the frequency distribution for a set of scores. The most important of these are the mean and standard deviation, which measure the center and spread, respectively, of a frequency distribution. The standard deviation of a set of scores is a meaningful measure of variability when interpreted using the empirical rule. Numerical descriptive measures of a population are called *parameters* and numerical descriptive measures computed from a sample are called *statistics*.

Numerical descriptive measures are suitable for both description and inference making. We can use a numerical descriptive measure of the sample — say, the sample mean — to estimate a parameter such as the population mean. The great advantage of the numerical descriptive measure in making inferences is that we can give a quantitative measure of the goodness of the inference. In particular, we will show that the sample mean lies within a specified distance of the population mean with a predetermined probability.

KEY WORDS

Box plot   A graphical display of quantitative data that builds on the information presented in a stem-and-leaf plot.

Coefficient of relative variation (CRV)   The standard deviation expressed as a percentage of the mean $\bar{X}$.

Empirical rule   A rule that states approximately what percentage of the scores in a mound-shaped distribution lies within one, two, or three standard deviations of the mean $\bar{X}$.

Extreme outlier   A score in a box plot beyond an outer fence on either side.

Grouped data   Data grouped in a frequency table.

Index of qualitative variation   The total number of observed differences expressed as a percentage of the maximum number of possible differences.

Interquartile range (IQR)   The difference between the upper and lower quartiles of a set of scores.

Lower quartile   The 25th percentile of a large set of scores. Twenty-five percent of the scores fall below the lower quartile and 75 percent above it.

Mean   The sum of a set of scores divided by the number of scores in the set. Also called the *arithmetic mean.*

Median   The middle score for an odd number of scores arranged in increasing order. The average of the two middle scores for an even number of scores arranged in increasing order. For a large set of scores, the median is the 50th percentile.

Mild outlier   A score in a box plot beyond an inner fence on either side.

Mode   The score or measurement that occurs with the greatest frequency in a set.

Parameter   A numerical descriptive measure of a population.

Percentile   The score in a distribution corresponding to a percentile rank.

Percentile rank   The position of a score expressed as a fraction or percentage of scores above or below it. It is used to locate an observation in relation to other observations.

Range   The difference between the largest and smallest scores in a set.

Standard deviation   The positive square root of the variance for a set of scores.

Statistic   A numerical descriptive measure of a sample.

Upper quartile   The 75th percentile of a large set of scores. Seventy-five percent of the scores fall below the upper quartile and 25 percent above it.
Variance   The sum of the squared deviations of the scores about their mean divided by $n - 1$ for a sample and by n for a population.

KEY FORMULAS

Sample median (grouped data)	M_d	$= L + \dfrac{i}{f_m}\,(50\% \text{ of } n - cf_b)$
Sample mean (ungrouped data)	$\bar{X}$	$= \dfrac{\Sigma X}{n}$
Sample mean (grouped data)	$\bar{X}$	$= \dfrac{\Sigma fX}{n}$
Pth percentile	P_p	$= L + \dfrac{i}{f_p}\,(P\% \text{ of } n - cf_b)$
Sample variance (ungrouped data)	s^2	$= \dfrac{\Sigma(X - \bar{X})^2}{n - 1}$ or
	s^2	$= \dfrac{1}{n-1}\left[\Sigma X^2 - \dfrac{(\Sigma X)^2}{n}\right]$
Sample variance (grouped data)	s^2	$= \dfrac{\Sigma f(X - \bar{X})^2}{n - 1}$ or
	s^2	$= \dfrac{1}{n-1}\left[\Sigma fX^2 - \dfrac{(\Sigma fX)^2}{n}\right]$
Sample standard deviation	s	$= \sqrt{s^2}$
Coefficient of relative variation		$\text{CRV} = \dfrac{s}{\bar{X}} \times 100$

SUPPLEMENTARY EXERCISES FOR CHAPTER 4

64. The accompanying data represent the ratio of male to female executives in ten corporations.

12.67	18.14	13.35	17.74	16.91
12.15	15.73	11.85	14.65	10.28

    a. Round the data to the nearest tenth.

    b. Compute the mode for the 10 rounded scores.

    c. Compute the median for the 10 rounded scores.

    d. Compute the mean for these 10 scores.

    e. Compute the standard deviation.

65. What is the range for the sex ratios in Exercise 64?

66. Use the data in Table 4.2 to compute the 30th percentile.

67. Randomly select 10 cities from the North in Table 3.4 and 10 from the South. Given these two samples of crime rates, compute the mean and standard deviation for each sample and then find the coefficient of variation.

68. The accompanying data represent a sample of 10 measurements on the degree of urbanization of 10 localities:

$$63, \quad 56, \quad 32, \quad 56, \quad 48, \quad 45, \quad 45, \quad 96, \quad 57, \quad 71$$

    a. Compute the range.

    b. Calculate the mean and standard deviation.

    c. Use the range approximation of Section 4.12 to check your calculation of s.

69. The mean contribution per person for a college alumni fund drive was $100.50, and the standard deviation was $38.23. What is the contribution of the person who is 1 standard deviation below the mean? 1 standard deviation above the mean?

70. Discuss which measure of central tendency would be more appropriate for describing the central tendency of the distribution of alumni contributions of Exercise 69.

71. Would you use the standard deviation rule to describe the distribution of alumni contributions of Exercise 69?

72. Seven different families have the following number of children: 2, 1, 1, 0, 4, 5, and 2. Find the mean and standard deviation. Check your calculation of s by using the range approximation of Section 4.12.

73. Using the data in Exercise 64, estimate the standard deviation. (*Hint*: See Section 4.12.) Compute s and compare this value with your approximation.

74. From the accompanying scores on the percentage of family income allocated to rent, a researcher calculated s to be .263. On what grounds might we doubt the researcher's accuracy? What is the correct value (to the nearest hundreth)?

17.2	17.1	17.0	17.1	16.9
17.0	17.1	17.0	17.3	17.2
17.1	17.0	17.1	16.9	17.0
17.1	17.3	17.2	17.4	17.1

75. One hundred twenty-eight individuals were given a test for social awareness. The scores produced a mean of 92 and a standard deviation of 10 on a scale of 100. Would you expect the distribution of these 128 scores (where a score cannot exceed 100) to be mound-shaped? Why?

76. One hundred fundamentalist ministers were administered a 40-item test on the causes of mental illness. Compute the mean and standard deviation for the scores in the accompanying table.

EXERCISE 76

Test data for 100 fundamentalist ministers

Class Interval	f	X_c	fX_c	fX_c^2
34–35	4	10		
32–33	0	9		
30–31	2	8		
28–29	6	7		
26–27	3	6		
24–25	5	5		
22–23	6	4		
20–21	6	3		
18–19	7	2		
16–17	9	1		
14–15	22	0		
12–13	10	−1		
10–11	8	−2		
8– 9	6	−3		
6– 7	6	−4		

77. Compute the mode for the data in Exercise 76.

78. What is the median for the data of Exercise 76?

79. A random sample of 15 students from a total of 200 enrolled in a course called "Statistics for the Social Sciences" were given a pencil-and-paper IQ test. The results are as follows:

10	7	14	19	17
17	16	16	16	20
15	14	12	15	8

Determine the mean, median, and mode. Compare your answers.

80. Determine the standard deviation for the ungrouped data of Exercise 79.

81. Experience with students from previous classes suggested that the average (mean) score for the pencil-and-paper test of Exercise 79 was 25. Based on the empirical rule, what conclusions might you draw concerning the class of 200 students?

82. Check your computation of the standard deviation in Exercise 80 by comparing it with the range estimate of the standard deviation.

83. The levels of educational attainment (in years) of 15 heads of households living in an upper-middle-class residential area are as follows:

12	7	14	21	19
16	16	18	16	20
15	14	12	15	8

Determine the mean, median, and mode. Compare your answers.

84. Determine the standard deviation for the ungrouped data of Exercise 83.

85. Using the data in the accompanying table, construct a stem-and-leaf plot.

EXERCISE 85

Median values of homes in lower-class neighborhoods (dollars)

20,700	13,600	14,400	11,300	12,000	13,000
12,800	17,500	13,000	12,800	10,500	16,300
16,400	17,600	11,400	13,000	14,600	16,800
16,400	13,800	12,400	14,600	11,100	22,400
20,600	19,800	12,100	15,000	12,000	21,900
18,200	17,500	15,100	12,200	16,300	18,500
25,500	17,300	17,100	12,600	14,000	15,400
18,900	14,500	21,300	12,500	14,100	23,100
22,500	18,000	18,700	12,200	15,300	22,700
23,400	13,900	17,100	11,200	17,300	35,100

86. Construct a box plot for the data in Exercise 85. Interpret your findings.

87. Refer to Exercise 84. Check your computation of the standard deviation by comparing it with the range estimate of the standard deviation. Comment.

88. Refer to Exercise 75, Chapter 3, pertaining to the percentage increase in teachers' salaries for one year, by state.
  a. Determine the mode.
  b. Compute the median.
  c. Calculate the mean.
  d. Calculate the standard deviation.

89. Refer to Exercise 76, Chapter 3, pertaining to infant mortality rates, by state.
   a. Determine the mode.
   b. Compute the median.
   c. Calculate the mean using the coded formula with m equal to the midpoint of the interval 10.5–10.9.
   d. Calculate the standard deviation using the coded formula with m equal to the midpoint of the interval 10.5–10.9.
   e. Calculate the interquartile range.

90. Refer to Exercise 79, Chapter 3, pertaining to the projected percentage increase in population between 1985 and 2000.
   a. Determine the mode.
   b. Compute the median.
   c. Calculate the mean using the coded formula with m equal to the midpoint of the interval 15–19.
   d. Calculate the standard deviation using the coded formula with m equal to the midpoint of the interval 15–19.
   e. Calculate the interquartile range.

91. During the years 1800 to the present, the reigns of Catholic pontiffs (popes) were as shown in the table.

EXERCISE 91

Duration of reigns for
Catholic pontiffs
(1800 to present)

Pope	Years of Reign	Pope	Years of Reign
Pius VII	1800–1823	Benedict XV	1914–1922
Leo XII	1823–1829	Pius XI	1922–1939
Pius VIII	1829–1830	Pius XII	1939–1958
Gregory XVI	1831–1846	John XXIII	1958–1963
Pius IX	1846–1878	Paul VI	1963–1978
Leo XIII	1878–1903	John Paul I	1978–1978
St. Pius X	1903–1914	John Paul II	1978–present

   a. Determine the range and quartiles for the length of reign for the pontiffs listed.
   b. Does the distribution of length of reign appear to be mound-shaped?

92. The data shown here summarize the number of people below the poverty level in the United States, by state. Compute the mean, median, and mode.

EXERCISE 92

Number of people be-
low poverty level (per
1000 U.S. population),
by state

State	Number below Poverty Level (1000)	State	Number below Poverty Level (1000)
Alabama	684	Missouri	592
Alaska	39	Montana	95
Arizona	331	Nebraska	159
Arkansas	417	Nevada	67
California	2611	New Hampshire	78
Colorado	289	New Jersey	699
Connecticut	262	New Mexico	222
Delaware	69	New York	2344
Dist. of Columbia	115	North Carolina	827
Florida	1245	North Dakota	1108
Georgia	869	Oklahoma	391
Hawaii	92	Oregon	291
Idaho	118	Pennsylvania	1213
Illinois	1284	Rhode Island	94
Indiana	523	South Carolina	479
Iowa	266	South Dakota	107
Kansas	232	Tennessee	760
Kentucky	657	Texas	2055
Louisiana	777	Utah	154
Maine	140	Vermont	56
Maryland	409	Virginia	594
Massachusetts	547	Washington	410
Michigan	1004	West Virginia	276
Minnesota	370	Wisconsin	388
Mississippi	600	Wyoming	37

Note: The data for Ohio were not available at this time.

93. Refer to Exercise 92. The output shown here displays a stem-and-leaf plot and a box plot. Discuss the characteristics of the data.

EXERCISE 93

```
MTB > stem leaf 'POVERTY'

Stem-and-leaf of POVERTY   N = 50
Leaf Unit = 100

    15     0 000000000111111
   (11)    0 22222223333
    24     0 44445555
    16     0 666677
    10     0 88
     8     1 01
     6     1 222
     3     1
     3     1
     3     1
     3     2 0
     2     2 3
     1     2
     1     2 6

MTB > boxplot 'POVERTY'
```

```
         ------------
      --I    +    I------------            *      *      O
         ------------
      +---------+---------+---------+---------+---------+------POVERTY
      0        500      1000      1500      2000      2500
```

94. Using Database A, Appendix Table 7, follow the rules for constructing a frequency distribution for the number of acts that students define as serious crimes, for social science students only ($n = 41$). Set $i = 2$. Then compute the standard deviation.

95. Using Database A again, construct a skeleton box plot for ungrouped information on the number of acts judged to be serious crimes by the first 100 students.

96. Refer to Exercise 95. Expand the skeleton box plot to include the following:
    a. lower inner fence
    b. upper inner fence
    c. lower outer fence
    d. upper outer fence

97. Refer to Exercises 95 and 96. Continue to expand the skeleton box plot to include the following:
    a. lower adjacent score
    b. upper adjacent score
    c. all mild outliers
    d. all extreme outliers

98. Calculate the standard deviation for the data in Exercise 86, Chapter 3, on the level-of-technology measurements for all 60 nations shown in Database B, Appendix Table 8.

99. For the ungrouped data used in Exercise 86, Chapter 3, construct a skeleton box plot on the level of technology measurements.

100. Refer to Exercise 99. Expand the skeleton box plot to include the following:
  a. lower inner fence
  b. upper inner fence
  c. lower outer fence
  d. upper outer fence

101. Refer to Exercises 99 and 100. Continue to expand the skeleton box plot to include the following:
  a. lower adjacent score
  b. upper adjacent score
  c. all mild outliers
  d. all extreme outliers

102. Refer to the clinical trial database in Appendix Table 9 and compute the mean, range, and standard deviation of the HAM-D total score for the four treatment groups.

103. Refer to Exercise 102. Complete a profile of the four treatment groups by computing the mean, range, and standard deviation for the anxiety, retardation, sleep disturbance, and total score from the HAM-D scale. Are there any obvious differences among the groups following the treatment period?

104. Refer to Exercise 102. Combine the OBRIST scores for the four treatment groups of the clinical trial database.
  a. Construct a histogram and determine the mean and median from the histogram.
  b. Compute the actual sample mean and median for the combined data and compare these values to the approximation obtained from part (a).

105. Using Database D, Appendix 10 (refer to Exercise 96, Chapter 3), with the rounded rates of forcible rape for the 30 states, complete the following operations:
  a. Construct a frequency distribution with seven class intervals, following the guidelines for constructing frequency distributions.
  b. Compute the mode for the grouped data.
  c. Compute the mean and the standard deviation of the grouped data, setting the midpoint of the fourth interval equal to 0.
  d. Compute the median, 25th percentile, and 75th percentile.
  e. Check your calculation of s by using the range approximation of Section 4.12.

106. Using Database D, Appendix Table 10, construct a frequency distribution for population density of the 30 states. Use seven categories, but follow the other rules in establishing a frequency distribution.

107. Refer to Exercise 106. Complete the following:
  a. Compute the mode for the grouped data.
  b. Compute the mean and the standard deviation of the grouped data, setting the midpoint of the fourth interval equal to 0.
  c. Compute the median, 25th percentile, and 75th percentile.

d. Check your calculation of s by using the range approximation of Section 4.12.

108. Using Database B, Appendix Table 8 (see Exercise 99, Chapter 3, involving infant mortality rates), perform the following operations:
a. Compute the mode for the grouped data.
b. Compute the mean and the standard deviation of the grouped data, setting the midpoint of the fourth interval equal to 0.
c. Compute the median, 25th percentile, and 75th percentile.
d. Check your calculation of s by using the range approximation of Section 4.12.

109. Using Database B, Appendix Table 8 (see Exercise 100, Chapter 3, involving per capita GNP in U.S. dollars), perform the following operations:
a. Compute the mode for the grouped data.
b. Compute the mean and the standard deviation of the grouped data, setting the midpoint of the fourth interval equal to 0.
c. Compute the median, 25th percentile, and 75th percentile.
d. Check your calculation of s by using the range approximation of Section 4.12.

110. Using Database B, Appendix Table 8 (see Exercise 101, Chapter 3, involving life expectancies), perform the following operations:
a. Compute the mode for the grouped data.
b. Compute the mean and the standard deviation of the grouped data, setting the midpoint of the third interval equal to 0.
c. Compute the median, 25th percentile, and 75th percentile.
d. Check your calculation of s by using the range approximation of Section 4.12.

111. Repeat Exercise 110 using 10 categories. Compare all of your results with those from Exercise 108. Comment on the appropriateness of using 5 categories as against using 10. (Note: For computing mean and standard deviation, set midpoint of your first interval equal to 0 — that is, the interval containing the lowest values.)

112. Using Database B, Appendix Table 9, construct a skeleton box plot for ungrouped information on the infant mortality rates. Expand the skeleton box plot to include the following:
a. lower inner fence
b. upper inner fence
c. lower outer fence
d. upper outer fence

113. Using Database B, Appendix Table 9, construct a skeleton box plot for ungrouped information on the per capita GNP in U.S. dollars. Expand the skeleton box plot to include the following:
a. lower inner fence
b. upper inner fence

    c. lower outer fence

    d. upper outer fence

114. Using Database B, Appendix Table 9, construct a skeleton box plot for ungrouped information on life expectancy. Expand the skeleton box plot to include the following:

    a. lower inner fence

    b. upper inner fence

    c. lower outer fence

    d. upper outer fence

115. If your data of interest were already in the form of a frequency distribution with intervals where $i = 5$, could you construct a skeleton box? Comment.

CHAPTER 5

PROBABILITY, INFERENCES, AND SAMPLING DISTRIBUTIONS IN THE SOCIAL SCIENCES

GENERAL OBJECTIVES

We all make inferences. Social researchers are no different, but they make inferences (decisions or predictions) based on sample data. This chapter discusses the important role of probability in their making inferences. It also sets the stage for making inferences by introducing a variety of specific distributions, each with its own properties, that are found in social research.

SPECIFIC OBJECTIVES

1. To show how probability can be used to make inferences more precise and plausible.
2. To discuss the nature of probability itself and to illustrate how to find the probability of an outcome.
3. To highlight the differences between discrete and continuous variables, especially as these differences influence probability statements.
4. To introduce the binomial, a very useful discrete variable.
5. To introduce the normal probability distribution, a distribution involving a continuous variable.
6. To show how to use the tabulated areas (probabilities) under the normal curve.
7. To illustrate how and when the normal curve can be used as a close approximation to a binominal distribution.

5.1   INTRODUCTION

We stated in Chapter 1 that social researchers use inferential statistics to make statements about a population based on information contained in a sample. Because populations are sets of scores, we need a way to state an inference about them. Graphical and numerical descriptive techniques were presented in Chapters 3 and 4, respectively. Now let us examine probability, the mechanism for making inferences. This idea is best illustrated by means of an example.

Martha Jones, a candidate for Congress, publicly announces that her forthcoming election is a guaranteed success, and she forecasts victory by a substantial margin in all precincts of her district. Somewhat dubious about her claims, a local television station randomly selects 20 names from the voter registration list, calls each voter, and asks the voters for whom they will vote in the upcoming election. Not one of the 20 voters states that he or she will vote for Jones — all favor her opponent. What do you conclude about Jones's claim to victory in the sampled area?

If Jones were correct in her claim of victory, at least half the voters in the district would favor her, and somewhat near this same proportion should be observed in the sample. As it turned out, none of the voters in the sample favored Jones, a result highly contradictory to her claim. Hence we infer that the proportion of voters in the population (the district) favoring Jones is less than $\frac{1}{2}$ and that she will lose the district. We conclude that Jones will lose because the sample yielded results highly contradictory to her claim. By *contradictory* we do not mean that it is impossible to select at random 0 voters who favor Jones out of the 20 sampled. We mean, rather, that such a draw is highly improbable, assuming Jones's claim of victory is correct. Thus we measure the degree of contradiction to Jones's claim of victory in terms of the *probability* of the observed sample.

To get a better view of the role that probability plays in making this inference, suppose that the sample produced 9 voters in favor of Jones and 11 in favor of her opponent. Would we consider this result highly improbable and reject Jones's claim? How about 7 in favor and 13 against — or 5 in favor and 15 against? Where do we draw the line? At what point do we decide that the result of the observed sample is so improbable, assuming Jones's claim to be correct, that we disagree with her claim? To answer this question, we must know how to find the **probability** of obtaining a particular sample outcome. Knowing this probability, we can determine whether we agree or disagree with Jones's claim. **Probability is the tool that enables us to make an inference.**

It must be emphasized that our line of reasoning here is perfectly consistent with the logic employed in our daily decision making. A trial jury convicts an indicted person if the prosecution's evidence is highly contradictory to the person's claim of innocence. Because all pertinent information may not be presented during a trial, and because some of the information presented during the trial may be incorrect or misleading, the jury faces some degree of uncertainty in reaching a decision, and probability enters the picture. The difference between the statistical and the lay approach to decision making is that we will not rely on our own intuition or biases to make decisions. Rather, we will evaluate the probability of the sample outcome objectively before reaching a decision.

Since probability is the tool for making inferences, we might ask: What is probability? In the preceding discussion we used the term *probability* in its everyday sense. Let us examine this idea more closely.

5.2   WHAT IS PROBABILITY?

Statistical techniques are used in social research because we deal with events that are difficult to predict in advance. For example, it would be difficult to predict the status of an underdeveloped nation in the year 2000. The future status of any society is likely to vary, depending on such things as the balance of payments, the introduction of modern medicine, and the decline of death and birth rates. This kind of complexity creates a need for inferences in the social sciences — and especially for the appropriate statistical tools for making inferences. Probability is one of these tools.

Observations of social phenomena can result in many different outcomes, some of which are more likely than others. Numerous attempts have been made to give a precise definition for the probability of an outcome. We will cite a few of these.

The first interpretation, called the **classical interpretation of probability**, arose from games of chance. Typical probability statements of this type are "The probability that a flip of a balanced coin will show heads is $\frac{1}{2}$" and "The probability of drawing an ace when a single card is drawn from a standard deck of 52 cards is $\frac{4}{52}$." The numerical values for these probabilities arise from the nature of the games. A coin flip has two possible outcomes (a head or a tail); the probability of a head should then be $\frac{1}{2}$ (1 out of 2). Similarly, there are 4 aces in a standard deck of 52 cards, so the probability of drawing an ace in a single draw is $\frac{4}{52}$, or 4 out of 52.

In the classical interpretation of probability, each possible distinct result is called an **outcome**; an **event** is identified as a collection of outcomes. The probability of an event E under the classical interpretation of probability is computed by taking the ratio of the number of outcomes N_E favorable to event E to the total number N of possible outcomes.

$$P(\text{event } E) = \frac{N_E}{N}$$

The applicability of this interpretation depends on the assumption that all outcomes are equally likely. If this assumption does not hold, the probabilities indicated by the classical interpretation of probability will be in error.

A second interpretation of probability is called the **relative frequency concept of probability**. If an experiment is repeated a large number of times and event E occurs 30% of the time, then .30 should be a very good approximation to the probability of event E. Symbolically, if an experiment is conducted n different times and if event E occurs on n_E of these trials, then the probability of event E is approximately

$$P(\text{event } E) \approx \frac{n_E}{n}$$

We say "approximately" because we think of the actual probability $P(\text{event } E)$ as the relative frequency of the occurrence of event E over a very large number of observations or repetitions of the phenomenon. The fact that we can check probabilities that have a relative frequency interpretation (by simulating many repetitions of the experiment) makes this interpretation very appealing and practical.

The third interpretation of probability can be used for problems for which it is difficult to imagine a repetition of an experiment. These are "one-shot" situations. For example, the director of a state welfare agency who estimates the probability that a proposed revision in eligibility rules will be passed by the state legislature would not be thinking of a long series of trials. Rather, the director would use a **personal** (or *subjective*) **probability** to make a statement of belief regarding the likelihood of a one-shot event, such as the passage of the proposed legislative revision. The problem with subjective probabilities is that they can vary from person to person and cannot be checked.

Of the three interpretations presented, the relative frequency concept seems to be the most reasonable, since it provides a practical interpretation of the probability for most events of interest. Even though we will never run the necessary repetitions of the experiment to determine the exact probability of an event, the fact that we could check the probability of an event gives meaning to the relative frequency concept. Throughout the remainder of this text, we will lean heavily on this interpretation of probability.

5.3   FINDING THE PROBABILITY OF AN OUTCOME

In the preceding section we discussed three different interpretations of probability. We will use the classical interpretation and the relative frequency concept to illustrate the computation of the probability of an event. Consider an experiment that consists of tossing two coins, a penny and a dime, and observing the upturned faces. There are four possible outcomes:

- TT: tails for both coins
- TH: tail for the penny, head for the dime
- HT: head for the penny, tail for the dime
- HH: heads for both coins

What is the probability of observing exactly one head from the two coins?

This probability can be obtained easily if we can assume that all four outcomes are equally likely. In this case that seems quite reasonable. Then, by the previous sections, there are $N = 4$ possible outcomes, and $N_E = 2$ of these are favorable for the event of interest, observing exactly one head. Hence, by the classical interpretation of probability,

$$P(\text{exactly 1 head}) = \frac{2}{4} = \frac{1}{2}$$

We could also obtain this result using the relative frequency concept. Suppose that a penny and a dime were tossed 2000 times, with the results as shown in Table 5.1. Note that this approach yields approximate probabilities that are in agreement with our intuition. That is, intuitively we might expect these outcomes to be equally likely and that each would occur with a probability equal to $\frac{1}{4}$, or .25. This assumption was made for the classical interpretation.

TABLE 5.1

Results of 2000 toss-
ings of a penny and a
dime

Outcome	Frequency	Relative Frequency
TT	474	474/2000 = .237
TH	502	502/2000 = .251
HT	496	496/2000 = .248
HH	528	528/2000 = .264

If we wish to find the probability of tossing two coins and observing exactly one head, we have, from Table 5.1,

$$P(\text{exactly 1 head}) \approx \frac{502 + 496}{2000} = .499$$

This is very close to the theoretical probability, which we have shown to be .50.

EXERCISES

1. Are social data subject (amenable) to the notions of probability? Explain.

2. What is meant by the relative frequency concept of probability?

3. Conduct a class experiment in which each student flips two coins and records the number of heads. Repeat this experiment 10 times and combine the class results in a table similar to Table 5.1. Compare the two tables and comment on the differences in relative frequencies.

4. For each of the following situations, indicate which interpretation of probability seems most appropriate. (*Note:* There may be some argument about which interpretation is the best.)

   a. A newly married couple has a probability of .40 of remaining together as husband and wife for more than 5 years.

   b. The probability of a male college graduate living beyond the age of 65 is .60.

   c. The probability that additional tax legislation will be passed by Congress this session is .10.

   d. The probability that a city selected at random will have an unemployment rate of 18% is .30.

   e. The probability of drawing an SMSA (from Table 3.4) with a violent crime rate of 195 is .04.

   f. The probability of selecting a household at random within a city for which the head of the household is unemployed is .10.

5. Give your own personal probability for each of the following situations. It would be instructive to tabulate these probabilities for the entire class. Where are there large discrepancies?

   a. The federal budget will be balanced within the next five years.

   b. You will go on to graduate school upon graduation.

   c. The Democratic nominee will be elected president in the next presidential election.

   d. It will rain tomorrow.

6. List five events, other than those in Exercise 5, for which you think you can specify a realistic probability. State the probability for each event and indicate why you are confident that the specified probability is realistic.

5.4   VARIABLES: DISCRETE AND CONTINUOUS

In Chapter 2 we distinguished between quantitative and qualitative variables. We will now return to that distinction.

Most social events of interest result in numerical observations or measurements. If a quantitative variable measured (or observed) in an experiment is denoted by the symbol X, we are interested in the values that X can assume. These values are called *numerical outcomes*. The number of students in a class of 50 who earn an A in their criminology course is a numerical outcome. The percentage of registered voters who cast ballots in a given election is also a numerical outcome.

Variables are classified as one of two types.

DEFINITION 5.1 | When observations on a quantitative variable can assume only a countable number of values, the variable is called a **discrete variable**.

Examples of discrete variables are:

1. number of homicides during a particular year
2. number of accidents per year at an intersection
3. number of voters in a sample favoring Jones

Note that it is possible to count the number of values that each of these variables can assume.

DEFINITION 5.2 | When observations on a quantitative variable can assume any one of the countless number of values in a line interval, the variable is called a **continuous variable**.

For example, the daily maximum temperature in Rochester, New York, can assume any of the infinitely many values on a line interval. It could be 89.6, 89.799, or 89.7611114. Typical continuous variables are temperature, pressure, height, weight, and distance.

The distinction between discrete and continuous variables is pertinent when we are seeking the probabilities associated with specific values of a random variable. The need for the distinction will be apparent when probability distributions are discussed in Sections 5.5 and 5.7.

5.5   PROBABILITY DISTRIBUTIONS FOR DISCRETE VARIABLES

As previously stated, we need to know the probability of observing a particular sample outcome in order to make an inference about the universe from which the sample was drawn. To do this, we need to know the probability associated with each value of the variable X. Viewed as relative frequencies, these probabilities generate a distribution of theoretical relative frequencies called the *probability distribution of X*. Probability distributions differ for discrete and continuous variables, but the interpretation is essentially the same for both.

The **probability distribution for a discrete variable** displays the probability $P(X)$ associated with each value of X. This display can be presented as a table, a graph, or a formula. To illustrate, consider the tossing of two coins in Section 5.3, and let X be the number of heads observed. Then X can take the values 0, 1, or 2. From the data of Table 5.1, we can determine the approximate probability for each value of X, as given in Table 5.2. We point out that the relative frequencies in the table are very close to the theoretical relative frequencies (probabilities), which can be shown to be .25, .50, and .25 using the classical interpretation of probability. If we had employed 2,000,000 tosses of the coins instead of 2000, the relative frequencies for $X = 0$, 1, and 2 would be indistinguishable from the theoretical probabilities.

TABLE 5.2

Empirical sampling results for the number of heads in 2000 tosses of two coins

X	Frequency	Relative Frequency
0	474	.237
1	998	.499
2	528	.264

The probability distribution for X, the number of heads in the toss of two coins, is shown in Table 5.3. It is presented graphically as a probability histogram in Figure 5.1.

TABLE 5.3

Probability distribution for the number of heads when two coins are tossed

X	$P(X)$
0	.25
1	.50
2	.25

The probability distribution for this simple discrete variable illustrates three important properties of discrete variables.

FIGURE 5.1

Probability distribution
for the number of
heads when two coins
are tossed

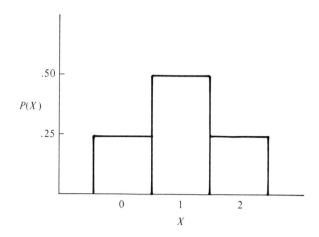

PROPERTIES OF DISCRETE VARIABLES

1. The probability associated with every value of X lies between 0 and 1.
2. The sum of the probabilities for all values of X equals 1.
3. The probabilities for a discrete variable are additive. Hence the probability that $X = 1$ or 2 is equal to $P(1) + P(2)$.

The relevance of the probability distribution to statistical inference can be illustrated by reconsidering the case of candidate Jones (Section 5.1). Jones claims that she would win the district, but we concluded that she would lose, because it seemed intuitively improbable that she could win when none of the 20 sampled voters favored her. Although satisfied with our inference, we noted that less conclusive results (say, 7 in favor, 13 against) would require more than an intuitive assessment of the probability of the observed sample. Now we will show how these probabilities can be obtained.

If Jones had at least 50% of the votes (let us give her the benefit of the doubt and say exactly 50%), then drawing a single voter at random from the population of responses for all voters in the precinct would be equivalent to tossing a balanced coin. If the head denotes a preference for Jones and a tail denotes a preference for her opponent, the selection of 20 voters would be analogous to tossing 20 coins and observing X, the number of heads (those favoring Jones), in the sample. You will note that this experiment is just a simple extension of the tossing of two coins in Section 5.3.

The probability distribution for X could be obtained by using the relative frequency approach. Many repetitions of 20 coin tosses would result in a

FIGURE 5.2

Probability distribution
for *X*, the number of
voters who favor
Jones in a sample of
n = 20.

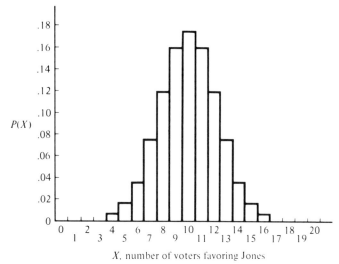

X, number of voters favoring Jones

(*Note*: The probability that $X = 0, 1, 2, 3, 17, 18, 19,$ or 20 is small and does not appear in the figure.)

probability distribution of *X*, the number of voters favoring Jones (number of heads), as shown in Figure 5.2. Note that the possible values of *X* are 0, 1, 2, . . . , 20.

Observe that $X = 10$ occurs with the largest probability, which is what we would expect if 50% of the voters favor Jones. We also note that it is highly improbable that we would draw a sample with as few as $X = 3$ or, for that matter, even $X = 5$. That is, from Figure 5.2 we see that the probability of *X* being 3 or less is practically zero, and the probability of *X* being 5 is about .02, which is very small in comparison to the probability of *X* being, say, 10. **Since the improbable result that none in a sample favor Jones ($X = 0$) is highly contradictory to her claim that she will win the district, we infer that the population of voter results contains less than 50 % favoring her and therefore that she will lose the district.**

The example illustrates the important role of probability in making inferences. We have used the probability distribution of a discrete variable to make an inference about a very real population that is of interest to both Jones and the general public.

5.6   A USEFUL DISCRETE VARIABLE: THE BINOMIAL

Many populations of interest to business persons and scientists can be viewed as large sets of 0s and 1s. For example, consider the set of responses of all adults in the United States to the question, "Do you favor the development of nuclear energy?" If we disallow "no opinion," the responses will constitute a set of "yes" responses and "no" responses. If we assign a 1 to each "yes" and a 0 to each "no," then the population will consist of a set of 0s and 1s, and the sum of the 1s will equal the total number of persons favoring the development of nuclear power. The sum of the 1s divided by the number of adults in the United States will equal the proportion of people who favor the development.

Gallup and Harris polls are examples of the sampling of 0-1 populations. People are surveyed, and their opinions are recorded. Based on the sample responses, Gallup and Harris estimate the proportions of people in the population who favor some particular issue or possess some particular characteristic.

Similar surveys are conducted in the biological sciences, engineering, and business, but they may be called experiments rather than polls. For example, experiments are conducted to determine the effect of new drugs on small animals, such as rats or mice, before the drugs are administered to larger animals and, eventually, human subjects. Many of these experiments bear a marked resemblance to a poll, in that the experimenter records only whether the drug is effective. Thus, if 300 rats are injected with a drug and 230 show a favorable response, the experimenter has conducted a "poll" of rat reaction to the drug — 230 "in favor" and 70 "opposed."

Similar "polls" are conducted by most manufacturers to determine the fraction of a product that is of good quality. Samples of industrial products are collected before shipment, and each item in the sample is judged "defective" or "acceptable" according to criteria established by the company's quality control department. Based on the number of defectives in the sample, the company can decide whether the product is suitable for shipment. Note that this example, as well as those preceding, has the practical objective of making an inference about a population based on information contained in a sample.

The public opinion poll, the consumer preference poll, the drug-testing experiment, and the industrial sampling for defectives are all examples of a common, frequently conducted sampling situation known as a *binomial experiment*. The binomial experiment is conducted in all areas of science and business. It differs from one situation to another only in the nature of objects being sampled (people, rats, electric light bulbs, oranges). Thus it is useful to define its characteristics. We can then apply our knowledge of this one kind of experiment to a variety of sampling experiments.

For all practical purposes, the binomial experiment is identical to the coin-tossing example of previous sections. Here n different coins are tossed, and we are interested in the number of heads observed. We assume that the probability of tossing a head on a single trial is p (p may equal .50, as it would for a balanced coin, but in many practical situations p will take some other value between 0 and 1). We also assume that the outcome for any one toss is unaffected by the results of any preceding tosses. The characteristics of a binomial experiment can be summarized as follows.

| DEFINITION 5.3 | A **binomial experiment** possesses the following properties: |

1. The experiment consists of n identical trials.
2. Each trial results in one of two outcomes. We will label one outcome a success and the other a failure.
3. The probability of success on a single trial is equal to p, and p remains the same from trial to trial.
4. The trials are independent; that is, the outcome of one trial does not influence the outcome of any other trial.
5. The experimenter is interested in X, the number of successes observed during the n trials.

Now let us check our ability to identify a binomial experiment.

| EXAMPLE 5.1 | A survey is conducted to determine the proportion of college students who favor a policy of mandatory drug testing of athletes. A random sample of 300 students is selected, each student is interviewed, and the number favoring mandatory drug testing is recorded. Is this sampling a binomial experiment? |

SOLUTION

To answer this question, we check each of the five characteristics of the binomial experiment to determine if they are satisfied.

1. Are there n identical trials? Yes; there are $n = 300$ interviews, all the same.
2. Does each trial result in one of two outcomes? Yes; each student interviewed either favors or does not favor the mandatory drug testing of athletes.
3. Is the probability of success the same from trial to trial? Yes. If we let success denote a person favoring the policy, then (assuming that the number of students is large) the probability of drawing a student favoring mandatory drug testing will remain constant from trial to trial, for all practical purposes.
4. Are the trials independent? Yes; the outcome of one interview is unaffected by the results of the other interviews.

5. Is the random variable of interest to the experimenter the number of successes X in the sample? Yes; we are interested in the number of students in the sample of 300 favoring mandatory drug testing of athletes. The sample proportion ($X/300$) would be an *estimate* of the proportion of all students who favor the policy.

Since all five characteristics are satisfied, the survey represents a binomial experiment.

EXAMPLE 5.2

A professor interviews 75 students in a class of 100 to estimate the proportion of students who expect to obtain a C or better in her course. Is this a binomial experiment?

SOLUTION

Check this experiment against the five characteristics of a binomial.

1. Are there identical trials? Yes; each of 75 students is interviewed.
2. Does each trial result in one of two extremes? Yes; each student either does or does not expect to obtain a grade of C or higher.
3. Is the probability of success the same from trial to trial? No. If we let success denote a student expecting to obtain a C or higher, then the probability of success can change considerably from trial to trial. For example, suppose that, unknown to the professor, 70 of the 100 students expect to obtain a grade of C or higher. Then p, the probability of success for the first student interviewed, is $\frac{70}{100} = .70$. If the student is a failure (does not expect a C or higher), the probability of success for the next student is $\frac{70}{99} = .71$. Suppose that after 50 students have been interviewed, 40 were successes and 10 were failures. Then the probability of success for the next (51st) student is $\frac{40}{50} = .80$.

This example shows how the probability of success can change substantially from trial to trial in situations where the sample size is a relatively large portion of the total population size. This experiment does not satisfy the properties of a binomial experiment.

It should be noted that very few real-life situations perfectly satisfy the requirements stated in Definition 5.1. However, for many the lack of agreement is so small that the binomial experiment still provides a very good model for reality.

Having defined the binomial experiment and suggested several practical applications, we now examine the probability distribution for the binomial variable X, the number of successes observed in n trials. Although it would be possible to approximate $P(X)$, the probability associated with a value of X in a binomial experiment, by using a relative frequency approach, it is easier to make use of a general formula for binomial probabilities.

FORMULA FOR COMPUTING $P(X)$ IN A BINOMIAL EXPERIMENT

The probability of observing X successes in n trials of a binomial experiment is

$$P(X) = \frac{n!}{X!(n-X)!} p^X q^{n-X}$$

where

n = number of trials
p = probability of success in a single trial
$q = 1 - p$
X = number of successes in n trials
$n! = n(n-1)(n-2)\cdots(1)$

As indicated in the preceding formula, the notation $n!$ (referred to as n factorial) is used for the product

$$n! = n(n-1)(n-2)\cdots(1)$$

For $n = 3$,

$$3! = (3)(3-1)(3-2) = (3)(2)(1) = 6$$

Similarly, for $n = 4$,

$$4! = (4)(3)(2)(1) = 24$$

We also note that 0! is defined to be equal to 1.

To see how the formula for binomial probabilities can be used to calculate the probability for a specific value of X, consider the following examples.

EXAMPLE 5.3

An experiment consists of tossing a coin two times. If the probability of a head is .5, compute the probability distribution for X, the number of heads, using the binomial formula $P(X)$. Compare your results to those given in Table 5.3.

SOLUTION   Using the formula

$$P(X) = \frac{n!}{X!(n-X)!} p^X q^{n-X}$$

and substituting $n = 2$, $p = .5$ and $X = 0, 1, 2$, we obtain

$$P(X = 0) = \frac{2!}{0!2!} (.5)^0 (.5)^2 = .25$$

$$P(X = 1) = \frac{2!}{1!1!} (.5)^1 (.5)^1 = .50$$

$$P(X = 2) = \frac{2!}{2!0!} (.5)^2 (.5)^0 = .25$$

Note that these results are identical to those presented in Table 5.3.

EXAMPLE 5.4   Suppose that a sample of households is randomly selected from all the households in a city and that in 10% of the households throughout the city, the head of the household is unemployed. If we select a sample of 5 households, what is the probability that all 5 heads of household are employed?

SOLUTION   Carefully define which outcome you wish to call a success. For this example we will define a success as "being employed." Then the probability of success when a single head of household is selected from the population is $p = .9$ (because the proportion of unemployed is .1). Since we wish to find the probability that $X = 5$ (all 5 are employed) in $n = 5$ trials, we have

$$P(X) = \frac{n!}{X!(n-X)!} p^X q^{n-X}$$

or

$$P(5) = \frac{5!}{5!(5-5)!} (.9)^5 (.1)^0 = \frac{5!}{5!0!} (.9)^5 (1) = (.9)^5 = .590$$

That is, the probability that all 5 heads of household (in a sample of 5) are employed is .590.

The binomial probability distribution for $n = 5$ and $p = .9$ is shown in Figure 5.3. The probability of observing $X = 5$ employed in a sample of 5 is shaded in the figure.

FIGURE 5.3

The binomial probability distribution when $n = 5$ and $p = .9$

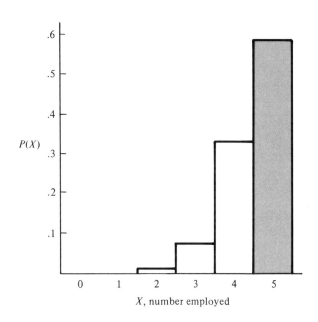

EXAMPLE 5.5

Refer to Example 5.4 and calculate the probability that exactly 1 head of household in the sample of 5 households will be unemployed. What is the probability of 1 or fewer being unemployed?

SOLUTION

Since X is the number of employed in the sample of $n = 5$, 1 unemployed person would correspond to $X = 4$ employed. Then

$$P(4) = \frac{5!}{4!(5 - 4)!}(.9)^4(.1)^1$$

$$= \frac{(5)(4)(3)(2)(1)}{(4)(3)(2)(1)(1)}(.9)^4(.1) = 5(.9)^4(.1) = .328$$

Thus the probability of drawing $X = 4$ employed heads of household in a random sample of $n = 5$ is .328, or roughly one chance in three.

The outcome "1 or fewer unemployed" is the same as the outcome "4 or 5 employed." Since X is the number employed, we seek the probability that $X = 4$ or 5. Because the probabilities associated with values of a discrete variable are additive, we have

$$P(X = 4 \text{ or } 5) = P(4) + P(5) = .328 + .590 = .918$$

That is, the probability that a random sample of $n = 5$ households will yield either 4 or 5 employed heads is .918. This high probability is consistent with our intuition, because we would expect the number of employed in the sample to be large if 90% of all heads of household in the city are employed.

EXAMPLE 5.6

A labor union's examining board for the selection of apprentices has a record for admitting 70% of all applicants who satisfy a set of basic requirements. Five members of a minority group recently came before the board, and 4 out of 5 were rejected. First, let us reason from the population to the sample and find the probability that 1 or fewer would be accepted if p is really .7. We will then reason in reverse and use our intuition to decide whether the board applied a lower probability of acceptance when reviewing the 5 members of the minority group.

SOLUTION

Let X be the number selected out of the 5 examined. The probability of the event that $X = 0$ or 1 is

$$P(X = 0 \text{ or } 1) = P(0) + P(1)$$

Since we regard "acceptance" as a success, $p = .7$. Using $n = 5$ and substituting into the formula

$$P(X) = \frac{n!}{X!(n - X)!} p^X q^{n-X}$$

we have

$$P(0) = \frac{5!}{0!(5 - 0)!}(.7)^0(.3)^5 = \frac{5!}{(1)5!}(.7)^0(.3)^5 = .002$$

$$P(1) = \frac{5!}{1!(5 - 1)!}(.7)^1(.3)^4 = \frac{(5)(4)(3)(2)(1)}{(1)(4)(3)(2)(1)}(.7)^1(.3)^4 = .028$$

Then

$$P(X = 0 \text{ or } 1) = P(0) + P(1) = .002 + .028 = .030$$

This indicates that if the examinations are independent and the committee is accepting each applicant with a probability equal to .7, the probability that only 1 or fewer of the 5 is selected is 3 chances in 100. We would regard this improbable occurrence ($X \leq 1$) as a rare event.

Now let us reason from the sample to the population. Having observed the rare event $X \leq 1$, we could draw one of two conclusions. Either we have been unlucky and observed an unlikely event, or the board is currently admitting with a probability less than .7. We are inclined to accept the latter conclusion. Note that we do not conclude that the board is necessarily biased against the minority group. A lower probability of acceptance (which appears to exist) may also have been caused by an excess of apprentices in this particular labor speciality.

The purpose of this section is to present the binomial probability distribution so that you can see how binomial probabilities are calculated and calculate them for small values of n, if you so desire. In practice, n is usually large (in national surveys, sample sizes as large as 1500 are common), and the computation of the binomial probabilities is very tedious. Fortunately, these computations can be avoided. Binomial probabilities have been calculated on an electronic computer for various values of n and are readily available in tabulated form (see the references at the back of the book). For many situations, exact values of the probabilities are unnecessary. We will present a single procedure in Section 5.10 for obtaining approximate values for binomial probabilities that we can use in making inferences.

We have discussed probability distributions for discrete variables and have given an example of a very useful discrete variable, the binomial. We proceed in the next section with a discussion of probability distributions for continuous variables.

EXERCISES

7. If $n = 5$, what is $n!$? What is $0!$?

8. Consider the following class experiment: Toss three coins and observe the number of heads X. Let each student repeat the experiment 10 times, combine the class results, and construct a relative frequency table for X. Note that these relative frequencies give approximations to the actual probabilities that $X = 0$, 1, 2, or 3. (*Note*: Calculate the actual probabilities by using the binomial formula $P(X)$ to compare the approximate results with the actual probabilities.)

9. Examine the accompanying newspaper clipping. Does this sampling appear to satisfy the characteristics of a binomial experiment?

Poll Finds Opposition to Phone Taps

New York — People surveyed in a recent poll indicated they are 81 to 13 percent against having their phones tapped without a court order.

The people in the survey, by 68 to 27 percent, were opposed to letting the government use a wiretap on citizens sus-pected of crimes, except with a court order.

The survey was conducted with 1495 households and also found the following results:

— The people surveyed are 80 to 12 percent against the use of any kind of electronic spying device without a court order.

— Citizens are 77 to 14 percent against allowing the government to open their mail without court orders.

— They oppose, by 80 to 12 percent, letting the telephone company disclose records of long distance phone calls, except by court order.

For each of the questions, a few of those in the survey had no responses.

10. A survey was conducted to investigate the attitudes of nurses working in Veterans Administration hospitals. A random sample of 1000 nurses was contacted using a mail questionnaire, and the number of nurses favoring or opposing a particular issue was recorded. If we confine our attention to the nurses' responses to a single question, would this sampling represent a binomial experiment? As with most mail surveys, some of the nurses will not respond. What effect might nonresponders in the sample have on the estimate of the percentage of all Veterans Administration nurses who favor the particular proposition?

11. A criminologist claims that the probability of reform for a first-offender embezzler is .9. Suppose that we define "reform" as meaning that the person commits no criminal offenses within a 5-year period. Three paroled embezzlers were randomly selected from prison records, and their behavioral histories were examined for the 5-year period following prison release. What is the probability that all 3 were reformed? At least 2?

12. A community is evenly divided between black families and white families. If a random sample of 10 families is selected to be interviewed concerning the rezoning of a school district, what is the probability that all families are white? What is the probability that all 10 are black families? Comment. If all 10 families selected were either all white or all black, would you suspect a racial bias in the selection of the sample? (*Note:* Your decision should be made on the basis of probability.)

13. Refer to Exercise 12. Suppose that the sample contained only 5 families and that 4 of the 5 were white. What is the probability of selecting 4 or more whites in a random sample of 5? Does the sample suggest racial bias in the selection? (Base your decision on the calculated probability.)

14. Read the accompanying news clipping. Explain why this might or might not be a binomial experiment. What information, missing in the article, is needed to conclude firmly that the survey is a binomial experiment?

Study of Divided Families Shows Positive Attitudes

Chicago — A study of divorced mothers and their children has revealed some positive attitudes among members of divided families. Perhaps a broken home is not the psychological disaster for family members that society has suspected.

The study, involving 20 mothers with one or more children between the ages of 6 and 18, was conducted to determine the basic concerns of divorced mothers and their children. There were 20 mothers and 35 children involved in the study.

All the women were working full time. Most of them had made plans toward bettering their earning power. The women had been divorced from 3 months to 15 years. The educational level of the women in the study was high compared with the national average: 12 years to 18 years of education.

A key aim of the study was to determine the feelings of the women and their children about their acceptance in society.

Eighty-six percent of the children felt that at school they were treated the same as children whose parents were married. Children age 10 through 12 especially preferred that teachers and friends be told about the home situation. They wanted news of the divorce not to come as a surprise to others or to be a source of embarrassment for them.

In general, the children were doing well in school and even excelled in some areas.

Although the trend among most of the women was to socialize mainly with single persons, 80 percent of them felt accepted in their neighborhoods. Half of them said they felt accepted at church.

Among the children, 91 percent indicated they were treated no differently at Sunday school. Ninety percent of the sample were active church members.

Most of the women, 85 percent, said that after their divorces their attitudes toward divorce had shifted from negative to positive. The same proportion saw advantages for their children, in terms of understanding life and people, as a result of the divorce.

15. For the accompanying survey, answer the following questions:

  a. Does this appear to be a binomial experiment?

  b. Explain why it might or might not satisfy the five characteristics of a binomial experiment.

Alcoholism Reported Up in Army

Large numbers of young American soldiers are becoming alcoholics. This parallels the increase of alcohol abuse among young civilians, researchers report.

In a study of 1873 Army men randomly selected from bases of the United States, nearly 2 out of every 5 soldiers were found to be either actual alcoholics, borderline alcoholics, or potential alcoholics.

The study showed that the largest percentage of problem drinkers were under age 20 and had ranks below sergeant.

5.7 PROBABILITY DISTRIBUTIONS FOR CONTINUOUS VARIABLES

You will recall that a continuous random variable can assume values associated with infinitely many points in a line interval. Without elaboration, we state that it is impossible to assign a small amount of probability to each value of x (as was done for a discrete random variable) and retain the property that the probabilities sum to 1. For example, suppose that the Social Security Administration is examining the distribution of ages for those receiving disability benefits under Social Security. Although we usually display ages to the nearest year for adults, we could use decimals to be more specific. We might have ages of 65.3 years, 65.328 years, 65.3286417 years, and so on. With this degree of accuracy, the variable age could be considered continuous; clearly it would be difficult to assign a small amount of probability to each and every age while retaining the property that the sum of the probabilities equals 1.

We overcome this difficulty by reverting to the concept of the relative frequency histogram of Chapter 3, where we talked about the probability of X falling in a given interval. Recall that the relative frequency histogram for a population containing a large number of measurements will almost be a smooth curve, because the number of class intervals can be made large and the width of the intervals decreased. Thus we envision a smooth curve that provides a model for the population relative frequency distribution generated by repeated observation of a continuous random variable. This will be similar to the curve shown in Figure 5.4a.

Recall that the histogram relative frequencies are proportional to areas over the class intervals and that these areas can be interpreted probabilistically. That is, if a score is randomly selected from the set, the probability that it will fall in an interval is proportional to the histogram area above the interval. Since a population is the whole (100%, or 1), we want the total area

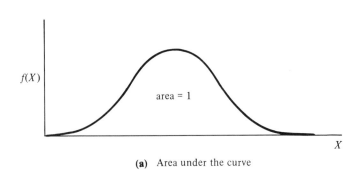

(a) Area under the curve

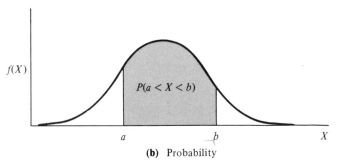

(b) Probability

under the probability curve to equal 1. If we let the total area under the curve equal 1, then areas over intervals are exactly equal to the corresponding probabilities.

The graph for the **probability distribution of a continuous variable** is shown in Figure 5.4a. The ordinate (height of the curve) for a given value of X is denoted by the symbol $f(X)$. Many people are tempted to say that $f(X)$, like $P(X)$ for the binomial variable, designates the probability associated with the continuous variable X. However, as we mentioned before, it is impossible to assign a probability to each of the infinitely many possible values of a continuous variable. Thus all we can say is that $f(X)$ represents the height of the probability distribution for a given value of X.

The probability that a continuous variable falls in an interval (say, between two points a and b) follows directly from the probabilistic interpretation of the area over an interval in the relative frequency histogram (Section 3.8). It is equal to the area under the curve over the interval a to b, as shown in Figure 5.4b. This probability is written $P(a < X < b)$.

Curves of many shapes can be used to represent the population relative frequency distribution for values associated with a continuous variable. Fortunately, the areas under these curves have been tabulated and are ready for use. Thus, if we know that student examination scores possess a particular probability distribution, as in Figure 5.5, and if areas under the curve have been tabulated, we can find the probability that a particular student will score more than 80% by looking up the tabulated area, which is shaded in Figure 5.5.

Most data collected on continuous variables in nature possess mound-shaped frequency distributions, and many of these are nearly bell shaped. A continuous variable (the normal) and its probability distribution (the bell-shaped normal curve) provide a good model for these types of data. The normally distributed variable also plays a very important role in statistical inference. We will study its bell-shaped probability distribution in detail in the next section.

FIGURE 5.5

Hypothetical probability distribution for students' examination scores

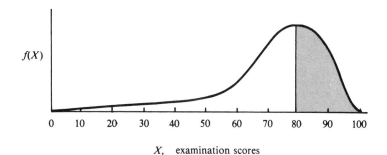

$f(X)$

0   10   20   30   40   50   60   70   80   90   100

X,   examination scores

5.8   A USEFUL CONTINUOUS VARIABLE: THE NORMAL PROBABILITY DISTRIBUTION

Recall that probability is the tool to make inferences about a population or universe, based on information contained in a sample. A prerequisite for making the inference is knowledge of the probability distribution for the variable measured in the experiment.

With this background, it would seem natural to present many different variables with probability distributions, so that these distributions could be used to approximate distributions observed in nature. Fortunately, this task can be greatly simplified, because a large number of experimental populations often possess mound-shaped frequency distributions that approximate the bell shape of the normal curve (see Figure 5.6).

The normal curve, which is the probability distribution for a normal variable, is an excellent model for the relative frequency distribution of many social variables. It is not necessary to write a mathematical expression for the normal curve; instead we will portray it graphically and identify some of its important properties. These properties are as follows:

1. The normal curve is bell shaped (see Figures 5.6 and 5.7). The area within 1 standard deviation of the mean is .6826; within 2 standard deviations, the area is .9544.
2. The normal curve is symmetrical about its mean μ (see Figure 5.6).
3. The location and spread of the normal curve depend on the values of μ and σ. For example, three normal curves with different means and standard deviations are shown in Figure 5.7.

The normal curve is useful because of the frequent occurrence of near-normal relative frequency distributions of social data.

FIGURE 5.6

Normal probability distribution

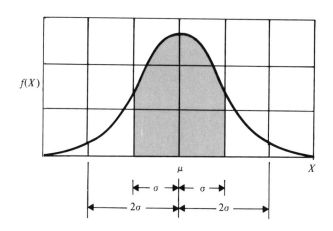

FIGURE 5.7

Three normal curves
with different means
and standard devia-
tions

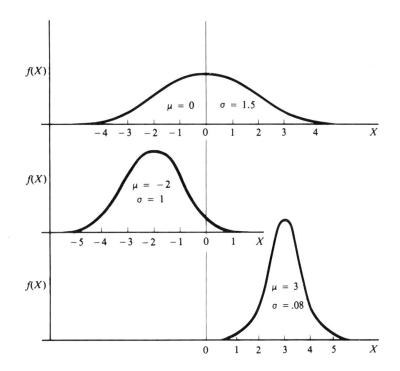

5.9   TABULATED AREAS UNDER THE NORMAL CURVE

You will recall that we must know the probability of a sample in order to make inferences about a population or universe. Hence we must be able to calculate the probability that a variable with a normal probability distribution will fall in a specified interval. For example, if X is normally distributed with mean μ and standard deviation σ, we need to know the probability that X lies in an interval between two points a and b. Recall that probabilities for continuous variables correspond to areas under a smooth curve. The shaded portion of Figure 5.8 represents the area under a normal curve between

FIGURE 5.8

Area under a normal
curve

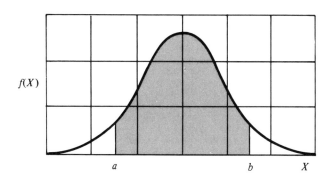

points a and b and corresponds to the probability that X will fall within the interval.

The desired area can be obtained by using a table giving areas under the normal curve. Unfortunately, there are infinitely many normal distributions corresponding to the possible values of the parameters μ and σ. It would be an impossible task to provide tables of areas for every normal distribution, but we have an easy way to circumvent this difficulty.

Appendix Table 1 gives areas under the normal curve between the mean and a measurement located z standard deviations to the right of μ. A typical tabulated area is shown in Figure 5.9. Areas to the left of the mean need not be tabulated, because the normal curve is symmetrical about the mean. The area between the mean and a point 2σ to the right is the same as the area between the mean and a similar point 2σ to the left.

The number z of standard deviations is given to the nearest tenth in the left-hand column of Appendix Table 1. Adjustments for values of z to the nearest hundredth are given in the top row of the table. Entries in the table are the areas corresponding to particular values of z. For example, the area between the mean and a point $z = 2$ standard deviations to the right of the mean is shown in the second column of the table opposite $z = 2.0$. This area, shaded in Figure 5.10a, is .4772. The area between the mean and a point 2 standard deviations to the left of the mean, shown in Figure 5.10b, is also .4772. Then the area *within* 2 standard deviations of the mean is 2(.4772) = .9544. This explains the origin of the phrase "approximately 95%" in the empirical rule.

Similarly, the area 1 standard deviation to the right of the mean (i.e., $z = 1$) is .3413. The area *within* 1 standard deviation of the mean is .6826, or approximately 68%, as stated in the empirical rule. This area is shown in Figure 5.11.

FIGURE 5.9

Tabulated area under the normal curve

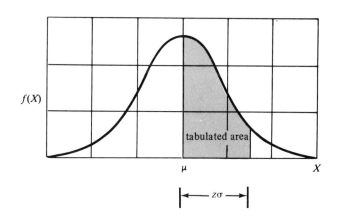

FIGURE 5.10

Tabulated area corre-
sponding to $z = 2$

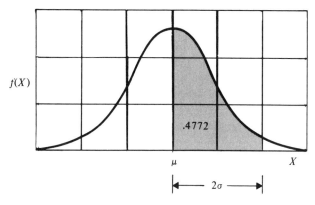

(a) Area to the right of μ

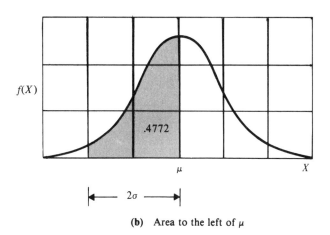

(b) Area to the left of μ

FIGURE 5.11

Area within 1 standard
deviation of μ

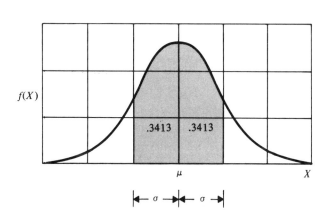

FIGURE 5.12

Area corresponding to $z = 1.64$

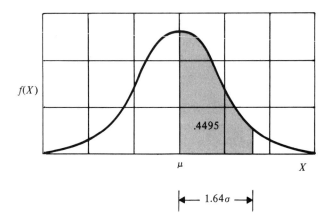

Suppose we wish to find the area corresponding to $z = 1.64$. Proceed down the left column to the row $z = 1.6$ and across the top of the table to the .04 column. The intersection of the $z = 1.6$ row with the .04 column gives the desired area, .4495. This area is shown in Figure 5.12.

To determine how many standard deviations a measurement X lies from the mean μ, we first determine the distance between X and μ. Recall that this distance is

$$\text{distance} = X - \mu$$

The distance between X and μ can then be converted into a number of standard deviations called a **z-score** by dividing by the standard deviation σ of X:

$$z = \frac{\text{distance}}{\text{standard deviation}} = \frac{X - \mu}{\sigma}$$

Note that we are merely coding the value X by subtracting μ and dividing by σ. Figure 5.13 illustrates values of z corresponding to specific values of X.

FIGURE 5.13

Relationship between specific values of X and $z = (X - \mu)/\sigma$

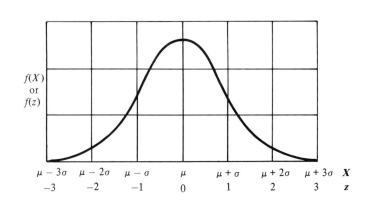

Thus a value of X 2 standard deviations below (to the left of) μ corresponds to a z-score of -2.

To calculate the area under a normal curve between the mean μ and a specified value X to the right of the mean, we first compute the z-score for the observed value of X, using the formula

$$z = \frac{X - \mu}{\sigma}$$

We then refer to Appendix Table 1 and obtain the entry corresponding to the calculated value of z. This entry is the desired area (probability) under the curve between μ and the specified value of X.

We will illustrate the use of the table of normal curve areas by a simple example. Then we will proceed to some practical applications.

EXAMPLE 5.7

Suppose that X is a normally distributed variable with a mean $\mu = 8$ and a standard deviation $\sigma = 2$. Find the probability that X lies in the interval from 8 to 11. That is, what proportion of the total area lies under the curve between 8 and 11? (See the shaded portion of Figure 5.14.)

FIGURE 5.14

Area under the normal curve between $\mu = 8$ and $X = 11$

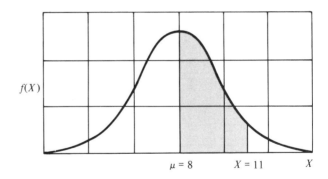

SOLUTION

To determine the desired area, we compute a z-score for $X = 11$.

$$z = \frac{X - \mu}{\sigma} = \frac{11 - 8}{2} = 1.50$$

Thus $X = 11$ lies 1.50 standard deviations above (to the right of) $\mu = 8$. The corresponding area can then be determined from the entry in Appendix Table 1 opposite $z = 1.50$. We see that the desired area is .4332 (see Figure 5.15). Therefore the probability that X lies between 8 and 11 is .4332.

FIGURE 5.15

Area between $\mu = 8$
and $X = 11$ is .4332

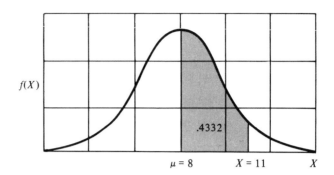

EXAMPLE 5.8

The quantitative portion of a nationally administered achievement test is scaled so that the mean score is 500 and the standard deviation is 100. If we assume that the distribution of scores is normal (bell shaped), what proportion of the students throughout the country should score between 500 and 682? What proportion should score between 340 and 682?

SOLUTION

Consider Figure 5.16. To answer the first question, we first compute the area A_1 between $\mu = 500$ and $X = 682$:

$$z = \frac{X - \mu}{\sigma} = \frac{682 - 500}{100} = 1.82$$

The tabulated area for this value of z is $A_1 = .4656$. Thus we expect 46.56% of the students to score between 500 and 682. The area between 340 and 682 is equal to the sum of A_1 and A_2 in Figure 5.16. To find A_2, we compute the z-score for $X = 340$.

$$z = \frac{X - \mu}{\sigma} = \frac{340 - 500}{100} = -1.60$$

FIGURE 5.16

Area between $X = 340$
and $X = 682$

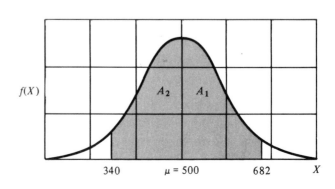

(A negative value of z indicates a point to the left of the mean.) The appropriate area (found by ignoring the negative sign) is then .4452. We would expect the proportion of students scoring between 340 and 682 to be

$$A_1 + A_2 = .4656 + .4452 = .9108$$

EXAMPLE 5.9

A researcher found that the length of time for five-person groups to reach consensus on an abortion policy has a normal distribution with $\mu = 2.2$ hours and $\sigma = .25$. What is the probability that a randomly selected group will reach consensus in less than 1.50 hours? In a particular experiment a group consisting of five persons with very distinct opinions reached consensus in 1.50 hours. Would you suspect that the members of the groups had discussed the issue beforehand?

SOLUTION

A sketch of the desired area P is shown in Figure 5.17. First we compute the z-score:

$$z = \frac{X - \mu}{\sigma} = \frac{1.50 - 2.2}{.25} = -2.8$$

FIGURE 5.17

Probability that a group requires less than 1.50 hours to reach consensus

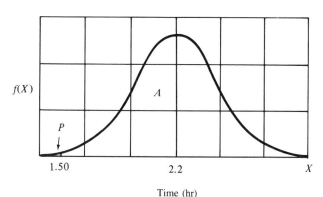

Time (hr)

The area A corresponding to $z = 2.8$ is .4974. The area on one side of the mean is .5, so the desired area is

$$P = .5 - A = .0026$$

This probability is quite small, which means that the group's spectacular feat is indeed a rare event, or else the members of the group have taken exceptional steps to reach a consensus. Although rare events do occur sometimes, we would be inclined to accept the latter explanation.

In this section we have shown how to find areas under a normal curve. To do this, we converted the distance between a measurement X and the mean μ into a z-score and then referred to Appendix Table 1 for the area. These areas are equal to the probabilities that measurements will fall in particular intervals.

EXERCISES

16. Using Appendix Table 1, find the area under the normal curve over the intervals identified by the following z-scores:

   a. 0 to $+1.00$ **b.** 0 to $+2.00$ **c.** 0 to $+1.43$

   d. $+.73$ to $+.98$ **e.** $-.37$ to $+.37$ **f.** -1.43 to 0

17. Repeat Exercise 16 for these z-scores:

   a. -2.58 to -1.00 **b.** $-.61$ to $+1.78$

   c. $+1.00$ to $+2.00$ **d.** $+2.00$ to $+3.00$

18. Repeat Exercise 16 for these z-scores:

   a. $-.31$ to $+.56$ **b.** $+.29$ to $+.68$

   c. -1.64 to $+1.64$ **d.** -2.40 to $-.87$

19. Repeat Exercise 16 for these z-scores:

   a. -1.56 to $+1.36$ **b.** $+1.65$ to $+2.00$

   c. -1.04 to $+1.27$ **d.** $-.39$ to $+1.83$

20. Find the value of z such that 25% of all the scores in the distribution are to the left of z.

21. Find the value of z such that 17% of all the scores in the distribution are to the right of z.

22. A normally distributed variable X possesses a mean of 8 and a standard deviation of 3. Find the z-score corresponding to $X = 8.5$.

23. Refer to Exercise 22. Find the X-score corresponding to $z = -.86$.

24. Refer to Exercise 22. Find the z-score corresponding to $X = 6.7$.

25. Refer to Exercise 22. Find the probability that X lies in the interval 7.4 to 8.3.

26. Refer to Exercise 22. Find the probability that X lies outside the interval 7.8 and 9.1.

27. Annual incomes for intracity social workers throughout the country are assumed to be normally distributed with $\mu = \$28,500$ and $\sigma = \$1600$. What proportion of social workers receive an income greater than \$30,000? Less than \$25,500?

5.10   NORMAL APPROXIMATION TO THE BINOMIAL

In Section 5.8 we indicated that the normal curve provides a good model for the relative frequency distributions of many social variables that can be observed and studied. Now that we know how to compute probabilities associated with a normal variable, we can apply what we know to determine probabilities for the many variables (both discrete and continuous) for which the normal variable is a good model. We will illustrate how this works using the binomial variable.

The binomial distribution for the number X of voters favoring Jones (Section 5.5) provides an excellent example of a situation in which a normal curve can be used to calculate probabilities for another distribution. The probability distribution for X (Figure 5.2) is shown in Figure 5.18 with a normal curve superimposed. Note how well the normal curve approximates the actual probability distribution for X.

The normal distribution that provides the best approximation to the binomial probability distribution has the mean and the standard deviation equal to the mean and the standard deviation of a binomial variable. These are given by the next two formulas.

MEAN AND STANDARD DEVIATION OF A BINOMIAL VARIABLE

$$\mu = np$$

$$\sigma = \sqrt{npq}$$

where p is the probability of success in a given trial and $q = 1 - p$.

The approximating normal curve to the distribution of X for the Jones survey, Figure 5.19, is based on $p = .5$ (assuming that 50% of the voters favor Jones) and $n = 20$. Then

$$\mu = np = 20(.5) = 10$$

$$\sigma = \sqrt{npq} = \sqrt{20(.5)(.5)} = 2.24$$

We have not explained how to draw the approximating normal curve, because this is unimportant. The relevant point to note is that we would *not expect* X to fall more than 1.96 standard deviations ($1.96\sigma = 1.96 \times 2.24 = 4.39$) away from the mean $\mu = 10$, because the probability of this occurrence is quite small. By using the properties of a normal curve, we can determine that the probability that X lies more than 1.96 standard deviations away

FIGURE 5.18

Probability distribution
for the number of
voters favoring Jones
in a sample of $n = 20$,
and the approximating
normal curve

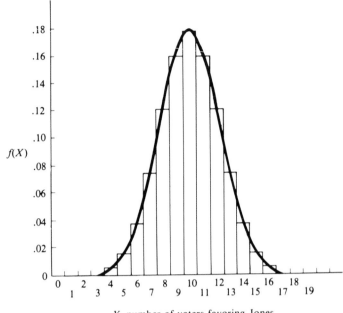

X, number of voters favoring Jones

FIGURE 5.19

Approximating normal
curve for the Jones
survey

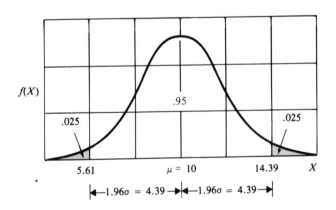

from μ is .05. This probability is shown in Figure 5.19 as the shaded area, based on $1.96\sigma = 4.39$.

Recall the situation surrounding the Jones survey. A random sample of $n = 20$ prospective voters was selected; each person in the sample was asked if he or she favored Jones in the upcoming election. We have seen that the probability of observing $X = 0$ for a binomial variable with $n = 20$ and $p = .50$ is very small (see Figure 5.2), and hence we rejected Jones's claim to victory in the upcoming election.

The same conclusion could be drawn using the normal approximation to the binomial. The normal curve that offers the best approximation to a binomial distribution when $n = 20$ and $p = .5$ has $\mu = np = 10$ and $\sigma = \sqrt{npq} = 2.24$. As we have seen, we would be unlikely to observe a value of X beyond 1.96σ (4.39) on either side of μ. More specifically, a value of $X = 0$, which has a z-score of

$$z = \frac{0 - 10}{2.24} = -4.46$$

is extremely unlikely, assuming that Jones will win. Hence we conclude that she will not win the election.

You might ask why we are using the probability distribution of a continuous variable (the normal) to approximate the probability distribution for a discrete variable (the binomial). The reason is that although we have a formula for computing the probability $P(X)$ associated with any value of the binomial variable X, computation of $P(X)$ is difficult for large values of the sample size n. Imagine having to calculate the probability that X is 468 or less for a survey of $n = 1000$ persons when $p = .5$. The calculation of $P(X = 468)$ could be difficult in itself, but the desired probability would require similar calculations for $X = 467, 466, 465, \ldots, 0$. This would be nearly an impossible task. Fortunately, probabilities associated with a normal variable are easier to compute. Then, if we can approximate the binomial distribution with a normal curve, we can approximate probabilities associated with a binomial variable using normal curve areas.

EXAMPLE 5.10

In a national survey to determine the proportion of voters favoring the Republican presidential candidate, a sample of 1000 voters was polled to determine each person's preference. Let X denote the number of persons favoring the Republican in the 1000 sampled. Assume that 50% of the registered voters favor the Republican. Find the mean and standard deviation of the random variable X. Find the probability that $X = 467, 466, 465, \ldots, 0$.

SOLUTION

This election survey satisfies the properties of a binomial experiment ($n = 1000$, $p = .5$). The mean and standard deviation of the binomial random variable X are

$$\mu = np = 1000(.5) = 500$$
$$\sigma = \sqrt{npq} = \sqrt{1000(.5)(.5)} = \sqrt{250} = 15.81$$

The z-score corresponding to $X = 467$ is

$$z = \frac{467 - 500}{15.81} = -2.09$$

Hence, from Appendix Table 1, the probability of observing $X \leq 467$ is .0183. This probability of .0183 found by using the normal approximation to the binomial is very close to the actual probability, which can be computed by using the binomial formula of Section 5.6.

The probability distribution for X is shown in Figure 5.20.

FIGURE 5.20

Normal curve for
Example 5.10

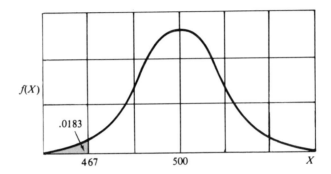

You will readily see how inference can enter this example. Suppose that X assumed an improbable value; that is, suppose that we drew a sample of 1000 persons and observed 467 or fewer who favored the Republican candidate. Since the probability of this occurrence is approximately .0183, we could infer either that we observed a rare event (assuming that 50% of the voting public favors the Republican) or that less than 50% of the voters favor the candidate. We would be inclined to choose the latter interpretation.

One final question should be answered. When is the normal approximation to the binomial valid? That is, when is it appropriate to use the approximation and when should we avoid it? The normal approximation to the binomial with $\mu = np$ and $\sigma = \sqrt{npq}$ is appropriate if the sample size n satisfies the following inequality:

$$n \geq \frac{5}{\min(p, q)}$$

That is, use the normal approximation if n is greater than (or equal to) 5 divided by the smaller of the quantities p and q. For example, if p is assumed to be .1 (and hence $q = .9$), the sample size would have to be greater than or equal to $5/.1 = 50$. Similarly when $p = .6$ (and hence $q = .4$), the normal approximation to the binomial would be valid if $n \geq 5/.4$, or 13.

This rule gives the minimum requirement for n. The larger the sample size for a given value of p, the better the approximation will be.

EXERCISES

28. List three important properties of a normal probability distribution.

29. What is the formula for the mean of the binomial distribution? The standard deviation?

30. Assume that 50% of the residents of a city are female. Suppose that of 1000 workers employed by a large contractor, only 48 are women. If the workers were randomly selected from the city, what is the mean number of females you would expect to be employed by the contractor? What is the standard deviation?

31. Refer to Exercise 30. Does the observation that only 48 of the employees are women suggest bias on the employer's part (assuming that sampling was random)? What is the fallacy in this argument?

32. Previous experience indicates that 1 out of every 100 major crimes in a large city is murder. A new crime prevention program has been in effect for a year. During the year the city experiences 3000 major crimes. From past experience, what is the average number of murders that you would expect? What is the standard deviation?

33. Refer to Exercise 32. Suppose that the observed number of murders in the city was 10. In light of past experience, is this a highly improbable event? Would you conclude that the new program has been effective?

34. An election poll shows that 516 of 1218 voters sampled favor the reelection of Senator Smith. Do you think the senator will win the election?

5.11   RANDOM SAMPLING

We have talked about finding the probability distribution of a variable by observing the frequency of occurrence of values of X in many repetitions of an experiment. Frequently the experiment will involve the random selection of one or more measurements from a population. We now give more precise meaning to the term *random sampling*.

DEFINITION 5.4	A *sample of one measurement* from a population of N measurements is said to be a **random sample** if each of the N measurements has an equal probability of being selected.

The notion of sampling can be extended to the selection of more than one measurement — say, n measurements. For purposes of illustration we will take a population that contains a very small number of measurements — say, $N = 4$ — which are 1, 2, 3, and 4. We will further assume that we wish to select a random sample of $n = 2$ from the $N = 4$. How many different (distinct) samples could we select? The six distinct samples are listed in Table 5.4.

TABLE 5.4

Samples of four measurements

Sample	Measurements in Sample
1	1, 2
2	1, 3
3	1, 4
4	2, 3
5	2, 4
6	3, 4

A *random sample* of 2 measurements from the population of 4 would give each of the 6 different samples the same probability of selection.

DEFINITION 5.5

A *sample of* n *measurements* is a **random sample** if each sample of size n has an equal probability of being selected.

It is unlikely that we could ever achieve a truly random sample, because the probabilities of selection will not always be exactly equal, but we do the best we can. Random sampling can be achieved (for all practical purposes) by ensuring that we have thoroughly mixed the elements in the population before selecting the sample. For example, card shuffling, although never perfect, is an attempt to distribute a random sample of cards to each player.

The simplest and most reliable way to select a random sample of n elements from a large population is to employ a table of random numbers, such as Appendix Table 6. Random number tables are constructed so that integers occur randomly and with equal frequency. For example, suppose that the population contains 1000 elements. Number the elements in sequence from 1 to 1000. Then turn to a table of random numbers, such as the excerpt shown in Table 5.5.

TABLE 5.5

Portion of a table of random numbers

10480	15011	01536
22368	46573	25595
24130	48360	22527
42167	93093	06243

Select n of the random numbers in order.

The numbers of the population elements to be included in the random sample are determined by the first three digits of the random numbers (unless the first four digits are 1000). Using Table 5.5, if $n = 5$, we would include elements numbered 104, 223, 241, 421, and 150. To avoid using the same sequence of random numbers over and over, the experimenter should select different starting points in Appendix Table 6 to begin the selection of random numbers for different samples.

What is the importance of random sampling? A basic reason for using random sampling is to ensure that inferences from the sample data are not distorted by a *selection bias*. A selection bias exists whenever there is a systematic tendency to overrepresent or underrepresent some part of the population. For example, a survey of households conducted entirely during the week between the hours of 9 A.M. and 5 P.M. would be severely biased towards households with at least one member at home. Hence any inferences made from the sample data would be biased towards the attributes or opinions of those families with at least one member at home and might not be truly representative of the population of all households in the region.

Even with the use of a table of random numbers, careful planning and a certain amount of ingenuity are required to have even a decent chance of approximating random sampling. This is especially true when the universe of interest involves people. People can be difficult to work with; they have a tendency to discard mail questionnaires and refuse to participate in personal interviews. Hence, unless we are very careful, the data we obtain may be full of biases having unknown effects on the inferences we are attempting to make.

We will not explore the topic of random sampling further in this text; entire courses at the undergraduate and graduate levels can be devoted to sample survey research methodology. The important point for us to remember is that data from a random sample will provide the foundation for making statistical inferences in later chapters. Random samples are not easy to obtain, but with care we can avoid many potential biases that could affect the inferences we make.

EXERCISES

35. Define what is meant by a random sample. Is it possible to draw a truly random sample? Comment.

36. Suppose that we wish to draw a random sample of $n = 20$ households from a city that contains 75,000 households. Further, suppose that the households have been identified and numbered. Use Appendix Table 6 to identify the households to be included in a random sample.

37. As a class exercise, have each student scan a recent copy of a newspaper or newsmagazine in which the results of a survey are given, and report the results of the survey to the class. Discuss whether the survey results were obtained from a random sample. What difference does it make?

38. One way to audit expense accounts for a large social research consulting firm would be to sample all reports dated the last day of each month. Comment on whether this would constitute a random sample.

5.12   THE SAMPLING DISTRIBUTION FOR $\bar{X}$

What happens when we draw a random sample from a population and compute the sample mean? How close does this computed statistic $\bar{X}$ lie to the corresponding population parameter μ? Similar questions might be asked concerning other statistics (for example, the median, the standard deviation, and others) when they are computed from sample data. To answer this question, we employ the same reasoning we used in analyzing Jones's prospects for election in Section 5.1. We will use the relative frequency approach of Section 5.3 to approximate the probability distribution for the sample mean, called the **sampling distribution for $\bar{X}$**. We do this by drawing samples of the same size over and over again from the population or universe of interest, each time computing the value of the sample mean. The resulting relative frequency histogram for the sample mean gives an approximation to the sampling distribution for $\bar{X}$.

We can illustrate this process by working with a known universe of scores. To illustrate and to make this example manageable, we will take the 90 rates of reported rape of Table 5.6 as our population and randomly draw 50 samples of 5 scores. For example, numbering the cities from 1 to 90 and using the table of random numbers, Appendix Table 6, we could proceed down column 1 and use the first two digits of each five-digit random number. For our first sample of random numbers, we obtain the numbers 10, 22, 24, 42, and 37, and we would select the rape rates from the cities assigned these numbers. The result of this first sample is shown in Table 5.7. The sample mean from the first sample is

$$\bar{X} = \frac{\Sigma X}{n} = \frac{196}{5} = 39.2$$

We repeat this procedure 49 more times to acquire 49 new samples. The means of the 50 samples are listed in Table 5.8.

To see how the sampling distribution of the sample mean $\bar{X}$ relates to the original distribution for the 90 rape rates, we can construct histograms for both sets of measurements. These are displayed in Figure 5.21.

	South	Rate	North	Rate	West	Rate
TABLE 5.6	Albany, GA	52	Akron, OH	39	Bakersfield, CA	58
Rate of reported rape	Asheville, NC	31	Allentown, PA	18	Brownsville, TX	18
for 90 SMSAs selected	Atlanta, GA	57	Ann Arbor, MI	87	Colorado Springs, CO	69
from the North, South,	Augusta, GA	40	Atlantic City, MI	54	Denver, CO	47
and West	Birmingham, AL	48	Benton Harbor, MI	100	Fresno, CA	65
	Charlotte, NC	45	Boston, MA	32	Galveston, TX	46
	Chattanooga, TN	38	Buffalo, NY	34	Houston, TX	61
	Colombia, SC	53	Canton, OH	30	Kansas City, KA	51
	Columbus, GA	48	Cincinnati, OH	36	Lawton, OK	48
	Fayetteville, AR	27	Cleveland, OH	53	Lubbock, TX	58
	Florence, SC	63	Columbus, OH	59	Modesto, CA	40
	Fort Lauderdale, FL	45	Dayton, OH	48	Oklahoma City, OK	58
	Gadsden, AL	24	Evansville, IN	21	Oxnard, CA	33
	Greensboro, NC	28	Gary, IN	31	Pueblo, CO	68
	Hickory, NC	13	Jersey City, NJ	34	Redding, CA	43
	Jackson, MS	41	Johnstown, PA	15	Reno, NV	81
	Knoxville, TN	27	Kenosha, WI	40	Sacramento, CA	50
	Lake Charles, LA	30	Madison, WI	24	St. Louis, MO	27
	Lexington, KY	32	Mansfield, OH	30	Salinas, KA	44
	Macon, GA	30	Milwaukee, WI	35	Salt Lake City, UT	32
	Mobile, AL	40	Minneapolis, MN	43	San Diego, CA	36
	Monroe, LA	45	Muskegon, MI	57	San Jose, CA	46
	Nashville, TN	59	Newark, NJ	56	Seattle, WA	59
	Norfolk, VA	42	Philadelphia, PA	38	Sioux City, IA	24
	Ocala, FL	48	Pittsfield, MA	41	Spokane, WA	34
	Richmond, VA	45	Portland, ME	21	Stockton, CA	41
	Savannah, GA	56	Racine, WI	49	Tacoma, WA	86
	Shreveport, LA	44	Reading, PA	14	Tucson, AR	55
	Washington, DC	34	Syracuse, NY	23	Victoria, TX	32
	Wilmington, DE	41	Vineland, NJ	55	Waco, TX	45

Source: U.S. Department of Justice, *Uniform Crime Reports for the United States.*
Note: Rates represent the number of reported rapes per 100,000 inhabitants, rounded to the nearest whole number.

TABLE 5.7

Results of sample 1

City Number	City	Rape Rate
10	Fayetteville, AR	27
22	Monroe, LA	45
24	Norfolk, VA	42
48	Dayton, OH	48
37	Buffalo, NY	34

TABLE 5.8

Means of 50 random samples of size 5 selected from the 90 rates of reported rapes in Table 5.6

39.0	39.0	36.6	36.6	40.8
56.2	39.6	42.0	38.4	62.6
41.6	46.4	37.4	46.0	43.4
52.6	35.8	50.2	49.8	44.0
40.0	47.2	38.8	41.6	43.2
45.6	41.0	35.8	53.2	35.2
46.2	50.0	45.4	46.4	44.4
35.2	42.0	42.6	58.2	36.8
47.4	46.8	41.6	47.4	55.6
39.2	45.8	37.4	41.8	27.8

As can be seen from Figure 5.21, the original population is certainly not mound shaped or symmetrical. In fact, the distribution is skewed to the right (tails off to the right). However, even with a small number of samples (50) and a small number of measurements per sample (5), the sampling distribution $\bar{X}$ is beginning to look bell shaped. In fact, most of the sample means are grouped closely about the mean of the population (which in this case can be computed to be $\mu = 43.31$).

The illustration we have presented could have been made more convincing by working with a much larger population and by taking a larger number of samples, with more observations in each sample. The important point to note is that in repeated sampling, $\bar{X}$ will be approximately normally distributed with mean μ and standard deviation $\sigma/\sqrt{n}$, called the **standard error of the mean**. The approximation will be more precise as n, the sample size for each sample, increases. Thus the frequency histogram for $\bar{X}$ would have been even more bell shaped if n had been 10 rather than 5, or 15 rather than 10, and so on.

Of course, in a practical situation we would not have the results of a sampling experiment available. But we will see in Chapter 6 that the sampling distributions (frequency histograms) for statistics (such as the sample mean

FIGURE 5.21

Relative frequency
histograms for the
rates of reported rapes
in Table 5.6

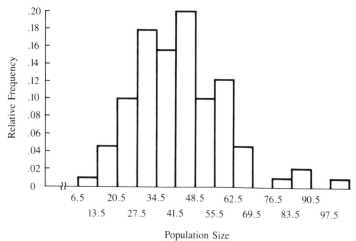

(a) Original population

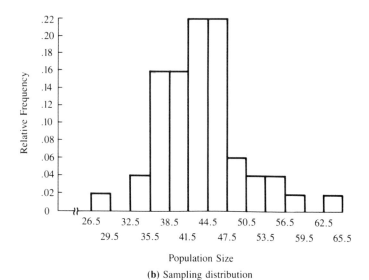

(b) Sampling distribution

$\overline{X}$, the sample proportion, etc.) are well-known. Although different statistics have different sampling distributions, we will use knowledge of these distributions to say, with a given probability, how close a single statistic will lie to the corresponding population parameter.

You may be dismayed to note how little accuracy we acquire in estimating a population mean rape rate based on a sample of five metropolitan areas. In Chapter 6 you will learn that the accuracy increases if you select a larger sample.

SUMMARY

Recall that social researchers frequently wish to make an inference about a population or universe, based on information contained in a sample. Anyone can use sample data to estimate the proportion of voters favoring candidate Jones, but the real question is, How far does the estimate lie from the true proportion? How much faith can we place in the inference? In a nutshell, what is the probability that the estimate will differ from the actual value by a specific amount — say, 5%? To answer this question, we must know the probabilities associated with values of the sample proportion favoring Jones; that is, we must know its sampling distribution. This probability is at the heart of the science of inference making.

Variables can be of two types, discrete and continuous. Their probability distributions can be derived mathematically by using the theory of probability or acquired empirically by repeating the phenomenon a large number of times and then constructing a frequency histogram of the results. Each probability distribution is a model for the population relative frequency histogram, and each can be described by a mean, a standard deviation, or any of the other numerical descriptive measures discussed in Chapter 4.

In this chapter we demonstrated the role that probability plays in making inferences and explained in general terms how you can find the probabilities associated with values of a variable that appear in a sample. The binomial and normal variables occupy prominent positions in statistical methodology. The binomial variable crops up in the conduct of many social science sample surveys, such as the number of persons in the sample who favor a particular issue, support a particular political candidate, or, in general, possess a specific attribute. The normal variable assumes a position of prime importance in the social sciences, because so many variables of interest have frequency distributions that are approximately normal. Even the binomial variable possesses a distribution that is approximately normal for large sample sizes. Consequently, we can often make approximate probability statements about observed sample results by using the areas (probabilities) under a normal probability distribution.

We will apply these results in Chapters 6 and 7. Specifically, we will consider ways to estimate parameters of populations and to judge how far away from the parameter our estimate might be. Or we might wish to hypothesize something about the population parameters and use the sample data to reach a decision concerning the believability of the hypothesis. These concepts, based on single samples from populations, will be developed in Chapters 6 and 7. Methods for comparing parameters from two or more populations are considered in subsequent chapters.

KEY WORDS

Binomial experiment   Experiment involving n identical, independent, dichotomous trials.

Binomial variable   A discrete variable representing the number of successes in n identical, independent, dichotomous trials.

Classical interpretation of probability   The probability of an event E occurring is computed by taking the ratio of the number of outcomes N_E favorable to event E to the total number N of possible outcomes.

Continuous variable   Observations on a continuous quantitative variable can assume any one of the countless number of values in a line interval.

Discrete variable   Observations on a discrete quantitative variable can assume only a countable number of values.

Event   A collection of outcomes.

Mean of a binomial variable np

Normal curve   Bell-shaped curve representing the probability distribution for a normal variable.

Outcome   Distinct possible result from an experiment.

Personal probability   A statement of belief regarding the likelihood of a one-shot event.

Probability   The likelihood that an event will occur when an experiment is conducted once.

Probability distribution of a continuous variable   Smooth curve that gives the theoretical relative frequency distribution for a continuous variable.

Probability distribution of a discrete variable   A listing, formula, or histogram giving the probability associated with each value of a discrete variable.

Random sample   A sample size of n measurements is called random if each sample size n has an equal probability of being selected.

Relative frequency concept of probability   The probability of an event E occurring is approximately n_E/n where event E occurs n_E times in an experiment conducted n different times.

Sampling distribution for $\bar{X}$ The probability distribution for the sample mean.

Standard deviation of a binomial variable $\sqrt{npq}$

Standard error of the mean   The standard deviation of the sampling distribution for $\bar{X}$.

z-score   A standard score; $z = (X - \mu)/\sigma$.

KEY FORMULAS

Binomial probability $P(X)$

$$P(X) = \frac{n!}{X!(n-X)!} p^X q^{n-X}$$

z-score

$$z = \frac{X - \mu}{\sigma}$$

Mean and standard deviation of a binomial variable

$$\mu = np$$
$$\sigma = \sqrt{npq}$$

Mean and standard error of $\bar{X}$

$$\mu_{\bar{X}} = \mu$$
$$\sigma_{\bar{X}} = \frac{\sigma}{\sqrt{n}}$$

SUPPLEMENTARY EXERCISES FOR CHAPTER 5

39. What is probability? Briefly describe its utility in the social sciences.

40. What are the differences between the probability distributions for discrete and continuous variables?

41. If a population contains 5 scores of alienation, how many distinctly different samples of 2 scores can be selected? (*Hint*: See Section 5.11.)

42. Discuss the logic behind the relative frequency approach to probability. Set up an empirical sampling procedure of your own to ascertain the probability of an event of your choice.

43. What is a binomial experiment? Give three examples of a binomial experiment of interest to the social scientist.

44. Prenursing students throughout the country were administered an examination to determine their knowledge of personal hygiene. If we assume that the population of scores was normally distributed with a mean of 50 and a standard deviation of 3.5, approximately what percentage of the population would you expect to fall in these intervals?
    a. 47 to 55　　**b.** 44.8 to 48.9　　**c.** below 58

45. Define z in terms of X, a normally distributed variable with a mean μ and a standard deviation σ.

46. Using Appendix Table 1, calculate the area under the normal curve between these z-scores:

    a. $z = 0$ and $z = +1.5$ **b.** $z = 0$ and $z = +1.8$

47. Repeat Exercise 46 for these z-scores:

    a. $z = 0$ and $z = +2.5$ **b.** $z = -1.5$ and $z = 0$

48. Repeat Exercise 46 for these z-scores:

    a. $z = -.8$ and $z = 0$ **b.** $z = -.8$ and $z = +.8$

49. Repeat Exercise 46 for these z-scores:

    a. $z = -1.96$ and $z = +1.96$ **b.** $z = -2.58$ and $z = +2.58$

50. Repeat Exercise 46 for these z-scores: .

    a. $z = -.12$ and $z = +1.80$ **b.** $z = +1.65$ and $z = +2.0$

51. Find the value of z such that 30% of the area lies to its right.

52. Find the value of z such that 5% of the area lies to its right.

53. Find the value of z such that 2.5% of the area lies to its right.

54. A normally distributed variable X has a mean of 7 and a standard deviation of 2. Find the z-value corresponding to $X = 6$.

55. Refer to Exercise 54. Find the value of z corresponding to $X = 8.5$.

56. Refer to Exercise 54. Find the probability that X lies in the interval 6 to 8.5.

57. One week before an important vote, a survey of members of a large all-male student organization indicated that 40% were in favor of changing their constitution to admit women members. Two days before the vote, the campus student government suggested that it would withhold operating funds for the organization if it did not vote to admit women as members. That same day 50 members were polled at random to ascertain their opinion on the issue, and 30 said they would vote for the constitutional change. Assuming that 40% of the entire membership still favor female members, what are the mean and standard deviation of the number favoring a constitutional change in a random sample of 50 members? (Assume that the student organization is large enough that the sampling satisfies the assumptions required of a binomial experiment.)

58. Refer to Exercise 57. Based on the fact that 30 of the 50 favored a constitutional change, would you conclude that opinions seem to have changed following the student government announcement?

59. Find the z-score such that 28% of the scores are less than that value of z.

60. In a distribution of birth rates, the mean is 18.5, and the standard deviation is 4.8. Find the z-score for a birth rate of 21.2. Would you be surprised to find a birth rate of 2.2? Why?

61. Thirty percent of all children in a large public school were found to exhibit signs of malnutrition. If a random sample of 100 students is to be selected from the school, give the mean and standard deviation of a normal approximation to X, the number of children in the sample exhibiting signs of malnutrition.

62. From returns in previous years, it was found that approximately 70% of the tax returns in a given income category were incorrectly prepared. Assuming that 70% of the returns will be incorrect this year also, find the mean and standard deviation of the random variable X, the number of tax returns incorrectly prepared in a random sample of 5000 returns. Use this information to describe the variability of X in repeated sampling.

63. If 2600 of the 5000 sampled returns (of Exercise 62) are prepared incorrectly, would you anticipate that approximately 70% of all the returns this year will be incorrectly prepared? Explain.

64. Find the value of z such that 1% of the area lies to its right.

65. Find the value of z such that 10% of the area lies to its right.

66. The hourly local union wage for a particular type of construction worker has a national average of \$15.30 and a standard deviation of .63. Find the proportion of local unions for which the compensation is more than \$16.00 per hour. If there were 850 such local unions, how many unions would have compensation in excess of \$16.00 per hour, if we assume that the population of all local wages is normally distributed?

67. In a study of suburban communities with a given level of industrial progress, an index of population growth and ecological awareness was developed. If the distribution of index scores is assumed to be normal with a mean of 50 and a standard deviation of 10, determine the probability of observing a suburban community with a score above 66.7.

68. The probability of a married woman having her first child during the fourth year of her marriage is .250; during the fifth year, .205; during the sixth year, .164; and during the seventh year or later, .306. What is the probability of a married woman having her first child during either the fourth or the sixth year of marriage?

69. A recent survey taken by the *New York Times* showed that 90% of those interviewed thought that there would be better government if there were more females in Congress. If .90 is the true population proportion, what is the probability that 340 or fewer agree with this proposal in a sample of 400?

70. A survey was conducted to determine the attitudes of physicians working in public hospitals. A sample of 1000 physicians was contacted using a mailed questionnaire, and the number favoring or opposing free abortions for unwed teenage mothers was recorded. If 80% of the physicians responded to the survey, would you regard this as a binomial experiment? If 65% of the 800 who responded favored free abortions, what conclusion would you draw?

71. A random sample of 10 members was obtained to ascertain opinions concerning a new wage package proposal to a local union by union leaders. If we assume that $p = .6$ of all the members who disagree with the wage package, compute the following probabilities:

    a. all disagree   **b.** exactly 6 disagree
    c. 6 or more disagree   **d.** all agree

72. An experiment is conducted to test the effect of an anticoagulant drug on rats. A random sample of 4 rats is employed in the experiment. If the drug manufacturer claims that 80% of the rats will be favorably affected by the drug, what is the probability that none of the 4 experimental rats will be favorably affected? One of the 4? One or none?

73. Refer to Database A in Appendix Table 7. Using the relative frequency concept of probability, what is the probability of a student being
    a. a social science major?
    b. married?
    c. from a high-income family?

74. Refer to Exercise 94 in Chapter 4, involving Database A. What is the z-score for a student who states that 22 acts should be declared serious crimes?

75. Refer to Exercise 74. What raw scores correspond to the following z-scores? Because the data are discrete whole numbers, round each answer to the nearest whole number.
    a. -1.58 b. $+2.23$ c. $+1.00$

76. Refer to Exercise 98 in Chapter 4, involving Database B. What is the probability of a nation having a level-of-technology score of 40 or above?

77. Refer to Exercise 76. How many nations have level-of-technology scores below $z = -1.20$?

78. Refer to Database C, Appendix Table 9. Consider the HAM-D total scores for the four treatment groups in the clinical trials. If we assume that the mean for the combined scores is 14.2 and the standard deviation is 6.3, determine z-scores for total scores of 5, 16, and 24.

79. Refer to Exercise 78. What total scores correspond to z-scores of -1.00, 0.00, and $+2.00$, respectively?

80. Refer to Exercise 78. If the combined HAM-D total scores are assumed to be normally distributed, determine the probability of having a total score higher than 24; less than 10.

81. Refer to Exercise 105 in Chapter 4. Using the relative frequency concept of probability, answer the following:
    a. What is the probability of a state having a forcible rape rate of 38 or above?
    b. What is the probability of a state having a forcible rape rate between 35 and 45?
    c. What is the probability of a state having a forcible rape rate of 27 or below?
    d. What are the corresponding rape rates for the following z-scores?

$$
\begin{array}{ccc}
-1.44 & +2.09 & -0.17 \\
-0.67 & -0.99 & +1.53 \\
+1.91 & +0.81 & -1.19
\end{array}
$$

82. Refer to Exercise 107 in Chapter 4. Using the relative frequency concept of probability, answer the following:

a. What is the probability of a state having a population density of 200 or above?

b. What is the probability of a state having a population density between 67 and 121?

c. What is the probability of a state having a population density of 39 or below?

d. What are the corresponding population densities for the following z-scores?

$$
\begin{array}{ccc}
-1.31 & +0.19 & -0.71 \\
-0.76 & -0.55 & +1.35 \\
+1.14 & +0.62 & -1.45
\end{array}
$$

83. Refer to Exercise 108 in Chapter 4. Using the relative frequency concept of probability, answer the following:

a. What is the probability of a nation having an infant mortality rate of 97 or above?

b. What is the probability of a nation having an infant mortality rate between 61 and 103?

c. What is the probability of a nation having an infant mortality rate of 27 or below?

d. What are the corresponding infant mortality rates for the following z-scores?

$$
\begin{array}{ccc}
-0.39 & +1.19 & -0.72 \\
-1.35 & -0.66 & +1.32 \\
+1.79 & +0.26 & -1.05
\end{array}
$$

84. Refer to Exercise 109 in Chapter 4. Using the relative frequency concept of probability, answer the following:

a. What is the probability of a nation having a per capita GNP of $7122 or above?

b. What is the probability of a nation having a per capita GNP between $13,320 and $19,593?

c. What is the probability of a nation having a per capita GNP of $819 or below?

d. What percentage of nations have per capita GNPs between the following pairs of z-scores?

$$
\begin{array}{cc}
-0.39 \text{ and } +1.19 & -0.72 \text{ and } -1.35 \\
-0.66 \text{ and } +1.32 & +0.26 \text{ and } +1.79
\end{array}
$$

85. Refer to Exercise 110 in Chapter 4. Using the relative frequency concept of probability, answer the following:

a. What is the probability of a nation having a life expectancy of 61 or above?

b. What is the probability of a nation having a life expectancy between 67 and 74?

c. What is the probability of a nation having a life expectancy of 59 or below?

d. What percentage of nations have life expectancies between the following pairs of z-scores?

$$-1.39 \text{ and } +0.19 \qquad -0.27 \text{ and } -1.53$$
$$-0.99 \text{ and } +1.52 \qquad +0.62 \text{ and } +1.97$$

CHAPTER 6

CONCEPTS OF ESTIMATION: THE ONE-SAMPLE CASE

GENERAL OBJECTIVES

Inferences are often haphazard and based on personal biases; decisions and predictions have been made since the very beginning of humankind. Today, more than ever, it is vitally important that complex social organizations and societies make reasonable inferences based on solid information. Unfortunately, in most situations one must still make inferences in the face of uncertainty, since all the relevant information is not known. This is where statistics, using probability concepts, can be of help. This chapter helps us understand how statistics can be used to make inferences using estimation procedures based on data from a single sample.

SPECIFIC OBJECTIVES

1. To introduce the idea that the research question asked dictates whether a parameter should be estimated or a specific hypothesis tested.
2. To distinguish between point and interval estimates.
3. To show how to construct and interpret an interval estimate of a population mean, based on data from a single random sample.
4. To show how to construct and interpret an interval estimate of the binomial parameter p, based on data from a single random sample.
5. To give guidance in determining how large a sample must be to construct an interval estimate with a specific degree of confidence and a specified width.

6.1 INTRODUCTION

Inference — specifically, decision making and prediction — is centuries old and plays an important role in our lives. Each of us is faced daily with personal decisions and situations that require predictions about the future. State agencies are concerned with predicting the number of welfare recipients and the average amount paid per person in a given year. A social researcher may wish to estimate the mobility of a particular segment of our society. A political scientist seeks to know whether people's opinions about particular penal reforms are related to political party affiliation. The inferences that these individuals make should be based on relevant facts, which we call *observations* or *data*.

In many practical situations the relevant facts are abundant, seemingly inconsistent, and in many respects overwhelming. As a result, our careful decision or prediction is often little better than anybody's outright guess. The reader need only refer to the "Market Views" section of the *Wall Street Journal* to observe the diversity of expert opinion about future stock market behavior. Similarly, a visual analysis of data from a sample survey often yields conflicting conclusions by social researchers. Many individuals feel that their own built-in inference-making equipment is quite good. However, experience suggests that most people are incapable of using large amounts of data, mentally weighing each bit of relevant information, and arriving at a good inference. (You may test your individual inference-making ability on the exercises in this chapter and Chapter 7. Scan the data and make an inference before using the appropriate statistical procedure. Compare the results.)

As social researchers we make use of statistical results rather than relying on our intuition. We employ statistical techniques to aid in making inferences. Earlier, we touched on some of the notions involved in statistical inference; we will collect our thoughts at this point in a presentation of some of the basic ideas involved in statistical inference.

The objective of inferential statistics is to make inferences about a population or universe based on information contained in a sample. Since populations are characterized by numerical descriptive measures called parameters, statistical inference is concerned with making inferences about population parameters. Typical population parameters are the mean, the standard deviation, the area under the probability distribution above or below some value of a variable, and the area between two values of a variable. Indeed, the practical problems mentioned in the first paragraph of this section can be restated in the framework of a population with a specified parameter of interest. For example, in trying to predict the average amount of money paid per person to welfare recipients in a given year, the population of interest is the set of all yearly welfare payments, and we are interested in estimating the value of the population mean μ.

Procedures for making inferences about parameters fall into one of two categories. Either we try to *estimate* (predict) the population parameter of interest, or we *conduct a statistical test* about the value of the parameter. These two inference-making procedures are quite different and are contrasted by the following questions. In estimating a population parameter we are asking the question, "What is the value of the population parameter?" In a statistical test we are asking the question, "Is the parameter equal to this specific value?"

The first procedure, estimating, reflects an experimental situation in which we may know very little about the parameter of interest. For example, in a preliminary study of service personnel returning from a tour of duty overseas, social researchers might wish to administer a political awareness questionnaire to a sample of returnees. Because of the ever-changing political situation, information from recent returnees would be helpful in constructing an appropriate format for the present debriefing sessions. The sample information could be used to estimate the average political awareness of service personnel and might be helpful in developing the debriefing sessions.

In contrast, consider a situation in which we are interested in the effectiveness of an extensive birth control campaign to educate the people of a developing nation. Information prior to the campaign suggested that approximately 10% of the family units regularly used recognized methods of birth control. One year after the campaign, we would be interested in testing the hypothesis that the percentage of families practicing birth control is greater than 10%. Note that in this situation we are not asking, "What is the percentage of family units practicing birth control?" Rather, we are asking, "Is the percentage greater than 10%?"

Any statement about statistical inference would be incomplete without reference to a measure of goodness for an inferential procedure; with such a reference one procedure can be compared with another. More than comparing different procedures, we would like to state the goodness of a particular inference in a given situation. For example, we may not only want to predict the number of unemployed persons of a given ethnic background, but also to know how accurate our prediction is. Is it correct to within 1000, or 10,000, or 1,000,000? **In a practical situation a statistical inference contains two elements: the inference itself and a measure of its goodness.**

Before concluding this introductory discussion of inference, we should answer a question that frequently disturbs the beginner: Which method of inference should be used? That is, should the parameter be estimated, or should we test a hypothesis concerning its value? The answer to this question is dictated basically by the research question that has been posed, and in some cases it is a personal preference. Many substantive problems involve testing hypotheses about parameters; others involve making estimates. We will employ estimation procedures in this chapter and tests of hypotheses in Chapter 7. In both chapters we will confine our attention to inferences based on a single sample selected from a population or universe.

EXERCISES

1. Suppose that a researcher is interested in determining the percentage of registered Democrats in a large voting district who favor capital punishment. Identify the population of interest.

2. Refer to Exercise 1. Is the researcher faced with a problem involving estimation or testing of a hypothesis? How might you specify a measure of goodness?

3. Suppose the researcher of Exercise 1 wishes to determine whether the percentages of Republicans and Democrats favoring capital punishment differ. Identify the population(s) and parameter(s) of interest. Indicate whether the researcher is faced with an estimation or a testing problem.

4. A researcher is interested in estimating the percentage of registered voters in her state who have voted in at least one state or federal election in the past two years. Identify the population of interest. How might you select the voters to be included in the sample?

6.2   ESTIMATION OF A POPULATION MEAN

Many practical problems require the estimation of a population mean μ. For example, a social researcher may want to estimate the average reaction time of patients to a particular stimulus, or the mean increase in wages for various unions, or the mean family income in a ghetto area. In this section we will discuss both point and interval estimation of a population mean μ.

Estimation procedures can be divided into two types. We can calculate a single number, called a **point estimate**, from the sample data and use this value to estimate the parameter of interest. Or we can compute two numbers from the sample data and use the interval formed by the two numbers as an **interval estimate** of the parameter of interest. The distinction between the two is quite simple. In the former case we compute one number and infer that the parameter is that value. In the latter case we compute two numbers and infer that the parameter lies in the interval between them.

As social researchers, we will seldom be concerned with point estimates by themselves for estimating population parameters, since such estimates are invariably in error. Instead we deal almost exclusively with interval estimates. For example, a statement that 39% of respondents favored a proposed loan forgiveness program is less useful than one such as "the favorable response rate is estimated to be 39% ± 2%."

Given the sampling distribution of $\overline{X}$ and areas under a normal curve, we can develop the basic concepts of interval estimation for μ. Before we do this, though, we need to expand on the properties of the sampling distribution for $\overline{X}$. These are listed next.

PROPERTIES OF THE SAMPLING DISTRIBUTION OF $\overline{X}$

The sampling distribution of $\overline{X}$, obtained by drawing many samples of size n from the same population and calculating $\overline{X}$ for each sample, has the following properties, regardless of the form of the population from which the sample measurements are drawn:

1. The mean of the sampling distribution of $\overline{X}$ is μ, the same as the mean for the population from which the sample measurements are drawn (see Figure 6.1a).

2. The standard deviation of the sampling distribution of $\overline{X}$ is

$$\sigma_{\overline{X}} = \frac{\sigma}{\sqrt{n}}$$

where σ is the standard deviation of the original population and n is the sample size. Note that the symbol $\sigma_{\overline{x}}$ is used to denote the standard deviation of the sampling distribution of $\overline{X}$; it is called the **standard error of the mean**.

3. When n is large (30 or more), the sampling distribution of $\overline{X}$ is approximately normally distributed (see Figure 6.1b).

The ideas behind constructing an interval estimate for a population mean μ can be illustrated best by way of an artificial example. Suppose that a random sample of size $n = 36$ is selected from a population with unknown mean μ and known standard deviation $\sigma = 24$. The sampling distribution of $\overline{X}$ will be normal with mean μ and standard error $\sigma_{\overline{X}} = \sigma/\sqrt{n} = \frac{24}{6} = 4$. Thus the interval $\mu \pm 1.96(4)$ includes 95% of the $\overline{X}$s in repeated sampling, as illustrated in Figure 6.2. Looked at slightly differently, anytime the observed value of $\overline{X}$ lies in the interval $\mu \pm 1.96(4)$, the interval $\overline{X} \pm 1.96(4)$ will enclose (or capture) μ. This is shown in Figure 6.3. Since in repeated sampling there is a 95% chance that $\overline{X}$ lies in the interval $\mu \pm 1.96(4)$, there is a 95% chance

FIGURE 6.1

Distribution for the
original population X
and sampling distribu-
tion for $\bar{X}$

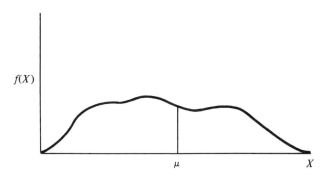

(a)   Distribution for X with mean μ and standard deviation σ

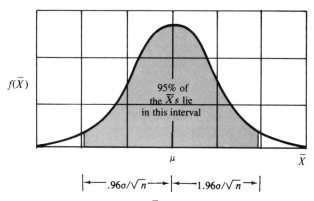

(b)   Sampling distribution for $\bar{X}$ with mean μ and standard error $\sigma/\sqrt{n}$

FIGURE 6.2

Sampling distribution
of $\bar{X}$ with $\sigma_{\bar{x}} = 4$

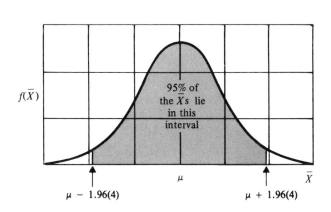

FIGURE 6.3

Observed value of $\bar{X}$ and the interval $\bar{X} \pm$ 1.96(4)

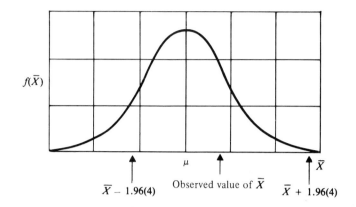

$f(\bar{X})$

μ

$\bar{X}$

$\bar{X} - 1.96(4)$ Observed value of $\bar{X}$ $\bar{X} + 1.96(4)$

that the interval $\bar{X} \pm 1.96(4)$ will enclose μ. This idea is illustrated in Figure 6.4. Twenty different samples were drawn from a population with mean μ and standard deviation σ. For each sample an interval estimate was computed using the formula $\bar{X} \pm 1.96\sigma_{\bar{X}}$. Note that although the intervals bob about, most of them intersect the vertical line and hence contain μ. In fact, if we

FIGURE 6.4

Twenty interval esti-mates computed by using $\bar{X} \pm 1.96\sigma_{\bar{X}}$

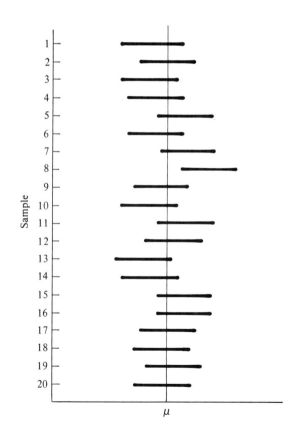

Sample

μ

repeated this process over and over again, 95% of the intervals formed would contain μ.

In practice we take only a single sample from the population of interest and compute the sample mean. The interval estimate $\bar{X} \pm 1.96\sigma_{\bar{X}}$ that we construct from the sample data is called a 95% **confidence interval** for the population mean μ.

LARGE-SAMPLE 95% CONFIDENCE INTERVAL FOR μ

$$\bar{X} \pm 1.96\sigma_{\bar{X}}$$

(*Note*: If σ is unknown, substitute s for σ. The sample size must be 30 or more so that s will be a good approximation for σ. A confidence interval for $n < 30$ is presented in Chapter 7.)

We illustrate these ideas with an example.

EXAMPLE 6.1

The hourly wages in a particular labor union are assumed to be normally distributed. A random sample of 70 employee records is examined, and the sample mean and standard deviation are $\bar{X} = \$13.00$ and $s = \$2.20$, respectively. Estimate μ using a 95% confidence interval.

SOLUTION

Since the sample size n is greater than 30, we can use the large-sample (30 or more) confidence interval. Since no prior estimate of σ is available, we must replace σ with s. Then

$$\frac{\sigma}{\sqrt{n}} \approx \frac{s}{\sqrt{n}} = \frac{2.20}{\sqrt{70}}$$

The lower point for the confidence interval, called the **lower confidence limit**, is

$$\bar{X} - \frac{1.96\sigma}{\sqrt{n}}$$

Substituting s for σ, we have

$$\bar{X} - \frac{1.96s}{\sqrt{n}} = 13.00 - (1.96)\frac{2.20}{\sqrt{70}} = 13.00 - .515 = 12.485$$

Similarly, the **upper confidence limit** with s substituted for σ is

$$\bar{X} + \frac{1.96s}{\sqrt{n}} = 13.00 + (1.96)\,\frac{2.20}{\sqrt{70}} = 13.515$$

Rounding these limits to the nearest cent, the 95% confidence interval for the true mean hourly wage is \$12.48 to \$13.52.

There are many different confidence intervals for μ. For example, the interval $\mu \pm 2.58\sigma_{\bar{X}}$ would include 99% of the $\bar{X}$s in repeated sampling (see Figure 6.5), and the interval $\bar{X} \pm 2.58\sigma_{\bar{X}}$ forms a 99% confidence interval for μ. For a given set of sample measurements, we will choose an appropriate degree of confidence and the corresponding formula for the confidence interval. One confidence interval will be computed and used as an interval estimate of μ.

The formula for a general $100(1 - \alpha)$% confidence interval for μ is shown next.

FIGURE 6.5

Sampling distribution of $\bar{X}$ and the interval $\mu \pm 2.58\sigma_{\bar{X}}$

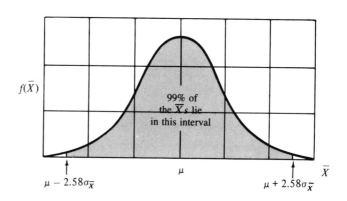

LARGE-SAMPLE $100(1 - \alpha)$% CONFIDENCE INTERVAL FOR μ

$$\bar{X} \pm z_{\alpha/2}\sigma_{\bar{X}}$$

where $\sigma_{\bar{X}} = \sigma/\sqrt{n}$ and $z_{\alpha/2}$ is the tabulated value in Table 6.1 cutting off a right-tail area of $\alpha/2$. The values of z for a 90%, 95%, and 99% confidence interval for μ are 1.645, 1.96, and 2.58, respectively. We assume that σ is known or that the sample size is large enough to replace σ with s.

TABLE 6.1

Common values of the
confidence coefficient
and the corresponding
values of z

Degree of Confidence $100(1 - \alpha)\,\%$	Tabled z-value $z_{\alpha/2}$
68%	1.00
80%	1.282
90%	1.645
95%	1.96
98%	2.33
99%	2.58

The quantity $z_{\alpha/2}$ is a value of z with an area $\alpha/2$ to its right. In other words, beyond a distance of $z_{\alpha/2}$ standard deviations to the right of μ, there is an area of $\alpha/2$ under the normal curve. For example, when the confidence coefficient is $1 - \alpha = .95$, and hence $\alpha = .05$, we determine $z_{.025}$, the value of z with an area $\alpha/2 = .025$ to its right. Since Appendix Table 1 is constructed to give areas under a normal curve between μ and a value to the right (or left) of μ, we can use Appendix Table 1 to determine the value of $z_{\alpha/2}$ by looking up the z-score corresponding to an area of $(1 - \alpha)/2$. This value of z will be $z_{\alpha/2}$ (see Figure 6.6). Common values for the degree of confidence and corresponding $z_{\alpha/2}$ values are shown in Table 6.1.

FIGURE 6.6

Interpretation of $z_{\alpha/2}$

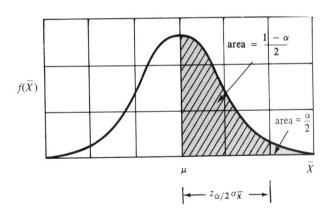

Before we leave interval estimation of μ, three points deserve further comment.

1. Sometimes students use 1.96σ to determine the confidence interval rather than $1.96\sigma_{\bar{X}}$. Remember, if we want to describe the variability of the distribution of $\bar{X}$, we must use $\sigma_{\bar{X}}$, the standard error of the sampling distribution of $\bar{X}$. The quantity σ is the standard deviation of the population from which the sample was drawn.

2. We sometimes have to approximate σ in calculating the confidence interval. We often use the sample standard deviation s to estimate σ. This approximation will be reasonably good when n is large (say, 30 or more).

3. You will note that the standard error of $\bar{X}$ depends on the standard deviation σ of the population and the sample size n. Thus

$$\sigma_{\bar{X}} = \frac{\sigma}{\sqrt{n}}$$

Although it is not obvious that the formula should take this form, it is clear that the greater the variation of the population as measured by σ, the greater will be the variation in the distribution of the $\bar{X}$s. Similarly, as the sample size n increases, we would expect the amount of information to increase, and hence the variability of the distribution of $\bar{X}$ to decrease. The sampling distributions of $\bar{X}$ based on samples of 5 and 25 drawn from a normal distribution are superimposed on the probability distribution for a normal population in Figure 6.7.

FIGURE 6.7

Sampling distribution of $\bar{X}$ based on samples of 5 and 25 from a normal population

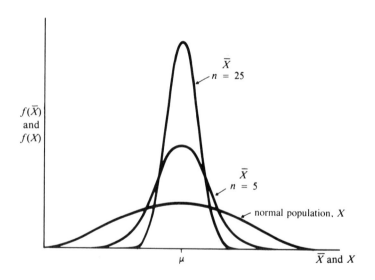

EXERCISES

5. Distinguish between the populations associated with σ and with $\sigma/\sqrt{n}$.

6. What interpretation can we give to the interval $\bar{X} \pm 1.96\sigma/\sqrt{n}$?

7. A random sample of $n = 36$ labor contracts showed an average hourly wage increase of $.75 and a standard deviation of $.32. Estimate the mean hourly

wage increase for all unions, using a 90% confidence interval. Interpret your result.

8. A random sample of $n = 40$ inner-city birth rates produced a sample average of 35 per thousand and a standard deviation of 6.3. Estimate the mean inner-city birth rate, using a 95% confidence interval.

9. A medical research team studied the effect of a diuretic using 30 healthy adults. The team reported that the urinary output of each person was carefully monitored for 24 hours following dosing, and the sample mean turned out to be 3300 milliliters with a standard deviation of 500. Construct a 95% confidence interval for μ.

10. Refer to Exercise 9. Assuming s remains constant, determine the width of a 95% confidence interval for μ based on sample sizes of 60, 90, and 120. Discuss the effect of sample size on the width of a confidence interval.

11. Refer to Exercise 9. How would the confidence interval change if we used either a 90% or a 99% confidence interval? In general, what happens to a confidence interval as the confidence level is increased for a fixed sample size?

12. Stafford and Reske (1990) explored the tendency for young couples to idealize each other, especially if they are involved in a long-distance relationship. They interviewed 34 geographically close (GC) couples and 37 long-distance (LD) couples. Subjects were scored on a premarital adjustment scale (PAS), idealistic distortion scale (IDS), and the frequency of interaction scale (FIS). The higher the score, the greater the perceived premarital adjustment, the more distortion, or the more frequently the couple interacted, respectively. Means and standard deviations are shown in the accompanying table.

EXERCISE 12

Means and standard deviations for geographically close and long-distance relationships

Scale	Geographically Close		Long Distance	
	Mean	**SD**	**Mean**	**SD**
premarital adjustment (PAS)	108.8	16.6	119.1	15.4
idealistic distortion (IDS)	16.5	2.8	18.1	2.7
frequency of interaction (FIS)	7.3	4.1	2.7	2.0

Source: Adapted from Laura Stafford and James R. Reske, "Idealization and Communication in Long-Distance Premarital Relationships," *Family Relations* 39 (1990), p. 276. Copyrighted 1990 by the National Council on Family Relations, 3989 Central Ave., N. E., Suite #550, Minneapolis, MN 55421. Reprinted by permission.

    a. Construct a 95% confidence interval and then a 90% confidence interval for the PAS mean for geographically close relationships.
    b. Construct a 95% confidence interval and then a 90% confidence interval for the PAS mean for long-distance relationships.

c. Construct a 90% confidence interval and then a 99% confidence interval for the IDS mean for geographically close relationships.

d. Construct a 90% confidence interval and then a 99% confidence interval for the IDS mean for long-distance relationships.

e. Construct a 90% confidence interval and then a 99% confidence interval for the FIS mean for geographically close relationships.

f. Construct a 90% confidence interval and then a 95% confidence interval for the FIS mean for long-distance relationships.

6.3   ESTIMATION OF THE BINOMIAL PARAMETER p

The point estimate we will use for the binomial parameter p is one that you would choose intuitively. Let p be the proportion of elements in the population that are classified as successes. Then the best estimate of p would appear to be the proportion of the observed sample that are successes. If X represents the number of successes in n trials, the sample proportion of successes, denoted by the symbol $\hat{p}$ (read "p hat"), is

$$\hat{p} = \frac{\text{number of successes}}{\text{number of trials}} = \frac{X}{n}$$

In Chapter 5 we noted that the binomial variable X possesses a mound-shaped probability distribution that approaches the normal curve as n becomes large. The **sampling distribution for $\hat{p}$** (the sample proportion) will possess the same shape as the distribution for X (the number of successes), except that the mean and standard error will be different.

MEAN AND STANDARD ERROR OF THE SAMPLING DISTRIBUTION $\hat{p}$

$$\mu_{\hat{p}} = p$$

$$\sigma_{\hat{p}} = \sqrt{\frac{pq}{n}}$$

where $q = 1 - p$.

As with the point estimate of μ, we seldom concern ourselves with the point estimate of the binomial parameter p. Instead, we move directly to the interval estimate. A 95% confidence interval for estimating the population proportion p has the same form as a 95% confidence interval for a population mean μ (see Section 6.2). We know from the sampling distribution of $\hat{p}$ that the interval $p \pm 1.96\sigma_{\hat{p}}$ includes 95% of the sample proportions $\hat{p}$ in repeated sampling. Consider the interval $\hat{p} \pm 1.96\sigma_{\hat{p}}$. Anytime $\hat{p}$ lies in the interval $p \pm 1.96\sigma_{\hat{p}}$, the interval $\hat{p} \pm 1.96\sigma_{\hat{p}}$ contains p. This occurs with probability equal to .95.

In a given situation we will calculate only one interval estimate by using the formula $\hat{p} \pm 1.96\sigma_{\hat{p}}$. This interval estimate is called a 95% confidence interval for p.

95% CONFIDENCE INTERVAL FOR p

$$\hat{p} \pm 1.96\sigma_{\hat{p}}$$

where $\sigma_{\hat{p}} = \sqrt{pq/n}$. Since p and $q = 1 - p$ are unknown, we substitute $\hat{p}$ and $\hat{q} = 1 - \hat{p}$ in the formula for $\sigma_{\hat{p}}$.

We illustrate these ideas with an example.

EXAMPLE 6.2

A sample of 1000 working class people in Great Britain was interviewed to determine political party affiliations. In the sample, 680 identified with the major left-of-center party. Use a 95% confidence interval to estimate the true proportion p of Great Britain's working class that identifies with the left-of-center party.

SOLUTION

The point estimate of p is

$$\hat{p} = \frac{X}{n} = \frac{680}{1000} = .68$$

Substituting $\hat{p} = .68$ and $\hat{q} = 1 - \hat{p} = .32$ for p and q, respectively, the 95% confidence interval has a lower limit of

$$\hat{p} - 1.96\sqrt{\frac{\hat{p}\hat{q}}{n}} = .68 - 1.96\sqrt{\frac{(.68)(.32)}{1000}}$$
$$= .68 - 1.96\sqrt{.000218}$$
$$= .68 - 1.96(.0148) = .68 - .03 = .65$$

and an upper limit of

$$\hat{p} + 1.96\sqrt{\frac{\hat{p}\hat{q}}{n}} = .68 + .03 = .71$$

The appropriate 95% confidence interval for p is then .65 to .71. We do not know whether this interval contains the parameter p. However, since 95% of the intervals $\hat{p} \pm 1.96\sigma_{\hat{p}}$ contain p in repeated sampling, we are 95% confident that the interval .65 to .71 includes the true proportion of Great Britain's working class that identifies with the left-of-center political party.

In Section 6.2 we indicated that it is possible to construct a general confidence interval for μ with confidence coefficient $1 - \alpha$ using the formula $\bar{X} \pm z_{\alpha/2}\sigma_{\bar{X}}$. The corresponding general formula for p is given next.

$100(1 - \alpha)$% CONFIDENCE INTERVAL FOR p

$$\hat{p} \pm z_{\alpha/2}\sigma_{\hat{p}}$$

where $\sigma_{\hat{p}} = \sqrt{pq/n}$.

Recall that the z-values corresponding to 90%, 95%, and 99% confidence intervals are, respectively, 1.645, 1.96, and 2.58 (see Table 6.1).

EXERCISES

13. Fifty United Nations ambassadors were randomly interviewed just prior to a major vote on mandatory severe sanctions against nations that harbor terrorists. Thirty stated that their governments had instructed them to vote for the severe sanctions. Find a 95% confidence interval for the nations favoring mandatory severe sanctions.

14. A sample of 100 university athletic directors was interviewed at the NCAA annual meetings. In the sample, 45 athletic directors favored a plan whereby football and basketball athletes would receive a salary equal to the minimum wage for each hour of official sports-related participation. Using a 98% confidence interval, estimate the true proportion of athletic directors who favor the plan.

15. A survey was conducted to investigate the proportion of registered nurses in a particular state who are actively employed. A random sample of $n = 400$ nurses selected from the state registry showed 274 actively employed. Find a 95% confidence interval for the proportion of registered nurses actively employed.

16. Refer to Exercise 15. Find both a 90% and 99% confidence interval for the proportion of registered nurses actively employed.

17. A survey conducted to determine the proportion of college students favoring "more than equal" job rights opportunities for women (to offset past injustices) showed 258 of a random sample of 1000 favoring the proposal. Estimate the proportion of students in the entire population favoring the proposal, using a 99% confidence interval.

18. A random sample of 300 families in a city showed 23 earning salaries that placed them in a "poverty" category. Estimate the proportion of "poverty" families in the city, using a 90% confidence interval.

19. Refer to Exercise 18. Estimate the proportion, using a 99% confidence interval. Compare the properties of the two interval estimates and note the relation between interval width and degree of confidence.

20. Farber (1990) reports that the out-of-wedlock birth ratio is 90% for black teens and 45% for white teens. Assume that Farber's findings are based on two random samples, one of 100 black teens and the other of 100 white teens. Estimate the true proportion of the out-of-wedlock births for black teens, using a 99% confidence interval. Repeat the same procedure for white teens.

6.4   CHOOSING THE SAMPLE SIZE FOR ESTIMATING A POPULATION MEAN OR PROPORTION

How can we determine the number of observations to be included in a sample? The implications of such a question are clear. Data collection costs money. If the sample is too large, time and talent are wasted. Conversely, it is wasteful if the sample is too small, because inadequate information has been purchased for the time and effort expended. Also, it may be impossible to increase the sample size at a later time. Hence the number of observations the experimenter should include in the sample will depend on the amount of information he or she wants to buy.

Suppose we wish to estimate the average dollar amount for accident claims filed against an insurance company. To determine how many claims to examine (or to sample), we would have to determine how accurate the company wants us to be. Thus we might specify that the width of a 95% confidence interval must be a given tolerable value — say, 10 units. That is, we want the confidence interval to be of the form $\bar{X} \pm E$.

Calculation of the required sample size for estimating can be done by formula. If a 95% confidence interval is to be of the form $\bar{X} \pm E$, then solve the expression

$$1.96\sigma_{\bar{X}} = E$$

for n. The width of the interval is $2E$.

SAMPLE SIZE REQUIRED FOR A 95% CONFIDENCE INTERVAL ON μ OF THE FORM $\bar{X} \pm E$

$$n = \frac{(1.96)^2 \sigma^2}{E^2}$$

You will note that determining a sample size to estimate μ requires knowledge of the population variance σ^2 (or standard deviation σ). We can obtain an approximate sample size by estimating σ^2, using one of these two methods:

1. Employ information from a prior experiment to calculate a sample variance s^2. This value is used to approximate σ^2.
2. Use information on the range of the observations to obtain an estimate of σ. (See Section 4.12.) The square of this value estimates σ^2.

We would then substitute the estimated value of σ^2 in the sample size equation to determine an approximate sample size n.

We illustrate the procedure for choosing a sample size with some examples.

EXAMPLE 6.3   Union officials are concerned about reports of inferior wages paid to employees of a company under their jurisdiction. It is decided to take a random sample of n wage sheets from the company to estimate the average hourly wage. If it is known that wages in the company have a range of $10 per hour, determine the sample size required to estimate the average hourly wage μ, using a 95% confidence interval of width equal to $1.20.

SOLUTION   Since we want a 95% confidence interval with width $1.20, $E = \$.60$. The value that we use to substitute for σ is range/4 = 2.50. Substituting into the formula for n, we have

$$n = \frac{(1.96)^2 (2.5)^2}{(.60)^2} = 66.69$$

To be on the safe side, we will round this number up to the next integer. Thus $n = 67$.

EXAMPLE 6.4

A federal agency has decided to investigate the advertised weight displayed on cartons of a certain brand of cereal. The company in question periodically samples cartons of cereal coming off the production line to check their weight. A summary of 1500 of the weights made available to the agency indicates a mean weight of 11.80 ounces per carton and a standard deviation of .75 ounce. Use this information to determine the number of cereal cartons the federal agency must examine to estimate the average weight of cartons produced now, using a 95% confidence interval of width .50.

SOLUTION

The federal agency has specified that the width of the confidence interval is to be .50, so $E = .25$. Assuming that the weights made available to the agency by the company are accurate, we can take $\sigma = .75$. The required sample size is

$$n = \frac{(1.96)^2(.75)^2}{(.25)^2} = 34.57$$

That is, the federal agency must obtain a random sample of 35 cereal cartons to estimate the mean weight to within $\pm.25$ ounce.

Determining the sample size for a 95% confidence interval on p of a fixed width is a similar process. By solving the expression

$$1.96\sigma_{\hat{p}} = E$$

for n, we obtain the following analogous formula:

SAMPLE SIZE REQUIRED FOR A 95% CONFIDENCE INTERVAL ON p OF THE FORM $\hat{p} \pm E$

$$n = \frac{(1.96)^2 pq}{E^2}$$

You will note that we must know p to find n. This seems to create a circular problem, since our final objective is to estimate p. Actually it is not as complicated as it appears.

The researcher often knows before the experiment begins that p lies in a fairly narrow range. For example, the proportion of the popular vote for a presidential candidate in a national election is often close to .50. Thus the researcher will substitute the value dictated by experience for p. A second method for finding p is to use data collected from a prior study to estimate p.

Finally, if you have no prior information, substitute $p = .50$. This will yield the largest possible sample size for the width that you have specified and thus give a conservative answer to the required sample size. The sample will likely be larger than required, but you will be on the safe side.

We illustrate the selection of sample size for estimating a binomial parameter p with an example.

EXAMPLE 6.5

In a national election poll we wish to estimate the proportion p of voters in favor of candidate A. How many people should be polled to estimate p with a 95% confidence interval of the form $\hat{p} \pm .02$?

SOLUTION

The researcher has specified that $E = .02$. The sample size n necessary to achieve the desired confidence interval for p is

$$n = \frac{(1.96)^2 pq}{E^2}$$

However, we must first estimate p. If a similar survey has been run recently, we could use the sample proportion to estimate p. Otherwise, we substitute $p = .5$ to obtain a conservative sample size (one that is likely to be larger than required). Assuming that no prior survey has been run, the sample size is

$$n = \frac{(1.96)^2 pq}{E^2} = \frac{(1.96)^2 (.50)(.50)}{.0004} = 2401$$

That is, 2401 potential voters must be polled to estimate the proportion favoring candidate A to within .02 of the actual unknown proportion p.

EXERCISES

21. Previous research indicates that the range for county divorce rates (number of divorces per 1000) is 3.2 to 13.2. Determine the size of sample required to estimate the average county divorce rate for this year, using a 98% confidence interval with $E = .4$.

22. Refer to Exercise 21. Assume that you did not have information about the range but knew that the standard deviation had been 1.5. Determine the sample size, using a 98% confidence interval with $E = .4$.

23. Refer to Exercises 21 and 22. How different are the two estimated sample sizes? How might you explain this difference?

24. Determine the sample size required to estimate the mean violent crime rate for all U.S. cities, using a 95% confidence interval of the form $\bar{X} \pm 50$. Assume that the range is 1036.

25. Assume that σ is approximately 225 for the data of Table 3.4. Determine the sample size required to estimate the mean violent crime rate for all U.S. cities, using a 95% confidence interval with $E = 20$.

26. Determine the sample size required to estimate p, the proportion of all Atlanta voters favoring a particular Democratic candidate, using a 95% confidence interval of the form $\hat{p} \pm .03$. Assume that 40% of the voters usually cast ballots for the Democratic candidate in Atlanta.

27. In estimating sample sizes to determine μ, describe the two methods for estimating σ. Develop a problem of interest to social researchers, first employing information from a prior experiment and then employing the range estimate.

28. Refer to Exercise 12. Recall that Farber (1990) reports that the out-of-wedlock birth rate is 90% for black teens and 45% for white teens.

a. Determine the sample size you would want in order to estimate the proportion of out-of-wedlock births for black teens, using a 95% confidence interval.
b. Determine the sample size you would want in order to estimate the proportion of out-of-wedlock births for white teens, using a 95% confidence interval.
c. Are the two sample sizes the same? Comment.

SUMMARY

Social researchers frequently sample to assess public opinions concerning a key political issue or to determine a characteristic of a social system. Such assessments are often phrased as an estimate of a population proportion or a population mean. Thus we might wish to know the proportion of alcoholics who successfully complete a rehabilitation program or the mean number of days of employment per year for blacks with a high school education. This chapter discusses how these estimates can be acquired and what they mean. The chapter also shows how to determine the size of a sample, depending on how much error we are willing to tolerate.

Given the appropriate data, anyone can construct estimates of the desired population parameters by using statistics (an objective procedure) or by using any subjective procedure. Regardless of how an estimate is obtained, the big question is how much reliance we can place on it. Is the estimate reasonably close to the population parameter?

Subjective procedures based on experience or intuition may or may not yield good estimates. They may be given by people who truly possess sufficient experience to yield satisfactory estimates, but how will you know when you have a person with this ability, and how will you know how accurate the estimate is? Or they may be presented by people who are inadequately prepared to do the job, but how will you know?

One of the major contributions of statistics is the feature that all inferences must be accompanied by a measure of their goodness. We talk of confidence intervals with specified degrees of confidence. This is the great advantage of statistics. By using statistical estimation procedures, we make an estimate and know how much we can rely on it.

In this chapter we emphasized the basic concepts of statistical estimation and illustrated these concepts by considering inferences based on single samples and on the estimation of population means and proportions. Having given a brief introduction to estimation, we turn in the next chapter to a second method of making inferences — testing hypotheses.

KEY WORDS

Confidence interval   Two numbers computed from sample data that form an interval estimate for some parameter.

Estimate   A number computed from sample data used to approximate a population parameter.

Interval estimate   The interval formed by the upper and lower limits of a confidence interval for a parameter.

Lower confidence limit   The smaller of the two numbers that form a confidence interval.

Point estimate   The value of the statistic, one number, used to estimate a parameter.

Sampling distribution for $\hat{p}$ Probability distribution of $\hat{p}$.

Standard error of the mean   The standard deviation of the sampling distribution for $\bar{X}$.

Upper confidence limit   The larger of the two numbers that form a confidence interval.

KEY FORMULAS

Mean and standard error for the sampling distribution for $\bar{X}$

$$\mu_{\bar{X}} = \mu$$

$$\sigma_{\bar{X}} = \frac{\sigma}{\sqrt{n}}$$

General large-sample $100(1 - \alpha)\,\%$ confidence interval for μ

$$\bar{X} \pm z_{\alpha/2}\sigma_{\bar{X}} \qquad \text{where} \qquad \sigma_{\bar{X}} = \frac{\sigma}{\sqrt{n}}$$

Mean and standard error for the sampling distribution for $\hat{p}$

$$\mu_{\hat{p}} = p$$

$$\sigma_{\hat{p}} = \sqrt{\frac{pq}{n}} \qquad \text{where} \qquad q = 1 - p$$

General large-sample $100(1 - \alpha)\,\%$ confidence interval for p

$$\hat{p} \pm z_{\alpha/2}\sigma_{\hat{p}} \qquad \text{where} \qquad \sigma_{\hat{p}} = \sqrt{\frac{pq}{n}}$$

Sample size for estimating μ to within $\pm\, E$ using a 95\,% confidence interval

$$n = \frac{(1.96)^2\sigma^2}{E^2}$$

Sample size for estimating p to within $\pm\, E$ using a 95\,% confidence interval

$$n = \frac{(1.96)^2 pq}{E^2}$$

SUPPLEMENTARY EXERCISES FOR CHAPTER 6

29. Sick leave records obtained from a random sample of 100 steelworkers showed a mean number of days of sick leave for the previous year equal to 25.6. If the sample standard deviation is 7.4, estimate the population mean number of days of sick leave for steelworkers last year, using a 95% confidence interval.

30. In a particular society, marriage counselors have found that the length of time from the first marriage to separation for divorced couples is 6.7 years. A random sampling of 80 divorced couples from a different society produced an average time to separation of 6.3 years and a standard deviation of 2.9 years. Estimate the mean length of time to separation, using a 95% confidence interval.

31. A random sample of 150 terms of sentence for a particular crime (first offense) showed a mean of 4.2 years and a standard deviation of 2.4 years. Estimate the mean term of prison sentence for the offense, using a 95% confidence interval.

32. If a sample of 180 voters goes to the polls and 50 vote for the Republican candidate, give a point estimate of the population proportion p casting votes for the Republican candidate. Evaluate your answer.

33. Use the information in Exercise 32 and establish a 95% confidence interval. As a campaign manager, which estimate would you prefer and why?

34. What are parameters and how do they differ from statistics?

35. Do we use estimates when the sample data collected constitute the population of interest? Why or why not?

36. Distinguish between a point and an interval estimate. What are the two basic procedures for making inferences? How do we measure the goodness of an interval estimation procedure?

37. A random sample of $n = 500$ insurance records of physicians, selected from the files of an insurance company, shows that 10% of the physicians have been involved in one or more lawsuits. Estimate the proportion of all physicians covered by the insurance company who have been involved in lawsuits, using a 95% confidence interval.

38. A social scientist reports that the average length of stay in 100 mental hospitals is 120 days. The sample involves hospitals rather than individuals. The standard deviation for the hospitals is 5.5. Find a 95% confidence interval for the average length of stay. Interpret your result.

39. Use the data in Exercise 38 to construct a 99% confidence interval for the average length of stay.

40. A researcher reports that 45% of a random sample of 1000 college students (sample size equals 1000) believe that the penalties for the possession of marijuana should be reduced. Give a 95% confidence interval for the proportion of all college students who favor this proposition.

41. Use the data in Exercise 40 to find a 99% confidence interval for the population proportion.

42. Explain in your own words the justification for the following statements: "If the sample is too large, time and talent are wasted; if the sample is too small, time and talent are wasted."

43. An industrial sociologist researching work characteristics in a manufacturing plant is interested in the average amount of time required by work groups to complete a complicated task. A previous study suggests that the standard deviation of the population is approximately 4.85 minutes. Use this information to determine the number of groups to be included in the study if the sociologist wants to estimate μ to within .5 minute.

44. If a public opinion pollster is interested in estimating the proportion of registered voters favoring a candidate to within .05 and if p is about .5, how large should the sample be?

45. Refer to Exercise 44. A fellow public opinion pollster argues that the population proportion is really in the neighborhood of .40. Does this produce a substantial change in the required sample size? Comment.

46. Give a 95% confidence interval for μ, the mean violent crime rate, using the data of Table 3.4.

47. We observe the percent of fathers and mothers that used certain strategies to cope with their child's cancer. For example, 52% of the mothers engaged in information seeking, while only 23% of the fathers did. Similarly, 32% of the mothers engaged in denial, while 50% of the fathers did. Use these data to obtain separate 95% confidence intervals for mothers and fathers regarding the percentage engaged in information seeking and the percentage exhibiting denial.

48. Use Database A, Appendix Table 7, and assume that these students constitute a random sample of all students. Use a 95% confidence interval to answer the following questions:

 a. What proportion of all students are in the social sciences?
 b. What proportion of all students have no religious preference?
 c. What proportion of all students are married?

49. Refer to Database B, Appendix Table 8, and assume that these nations constitute a random sample of all nations. Ten nations in the sample rank low in civil liberties; that is, they are in categories 11, 12, 13, or 14.

 a. Using a 95% confidence interval, what proportion of all nations are in categories 11, 12, 13, or 14?
 b. Determine the sample size required to estimate the proportion of all nations in categories 11, 12, 13, or 14 in the next survey, using a 98% confidence interval with $E = .05$.

50. Refer to Database C, Appendix Table 9. Construct a 95% confidence interval for the HAM-D total score of treatment group C. How would this interval change for a 99% confidence interval?

51. Refer to Exercise 50. Using the clinical trials data, give a 90% confidence interval for the HOPKINS OBRIST cluster score of treatment A.

52. Use Database D, Appendix Table 10, and assume that the 30 states represent a random sample of all political units. Use a 90% confidence interval to answer the following questions:

 a. What proportion of all units have abortion rates of 21.2 and above?
 b. What proportion of all units have abortion rates of 19.3 and below?
 c. What proportion of all units have forcible rape rates of 41.2 and above?
 d. What proportion of all units have forcible rape rates of 24.9 and below?

53. Repeat Exercise 52, using a 98% confidence interval to answer each of the questions.

54. Repeat Exercise 52, using a 99% confidence interval to answer each of the questions.

55. Refer to Exercise 52. What is the mean of the 30 abortion rates? Determine the sample size required to estimate the true mean, using a 95% confidence interval with $E = .07$.

56. Repeat Exercise 55, using a 98% confidence interval with $E = .04$.

CHAPTER 7

STATISTICAL TESTS
OF HYPOTHESES:
THE ONE-SAMPLE CASE

GENERAL OBJECTIVES

Social science knowledge must build on theory and prior research, and much of social research involves testing specific hypotheses that have been deduced from theory or prior research. This chapter introduces you to the mechanics of hypothesis testing. Specifically, it introduces tests of hypotheses about a population mean or proportion based on data from a single sample.

SPECIFIC OBJECTIVES

1. To define and explain the differences between null and research hypotheses.
2. To show the role of the test statistic in hypothesis testing, and to explain the four elements of a statistical test: research hypothesis, null hypothesis, test statistics, and rejection region.
3. To show that in the research process, you are always subject to making an incorrect decision.
4. To illustrate how to do a statistical test about a population mean based on a single sample.
5. To provide you with a guide on how to select research hypotheses and null hypotheses.
6. To illustrate how to do a statistical test about a binomial parameter p based on a single sample.
7. To introduce the concept of level of significance (p-value) for a statistical test.
8. To show that different procedures are involved in testing hypotheses, depending on the sample size.
9. To introduce the one-sample goodness-of-fit test: the chi-square test.

7.1   INTRODUCTION

In Chapter 5 we were concerned with determining the probability or likelihood of an observed event. In doing so we took the opportunity to use the calculated probability to make an inference about the population from which the sample was drawn. Social researchers routinely make such inferences. Our method was intuitive and based on the following reasoning. If we thought that a population parameter, such as the mean, was a specific value and then observed a highly contradictory value for the sample mean, we concluded that the hypothesized value of the parameter was incorrect or that the sample value did not reflect the population. **Contradictory sample results are those that are highly improbable.** The more improbable, the more contradictory are the results.

As social researchers, we begin a statistical test by stating two hypotheses about a parameter of the population. The first hypothesis is called the **research hypothesis**, the hypothesis we wish to verify. A research hypothesis is usually formed on the basis of theory or prior research. A statistical test of a hypothesis uses the technique of proof by contradiction. To verify the research hypothesis, we actually test a different or second hypothesis. The second hypothesis is referred to as the **null hypothesis**. Although it, too, relates to the population parameter of interest, the null hypothesis contradicts the research hypothesis. Thus, if we test the null hypothesis and find enough evidence to indicate that we should reject (nullify) the null hypothesis, we have actually verified our research hypothesis.

7.2   A STATISTICAL TEST OF A HYPOTHESIS

A statistical test of a hypothesis can be likened to a court trial. In the court trial the research hypothesis is that the defendant is guilty. The prosecution attempts to verify this hypothesis by showing that its opposite (that the defendant is not guilty) is false. The second hypothesis (the null hypothesis) is the hypothesis to be tested. If we can collect sufficient evidence to show that the null hypothesis is false, we have found sufficient evidence to support the research hypothesis.

How do we decide which hypothesis (the research or the null) is true? As with a court trial, evidence is collected and considered so that a decision can be reached. The sample information selected from the population represents the evidence in a statistical test. Whereas the jury weighs the evidence in a court trial and reaches a conclusion, we will use the sample data to compute a single quantity, called the **test statistic**. If the computed value of the test statistic is contradictory to the null hypothesis, we reject the null hypothesis and conclude that the research hypothesis is true. Similarly, in a court trial, if the evidence presented to the jury is highly contradictory to the hypothesis that the defendant is not guilty (the null hypothesis), the jury rejects the null hypothesis in favor of the research hypothesis (that the defendant is guilty).

How do we decide which values of the test statistic imply rejection of the null hypothesis and which do not? We consider the set of all values that the test statistic could possibly assume and then divide the set into two regions, one corresponding to a rejection region and the other to a nonrejection region. (How this division is made will be explained subsequently.) This situation is shown symbolically in Figure 7.1.

FIGURE 7.1

All possible values of a
test statistic

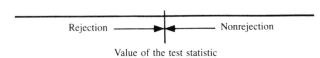

A point on the horizontal line in Figure 7.1 corresponds to a possible value of the test statistic. We symbolically divide all these values with a vertical line to obtain two sets, one corresponding to rejection and the other to nonrejection of the null hypothesis. **If the computed value of the test statistic falls in the rejection region, we reject the null hypothesis (which means that our research hypothesis is supported). Otherwise we fail to reject the null hypothesis (and thus our research hypothesis is not supported).** Note that Figure 7.1 shows how the rejection region might be located for one type of test. As you will see, for some tests the rejection region lies to the right (or left) of the nonrejection region, and for others it is located on either side of the nonrejection region.

You have probably observed that we use the terms "fail to reject" and "nonrejection" rather than the terms "accept" and "acceptance." This is because of an important principle in hypothesis testing procedures: **we can never prove that the null hypothesis is true.**

We can again compare these circumstances to the court trial. The defendant is not proven to be *innocent* of a crime; rather, the jury renders a verdict of *not guilty* based on the evidence presented.

We can now formalize our procedure for hypothesis testing. A statistical test consists of four parts: a research hypothesis, a null hypothesis, a test statistic, and a rejection region. These four parts are defined next.

FOUR ELEMENTS OF A STATISTICAL TEST

1. **Research hypothesis** A hypothesis about a population parameter that we wish to verify. Some people use the symbol H_1 to refer to the research hypothesis.

2. **Null hypothesis**   A hypothesis contradictory to the research hypothesis. It is the hypothesis to be tested. By contradicting the null hypothesis, we affirm the research hypothesis. Some people use the symbol H_0 to refer to the null hypothesis.
3. **Test statistic**   A quantity computed from the sample data. "Test statistic" will often be abbreviated as T.S. in this book.
4. **Rejection region**   A set of values for the test statistic that are contradictory to the null hypothesis and imply its rejection. "Rejection region" will often be abbreviated as R.R. in this book.

To summarize, a random sample is drawn from the population of interest, and a single number, the value of a test statistic, is computed from the sample values. The decision to reject or fail to reject the null hypothesis depends on the computed value of the test statistic.

EXAMPLE 7.1

In Section 5.1 we randomly sampled 20 voters from a district to determine whether the district favored Jones's election. Identify the four elements of a statistical test that will help us decide whether Jones will lose the district.

SOLUTION

Recall that in the sample poll of 20 district voters in Section 5.1, we observed that none of the 20 voters favored Jones, and we concluded that Jones would lose her district. We can formalize our intuitive inference-making procedure to illustrate a statistical test of a hypothesis about the parameter p, the proportion of voters in the district who favor Jones's election.

The general hypothesis that we wish to confirm is that Jones will lose the election. Rephrased in terms of a population parameter, the research hypothesis is that p, the proportion of all district voters favoring Jones, is less than .5. As stated previously, the null hypothesis is the hypothesis to be tested in a statistical test and is a hypothesis contradictory to the research hypothesis. One such contradictory hypothesis is that $p = .5$ (i.e., 50% of the voters favor Jones's election). Although there are many other hypotheses contradictory to the research hypothesis, this null hypothesis is the least we could expect if Jones were to win. The test statistic is X, the number of prospective voters in the sample who favor Jones's election.

To locate the rejection region, we consider all possible values that X can assume. In a sample of $n = 20$ prospective voters, X could assume a value of $0, 1, 2, \ldots, 20$. Small values of X will tend to contradict the null hypothesis and support the research hypothesis. Thus our rejection region would appear as shown in Figure 7.2, except that we must locate the dividing line between the two regions.

FIGURE 7.2

Rejection and nonre-
jection regions for
Example 7.1

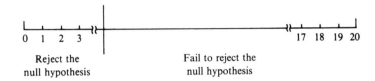

Reject the   Fail to reject the
null hypothesis   null hypothesis

How can we determine which small values of X are improbable? Recall from Section 5.10 that the probability distribution for X, the number of voters favoring Jones, in a sample of $n = 20$ can be approximated by a normal curve for which

$$\mu = np$$
$$\sigma = \sqrt{npq}$$

where $q = 1 - p$. Assuming that the null hypothesis is true (i.e., $p = .5$), then we have

$$\mu = 20(.5) = 10$$
$$\sigma = \sqrt{20(.5)(.5)} = 2.24$$

We can see that the values of X that are improbable (and small) are those that lie in the lower tail of the approximating normal distribution, as shown in Figure 7.3. For example, a value of X that lies more than 1.96σ below the mean $\mu = 10$ is clearly improbable. We can compute 1.96σ by substituting the value of σ; that is, $\sigma = 2.24$:

$$1.96\sigma = 1.96(2.24) = 4.39$$

Thus a value of X more than 1.96σ below $\mu = 10$ is a value below $10 - 4.39 = 5.61$, and we could locate the rejection region as shown in Figure 7.3.

FIGURE 7.3

Rejection region for a
test of the null hypoth-
esis that $p = .5$ when
$n = 20$, $\mu = 10$, and
$\sigma = 2.24$

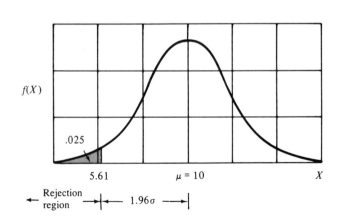

To summarize, the four parts of the statistical test for Example 7.1 are:

Research hypothesis: $p < .5$
Null hypothesis: $p = .5$
Test statistic: X
Rejection region: Reject the null hypothesis if X lies below 5.61.

Referring to the sample data, since the value of the test statistic ($X = 0$) falls in the rejection region, we reject the null hypothesis and conclude that the research hypothesis is true. That is, we infer that Jones will lose her district.

What is the probability that X will fall in the rejection region if the null hypothesis is true? From our knowledge of the areas under the normal curve, we know that the probability is approximately equal to .025. This probability, represented by the shaded portion of Figure 7.3, measures the risk of incorrectly rejecting the null hypothesis when it is true.

7.3   HOW GOOD IS OUR DECISION?

The goodness of a decision-making procedure, statistical or any other, can be measured by the probability of making an incorrect decision. The possible outcomes of a court trial are shown in Table 7.1. An error can be made either by convicting a person who is not guilty or by not convicting a guilty person. We wish to minimize the probabilities for making both types of incorrect decisions.

A statistical test of a hypothesis is subject to the same two types of errors that threaten a jury's decision. We might reject the null hypothesis when it is in fact true, or we might fail to reject the null hypothesis when it is false. These errors are called type I and type II errors, respectively (see Table 7.2).

TABLE 7.1

Possible outcomes of a court trial

	Unknown Truth	
Jury Decision	**Guilty**	**Not Guilty**
guilty	correct decision	incorrect decision
not guilty	incorrect decision	correct decision

TABLE 7.2

Decision table

	Null Hypothesis	
Decision	**False**	**True**
reject the null hypothesis	correct	type I error
fail to reject the null hypothesis	type II error	correct

DEFINITION 7.1	A **type I error** is committed if the null hypothesis is rejected when it is true. The **probability of a type I error** is denoted by α (the Greek letter alpha).

DEFINITION 7.2	A **type II error** is committed if the null hypothesis is not rejected when it is false. The **probability of a type II error** is denoted by β (the Greek letter beta).

The probability α of making a type I error is the probability of rejecting the null hypothesis when it is true. (Note that in Example 7.1 α was shown to be .025, the shaded portion of Figure 7.3.) The probability β of a type II error is the probability of failing to reject the null hypothesis when it is false and the alternative hypothesis is true. Although it is much more difficult to determine β than α, there is a relationship between these two probabilities. **For a given sample size, α and β are inversely related**; that is, as one goes up, the other goes down, as shown in Figure 7.4.

Returning to the court trial, rejecting the null hypothesis when it is true (a type I error) is equivalent to convicting a person who is not guilty. Thus we want the probability of convicting a person who is not guilty to be small. Failing to reject the null hypothesis when it is false (a type II error) resembles the freeing of a guilty person. This decision occurs with probability β. When laws protecting individual rights are strengthened, the probability α of convicting a person who is not guilty decreases; simultaneously, the probability β of letting a guilty person go free increases. As we relax the protection of individual rights, we increase α and decrease β.

As we will show later, the social researcher should specify α prior to running a statistical test. He or she may choose α to be .01, .05, or some other value. Specification of a value for α locates the rejection region for the test, but determination of β is more complicated and beyond the scope of this text. Hence in this text, if the value of the test statistic falls in the rejection region, we will reject the null hypothesis. Having specified α, we will know the risk of having made an incorrect decision. If the value of the test statistic does not

FIGURE 7.4

Relationships between α and β

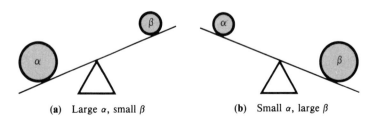

(a) Large α, small β (b) Small α, large β

fall in the rejection region, we will conclude that there is insufficient evidence to reject the null hypothesis, thus eliminating the possibility of a type II error. This decision is similar to the one a jury must face. If there is any doubt that the defendant is guilty, the jury must free him or her. In such a case the defendant is not said to be "innocent"; instead, the verdict is "not guilty," which implies that there was insufficient evidence to justify the rejection of the defendant's claim of innocence.

A discussion of several useful statistical tests should clarify what we have said about the decision-making process. These tests will be presented in the succeeding sections.

7.4   A STATISTICAL TEST ABOUT A POPULATION MEAN

The parameter of interest in many surveys or experiments is the population mean μ. For example, we may be interested in the mean reaction time to respond to a particular stimulus, the mean income for indigent families in a given community, the mean yield of oxygen in a chemical plant, or the mean level of impurities in a water supply. Recall that we could either estimate the value of the parameter μ or test a hypothesis concerning its value. In this section we will explain how to conduct a statistical test about a mean based on a random sample of n measurements selected from a population. The null hypothesis for the test will be that the population mean μ equals a specific value, denoted by the symbol μ_0.

Suppose that a union claims that the average annual wage for its members is $35,000 per year. If we doubt the truth of the claim and suspect that the actual annual wage is less than $35,000, we would select a random sample of n persons from the total membership and, using this information, decide whether there is sufficient evidence to indicate that μ is less than $35,000. The research hypothesis that we wish to verify is $\mu < \$35,000$, and a hypothesis contradictory to the research hypothesis is the null hypothesis $\mu = \$35,000$.

A logical test statistic for the test is the sample mean $\bar{X}$. We know from Chapter 6 that the sampling distribution of $\bar{X}$ is approximately normal, with mean μ and standard error $\sigma_{\bar{X}} = \sigma/\sqrt{n}$. Recall that σ is the standard deviation of the population from which the sample was drawn and that n is the number of measurements in the sample. Values of $\bar{X}$ much smaller than μ_0 in the lower tail of the sampling distribution (see Figure 7.5) will contradict the null hypothesis.

The contradictory values of $\bar{X}$ form a rejection region for our statistical test. If the sample mean falls in the rejection region of Figure 7.5, we will reject

FIGURE 7.5

Contradictory values of
$\overline{X}$ located in the lower
tail

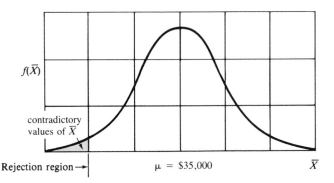

the null hypothesis ($\mu = \$35,000$) in favor of the research hypothesis ($\mu < \$35,000$). Note that we are attempting to verify (or affirm) the research hypothesis by contradicting the null hypothesis.

Let us see how the choice of α locates the rejection region. If we are willing to take the risk that one time in 40 we will incorrectly reject the null hypothesis, then $\alpha = \frac{1}{40} = .025$. An appropriate rejection region can be specified for this (or any other) value of α by referring to the sampling distribution of $\overline{X}$. Since the shaded area in Figure 7.5 corresponds to α, we must locate the rejection region such that an area of $\alpha = .025$ lies in the lower tail of the distribution of $\overline{X}$. From our knowledge of the normal curve, the rejection region must be located at a distance $1.96\sigma_{\overline{X}}$ below the mean $\mu = \$35,000$ (see Figure 7.6).

FIGURE 7.6

Rejection region

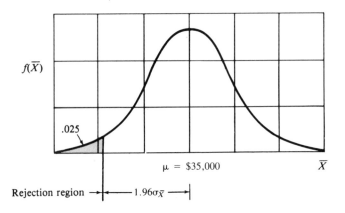

EXAMPLE 7.2   For the previous union situation, suppose that we obtained salary information for a random sample of 40 union employees. Assume further that the

sample mean wage and standard deviation were, respectively,

$$\bar{X} = \$34,250$$
$$s = 702$$

Locate the rejection region for a test of H_0: $\mu = \$35,000$ and H_1: $\mu < \$35,000$ for $\alpha = .025$.

SOLUTION

For $\alpha = .025$, we will locate the rejection region at a distance of $1.96\sigma_{\bar{X}}$ below $\mu = \$35,000$. Recall that $\sigma_{\bar{X}} = \sigma/\sqrt{n}$; since σ is unknown, we will substitute $s = 702$ for σ to obtain

$$\sigma_{\bar{X}} = \frac{s}{\sqrt{n}} = \frac{702}{\sqrt{40}} = 111$$

$$1.96\sigma_{\bar{X}} = 217.56$$

The rejection region is located below $\$35,000 - \$217.56 = \$34,782.44$ (see Figure 7.7). If the observed sample mean lies below $\$34,782.44$, we reject H_0: $\mu = \$35,000$ in favor of H_1: $\mu < \$35,000$.

FIGURE 7.7

Location of the union rejection region

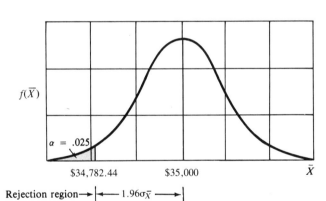

EXAMPLE 7.3

Refer to the union data and the results of Example 7.2 to reach a conclusion about H_0: $\mu = \$35,000$.

SOLUTION

To review, the four parts of the statistical test are:

H_1: $\mu < \$35,000$
H_0: $\mu = \$35,000$
T.S.: $\bar{X}$
R.R.: For $\alpha = .025$, reject H_0 if $\bar{X}$ lies below $\$34,782.44$.

Since the observed sample mean was $\bar{X} = \$34,250$, we reject the null hypothesis $\mu = \$35,000$ in favor of the research hypothesis $\mu < \$35,000$. The sample data support the assertion that the actual mean annual salary is less than that claimed by union officials.

The statistical test we conducted in Example 7.3 is called a **one-tailed test**, because the rejection region is located only in one tail of the sampling distribution. If, on the other hand, we had been interested in determining whether μ was greater than \$35,000, the research hypothesis would have been $H_1: \mu > \$35,000$, and large values of $\bar{X}$ located in the upper tail of the sampling distribution would have indicated rejection of the null hypothesis. This would also have been a one-tailed test, but the rejection region (for $\alpha = .025$) would have been as shown in Figure 7.8.

We can also formulate a two-tailed test when the research hypothesis is $H_1: \mu \neq \$35,000$. Here we would be interested in whether μ is larger or smaller than $\mu = \$35,000$, the value specified in the null hypothesis. For a **two-tailed test** we locate the rejection region in both tails of the sampling

FIGURE 7.8

Rejection region for $H_0: \mu = \$35,000$, $H_1: \mu > \$35,000$, and $\alpha = .025$

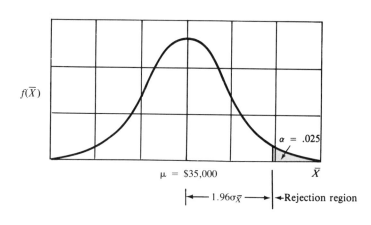

FIGURE 7.9

Rejection region for a two-tailed test with $\alpha = .05$

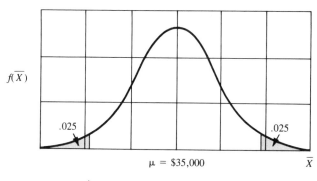

distribution of $\bar{X}$. The rejection region for $H_0: \mu < \$35{,}000$, $H_1: \mu \neq \$35{,}000$, and $\alpha = .05$ is shown in Figure 7.9.

EXAMPLE 7.4

A random sample of 30 SMSAs was selected, and the ratio (per 1000) of registered voters to the total number of persons 18 years and over for each area was recorded. Use the data given in Table 7.3 to examine the research hypothesis that μ, the average ratio (per 1000), is different from 675, last year's average ratio.

TABLE 7.3

Ratio of registered voters

802	497	653	600	729	812
751	730	635	605	760	681
807	747	728	561	696	710
641	848	672	740	818	725
694	854	674	683	695	803

SOLUTION

We can readily verify that the sample mean and standard deviation are

$$\bar{X} = 711.70$$
$$s = 84.15$$

The appropriate null hypothesis for the research hypothesis $H_1: \mu \neq 675$ is

$$H_0: \mu = 675$$

The test statistic is $\bar{X}$, and we will reject H_0 if the observed value of $\bar{X}$ lies more than 1.96 standard errors away from μ_0. For our data, substituting s for σ, we have

$$\sigma_X = \frac{\sigma}{\sqrt{n}} \approx \frac{84.15}{\sqrt{30}} = 15.36$$

$$1.96\sigma_{\bar{x}} \approx 1.96(15.36) = 30.11$$

The rejection region for this test is shown in Figure 7.10.

To summarize, the four parts of our statistical test are:

$H_1: \mu \neq 675$
$H_0: \mu = 675$
T.S.: $\bar{X}$
R.R.: With $\alpha = .05$, reject H_0 if $\bar{X}$ is greater than 705.11 or less than 644.89 (see Figure 7.10).

FIGURE 7.10

Rejection region for
Example 7.4

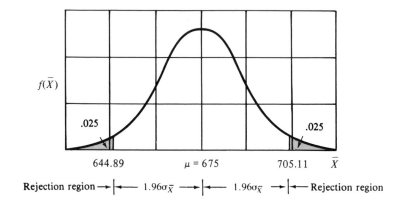

Since our observed 711.70 lies in the rejection region, we reject H_0: $\mu = 675$. Practically, since $\bar{X} = 711.70$ falls in the upper tail of the rejection region, we conclude that the average ratio is greater than last year's ratio of 675.

We summarize what we have learned about a statistical test for μ as follows.

STATISTICAL TEST ABOUT μ

Research hypothesis for a one-tailed test
  1. $H_1 : \mu > \mu_0$
  2. $H_1 : \mu < \mu_0$

Research hypothesis for a two-tailed test
  3. $H_1 : \mu \neq \mu_0$

Null hypothesis H_0: $\mu = \mu_0$ (the value of μ_0 will be clear from the research hypothesis developed for the study)

Test statistic $\bar{X}$

Rejection region for a one-tailed test with $\alpha = .025$
  1. R.R.: Reject H_0 if $\bar{X}$ is greater than $1.96\sigma_{\bar{X}}$ above μ_0.
  2. R.R.: Reject H_0 if $\bar{X}$ is less than $1.96\sigma_{\bar{X}}$ below μ_0.

Rejection region for a two-tailed test with $\alpha = .05$
  3. R.R.: Reject H_0 if $\bar{X}$ is more than $1.96\sigma_{\bar{X}}$ above or below μ_0.

Assumptions
  1. The variable X is measured on an interval or ratio scale.
  2. The sample measurements represent a random sample from the population or universe of interest.

3. The sampling distribution of $\overline{X}$ is approximately normal.
4. The sample size must be 30 or more if s is used to approximate the unknown standard deviation σ in $\sigma_{\overline{X}}$.

Note that the test procedure requires us to know σ. Since this will rarely be true, we must either have a good estimate of σ based on prior studies or use s, the standard deviation computed from the sample data. In order that s be a good approximation to σ, the number of measurements in the sample must be 30 or more. Inferences about μ based on small samples will be discussed later in this chapter.

EXERCISES

1. Use the data in Table 7.3 to test the null hypothesis $H_0: \mu = 700$ against the research hypothesis $H_1: \mu \neq 700$. (Use $\alpha = .05$.)

2. If $\overline{X} = 8.3$ and $s = 5.38$ for the murder rates of 90 cities, test the research hypothesis that the mean murder rate for all metropolitan areas is greater than 7.0. (Use $\alpha = .05$.)

3. Repeat Exercise 2, but assume that the sample size is 60. What would this do to your test and conclusion? Explain.

4. A study was conducted to determine whether the average amount of money expended per two-person household per week for food in a particular community differed from the national average ($182 per week). A random sample of $n = 100$ households in the community gave a mean of $188 and a standard deviation of $15.61. Do these data provide sufficient evidence to indicate that the mean household per-week expenditure for the community is different from the national average? (Use $\alpha = .05$. *Hint*: Specify the research and null hypotheses, then perform your test.)

5. The mean and standard deviation of a random sample of $n = 50$ measurements are $\overline{X} = 63.7$ and $s = 14.2$. Conduct a statistical test of $H_0: \mu = 68$ against the alternative $H_1: \mu < 68$, using $\alpha = .05$. List all parts of the test and your conclusion.

6. Refer to the previous exercise. How would your conclusions change if the research hypothesis were $H_1: \mu \neq 68$?

7. Researchers for the AFL-CIO sampled 100 counties at random. The average increase in salary for full-time workers over the previous year was $804 with a standard deviation of $1526.
   a. Test the null hypothesis that $\mu = \$850$. Set $\alpha = .05$.
   b. Test the null hypothesis that $\mu = \$766$. Set $\alpha = .05$.

8. Recall the Stafford and Reske (1990) study from Chapter 6. The researchers explored the tendency for young couples to idealize each other, especially if they are involved in a long-distance relationship. They interviewed 34 geographically close (GC) couples and 37 long-distance (LD) couples. Subjects were scored on a premarital adjustment scale (PAS), idealistic distortion scale (IDS), and frequency of interaction scale (FIS). The higher the score, the greater the perceived premarital adjustment, the more distortion, or the more frequently the couple interacted, respectively. Means and standard deviations are shown in the accompanying table.

EXERCISE 8

Means and standard deviations for geographically close and long-distance relationships

Scale	Geographically Close		Long Distance	
	Mean	SD	Mean	SD
premarital adjustment (PAS)	108.8	16.6	119.1	15.4
idealistic distortion (IDS)	16.5	2.8	18.1	2.7
frequency of interaction (FIS)	7.3	4.1	2.7	2.0

Source: Adapted from Laura Stafford and James R. Reske, "Idealization and Communication in Long-Distance Premarital Relationships," *Family Relations* 39 (1990), p. 276. Copyrighted 1990 by the National Council on Family Relations, 3989 Central Ave., N.E., Suite #550, Minneapolis, MN 55421. Reprinted by permission.

a. Conduct a statistical test of $H_0: \mu = 125$ for the PAS population mean for geographically close relationships, using $\alpha = .05$. Repeat the same test for long-distance relationships.
b. Conduct a statistical test of $H_0: \mu = 25$ for the IDS population mean for geographically close relationships, using $\alpha = .05$. Repeat the same test for long-distance relationships.
c. Conduct a statistical test of $H_0: \mu = 5$ for the FIS population mean for geographically close relationships, using $\alpha = .01$. Repeat the same test for long-distance relationships.

7.5   HOW TO SELECT THE RESEARCH AND NULL HYPOTHESES

As stated in Sections 7.1 through 7.3, the social researcher formulates two hypotheses when conducting a statistical test about a population parameter. The research hypothesis is the motivating hypothesis behind our test procedure. Once the research hypothesis is formulated, we specify a hypothesis (the null hypothesis) that is contradictory to the research hypothesis. The test procedure is then designed to verify the research hypothesis by showing that the null hypothesis is false. **A statistical test of a hypothesis employs the technique of proof by contradiction; that is, we try to support the research hypothesis by showing that the null hypothesis is false.**

EXAMPLE 7.5	To evaluate the success of a one-year experimental program designed to increase the mathematical achievement of underprivileged high school seniors, the statewide mathematics test scores for a sample of $n = 100$ underprivileged seniors were tested against the previous year's statewide average of 525 for underprivileged students. If we wish to test a hypothesis about the mean mathematics test score for all underprivileged students who might participate in the program, state the research and null hypotheses.
SOLUTION	The research (motivating) hypothesis for this study is that the experimental program will indeed improve mean test scores above the comparable figure of 525 for the previous year. Phrased in terms of the parameter μ, the research hypothesis is

$$H_1 : \mu > 525$$

One hypothesis contradictory to the research hypothesis would be that the experimental program had no effect on mathematics achievement; that is, the mean test score for students under the test program is identical to the previous year's average, 525. This contradictory hypothesis (or null hypothesis),

$$H_0 : \mu = 525$$

would be the hypothesis under test. We would try to verify the research hypothesis ($\mu > 525$) by showing that the null hypothesis ($\mu = 525$) is false.

EXAMPLE 7.6	A social researcher asserts that urban preschool children aged 3 to 5 watch an average of 22.6 hours of television per week. A marketing research firm believes that the claimed mean is too high. Set up a research hypothesis and a null hypothesis to test the marketing firm's contention.
SOLUTION	If the marketing firm says the claimed mean (22.6) is too high, then an appropriate research hypothesis is $H_1 : \mu < 22.6$; and the corresponding null hypothesis is $H_0 : \mu = 22.6$.

We have seen how to specify the research and null hypotheses for a few situations. The important thing to remember is that the research hypothesis indicates the form of the null hypothesis and locates the rejection region by specifying whether we have a one- or two-tailed test. You will gain more facility at formulating hypotheses as we continue to discuss appropriate tests for particular research problems.

7.6 z-SCORES AND THE CHOICE OF α

Now that we know how to conduct a statistical test for μ, we can simplify the mechanics of the test by measuring the distance between the observed value of the sample mean $\bar{X}$ and its hypothesized mean μ_0, using a z-score as the test statistic. z-scores were first discussed in Section 5.9 and can be applied here.

---

z-SCORE FOR $\bar{X}$

$$z = \frac{\text{distance}}{\text{standard error of } X} = \frac{\bar{X} - \mu_0}{\sigma/\sqrt{n}}$$

If $z = 2$, $\bar{X}$ lies 2 standard errors above the hypothesized mean. Similarly, if $z = -1$, then $\bar{X}$ is only 1 standard error below μ_0.

Consider the data of Example 7.4. We took a random sample of 30 SMSAs and computed the registration ratio for each area. Recall that we were to test

$$H_0 : \mu = 675$$

against the research hypothesis

$$H_1 : \mu \neq 675$$

by using $\bar{X}$ as the test statistic. For the probability of a type I error set at $\alpha = .05$, we were to reject the null hypothesis if the observed value of $\bar{X}$ was more than 1.96 standard errors ($1.96\sigma_{\bar{X}}$) away from the hypothesized mean of 675. Similarly, we could use z as the test statistic and reject the null hypothesis if the computed z-score is greater than 1.96 or less than -1.96. For the data of Example 7.4, the z-score is

$$z = \frac{\bar{X} - \mu_0}{\sigma_{\bar{X}}} = \frac{711.70 - 675}{84.15/\sqrt{30}} = 2.39$$

Since the value of z, 2.39, exceeds 1.96, we reject the null hypothesis and conclude that the mean registration ratio is different from 675.

FIGURE 7.11

Rejection region for a
one-tailed test with
$H_1: \mu > \mu_0$ when
$\alpha = .05$

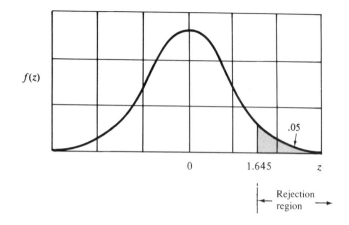

    Suppose that the social researchers of Example 7.4 were interested only in detecting whether the mean registration ratio was greater than the hypothesized mean, 675. For this situation we would reject the null hypothesis only for large values of $\bar{X}$, and hence we would locate all the rejection region in the upper tail of the distribution of $\bar{X}$. For $\alpha = .05$ we would reject the null hypothesis if $\bar{X}$ lies more than $1.645\sigma_{\bar{X}}$ above the hypothesized mean. This would be equivalent to a rejection for values of z greater than 1.645 (see Figure 7.11).

    In setting up a rejection region for any value of α (not necessarily .05), it becomes useful to define the quantity z_a to be the value in the z table (Appendix Table 1) with a specified area a to its right (see Figure 7.12). Since entries in the table represent areas from $z = 0$ out to a specified value of z, we can determine z_a by finding the z-value corresponding to a table entry $.5 - a$. Typical values of $.5 - a$ and z_a are given in Table 7.4. **Note that we use the symbol a to designate the desired tail area. For a one-tailed test, $a = \alpha$; for a two-tailed test, $a = \alpha/2$.**

    In general, we may run a statistical test of the null hypothesis $\mu = \mu_0$ by

FIGURE 7.12

Area under the curve
and to the right of z_a is
equal to a

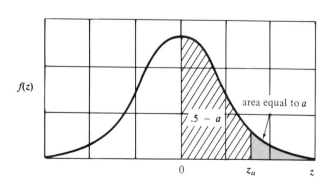

Desired Tail Area	Table Entry	
a	*.5 − a*	z_a
.005	.495	2.58
.01	.490	2.33
.025	.475	1.96
.05	.450	1.645
.10	.400	1.28

TABLE 7.4

Common values of α and z_a

using either a one- or a two-tailed test with a specified value of α. Research hypotheses and corresponding rejection regions are shown in Table 7.5.

EXAMPLE 7.7

Set up a rejection region for the mean registration ratio problem of Example 7.4 to test the null and research hypotheses shown here, using $\alpha = .01$.

$$H_0: \mu = 675$$
$$H_1: \mu < 675$$

SOLUTION

Using Table 7.5 for the one-tailed research hypothesis $\mu < \mu_0$, we will reject H_0 if the observed value of z is less than $-z_\alpha$. Substituting $\alpha = .01$, we will reject the null hypothesis if z is less than $-z_{.01}$. Referring to Table 7.4 (or Appendix Table 1), we have

$$z_{.01} = 2.33$$

For $H_1: \mu < 675$ we will reject $H_0: \mu = 675$ if the computed value of z is less than -2.33.

As noted previously, as the probability α of a type I error decreases, the probability β of a type II error increases. For this reason α is usually chosen to be .01, .05, or .10 for a statistical test.

TABLE 7.5

Rejection regions for the null hypothesis $\mu = \mu_0$, using a specified value of α

Research Hypothesis	Rejection Region
$H_1: \mu > \mu_0$	R.R.: Reject H_0 if $z > z_\alpha$
$H_1: \mu < \mu_0$	R.R.: Reject H_0 if $z < -z_\alpha$
$H_1: \mu \neq \mu_0$	R.R.: Reject H_0 if $z > z_{\alpha/2}$ or $z < -z_{\alpha/2}$

Note: Values of z_α or $z_{\alpha/2}$ can be obtained from Table 7.4 or Appendix Table 1.

EXERCISES

9. In testing the null hypothesis that $\mu = \mu_0$, the standard error of the distribution of $\bar{X}$ is $\sigma/\sqrt{n}$. How can we test the null hypothesis, since we do not know the standard deviation of the population?

10. Set up a rejection region for the mean of family incomes to test the null hypothesis $H_0: \mu = \$25,860$ against the research hypothesis $H_1: \mu \neq \$25,860$. (Use $\alpha = .02$.)

11. If the rejection region for a statistical test is located at $z > 1.645$ or $z < -1.645$, what is the probability of a type I error?

12. If the rejection region for a statistical test is located at $z > 1.645$, what is the probability of a type I error?

13. Sketch the rejection region for a test of $H_0: \mu = \mu_0$ for each of the following situations:
   a. R.R.: $z > 1.96$
   b. R.R.: $z < -1.96$
   c. R.R.: $z > 1.645$ or $z < -1.645$
   d. R.R.: $z > 2.33$

14. A random sample of $n = 36$ observations was obtained and used to test H_0: $\mu = 350$. If $\bar{X} = 375$ and $s = 40$,
   a. Test the research hypothesis $H_1: \mu > 350$, using $\alpha = .05$.
   b. Test the research hypothesis $H_1: \mu \neq 350$, using $\alpha = .05$.

15. Refer to Exercise 8, involving the Stafford-Reske study. Consider the three sets of means and standard deviations from their results for long-distance relationships.
   a. Test the research hypothesis $H_1: \mu > 130$ for the PAS findings, using $\alpha = .05$.
   b. Test the research hypothesis $H_1: \mu < 15$ for the IDA findings, using $\alpha = .02$.
   c. Test the research hypothesis $H_1: \mu > 4.1$ for the FIS findings, using $\alpha = .01$.

7.7   A STATISTICAL TEST ABOUT A BINOMIAL PARAMETER

Many surveys are conducted to make inferences about the proportion of people favoring a particular issue. A random sample of n people is selected from the total, and each is interviewed to determine his or her position, pro or con, on the issue. The number X in favor divided by the sample size n represents the sample proportion, and this quantity should come close to the true unknown population proportion. We will use the letter p to denote the population and $\hat{p} = X/n$ to denote the corresponding sample proportion.

You will note that this sampling procedure is a binomial experiment when the number of people in the group surveyed is large. The true proportion p in the population "in favor," then, represents the probability that the first person interviewed favors the issue. If the population is large relative to the sample size, the probability of interviewing a person "in favor" remains constant, for all practical purposes, as additional people are selected for the sample. A random selection of the sample produces independence (for all practical purposes) for the binomial trials and ensures the validity of the statistical procedures that follow. Surveys that satisfy these conditions may be viewed as binomial experiments.

You will note that the procedure employed to test the hypothesis that $p = .5$ for Jones's political survey in Section 7.1 was a test of a hypothesis concerning a binomial proportion p. We will now formalize this procedure and illustrate the test with an example.

The general procedure for a statistical test about p is identical to that for μ, with p replacing μ and $\hat{p}$ replacing $\bar{X}$. The following summary gives the three possible types of research hypotheses and corresponding rejection regions.

STATISTICAL TEST FOR A BINOMIAL PROPORTION p

Research hypothesis for a one-tailed test

Step 1

1. $H_1: p > p_0$
2. $H_1: p < p_0$

Research hypothesis for a two-tailed test

3. $H_1: p \neq p_0$

Step 2 → **Null hypothesis H_0:** $p = p_0$ (the value of p_0 will be clear from the research hypothesis developed for the study)

Test statistic

Step 3 ↗

$$z = \frac{\hat{p} - p_0}{\sigma_{\hat{p}}} \quad \text{where} \quad \sigma_{\hat{p}} = \sqrt{\frac{p_0 q_0}{n}} \quad \text{and} \quad q_0 = 1 - p_0$$

Rejection region for a one-tailed test and specified value of α

Step 4

1. R.R.: Reject H_0 if $z > z_\alpha$.
2. R.R.: Reject H_0 if $z < -z_\alpha$.

Rejection region for a two-tailed test and specified value of α

3. R.R.: Reject H_0 if $z > z_{\alpha/2}$ or $z < -z_{\alpha/2}$.

Note: We can select any value of α we desire, but generally we adopt $\alpha = .10$,

.05, or .01. The corresponding z_α or $z_{\alpha/2}$ values can be obtained from Table 7.4 or Appendix Table 1.

Assumptions

1. X is a binomial variable (see Section 5.6).
2. The distribution of $\hat{p} = X/n$ can be approximated by a normal distribution, and we can apply this test when both np_0 and nq_0 are 10 or more.

EXAMPLE 7.8

During the evening of the 1988 presidential election, the televised returns for a particular state showed 31,000 for Bush and 29,000 for Dukakis. Do these data, presented shortly after the closing of the polls, provide sufficient evidence to project a winner in the state?

SOLUTION

For a two-person race, if either candidate receives more than 50% of all the votes in the state, he or she is declared the winner. Letting p denote the proportion of voters that will cast a ballot for Bush, X the number of votes that Bush receives in the sample, and $\hat{p} = X/n$ the sample proportion, we wish to ascertain which of the candidates will win. In terms of the proportion of voters p who will cast a ballot for Bush, the research hypothesis can be restated as $p \neq .5$ (i.e., either p is greater than or less than .5).

The appropriate null hypothesis for the research hypothesis $H_1: p \neq .5$ is $H_0: p = .5$. From the sample data

$$n = 60{,}000$$

$$\hat{p} = \frac{31{,}000}{60{,}000} = .52$$

and

$$\sigma_{\hat{p}} = \sqrt{\frac{p_0 q_0}{n}} = \sqrt{\frac{.5(.5)}{60{,}000}} = .002$$

The rejection region for a two-tailed test with $\alpha = .05$ makes use of $z_{.025} = 1.96$. To summarize, the four parts of the statistical test are

$H_1: p \neq .5$

$H_0: p = .5$

T.S.: $z = \dfrac{\hat{p} - p_0}{\sigma_{\hat{p}}} = \dfrac{.52 - .50}{.002} = 10.0$

R.R.: For $\alpha = .05$, reject H_0 if $z > 1.96$ or $z < -1.96$.

Since the computed value of z (10.0) far exceeds 1.96, we reject H_0 in favor of the research hypothesis $H_1: p \neq .5$. Practically, since we rejected in the upper tail, we conclude that p is greater than .5 and that Bush should win the state.

You may be thinking that there is a flaw in our reasoning for the statistical test of Example 7.8. How can the 60,000 early returns constitute a *random* sample from the total of all votes cast in the state? Perhaps they all come from one or two urban areas where voting machines provide an early tabulation of voting results. If so, the proportion of voters favoring Bush in these urban areas might be quite different from the proportion favoring him throughout the entire state. The key to all election predictions is to obtain early returns from a random sample of precincts that are representative of a particular geographical region. Using the results from these precincts, the political analysts are able to project eventual winners long before all the votes have been tabulated. For our example we had to assume that the 60,000 early returns were representative of the entire state. The fact that $\hat{p} = .52$ fell so many standard deviations to the right of the hypothesized mean ($p_0 = .5$) reinforced our conclusion that Bush should win.

EXERCISES

16. Specify the four elements of a statistical test.

17. In dealing with proportions, when is a one-tailed test required?

18. In dealing with proportions, when is a two-tailed test required?

19. The proportion of counties in which the cost of living has actually decreased over the last 24 months is .20, based on a random sample of 100 counties. A national newsmagazine states that the true proportion is .30.
    a. What is the appropriate null hypothesis for this situation?
    b. What is the appropriate test statistic?
    c. Test the null hypothesis and set $\alpha = .05$.
    d. Do you accept the newsmagazine's claim? Why?

20. Out of a random sample of 1000 former prisoners who had undergone an intensive resocialization program while in prison, 362 stated that the program had been "extremely helpful" in assisting them adjust to out-of-prison life.
    a. What proportion of the prisoners reported that the program had been "extremely helpful"?
    b. A local political leader argues that the program was a waste of money and that less than .30 of the prisoners had profited from the program. Test the political leader's claim against the former prisoners' claim. Set $\alpha = .01$.

21. In a typical election year 45% of the voters in a county fail to vote in the local election. A local politician argues that this year the percentage of voters declining to vote will be 35% or less. Symbolically represent the research and null hypotheses.

22. The dropout rate at a college had been about 15% during the freshman year. College officials undertook a concerted campaign to counsel potential dropouts, hoping to reduce the rate dramatically. After two years of the program the dropout rate has been reduced to 10% for the 3000 freshman students. The college feels that the program was a success. Do you agree? Give statistical evidence to support your conclusion.

23. Naomi Farber (1990) reports that the out-of-wedlock birth ratio for white teens nationwide is 45. Based on a random sample of 100 white teens who gave birth to a baby, you find that 52 births to teens were out of wedlock.
    a. What is the appropriate null hypothesis for this situation?
    b. What is the appropriate test statistic?
    c. Test the null hypothesis and set $\alpha = .05$.
    d. If Farber's figure of 45 is accurate, what would you say about your figure of 52? Comment.

24. In the same study, Farber (1990) notes that the out-of-wedlock birth ratio for black teens is 90. You sample 100 births to black teens and find that 75 births were out of wedlock.
    a. Set up an appropriate null hypothesis, using $\alpha = .05$.
    b. What conclusions would you draw?

7.8 LEVEL OF SIGNIFICANCE OF A STATISTICAL TEST

In the previous sections we introduced a rather traditional approach to hypothesis testing. That is, we defined the parts of a statistical test along with the two types of errors and their associated probabilities α and β. In recent years many social researchers and other users of statistics have objected to this decision-based approach to hypothesis testing. Rather than running a statistical test with a preset value of α, they argue that we should specify the research and null hypotheses, collect the sample data, and determine the weight of the evidence for rejecting the null hypothesis. This weight, given in terms of a probability, is called the **level of significance** of the statistical test. We will first illustrate the calculation of a level of significance in an example.

EXAMPLE 7.9   Refer to the data of Example 7.4. Rather than specifying a preset value of α, determine the level of significance for a statistical test of $H_0: \mu = 675$ and $H_1: \mu > 675$.

SOLUTION   From the sample data, the computed value of the test statistic is

$$z = \frac{\overline{X} - 675}{s/\sqrt{n}} = \frac{711.70 - 675}{84.15/\sqrt{30}} = 2.39$$

The level of significance for this test (i.e., the weight of evidence for rejecting H_0) is the probability of observing a value of $\overline{X}$ greater than 711.70, assuming that the null hypothesis is true. This value can be computed by referring to Appendix Table 1 to determine the probability of observing a value of z greater than 2.39. This probability (sometimes designated by the letter p but not to be confused with the binomial p) is $.5 - .4916 = .0084$, as shown in Figure 7.13. Thus the level of significance for this test is .0084.

FIGURE 7.13

Level of significance
for Example 7.9

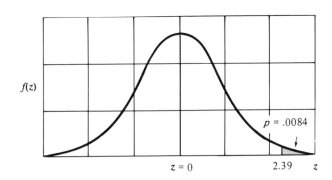

As can be seen from Example 7.9, the level of significance represents the probability of observing a sample outcome more contradictory to H_0 than the observed sample result. **The smaller the value of this probability, the heavier the weight of the sample evidence for rejecting H_0.** For example, a statistical test with a level of significance of $p = .01$ has more evidence for the rejection of H_0 than another statistical test with $p = .20$.

If the null and alternative hypotheses in Example 7.9, respectively, were

$$H_0: \mu = 675 \qquad \text{and} \qquad H_1: \mu < 675$$

and the computed value of $z = -2.39$, the level of significance would still be $p = .0084$ (see Figure 7.14).

For two-tailed tests (as determined by the form of H_1), we still compute the probability of obtaining a sample outcome more contradictory to H_0 than the observed result, but the level of significance is commonly taken to be twice this probability.

FIGURE 7.14

Level of significance
for $H_0: \mu = 675$,
$H_1: \mu < 675$, and
$z = -2.39$

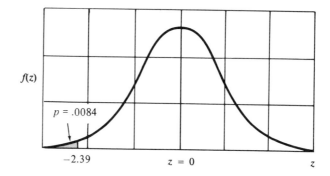

EXAMPLE 7.10 Give the level of significance for the test conducted in Example 7.4.

SOLUTION The null and research hypotheses, respectively, are

$$H_0: \mu = 675 \quad \text{and} \quad H_1: \mu \neq 675$$

and the computed value of z is 2.39. Since the probability of observing a value of z greater than 2.39 is .0084, the level of significance for the statistical test is

$$p = 2(.0084) = .0168$$

There is much to be said in favor of this approach to hypothesis testing. Rather than reaching a decision directly, the statistician (or person performing the statistical test) presents the experimenter with the weight of evidence for rejecting the null hypothesis. This experimenter can then draw his or her own conclusions. Many journals containing research results involving social data have followed this approach by reporting the findings of a statistical test in terms of its level of significance (p-value). Thus we might read that a particular test was significant at the $p = .05$ or perhaps the $p < .01$ level. By reporting results this way, we are left to draw our own conclusions.

However, one word of warning should be voiced. The $p = .05$ level of significance has become a magic level, and many people seem to feel that a particular null hypothesis should not be rejected unless the test achieves the .05 level. This, of course, has resulted in part from attitudes held by people who for many years have used the decision-based approach with α preset at .05. Keep this in mind when reading journal articles or reporting the results of statistical tests. **After all, statistical significance at a particular level does not dictate practical significance. Hence, after determining the level of significance of a test, the social researcher should always consider the practical significance of the finding.**

Throughout the text we will conduct statistical tests with both the decision-based approach and the level-of-significance approach, to familiarize you with both avenues of thought.

7.9   SMALL-SAMPLE TEST FOR A POPULATION MEAN

You will recall that the decision to reject a hypothesis about μ (Section 7.3) was based on the distance between $\bar{X}$ and the hypothesized value of μ. Too large a distance means that $\bar{X}$ is too many standard errors away from μ, based on the sampling distribution of $\bar{X}$.

As noted in previous sections, an easy way to measure the distance between the observed value of $\bar{X}$ and the hypothesized value of μ is to use the z-score,

$$z = \frac{\text{distance}}{\text{standard error of } \bar{X}} = \frac{\bar{X} - \mu_0}{\sigma/\sqrt{n}}$$

which expresses the distance between $\bar{X}$ and μ_0 in standard deviation units. If $z = 2$, it means that $\bar{X}$ lies 2 standard errors above the hypothesized mean. Similarly, $z = -1$ indicates that $\bar{X}$ is only 1 standard error below μ. **Using $\bar{X}$ or z as the test statistic leads us to the same conclusion; z merely counts the number of standard errors that $\bar{X}$ lies away from μ.**

This large-sample method for testing a hypothesis about μ is inappropriate for samples containing fewer than 30 scores when σ is unknown. Since we must sometimes use small samples because of cost, time, or other restrictions, and since σ is usually unknown for these practical situations, we need a small-sample procedure to test a hypothesis about μ. To illustrate, consider the following example.

A pharmaceutical firm has been conducting restricted studies on small groups of people to determine the effectiveness of a measles vaccine. The following scores are readings on the antibody strength for five individuals injected with the vaccine:

$$1.2, \quad 3.0, \quad 2.5, \quad 2.4, \quad 1.9$$

Use the sample data to test the hypothesis that the mean antibody strength for individuals vaccinated with the new drug is 1.6.

Problems of a similar nature were encountered by experimenters early in the twentieth century, when the only available test statistic was

$$z = \frac{\bar{X} - \mu}{\sigma/\sqrt{n}}$$

FIGURE 7.15

Standard normal *z* and
the *t* distribution for
n = 6 measurements

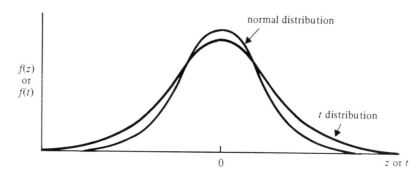

Faced with a small sample randomly selected from a normal population, they computed *s* to approximate σ and substituted it into the formula for *z*. Although aware that their procedure might be invalid, they took the only course open to them. That is, they used the *z*-test to test hypotheses about μ.

Many researchers of that day were quite concerned that their statistical tests were leading to incorrect decisions. One of these, W. S. Gosset, translated his curiosity into action. Gosset was a chemist for Guinness Breweries, and as you might suspect, he was only provided with small samples for use in tests of quality. He was faced with the problem of finding the probability distribution for

$$\frac{\bar{X} - \mu}{s/\sqrt{n}}$$

which is a small-sample *z* statistic with *s* substituted for σ. Gosset found that this test statistic, which he called *t*, possesses a probability distribution similar in appearance to the normal but with a wider spread. In fact, the smaller the sample size *n*, the greater the spread in the probability distribution for *t*. The standard normal distribution and a *t* distribution based on a sample of six measurements are shown in Figure 7.15.

Gosset published his work on the *t* distribution in 1908 under the pen name Student because of company policy. His publication included the exact form of the distribution as well as the tail-end of *t*, which are helpful in locating rejection regions. Gosset's statistic has many other applications in statistical decision making and has achieved a position of major importance in the field of statistics. His unique choice of a pen name has caused the statistic to be called **Student's *t*.**

PROPERTIES OF THE *t* DISTRIBUTION

1. The *t* distribution, like *z*, is mound shaped and symmetrical about $t = 0$ (see Figure 7.16).

FIGURE 7.16

The *t* distribution and
use of Table 7.6

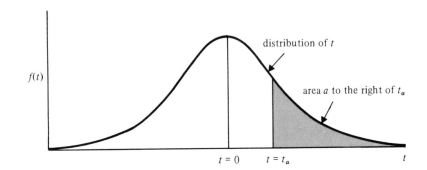

2. It is more variable than *z*, since both $\bar{X}$ and *s* change from sample to sample drawn from a population.
3. There are many *t* distributions. We determine a particular one by specifying a parameter, called the *degrees of freedom* (*d.f.*), that is directly related to the sample size *n*.
4. As the sample size *n* (or d.f.) gets large, the *t* distribution becomes a standard normal (*z*) distribution. Intuitively, this is reasonable, since *s* provides a better estimate of σ as *n* increases.

The values of *t* used to locate the rejection region (critical values) for a statistical test are presented in Appendix Table 2. Since the *t* distribution is symmetrical about $t = 0$, we give only right-tail values. A value in the left tail is simply the negative of the corresponding right-tail value. An entry in the table that corresponds to a certain number of degrees of freedom specifies a value of *t* — say, t_a — such that an area *a* lies to its right (see the shaded portion of Figure 7.16).

The format of Appendix Table 2 is shown in Table 7.6. Columns corresponding to various values of *a* are shown at the top of the table for $a = .10, .05, .025, .010,$ and $.005$. The quantity for the degrees of freedom is shown in the first column of the table. We will not explain the meaning of this term except to note that it is related to the sample size and, particularly, to

TABLE 7.6

Format of Appendix
Table 2

d.f.	$a = .10$	$a = .05$	$a = .025$	$a = .010$	$a = .005$
1	3.078	6.314	12.706	31.821	63.657
2	1.886	2.920	4.303	6.965	9.925
⋮	⋮	⋮	⋮	⋮	⋮
9	1.383	1.833	2.262	2.821	3.250

the amount of information available to estimate the unknown quantity σ. For the test statistic

$$t = \frac{\overline{X} - \mu}{s/\sqrt{n}}$$

the degrees of freedom will always be one less than the sample size — that is, $n - 1$.

The numbers recorded in Appendix Table 2 give the values of t_a. For example, suppose we have a sample of $n = 10$ measurements and wish to use a one-tailed t-test, rejecting in the upper tail of the t distribution, with the probability of a type I error being $\alpha = .05$. Then we would want to find the value of t_a corresponding to an area $a = .05$ (see Figure 7.17). To determine the value of t corresponding to $a = .05$ and $n = 10$, look at Appendix Table 2. Select the column corresponding to $a = .05$ and proceed down the column to d.f. $= n - 1 = 10 - 1 = 9$. The recorded value of t_a is 1.833. That value is shown in Figure 7.17.

FIGURE 7.17

Rejection region for a one-tailed t-test with $n = 10$ and $a = .05$

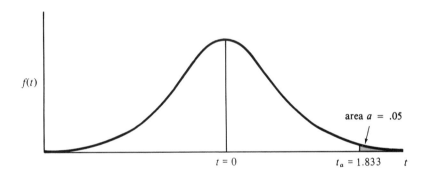

$f(t)$

area $a = .05$

$t = 0$ $t_a = 1.833$ t

EXAMPLE 7.11

Return to the pharmaceutical data on the measles vaccine and suppose that the regulations require that the mean antibody strength of a vaccine exceed 1.6 before it can be placed on the market. Test the research hypothesis that the firm's vaccine is marketable, using the following five measurements recorded for five people injected with the vaccine: 1.2, 3.0, 2.5, 2.4, and 1.9. (Use $\alpha = .05$.)

SOLUTION

The null hypothesis for this example is

$$H_0: \mu = 1.6$$

since we wish to establish the research hypothesis

$$H_1: \mu > 1.6$$

The test statistic is

$$t = \frac{\overline{X} - \mu}{s/\sqrt{n}}$$

Before computing t we must first obtain $\overline{X}$ and s for the sample data. Using a hand calculator or the shortcut formulas for $\overline{X}$ and s, it is easy to show that

$$\overline{X} = 2.2 \qquad \text{and} \qquad s = .682$$

Substituting into the test statistic, we calculate

$$t = \frac{2.2 - 1.6}{.682/\sqrt{5}} = \frac{.6(2.236)}{.682} = 1.97$$

To locate the rejection region for our test statistic, we must specify the degrees of freedom for our test. We simply state that d.f. $= n - 1$ for a small-sample test concerning μ. For a one-tailed test with a probability of a type I error being $\alpha = .05$, we can locate the rejection region from Appendix Table 2 for $a = .05$ and d.f. $= 4$. The table value of t is 2.132 (see Figure 7.18). Since the observed value of t, 1.97, does not fall in the rejection region, we have insufficient evidence to reject the null hypothesis that the mean antibody strength is 1.6.

FIGURE 7.18

Rejection region for $\alpha = .05$ and d.f. $= 4$ in Example 7.11

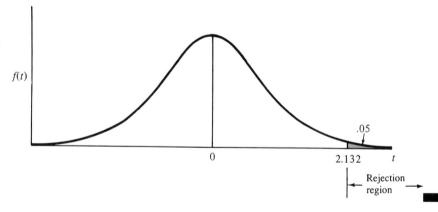

A summary of the elements of the Student's t-test for μ follows.

 STUDENT'S t-TEST FOR A POPULATION MEAN
Research hypothesis for a one-tailed test

1. $H_1: \mu > \mu_0$
2. $H_1: \mu < \mu_0$

Research hypothesis for a two-tailed test

   3. $H_1: \mu \neq \mu_0$

Null hypothesis $H_0: \mu = \mu_0$

Test statistic $t = \dfrac{\bar{X} - \mu_0}{s/\sqrt{n}}$

Rejection region for a one-tailed test with α specified and d.f. $= n - 1$

   1.   R.R.: Reject H_0 if $t > t_\alpha$.
   2.   R.R.: Reject H_0 if $t < -t_\alpha$.

Rejection region for a two-tailed test with α specified and d.f. $= n - 1$
   3.   R.R.: Reject H_0 if $t > t_{\alpha/2}$ or $t < -t_{\alpha/2}$.

Assumptions
   1.   The variable X is measured on an interval or ratio scale.
   2.   The sample measurements represent a random sample from a normal population.

The assumptions for using a t-test have just been indicated. The exact probability distribution of the quantity

$$\frac{\bar{X} - \mu}{s/\sqrt{n}}$$

depends on the form of the distribution from which the sample observations X were obtained. Only if these observations come from a normal distribution with mean μ and standard deviation σ will $(\bar{X} - \mu)/(s/\sqrt{n})$ possess a t distribution based on $n - 1$ degrees of freedom. Gosset's results, and hence the tail values in Appendix Table 2, are based on this assumption (that the original sample was selected from a population that possesses a normal probability distribution).

How restrictive is this assumption? In practice, provided the population of measurements is symmetrical, the results based on a t distribution will hold. This property of the t distribution and the common occurrence of mound-shaped distributions in practice make the Student's t invaluable for use in statistical inference.

How does one know what to do in practice? The answer is quite simple — look at the data. If a plot of the data (such as a histogram) suggests any gross skewness, there is a good chance that the population is skewed and hence the t method should not be used. In situations such as this, you should consult a professional statistician for an alternative method.

In addition to being able to run a t-test about μ, we can construct a confidence interval using t. The small-sample confidence interval for μ is identical to the large-sample confidence interval, with z replaced by t and σ replaced by s. The only restriction in using this confidence interval is that again we must assume that the sample is drawn from a population that is approximately normal.

GENERAL SMALL-SAMPLE CONFIDENCE INTERVAL FOR μ

$$\bar{X} \pm t_{a/2} \frac{s}{\sqrt{n}}$$

The value t_a corresponding to a 90%, 95%, or 99% confidence interval is found in Appendix Table 2 for d.f. $= n - 1$ and $a = .05, .025$, or $.005$, respectively.

We illustrate the use of the confidence interval with an example.

EXAMPLE 7.12

Use the sample data from Example 7.11 to estimate μ, the population mean antibody strength for individuals vaccinated with the new drug. Use a 95% confidence interval.

SOLUTION

Assuming that the data were drawn from a normal population, we can proceed with an analysis. For this example we have

$$\Sigma X = 11.00 \quad \text{and} \quad \Sigma X^2 = 26.06$$

Thus

$$\bar{X} = \frac{11}{5} = 2.2$$

$$s^2 = \frac{\Sigma X^2 - (\Sigma X)^2/n}{n - 1} = \frac{26.06 - (11)^2/5}{4}$$

$$= \frac{26.06 - 24.20}{4} = .465$$

$$s = \sqrt{.465} = .682$$

The general form of the confidence interval is

$$\bar{X} \pm t_a \frac{s}{\sqrt{n}}$$

From Appendix Table 2, for $a = .025$ and d.f. $= n - 1 = 4$, we determine that $t = 2.776$. Substituting into the formula, we obtain lower and upper confidence limits of

$$2.2 - \frac{2.776(.682)}{\sqrt{5}} = 2.2 - .847 = 1.353$$

$$2.2 + \frac{2.776(.682)}{\sqrt{5}} = 2.2 + .847 = 3.047$$

The 95% confidence interval is then 1.353 to 3.047. We note that this interval either does or does not enclose the true mean μ. However, in repeated sampling, 95% of the intervals calculated in this way will enclose μ. Hence we are 95% confident that the true mean antibody strength for the measles vaccine is in the interval 1.353 to 3.047.

EXERCISES

25. Why is z usually an inappropriate test statistic when the sample is small?

26. Set up the rejection region based on a t-test for $H_0: \mu = \mu_0$ when $\alpha = .05$ for the following research hypotheses:
   a. $H_1: \mu < \mu_0, n = 15$
   b. $H_1: \mu \neq \mu_0, n = 23$
   c. $H_1: \mu > \mu_0, n = 6$

27. Repeat Exercise 26 with $\alpha = .05$.

28. An experiment was conducted to determine the abrasion resistance of a new type of automobile paint. Twelve strips of metal were prepared with the new paint, and the abrasion resistance of each strip was measured. Use these data to construct a 95% confidence interval for μ, the mean abrasion resistance for the paint.

2.1	3.2	4.3	4.0
4.2	2.9	3.3	2.5
2.8	2.3	3.7	2.1

29. The divorce rate was determined for each of 10 counties. Use these data to construct a 90%, 95%, and 99% confidence interval for μ, the mean divorce rate for all U.S. counties.

6.4	3.5	7.1	4.2	5.1
3.6	5.3	6.2	4.8	4.1

30. Refer to Exercise 29. A divorce expert claims that the average divorce rate for counties is 5.1. Test his claim and set $\alpha = .02$.

31. The voter turnout in upper-middle-class areas of a city has averaged 650 voters for every 1000 registered voters. This year a random sample of five precincts shows turnouts of 635, 655, 640, 643, and 620 per 1000 registered voters. Do these data indicate a final average of less than 650? (Use a one-tailed test with $\alpha = .05$.)

32. An experiment was performed to determine if the use of pictures would facilitate or impede a child's ability to learn the meanings of words. A random sample of 10 kindergarten children was assigned to a class that used pictures to assist in learning. Each child was tested after the experimental period, and the number of words correctly identified from a total of 20 chosen for the test was recorded. This test was repeated for five successive days, and the score assigned to each student was the average of the five separate tests. These data are

$$12.0, \quad 13.6, \quad 15.2, \quad 14.4, \quad 17.8, \quad 8.2, \quad 9.6, \quad 16.0, \quad 12.2, \quad 18.8$$

We would like to compare the achievement of this experimental group of children with the performance of others who have not used pictures to aid (or impede) their ability to learn the meaning of words. Fortunately, sample test data have been collected over a long period of time for a very large group of children who have not employed pictures in their learning process. The mean for their tests was found to be 17.1.

Suppose we regard 17.1 as the true mean achievement for students who have learned without the use of pictures. Do the data given provide sufficient evidence to indicate that the use of pictures either improves (or impedes) word learning? That is, do the data provide sufficient evidence to show that the mean μ for the test group differs from 17.1? (Use $\alpha = .05$.)

7.10 ONE-SAMPLE GOODNESS-OF-FIT TEST: THE CHI-SQUARE TEST

Many studies, particularly in the social sciences, result in enumerative (or frequency) data for variables measured on nominal or ordinal scales. For instance, the classification of people into five income brackets would result in an enumeration or count corresponding to the number of people assigned to each of the five income classes. Or we might be interested in studying the reactions of hospital staffs to a particular stimulus in a psychological experiment. If hospital staffs collectively react in one of three ways when the stimulus is applied, and if a large number of hospitals are subjected to the stimulus, the experiment would yield three counts that indicate the number of different hospital staffs falling in each of the reaction classes. Similarly, a traffic study might require a count and classification of the types of motor vehicles that use a section of highway. An industry manufactures items that fall into one of three quality classes: acceptables, seconds, and rejects. A student of the arts might classify paintings in one of several categories, according to style and period, in order to study trends in style over time. We might wish to classify ideas within a philosophical study or a style in the field of literature. The results of an advertising campaign would yield count data that indicate a classification of consumer reaction. Indeed, many observations in the social sciences are not amenable to measurement on a continuous scale and hence result in count data.

The illustrations in the preceding paragraph exhibit, to a reasonable degree of approximation, the following characteristics, which define a **multinomial experiment.**

THE MULTINOMIAL EXPERIMENT
1. The experiment consists of n identical trials.
2. The outcome of each trial falls into one of k classes, or *cells.*
3. The probability that the outcome of a single trial will fall in a particular cell — say, cell i — is p_i ($i = 1, 2, 3, \ldots, k$) and remains the same from trial to trial. Note that

$$p_1 + p_2 + p_3 + \cdots + p_k = 1$$

4. The trials are independent.
5. The experimenter is interested in $n_1, n_2, n_3, \ldots, n_k$, where n_i ($i = 1, 2, 3, \ldots, k$) is equal to the number of trials in which the outcome falls in cell i. Note that

$$n_1 + n_2 + n_3 + \cdots + n_k = n$$

A multinomial experiment is analogous to tossing n balls at k boxes, where each ball must fall into one of the boxes. The boxes are arranged so that the probability that a ball will fall in a box varies from box to box but remains the same for a particular box in repeated tosses. Finally, the balls are tossed in such a way that the trials are independent. At the conclusion of the experiment, we observe n_1 balls in the first box, n_2 in the second, and so on, through n_k in the kth. The total number of balls is equal to

$$\Sigma n_i = n$$

You will note the similarity between the binomial and multinomial experiments; in particular, the binomial experiment represents the special case for the multinomial experiment when $k = 2$, $p_1 = p$, and $p_2 = q = 1 - p$. Working with the multinomial experiment, we will make inferences about the

k parameters p_1, p_2, p_3,..., p_k. In this chapter inferences about p_1, p_2, p_3,..., p_k will be expressed in terms of a statistical test of a hypothesis about their specific numerical values or their relationship to one another.

Suppose we know that the probability p_1 that a ball will land in cell 1 is .1. Then if we toss $n = 100$ balls at the cells, we would expect $100(.1) = 10$ balls to land in cell 1. Indeed, the expected number in cell i after n is np_i.

DEFINITION 7.3 In a multinomial experiment where each trial can result in one of k outcomes, the *expected number of outcomes of type i in n trials is np_i*, where p_i is the probability that a given trial results in outcome i.

In 1900 Karl Pearson proposed the following test statistic, which is a function of the squares of the deviations of the observed cell counts from their expected values. Letting O denote the observed cell count and E the expected count, Pearson's statistic is

$$\chi^2 = \sum \frac{(O - E)^2}{E}$$

Suppose that we hypothesize values for the cell probabilities p_1, p_2, p_3,..., p_k and calculate the expected cell counts, using Definition 7.3 to examine how well the data fit or agree with the hypothesized cell probabilities. Certainly, if our hypothesized value of each p is true, the cell counts should not deviate greatly from the expected cell counts. Large values of χ^2 would imply rejection of a null hypothesis. How large is large? The answer to this question can be found by examining the probability distribution of χ^2.

The quantity χ^2 possesses approximately a chi-square (χ^2) probability distribution in repeated sampling when n is large. For this approximation to be good, it is desirable that the expected number falling into each cell be 5 or more. We will not give the formula for the chi-square probability distribution, but we will characterize it by the following properties.

PROPERTIES OF THE CHI-SQUARE DISTRIBUTION

1. The chi-square distribution is not symmetrical (see Figure 7.19).
2. There are many chi-square distributions. We obtain a particular one by specifying the degrees of freedom associated with the chi-square distribution. (This number will change depending on the application.)

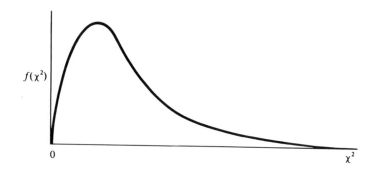

FIGURE 7.19

Chi-square probability distribution with d.f. = 4

The large values of χ^2 fall in the upper (right-hand) tail of the chi-square probability distribution.

The chi-square test for k specified cell probabilities, often called a **chi-square test for goodness of fit**, is based on $k - 1$ degrees of freedom. Upper-tail values of

$$\chi^2 = \sum \frac{(O - E)^2}{E}$$

are shown in Appendix Table 3. Entries in the table are chi-square values such that an area of size a lies to the right of χ_a^2 under the curve. We specify the degrees of freedom in the left-hand column of the table and the specified value of a in the top row of Appendix Table 3. For $a = .10$ and d.f. $= 14$, the tabulated value of the chi-square distribution is 21.0642 (see Figure 7.20).

The rejection region for the one-tailed test concerning k cell probabilities can be determined for a specified value of a type I error α using Appendix Table 3. If the observed value of χ^2 falls beyond the critical value, we reject the null hypothesis that specifies the k cell probabilities. We summarize the test procedure as follows.

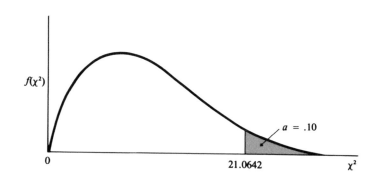

FIGURE 7.20

Tabulated value of the chi-square distribution with $a = .10$ and d.f. $= 14$

CHI-SQUARE GOODNESS-OF-FIT TEST

Research hypothesis   At least one of the cell probabilities differs from its hypothesized value.

Null hypothesis   Each of the k cell probabilities is specified.

Test statistic $\chi^2 = \sum \dfrac{(O - E)^2}{E}$

Rejection region   Reject the null hypothesis if χ^2 exceeds the tabulated value for d.f. $= k - 1$ and $a = \alpha$.

Assumptions

1.   The observed cell counts satisfy the properties of a multinomial experiment.
2.   The expected cell counts must be 5 or more.

EXAMPLE 7.13   Researchers studied a heroin epidemic in the San Francisco Bay area. A sample of 102 drug users was interviewed, and each subject was asked to name the kind of drug he or she first injected. These data are listed in Table 7.7. Because previous data were inadequate, it was hypothesized that the proportions of subjects reporting "type of first drug injected" would be $\frac{1}{3}$ for heroin, $\frac{1}{3}$ for speed, and $\frac{1}{3}$ for all others. Test the hypothesis that the cell probabilities for type of drug first injected do not differ from $\frac{1}{3}$. (Use $\alpha = .05$)

TABLE 7.7

Type of first drug injected by 102 subjects interviewed during a heroin epidemic

First Drug Injected	Number
heroin	42
speed	36
other	24
Total	102

Source: David B. Graeven and Andrew Jones, "Addicts and Experimenters: Dynamics of Involvement in an Adolescent Heroin Epidemic," National Institute on Drug Abuse Grant R01–DA00940 and California Department of Health Grant 75–53922.

SOLUTION

This experiment possesses the characteristics of a multinomial experiment with $n = 102$ trials and $k = 3$ outcomes:

- Outcome 1: First drug injected was heroin, with probability p_1.
- Outcome 2: First drug injected was speed, with probability p_2.
- Outcome 3: First drug injected was other than heroin or speed, with probability p_3.

The null hypothesis is

$$H_0: p_1 = p_2 = p_3 = \frac{1}{3}$$

which is to be tested against the research hypothesis that at least one of these probabilities differs from $\frac{1}{3}$. The observed and expected cell counts are given in Table 7.8. Note that the expected cell counts all exceed 5 and that the observed cell counts differ from the expected cell counts.

TABLE 7.8

Observed and expected cell counts for Example 7.13

Drug First Injected	Observed	Expected
heroin	42	$102(\frac{1}{3}) = 34$
speed	36	$102(\frac{1}{3}) = 34$
other	24	$102(\frac{1}{3}) = 34$

The test statistic is

$$\chi^2 = \sum \frac{(O - E)^2}{E}$$

$$= \frac{(42 - 34)^2}{34} + \frac{(36 - 34)^2}{34} + \frac{(24 - 34)^2}{34} = 4.94$$

The tabulated value of χ^2 for $a = .05$, with d.f. $= k - 1 = 3 - 1 = 2$, is 5.99. Since 4.94 does not exceed 5.99, we have insufficient evidence to indicate that the cell probabilities differ from $\frac{1}{3}$.

EXAMPLE 7.14   Researchers classified 129 Georgia residents by attitude toward locating mobile homes near Lake Russell. The observed and expected numbers for the null hypothesis $p_1 = p_2 = p_3 = \frac{1}{3}$ are given in Table 7.9. Perform a chi-square goodness-of-fit test on the data. (Use $\alpha = .05$.)

Attitude	Observed	Expected
favorable	32	43
neutral	24	43
unfavorable	73	43

TABLE 7.9

Distribution of attitudes about locating mobile homes near Lake Russell, Georgia

SOLUTION

Using the observed and expected cell counts in Table 7.9, we can compute χ^2:

$$\chi^2 = \sum \frac{(O - E)^2}{E}$$

$$= \frac{(32 - 43)^2}{43} + \frac{(24 - 43)^2}{43} + \frac{(73 - 43)^2}{43}$$

$$= \frac{(11)^2}{43} + \frac{(19)^2}{43} + \frac{(30)^2}{43} = 32.14$$

The tabulated value of χ^2 for $a = .05$ and d.f. = 2 is 5.99. Since $\chi^2 = 32.14$ exceeds 5.99, we reject the null hypothesis. There is a smaller number of favorable and neutral attitudes and a larger number of unfavorable attitudes than expected for $H_0: p_1 = p_2 = p_3 = \frac{1}{3}$.

EXERCISES

33. Describe the conditions under which the researcher is most likely to use the chi-square goodness-of-fit test for one sample.

34. Refer to Exercise 33. Write out the test statistic.

35. Refer to Exercise 33. What is the formula for determining the degrees of freedom?

36. Refer to Example 7.13. Assume that the expected frequencies are as follows: 20 for heroin, 30 for speed, and 53 for other. Perform a chi-square goodness-of-fit test. (Use $\alpha = .01$.)

37. Refer to Exercise 36. What conclusion would you draw from the chi-square test? Is it the same or different from the conclusion in Example 7.13? Why?

38. Using the national percentage distribution in Exercise 10, Chapter 3, determine the expected frequencies and then perform a chi-square goodness-of-fit test on the actual frequency count of the following sizes of six racial-ethnic groupings in a suburb of San Francisco. (Use $\alpha = .05$.)

62 Chinese, 26 Filipino, 10 Indian, 43 Japanese, 5 Korean, 4 Vietnamese

39. Repeat Exercise 38, using the national percentage distribution for Pacific Islanders in Exercise 10, Chapter 3. Actual frequencies in the suburb are listed below (use $\alpha = .05$):

52 Hawaiian   47 Guamanian   51 Samoan

40. Must the total expected frequency always equal the total actual frequency for a chi-square goodness-of-fit test? Explain.

41. In a classic study, Deutsch and Collins (1951) examined and evaluated the social psychological aspects of a social experiment involving racial attitudes. Integrated interracial projects were sponsored in several towns in Minnesota. A sample of 99 housewives was interviewed in Koaltown, Minnesota, to examine changes in their attitudes toward blacks. Deutsch and Collins indicate that the number of housewives in their study reporting favorable change, no change, and unfavorable change are, respectively, 58, 38, and 3. Test the hypothesis that the cell probabilities based on a similar Koaltown study do not differ from the original cell probabilities. The observed cell frequencies are shown in the accompanying table. (Use $\alpha = .01$.)

Exercise 41

Number of housewives in the Koaltown project reporting favorable change, no change, or unfavorable change in their attitudes toward blacks

Attitude	observed Number
favorable change	40
no change	40
unfavorable change	19
Total	99

42. Danziger and Radin (1990) reported on the living arrangements of 294 teenage mothers. They found 144 living alone, 75 living with their mother, and 65 living with both parents. Test the hypothesis that the cell probabilities for living arrangements of teenage mothers do not differ from .50, .25 and .25, respectively. (Use $\alpha = .05$.)

SUMMARY

Recall that the objective of statistics is to make an inference about a population, based on information contained in a sample. Chapters 2, 3, and 4 showed how we describe a set of measurements, thus providing us with a way to phrase an inference about a population. Chapter 5 introduced the concept of probability and probability distributions, providing us with the mechanism for making inferences. Chapter 6 and this chapter used this information in presenting the reasoning and methodology employed in statistical inference.

Since populations or universes are described by parameters, we can make inferences about them in two ways: we can test hypotheses about their values, or we can estimate them. Chapter 6 illustrated the reasoning employed in estimating population parameters (such as a mean or proportion) based on single samples selected from a population. Methods for testing hypotheses about population parameters, again based on single samples, are presented in this chapter.

The two methods for making inferences about population parameters are related to two of the steps in the scientific method. The scientific method may involve observation of nature to formulate a theory, followed by reobservation to test the theory against reality. The testing of hypotheses is a vital tool for determining whether observation agrees with theory. Estimation, the second method for making inferences about population parameters, attempts to determine the value of one or more parameters based on information contained in a sample. Unlike hypothesis testing, estimation does not ask, "Do the data provide sufficient evidence to indicate that μ differs from 80?" Rather it asks, "What is μ?"

A statistical test is composed of four parts: a research hypothesis, a null hypothesis, a test statistic, and a rejection region. The rejection region is a set of values of the test statistic that contradicts the null hypothesis. For a given value of α, we can determine whether to reject the null hypothesis by comparing the computed value of the test statistic to a value obtained from the appropriate table in the Appendix.

Several statistical tests were discussed in detail in this chapter. We began by presenting a statistical test concerning the large-sample test about a population (parameter) mean. The statistical test concerning the binomial parameter p was then presented and followed by the small-sample tests concerning a population mean. Finally, we presented a goodness-of-fit test, the chi-square. The goodness of a statistical test is measured by the values of the probability of rejecting the null hypothesis when it is true and of the probability of accepting the null hypothesis when it is false.

Note that the sample size n plays an important role in both estimation and testing hypotheses, because it measures the amount of data (and hence information) contained in the sample. As n increases, the width of a confidence interval decreases. When testing hypotheses where the data are quite variable and n is small, it is unlikely that we will reject the null hypotheses even when the null hypothesis is false. That is, the probability β of making a type II error will be large. This notion is important, because one frequently hears that "experts," panels, and high-level government commissions have found little effect of some drug on humans, that there is no difference in the effect of some social factor on the behavior or condition of various groups of people in our society, or that certain conditions have no effect on social behavior. These reports, which may vitally affect our society, are often based on pitifully small quantities of very variable data that do not support the experts' conclusions. In fact, the sample sizes employed are rarely revealed in the reports. The point here is clear. Before we place any weight on inferences made about data, we should look for a measure of goodness for the inference.

KEY WORDS

Chi-square test for goodness of fit   A test for k specified cell probabilities from a multinomial experiment.

Level of significance   The weight of the evidence for rejecting the null hypothesis in favor of the research hypothesis. This weight is expressed as a probability (p-value).

Multinomial experiment   An experiment that consists of n identical, independent trials, where each trial can result in one of k (a fixed number) of outcomes.

Null hypothesis   A hypothesis contradictory to the research hypothesis.

One-tailed test   The rejection region is allocated to one tail of the distribution.

Rejection region   A set of values for a test statistic that indicates rejection of the null hypothesis.

Research hypothesis   A hypothesis about a population parameter that we wish to verify.

Student's t   A particular symmetrical, mound-shaped distribution that possesses more spread than the standard normal probability distribution. Used for small samples.

Test statistic   A quantity computed from the sample data and used as a decision maker in a statistical test.

t-test   A statistical test for a population mean.

Two-tailed test   The rejection area divided evenly between the two tails of the distribution.

Type I error   Rejecting the null hypothesis when it is true.

Type II error   Failing to reject the null hypothesis when it is false and the research hypothesis is true.

z-score   Standardized score that is frequently used as a test statistic.

KEY FORMULAS

Large-sample test for μ ($n \geq 30$)

$$H_0: \mu = \mu_0$$

$$\text{T.S.: } z = \frac{\overline{X} - \mu_0}{\sigma/\sqrt{n}} \qquad (\textit{Note}: \text{If } \sigma \text{ is unknown, use } s.)$$

Test for p

$$H_0: p = p_0$$

$$\text{T.S.: } z = \frac{\hat{p} - P_0}{\sigma_{\hat{p}}} \qquad \text{where} \qquad \sigma_{\hat{p}} = \sqrt{\frac{p_0 q_0}{n}} \qquad \text{and} \qquad q_0 = 1 - p_0$$

Student's t-test for μ

$$H_0: \mu = \mu_0$$

$$\text{T.S.: } t = \frac{\overline{X} - \mu_0}{s/\sqrt{n}}, \text{d.f.} = n - 1$$

Goodness-of-fit test

$$H_0: \text{All cell probabilities are specified.}$$

$$\text{T.S.: } \chi^2 = \sum \frac{(O - E)^2}{E}, \text{d.f.} = k - 1$$

SUPPLEMENTARY EXERCISES FOR CHAPTER 7

43. Define what is meant by a type I error and a type II error.

44. What is a relationship between α and β for a fixed sample size?

45. How does increasing the sample size affect α and β?

46. During the 1988 Democratic primary campaign in California, a poll of 1000 registered Democrats showed 55% favoring Dukakis and 45% favoring Jackson. Do these data provide sufficient evidence to indicate that Dukakis would win the primary? Would you use a one-tailed or two-tailed test? (Use $\alpha = .05$.)

47. A sample of 30 SMSAs located in the West shows a mean fertility ratio of 350.4 and a standard deviation of 25.7. Test the null hypothesis $H_0: \mu = 360$, using a two-tailed test. (Use $\alpha = .01$.)

48. A study shows that 80% of college freshmen scoring above a certain cutoff point on a social science orientation test also passed principles of anthropology. This year 600 freshmen were tested, and of those scoring at or above the cutoff point, 450 passed and 150 failed principles of anthropology. Use the chi-square test for goodness of fit. Do the observed frequencies provide sufficient evidence to indicate that the failure rate in anthropology differs from that for the past year? (Use $\alpha = .05$.)

49. In a study of premarital pregnancy, a research team reports 30 such pregnancies in the lower social class, 20 in the middle social class, and 10 in the higher social class. If the expected frequencies are 20, 20, and 20, test the goodness of fit of the observed frequencies with the expected frequencies. What do these data suggest? (Use $\alpha = .05$.)

50. The flow of dollars to countries outside the United States affects the balance of payments. The level of balance of payments in turn reflects the health of our economy. If there is a deficit, we have more goods or funds leaving the country than are brought in through imports or investments. One major drain of dollars from the United States is through U.S. tourist expenditures in foreign countries. In a study to investigate the effect of the dollar exchange rate on travel to a particular country, social researchers examined the proportion of people issued passports. Of those issued passports in prior years, records indicate that 10% visited the country in question. One year after substantial changes in the exchange rate, a random sample of 400 holders of newly issued passports indicated that 23 planned to visit the country. Do these data provide sufficient evidence to indicate a difference in the proportions desiring to visit the country before and after the change in the exchange rate? (Suppose that you are willing to reject the null hypothesis when it is true with a probability of .05. That risk means that you will select $\alpha = .05$.)

51. The work of sociologists in studying the migration of individuals from urban and rural areas has been useful in developing projected labor needs and predicting the size and composition of the future work force. Early research suggests that the proportion of men age 30 or less who migrate from small communities in a particular state to urban areas is .38. A study of a particular small town showed a total of 92 migrators in a random sample of 200 males. Do the data suggest that the migratory proportion for this community differs from the value .38? (Use $\alpha = .05$.)

52. Results from a recent election survey of 1000 registered voters indicate that the reform party candidate received 550 votes. Do the data support the research hypothesis that the reform party candidate will poll more than 50% of the votes in the upcoming election?

53. To determine consistency in evaluating student behavior, two evaluators were presented with a group of 200 students for examination. Each student was examined by both of the evaluators. The evaluators agreed on 133 of the evaluations. Does this indicate that their agreement is due to reasons other than pure chance?

54. A hospital claims that the average length of patient confinement is 5 days. A study of the length of patient confinements on $n = 36$ people showed that $\bar{X} = 6.2$ and $s = 5.2$. Do these data present sufficient evidence to contradict the hospital's claim?

55. The opposition political party charges that 20% of the people receiving welfare fail to meet the specified requirements for qualifying for welfare. You draw a random sample of 800 persons currently receiving welfare and find that 12% fail to meet specified requirements. Test the hypothesis that the opposition party has overstated its claim. Would you use a one-tailed or two-tailed test? Would you set $\alpha = .05$ or $.01$? Why?

56. Using the information in Database A, Appendix Table 7, focus on the variable "income of parents." If the expected frequencies are 75 high, 75 medium, and 50 low, test the goodness of fit of the expected frequencies with the observed frequencies. What do the data suggest? (Use $\alpha = .01$.)

57. Refer to Exercise 56. Assume the expected frequencies are 60 high, 60 medium, and 80 low. Test the goodness of fit of the observed frequencies with the expected frequencies. What do the data suggest? (Use $\alpha = .05$.)

58. Computer output is shown here for a 90% confidence interval for μ and a statistical test of the null hypothesis $H_0: \mu = 675$, based on the data of Table 7.3.

   a. Identify the confidence interval.

   b. Interpret the results of the statistical test and compare your conclusion to that of Example 7.4.

Exercise 58

```
MTB > zinterval 90 84.15 'RATIO'

THE ASSUMED SIGMA =84.2

              N      MEAN     STDEV    SE MEAN    90.0 PERCENT C.I.
RATIO        30      711.7     84.2      15.4    (   686.4,    737.0)

MTB > ztest 675 84.15 'RATIO'

TEST OF MU = 675.000 VS MU N.E. 675.000
THE ASSUMED SIGMA = 84.2

              N      MEAN      STDEV    SE MEAN         Z     P VALUE
RATIO        30    711.700    84.151    15.364       2.39      0.017
```

59. Using the information in Database A, Appendix Table 7, focus on social science majors and their age. Test the hypothesis that the average age is 22.2 years for all social science majors. (Set $\alpha = .05$.)

60. Using the information in Database B, Appendix Table 8, focus on the degree to which civil liberties are denied in each nation. Combine nations with minimal denial of civil liberties (2s, 3s, and 4s) into category A; combine 5s, 6s, 7s, 8s, 9s, 10s, and 11s into category B; and combine 12s, 13s, and 14s into category C. Assume that the expected cell probabilities for each category are $\frac{1}{3}$, $\frac{1}{3}$, and $\frac{1}{3}$. Test the goodness of fit of the observed frequencies with the expected frequencies. (Set $\alpha = .05$.)

61. Using the information in Database C, Appendix Table 9, draw a random sample of 20 patients. Test the hypothesis that the mean of all patients is 50 for the OBRIST variable (HOPKINS OBRIST cluster totals). (Set $\alpha = .01$.)

62. Walsh (1990) studied the sentencing patterns of judges in felony assault cases in an Ohio metropolitan area. Of the 119 cases recommended by psychiatrists for probation, 58.8% were placed on probation and 41.2% were sent to prison. You repeat the study in your home town and find that of 200 cases, 42% were placed on probation and 58% were sent to prison. Test the goodness of fit of your observed frequencies with the expected frequencies based on the Ohio data. (Set $\alpha = .05$.)

63. Walsh (1990) also collected information about sentencing patterns when a probation officer recommended probation ($n = 81$). In the same Ohio metropolitan area, Walsh reports that 81.5% of the cases were placed on probation, and 18.5% were sent to prison. Again, you repeat the study in your home town and find that of 200 cases, 55% were placed on probation and 45% were sent to prison. Test the goodness of fit of your observed frequencies with the expected frequencies based on the Ohio data. (Set $\alpha = .05$.)

64. Using Database D, Appendix Table 10, and assuming that the 30 states represent a sample of all political units, test the following hypotheses, setting $\alpha = .01$.
   a. The average abortion rate is 27.5.
   b. The average murder rate is 9.4.
   c. The average forcible rape rate is 38.1.
   d. The average suicide rate is 13.2.

65. Meyer and Quadango (1990) studied the retirement situation of male auto workers. Their sample consisted of 147 retired men. The former auto workers' post-retirement household income was $10,000 or less for 21 men; $10,001 to $20,000 for 65 men; and over $20,000 for 61 men. Use the chi-square goodness-of-fit test and assume that the expected frequencies were 49, 49, and 49. (Set $\alpha = .01$.)

66. Popkin (1990) interviewed 149 randomly selected AFDC recipients in Chicago and discovered that 83% were black. Nationwide surveys indicate that 40.7% are black. A local Chicago reporter writes a story in which she argues that the Chicago figure does not differ significantly from the national pattern. Do you agree? Present a chi-square goodness-of-fit test to support your position.

67. Bumpass, Sweet, and Martin (1990) investigated patterns of remarriage after divorce, by examining population surveys. They looked at age at separation, duration of marriage, age at first marriage, children at separation, and race.
   a. For every 100 divorced people in each category, 89 people under 25 remarry, 78 between ages 25 and 29, 59 between ages 30 and 39, and 31 age 40 and over. Use the chi-square goodness-of-fit test among the three age categories in terms of likelihood to remarry after a divorce. (Set $\alpha = .05$.)
   b. For every 100 divorced people in each category, 89 people remarry when the first marriage lasts 0–1 year, 82 for 2–4 years, 76 for 5–9 years, and 52 for 10 and more years. Use a chi-square goodness-of-fit test among the four duration categories for the likelihood to remarry after a divorce. (Set $\alpha = .05$.)
   c. For every 100 divorced people in each category, 84 people remarry when

their age at first marriage was 14–17, 79 for age 18–19, 67 for age 20–22, and 51 for age 23 and above. Use a chi-square goodness-of-fit test among the four categories of age at first marriage for the likelihood to remarry after a divorce. (Set $\alpha = .01$.)

d. For every 100 divorced people in each category, 81 people with no children present at separation remarry, 73 people with 1–2 children, and 57 with 3 or more children. Use a chi-square goodness-of-fit test among the three categories regarding children. Interpret your results. (Set $\alpha = .05$.)

e. For every 100 divorced people in each category, 76 out of 100 white non-Hispanics remarry and 46 of 100 blacks do so. Use a chi-square goodness-of-fit test for the two racial categories. Interpret your results. (Set $\alpha = .01$.)

CHAPTER 8

ESTIMATION AND STATISTICAL TESTS OF HYPOTHESES: TWO SAMPLES

GENERAL OBJECTIVES

In this chapter we expand on the ideas introduced in Chapters 6 and 7: estimation and tests of hypotheses. Now, however, we will focus on estimation and statistical tests of hypotheses involving two samples rather than just one. Understanding these ideas is important to you from a very practical standpoint: Many research problems require comparisons between two samples.

SPECIFIC OBJECTIVES

1. To introduce a basic theorem: If two independent variables are normally distributed, the difference between the two variables will be normally distributed.

2. To highlight the properties of the sampling distribution for the difference between two sample means and between two sample proportions.

3. To illustrate how to test specific hypotheses involving differences between means or differences between proportions.

4. To show how to distinguish between large- and small-sample comparisons of two means.

5. To introduce the Mann-Whitney U-test, which can be used when the data are measured on an ordinal scale or when the assumptions underlying parametric tests are not met.

6. To introduce the paired t-test, which can be used to test hypotheses involving change over time in a variable for a set of cases (that is, there are measurements for each case at two points in time).

8.1   INTRODUCTION

Chapters 3 and 4 showed how to describe a set of measurements by using graphical and numerical descriptive methods. Chapter 5, which dealt with probability, probability distributions, and sampling distributions, set the stage for a discussion of inference by showing how we could interpret data from various populations using probability. Chapters 6 and 7 introduced the basic concepts of statistical inference making and applying them to estimation and statistical tests about μ and p using data from a single sample. So to date we have stated that the objective of statistics is to make inferences, explained how inferences are made, and given several practical illustrations. Where do we go now? The answer is to more applications of statistical inference. We will now consider inferences about the difference between two population means and the difference between two population proportions.

Rarely do we read a newsmagazine or Sunday newspaper without finding one or more articles comparing two populations. We might read that factory orders in July rose 1.7% (in comparison with June), that car production in September is scheduled to drop 4.5% (in comparison with August), that public school teachers of a certain state receive salaries less than the national average, or that the percentage of people suffering from arteriosclerosis is higher for individuals with cadmium in their water supply than for individuals without. All these examples compare two populations, based on information contained in samples selected from each.

How can we, as social researchers, tell whether the observed difference in the previous comparisons is real or whether it is due to random variation inherent in the sampling situations? People unfamiliar with research frequently answer this question by saying, "But you can see the difference, can't you? There is no question about it!" They forget that the difference they observe is based on sample values such as means, which vary in a random manner about the true population values. They confuse the observed difference between the *sample* means or percentages with those between the *populations*.

To further emphasize this point, let us consider an example. Many social researchers have been particularly interested in studying the influence of "labeling" on behavior. More specifically, it has been suggested that the performance of deviant acts is not really important to an individual's self-concept; rather, it is the labeling of a person as deviant by others that is crucial. To illustrate, let us compare two groups of individuals, in which each individual has been selling illegal drugs. Those individuals in group A have been publicly labeled as "drug pushers," whereas those in group B have escaped such labeling. As a hypothetical case, the results might show that 19 persons of 22 in group A have continued to push drugs, and 14 of 21 in group B have continued to do so. What do we conclude about the influence of labeling on drug pushing?

The proportions of drug pushers who continued to sell illegal drugs in the two groups appear to be substantially different: .86 versus .67. However, these proportions are estimates of binomial parameters based on relatively small samples. As a consequence, the sample estimates vary substantially about the true binomial parameters. Indeed, if the likelihood p of continuing to sell illegal drugs were identical for individuals in both groups, the difference between the two sample proportions, $.86 - .67 = .19$, could occur just due to chance.

It can be shown that the probability that the two estimates differ by as much as .19 is rather large. Hence there is *not* sufficient evidence to indicate a difference in the proportions of individuals in the two groups who have continued to sell illegal drugs. The true proportion for group A may be larger than for B, or vice versa, or the proportions may be equal. The relevant fact is that there is insufficient information in this study to indicate that the proportions of repeated drug-pushing activities differ between groups A and B. The technique employed in reaching this decision will be presented in Section 8.6.

8.2 THE SAMPLING DISTRIBUTION OF THE DIFFERENCE BETWEEN TWO SAMPLE STATISTICS

In many sampling situations we will select independent random samples from two populations in order to compare the population means or proportions. The statistics used to make these inferences will, in many cases, be the difference between the corresponding sample statistics. For example, suppose we select independent random samples of n_1 observations from one population and n_2 observations from a second population. We will use the difference between the sample means, $\bar{X}_1 - \bar{X}_2$, to make an inference about the difference between the population means, $\mu_1 - \mu_2$.

The following statistical theorem is of help in finding the sampling distribution of the difference between sample statistics computed from independent random samples:

THEOREM   If two independent variables X_1 and X_2 are normally distributed with means and variances (μ_1, σ_1^2) and (μ_2, σ_2^2), respectively, then the difference between the variables will be normally distributed with mean equal to $\mu_1 - \mu_2$ and variance equal to $\sigma_1^2 + \sigma_2^2$.*

This theorem can be directly applied to find the sampling distribution of the difference between two independent sample means or two independent sample proportions. Recall from Chapter 6 that if independent samples of size n_1 and n_2 are selected from two populations, 1 and 2, then when n_1 and n_2 are large, the sampling distributions of $\bar{X}_1$ and $\bar{X}_2$ will be approximately normal, with means and variances $(\mu_1, \sigma_1^2/n_1)$ and $(\mu_2, \sigma_2^2/n_2)$, respectively. Consequently, since $\bar{X}_1$ and $\bar{X}_2$ are independent, normally distributed variables, it follows from the theorem that the sampling distribution for the difference in the sample means, $\bar{X}_1 - \bar{X}_2$, will be approximately normal, with mean

$$\mu_{\bar{X}_1 - \bar{X}_2} = \mu_1 - \mu_2$$

and variance

$$\sigma_{\bar{X}_1 - \bar{X}_2}^2 = \sigma_{\bar{X}_1}^2 + \sigma_{\bar{X}_2}^2 = \frac{\sigma_1^2}{n_1} + \frac{\sigma_2^2}{n_2}$$

and standard error

$$\sigma_{\bar{X}_1 - \bar{X}_2} = \sqrt{\frac{\sigma_1^2}{n_1} + \frac{\sigma_2^2}{n_2}}$$

The sampling distribution of the difference between two independent, normally distributed sample means is shown in Figure 8.1.

PROPERTIES OF THE SAMPLING DISTRIBUTION FOR $\bar{X}_1 - \bar{X}_2$

1. The sampling distribution of $\bar{X}_1 - \bar{X}_2$ is approximately normal for large samples.
2. The mean of the sampling distribution, $\mu_{\bar{X}_1 - \bar{X}_2}$, is equal to the difference between the population means, $\mu_1 - \mu_2$.
3. The standard error of the sampling distribution is

$$\sigma_{\bar{X}_1 - \bar{X}_2} = \sqrt{\frac{\sigma_1^2}{n_1} + \frac{\sigma_2^2}{n_2}}$$

* The sum $X_1 + X_2$ of the variables will also be normally distributed with mean $\mu_1 + \mu_2$ and variance $\sigma_1^2 + \sigma_2^2$.

FIGURE 8.1

Sampling distribution for the difference between two sample means

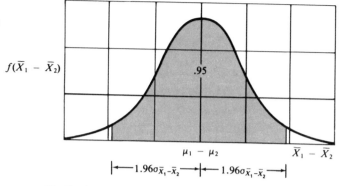

$f(\bar{X}_1 - \bar{X}_2)$

Similarly, the theorem enables us to find the sampling distribution for the difference in sample proportions, $\hat{p}_1 - \hat{p}_2$, computed from independent random samples of n_1 and n_2 observations, respectively, selected from two binomial populations. From Chapter 6 we know that for large samples, $\hat{p}_1$ and $\hat{p}_2$ will be approximately normally distributed, with means and variances $(p_1, p_1 q_1/n_1)$ and $(p_2, p_2 q_2/n_2)$, respectively. Hence it follows from the theorem that the sampling distribution for the difference in sample proportions, $\hat{p}_1 - \hat{p}_2$, will be approximately normally distributed, with mean

$$\mu_{\hat{p}_1 - \hat{p}_2} = p_1 - p_2$$

and variance

$$\sigma^2_{\hat{p}_1 - \hat{p}_2} = \frac{p_1 q_1}{n_1} + \frac{p_2 q_2}{n_2}$$

and standard error

$$\sigma_{\hat{p}_1 - \hat{p}_2} = \sqrt{\frac{p_1 q_1}{n_1} + \frac{p_2 q_2}{n_2}}$$

The sampling distribution for $\hat{p}_1 - \hat{p}_2$ is as shown in Figure 8.2.

FIGURE 8.2

Sampling distribution for the difference between two sample proportions

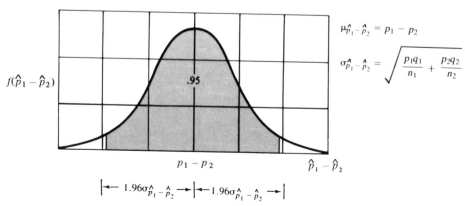

$f(\hat{p}_1 - \hat{p}_2)$

PROPERTY OF THE SAMPLING DISTRIBUTION FOR $\hat{p}_1 - \hat{p}_2$

1. The sampling distribution of $\hat{p}_1 - \hat{p}_2$ will be approximately normal for large samples.
2. The mean of the sampling distribution, $\mu_{\hat{p}_1 - \hat{p}_2}$, is equal to the difference between the means of the sampling proportions, $p_1 - p_2$.
3. The standard error of the sampling distribution is

$$\sigma_{\hat{p}_1 - \hat{p}_2} = \sqrt{\frac{p_1 q_1}{n_1} + \frac{p_2 q_2}{n_2}}$$

The sampling distribution for the difference between two sample means, $\bar{X}_1 - \bar{X}_2$, or the difference between two sample proportions, $\hat{p}_1 - \hat{p}_2$, can be used to answer the same types of questions asked about the sampling distributions for $\bar{X}$ and $\hat{p}$ in Chapter 7. Since the sample statistics are used to make inferences about corresponding population parameters, we can use the sampling distribution of a statistic to calculate the probability that the statistic will be within a specified distance of the population parameter. For example, we could use the sampling distribution of the difference in sample means to calculate the probability that $\bar{X}_1 - \bar{X}_2$ will be within a specified distance of the unknown difference in population means, $\mu_1 - \mu_2$. Inferences (estimations or tests) about $\mu_1 - \mu_2$ or $p_1 - p_2$ based on large samples will be discussed in succeeding sections of this chapter.

EXERCISES

1. If X_1 represents a measurement from a population with the mean equal to 250 and a standard deviation of 30, and X_2 represents a measurement from a population with the mean equal to 200 and a standard deviation of 40, describe the following:
   a. sampling distribution of $\bar{X}_1$ based on $n = 25$ measurements
   b. sampling distribution of $\bar{X}_2$ based on $n = 25$ measurements
   c. sampling distribution of $\bar{X}_1 - \bar{X}_2$ for $n_1 = n_2 = 25$

2. Refer to Exercise 1.
   a. Repeat parts (a) and (b) with $n = 100$. What effect does the increased sample size have?
   b. Describe the sampling distribution of $\bar{X}_1 - \bar{X}_2$ for $n_1 = n_2 = 100$, using the empirical rule.
   c. What relation is there between the sample size and the standard error in parts (a) and (b)?

3. Describe the sampling distribution for $\hat{p}_1 - \hat{p}_2$ based on the following conditions:
   a. $n_1 = n_2 = 100$; $p_1 = .4$, $p_2 = .2$
   b. $n_1 = 100$, $n_2 = 100$; $p_1 = .8$, $p_2 = .7$
   c. $n_1 = 200$, $n_2 = 50$; $p_1 = .4$, $p_2 = .55$

8.3 COMPARISON OF TWO POPULATION MEANS: LARGE-SAMPLE RESULTS

Populations are frequently compared by examining the difference in their means. We may wish to compare the mean suicide rates between two regions of a country or compare mean divorce rates between two races. For each of these problems we assume that we are sampling from two different populations or universes, the first with mean μ_1 and variance σ_1^2, the second with mean μ_2 and variance σ_2^2. Independent random samples of sizes n_1 and n_2 measurements are then drawn from populations 1 and 2, respectively. Finally, the estimates $\bar{X}_1$, s_1^2, $\bar{X}_2$, and s_2^2 of the corresponding population parameters are computed from the sample data. (See Table 8.1.)

TABLE 8.1

Notation for sampling
from two populations

	Population	
Characteristic	**1**	**2**
population mean	μ_1	μ_2
population variance	σ_1^2	σ_2^2
sample size	n_1	n_2
sample mean	$\bar{X}_1$	$\bar{X}_2$
sample variance	s_1^2	s_2^2

A logical estimate for the difference in population means is the difference in sample means, $\bar{X}_1 - \bar{X}_2$. As we have seen in Section 8.2, the difference in sample means has a sampling distribution (for large n) that is approximately normal, with mean and standard error given by

$$\mu_{\bar{X}_1 - \bar{X}_2} = \mu_1 - \mu_2 \quad \text{and} \quad \sigma_{\bar{X}_1 - \bar{X}_2} = \sqrt{\frac{\sigma_1^2}{n_1} + \frac{\sigma_2^2}{n_2}}$$

Knowing the properties of the normal curve and following the same logic applied in Chapter 6, it is possible to show that the form of a confidence interval for $\mu_1 - \mu_2$ is the same as that for μ with $\bar{X}$ replaced by $\bar{X}_1 - \bar{X}_2$ and σ_X replaced by $\sigma_{\bar{X}_1 - \bar{X}_2}$. This result is shown next.

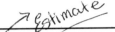
↗ Estimate

LARGE-SAMPLE 95% CONFIDENCE INTERVAL FOR $\mu_1 - \mu_2$

$$(\bar{X}_1 - \bar{X}_2) \pm 1.96\sigma_{\bar{X}_1 - \bar{X}_2}$$

where

$$\sigma_{\bar{X}_1 - \bar{X}_2} = \sqrt{\frac{\sigma_1^2}{n_1} + \frac{\sigma_2^2}{n_2}}$$

(*Note:* If σ_1^2 and σ_2^2 are unknown, we can substitute s_1^2 and s_2^2, respectively, provided the sample sizes n_1 and n_2 are equal to 30 or more. Also, for a 90% or 99% confidence interval, substitute 1.645 or 2.58, respectively, for the 1.96 that appears in the 95% confidence interval shown above.)

EXAMPLE 8.1

A study was conducted to determine if persons in suburban district 1 have a different mean income from those in district 2. A random sample of 50 homeowners was taken in district 1. Although we also wished to interview 50 homeowners in district 2, one person refused to provide the information requested even though we promised to keep it confidential, so only 49 observations were obtained from district 2. The data produced sample means and variances as shown in Table 8.2. Use these data to place a 95% confidence interval on $\mu_1 - \mu_2$.

TABLE 8.2

Income data for Example 8.1

	District	
Characteristic	**1**	**2**
sample size	$n_1 = 50$	$n_2 = 49$
sample mean	$\bar{X}_1 = 34{,}270$	$\bar{X}_2 = 32{,}780$
sample variance	$s_1^2 = 8740$	$s_2^2 = 6580$

SOLUTION

The difference in the sample means is

$$\bar{X}_1 - \bar{X}_2 = 34{,}270 - 32{,}780 = 1490$$

Since the sample variances are good estimates of σ_1^2 and σ_2^2 (which are unknown), we can substitute them into the formula for $\sigma_{\bar{X}_1 - \bar{X}_2}$ to obtain

$$\sqrt{\frac{\sigma_1^2}{n_1} + \frac{\sigma_2^2}{n_2}} \approx \sqrt{\frac{8740}{50} + \frac{6580}{49}} = 17.58$$

Hence $1.96\sigma_{\bar{X}_1 - \bar{X}_2} = 34.46$.

A 95% confidence interval for the difference in mean incomes for the two districts has a lower limit of

$$(\bar{X}_1 - \bar{X}_2) - 1.96\sigma_{\bar{X}_1 - \bar{X}_2} = 1490 - 34.46 = 1455.54$$

and an upper limit of

$$(\bar{X}_1 - \bar{X}_2) - 1.96\sigma_{\bar{X}_1 - \bar{X}_2} = 1490 + 34.46 = 1524.46$$

We are 95% confident that the difference in the population means lies in the interval 1455.54 to 1524.46.

The corresponding statistical test of a hypothesis about the difference between two population means μ_1 and μ_2 follows the logic developed for a test concerning a single population mean. The test procedure requires adequate sample sizes to estimate the population variances σ_1^2 and σ_2^2, because they will rarely be known. We suggest the requirement that n_1 and n_2 both be 30 or more. Then you can use s_1^2 and s_2^2 to approximate σ_1^2 and σ_2^2. Many students wonder what test can be used if one or more of the sample sizes is less than 30. We will present an appropriate small-sample test in Section 8.4 to cover this situation.

A summary of the elements in the large-sample test for the difference in means is given next.

LARGE-SAMPLE TEST FOR COMPARING TWO POPULATION MEANS

Research hypothesis for a one-tailed test

1. $H_1: \mu_1 - \mu_2 > 0$
2. $H_1: \mu_1 - \mu_2 < 0$

Research hypothesis for a two-tailed test

3. $H_1: \mu_1 - \mu_2 \neq 0$

Null hypothesis $H_0: \mu_1 - \mu_2 = 0$
Test statistic

$$z = \frac{\bar{X}_1 - \bar{X}_2}{\sigma_{\bar{X}_1 - \bar{X}_2}} \quad \text{where} \quad \sigma_{\bar{X}_1 - \bar{X}_2} = \sqrt{\frac{\sigma_1^2}{n_1} + \frac{\sigma_2^2}{n_2}}$$

Rejection region for a one-tailed test with α specified

1. R.R.: Reject H_0 if $z > z_\alpha$.
2. R.R.: Reject H_0 if $z < -z_\alpha$.

Rejection region for a two-tailed test with α specified

3. R.R.: Reject H_0 if $z > z_{\alpha/2}$ or $z < -z_{\alpha/2}$.

Assumptions

1. The variables being studied are measured on interval or ratio scales.
2. Random samples of n_1 and n_2 measurements are selected from populations 1 and 2, respectively.
3. The sampling distribution of $\bar{X}_1 - \bar{X}_2$ is approximately normal.
4. Both sample sizes must be 30 or more in order to replace the unknown population variances σ_1^2 and σ_2^2 by s_1^2 and s_2^2, respectively.

EXAMPLE 8.2

Two samples of 30 SMSAs were collected, one from the North and one from the West. Use the data of Table 8.3 to test the null hypothesis of equality of means for the rate of reported rapes in North and West. (Use $\alpha = .05$.)

SOLUTION

Using the data from Table 8.3, we find the following means and variances (subscript 1 is used for the North data and subscript 2 for the West):

$$X_1 = 40.6 \qquad X_2 = 48.5$$
$$s_1 = 376.36 \qquad s_2 = 259.21$$

We will investigate the research hypothesis that the mean reported rate of rape is higher for the West. Our research and null hypotheses can be written as follows:

$$H_1: \mu_1 - \mu_2 < 0$$
$$H_0: \mu_1 - \mu_2 = 0$$

The test statistic is

$$z = \frac{\bar{X}_1 - \bar{X}_2}{\sqrt{\dfrac{\sigma_1^2}{n_1} + \dfrac{\sigma_2^2}{n_2}}}$$

with the sample variances s_1 and s_2 replacing σ_1^2 and σ_2^2. Thus we have

$$z = \frac{40.6 - 48.5}{\sqrt{\dfrac{378.12}{30} + \dfrac{257.71}{30}}} = \frac{-7.9}{4.60} = -1.72$$

TABLE 8.3	North	Rate	West	Rate
Rate of reported rapes for 60 SMSAs selected from the North and West	Akron, OH	39	Bakersfield, CA	58
	Allentown, PA	18	Brownsville, TX	18
	Ann Arbor, MI	87	Colorado Springs, CO	69
	Atlantic City, NJ	54	Denver, CO	47
	Benton Harbor, MI	100	Fresno, CA	65
	Boston, MA	32	Galveston, TX	46
	Buffalo, NY	34	Houston, TX	61
	Canton, OH	30	Kansas City, KA	51
	Cincinnati, OH	36	Lawton, OK	48
	Cleveland, OH	53	Lubbock, TX	58
	Columbus, OH	59	Modesto, CA	40
	Dayton, OH	48	Oklahoma City, OK	58
	Evansville, IN	21	Oxnard, CA	33
	Gary, IN	31	Pueblo, CO	68
	Jersey City, NJ	34	Redding, CA	43
	Johnstown, PA	15	Reno, NV	81
	Kenosha, WI	40	Sacramento, CA	50
	Madison, WI	24	St. Louis, MO	27
	Mansfield, OH	30	Salinas, KA	44
	Milwaukee, WI	35	Salt Lake City, UT	32
	Minneapolis, MN	43	San Diego, CA	36
	Muskegon, MI	57	San Jose, CA	46
	Newark, NJ	56	Seattle, WA	59
	Philadelphia, PA	38	Sioux City, IA	24
	Pittsfield, MA	41	Spokane, WA	34
	Portland, ME	21	Stockton, CA	41
	Racine, WI	49	Tacoma, WA	86
	Reading, PA	14	Tucson, AR	55
	Syracuse, NY	23	Victoria, TX	32
	Vineland, NJ	55	Waco, TX	45

Source: U.S. Department of Justice, *Uniform Crime Reports for the United States.*

Note: Rates represent the number of reported rapes per 100,000 inhabitants, rounded to the nearest whole number.

For a one-tailed test with $\alpha = .05$, we will reject H_0 if z is less than -1.645. Since the computed value of z exceeds -1.645, we reject H_0 and conclude that the mean number of rapes is higher, on the average, for SMSAs in the West than in the North.

EXERCISES

4. Two hospitals studied the average number of days required to treat patients between the ages of 25 and 34. Random samples of 500 hospital patients were selected from each hospital. The sample means were 6.8 and 5.4 days and the sample standard deviations were 3.1 and 3.7 days, respectively. Estimate the difference $\mu_1 - \mu_2$ in mean stay, and construct a 95% confidence interval for $\mu_1 - \mu_2$.

5. Two random samples, one from 50 nonunionized companies and one from 50 unionized companies, were selected to compare the mean hourly income of nonunion and union workers. The 50 nonunionized companies offered a mean wage of $8.80 with a standard deviation of $.50, while the unionized companies offered a mean wage of $9.20 with a standard deviation of $.45. Do these data present sufficient evidence to indicate a difference in mean hourly wages between nonunion and union companies? (Use $\alpha = .05$.)

6. Two random samples of 100 adults each, selected from two ethnic minorities in a large city, were questioned concerning the number of years they attended public schools. Samples for the two ethnic minorities gave $\bar{X}_1 = 9.4$, $s_1 = 2.1$, $\bar{X}_2 = 10.2$, and $s_2 = 2.4$. Test to see if there is evidence of a real difference between the two population means. (Use $\alpha = .05$.)

7. David Monsees studied heterosexual experiences in Colombia, South America. Subjects recalled their age at their first coital experience. You hypothesize that males experience their first heterosexual activity at a younger age, on the average, than females. Using the data in the accompanying table, compute the means and variances. Do the data support your hypothesis? Explain.

EXERCISE 7

Age at first heterosexual (coital) experience

Age	Number of Males	Number of Females
8–9	1	0
10–11	5	0
12–13	42	16
14–15	68	77
16–17	64	74
18–19	72	70

Age	Number of Males	Number of Females
20–21	29	32
22–23	13	28
24–25	13	12
26–27	2	3
28–29	0	5
30–31	2	2
Total	311	319

Source: David M. Monsees, "Study of First Heterosexual Experience" (unpublished paper); by permission.

8. To reduce the growing national debt, legislation was introduced in Congress to reduce federal outlays to counties. Preliminary research indicates that the per capita reductions per year would vary between $25 and $128. A researcher sampled 100 rural counties and 100 urban counties and reported that the average per capita reduction for the rural counties would be $54 with a standard deviation of $16, and the reduction for the urban counties would be $80 with a standard deviation of $25. Test to see if there is evidence of a real difference in per capita reductions for rural and urban counties. (Use $\alpha = .01$.)

9. Refer to Exercise 8. Members of the House of Representatives were concerned that reductions in federal outlays be equitable. Their data showed that the mean per capita reduction for counties in Southern states would be $50 with a standard deviation of $30 for 50 counties, while the mean per capita reduction for 50 Northern states would be $75 with a standard deviation of $35. Test to see if there is evidence of a real difference in per capita reductions. What conclusions would you draw and why?

10. Using the original data from Table 5.6 pertaining to reported rate of rape, a researcher finds that the mean for 30 SMSAs in the South is 40.87. Means and variances for the North and West are reported in Example 8.2.
   a. Calculate the variance of the 30 SMSAs in the South.
   b. Test to see if there is evidence of a real difference in the reported rate of rape for the SMSAs in the South and the North. (Use $\alpha = .05$.) What conclusions do you draw?
   c. Test to see if there is evidence of a real difference in the reported rate of rape for the SMSAs in the South and West (Use $\alpha = .05$.)

11. Stafford and Reske (1990) explored the tendency for young couples to idealize each other, especially if they are involved in a long-distance relationship. They interviewed 34 geographically close (GC) couples and 37 long-distance (LD) couples. Subjects were scored on a premarital adjustment scale (PAS), idealistic

distortion scale (IDS), and frequency of interaction scale (FIS). The higher the score, the greater the perceived premarital adjustment, the more distortion, or the more frequently the couple interacted. Means and standard deviations are shown in the accompanying table.

Scale	Geographically Close		Long Distance	
	Mean	SD	Mean	SD
premarital adjustment	108.8	16.6	119.1	15.4
idealistic distortion	16.5	2.8	18.1	2.7
frequency of interaction	7.3	4.1	2.7	2.0

Source: Adapted from Laura Stafford and James R. Reske, "Idealization and Communication in Long-Distance Premarital Relationships," *Family Relations* 39 (1990), p. 276. Copyrighted 1990 by the National Council on Family Relations, 3989 Central Ave., N.E., Suite #550, Minneapolis, MN 55421. Reprinted by permission.

a. Test the null hypothesis of no difference between the two means on the premarital adjustment scale. (Set $\alpha = .05$.) Interpret your results.
b. Test the null hypothesis of no difference between the two means on the idealistic distortion scale. (Set $\alpha = .05$.) Interpret your results.
c. Test the null hypothesis of no difference between the two means on the frequency of interaction. (Set $\alpha = .01$.) Interpret your results.

8.4   COMPARISON OF TWO POPULATION MEANS: SMALL-SAMPLE RESULTS

The small-sample test of a hypothesis about the difference in two means is similar to the large-sample test, except that we make a few additional assumptions concerning the sampled populations.

As with large samples, the test statistic for small samples to test the null hypothesis $\mu_1 - \mu_2 = 0$ uses the difference in the sample means, $\bar{X}_1 - \bar{X}_2$. This difference is based on independent random samples of n_1 and n_2 observations, respectively, from the two populations. If the sample difference is too far away from $\mu_1 - \mu_2 = 0$, we reject the null hypothesis.

If we assume that both populations are normal, with means μ_1 and μ_2 but with the same variance σ^2, we can use a Student's t statistic for a test statistic for small samples:

$$t = \frac{\bar{X}_1 - \bar{X}_2}{s_p \sqrt{\frac{1}{n_1} + \frac{1}{n_2}}}$$

The quantity s in the test statistic is an estimate of the standard deviation σ for the two populations and is formed by combining information from the two samples. Thus we have

$$s_p = \sqrt{\frac{(n_1 - 1)s_1^2 + (n_2 - 1)s_2^2}{n_1 + n_2 - 2}}$$

A summary of the elements in the small-sample test for the difference in means is given as follows.

SMALL-SAMPLE t-TEST FOR COMPARING TWO MEANS

Research hypothesis for a one-tailed test

1. $H_1: \mu_1 - \mu_2 > 0$
2. $H_1: \mu_1 - \mu_2 < 0$

Research hypothesis for a two-tailed test

1. $H_1: \mu_1 - \mu_2 \neq 0$

Null hypothesis $H_0: \mu_1 - \mu_2 = 0$
Test statistic

$$t = \frac{\bar{X}_1 - \bar{X}_2}{s_p \sqrt{\frac{1}{n_1} + \frac{1}{n_2}}} \quad \text{where} \quad s_p = \sqrt{\frac{(n_1 - 1)s_1^2 + (n_2 - 1)s_2^2}{n_1 + n_2 - 2}}$$

Rejection region for a one-tailed test with α specified

1. R.R.: Reject H_0 if $t > t_\alpha$.
2. R.R.: Reject H_0 if $t < -t_\alpha$.

Rejection region for a two-tailed test with α specified

3. R.R.: Reject H_0 if $t > t_{\alpha/2}$ or $t < -t_{\alpha/2}$.

(*Note:* d.f. $= n_1 + n_2 - 2$)
Assumptions

1. The variables being studied are measured on interval or ratio scales.
2. Random samples of n_1 and n_2 measurements are obtained from populations 1 and 2, respectively.
3. Both populations are normal.
4. The populations' variances are identical (i.e., $\sigma_1^2 = \sigma_2^2$).

In fact, s_p^2 is a weighted average of the sample variances s_1^2 and s_2^2 and is sometimes called a *pooled estimate* of the variances (hence the subscript p). For the special case where the sample sizes are the same ($n_1 = n_2$), the formula for s_p^2 reduces to $s_p^2 = (s_1^2 + s_2^2)/2$, the mean of the two sample variances. The degrees of freedom for the test statistic are a combination of the degrees of freedom for the two samples:

$$\text{d.f.} = (n_1 - 1) + (n_2 - 1) = n_1 + n_2 - 2$$

The rejection region for the t-test is selected as for the test of a hypothesis about a single mean (Section 7.8). For a two-tailed test, we look up t_a in Appendix Table 2 corresponding to $a = \alpha/2$ and d.f. $= n_1 + n_2 - 2$. For a one-tailed test, we read the tabulated t-value corresponding to $a = \alpha$ with d.f. $= n_1 + n_2 - 2$.

EXAMPLE 8.3   Based on data contained in Appendix Table 8, Database B, life expectancies for each country in a random sample of five Latin American countries and a random sample of five African countries are shown in Table 8.4. Use the data to test the research hypothesis that, on the average, life expectancy is higher for Latin American countries than for African countries. (Use $\alpha = .05$.)

TABLE 8.4

Life expectancies in 5 Latin American and 5 African countries

Latin American	Life Expectancy	African	Life Expectancy
Bolivia	53	Egypt	60
Brazil	65	Ghana	55
Colombia	66	Nigeria	48
Peru	65	Senegal	46
Uruguay	71	Zaire	53

Source: Population Reference Bureau, *1990 World Population Data Sheet*, Population Reference Bureau, Inc. (Washington, D.C., 1990).

SOLUTION   The results of the computations for these data are shown in Table 8.5. Since the sample sizes are the same, the quantity s_p is the average of the sample variances:

$$s_p^2 = \frac{s_1^2 + s_2^2}{2} = \frac{44.0 + 31.3}{2} = 37.65$$

$$s_p = \sqrt{37.65} = 6.14$$

Characteristics	Latin American	African
sample size	5	5
sample mean	64.0	52.4
sample variance	44.0	31.3

TABLE 8.5

Computations for
Example 8.3

Denoting Latin American countries as population 1, we write the research
and null hypotheses as

$$H_1: \mu_1 - \mu_2 > 0$$
$$H_0: \mu_1 - \mu_2 = 0$$

The test statistic is

$$t = \frac{\bar{X}_1 - \bar{X}_2}{S_p\sqrt{\dfrac{1}{n_1} + \dfrac{1}{n_2}}} = \frac{64.0 - 52.4}{6.14\sqrt{\dfrac{1}{5} + \dfrac{1}{5}}} = \frac{11.60}{3.88} = 2.99$$

The rejection region (see Figure 8.3) for a one-tailed test with $\alpha = .05$ utilizes
a t-value from Appendix Table 2 with $a = .05$ and d.f. $= n_1 + n_2 - 2 = 8$.
This value is 1.860. Since the computed value of t is greater than 1.860, we
have sufficient evidence to reject the null hypothesis of equality of means for
the Latin American and African countries. Practically, it appears that Latin
American countries have a higher life expectancy.

Before concluding our discussion of the t-test, you might wonder whether
the assumptions of normal populations and equal variances ($\sigma_1^2 = \sigma_2^2$) must
hold in order for the t-test to be valid. The test functions satisfactorily for

FIGURE 8.3

Rejection region for t
in Example 8.3 when
$a = .05$ and d.f. $= 8$

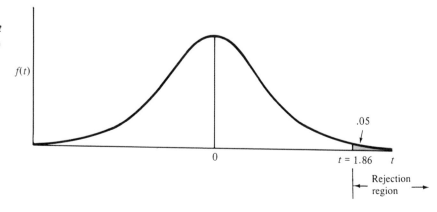

populations possessing mound-shaped probability distributions. The assumption is that $\sigma_1^2 = \sigma_2^2$ is more critical, but again it does not seriously affect the properties of the test if n_1 and n_2 are approximately equal. Consequently, the assumptions are not too restrictive, and the test has wide applicability. For now we will assume that $\sigma_1^2 \approx \sigma_2^2$ and that the two-sample t-test can be applied.

In addition to being able to test a hypothesis about two population means when using small sample sizes, we can also construct a small-sample confidence interval for $\mu_1 - \mu_2$. The formula for a small-sample 95% confidence interval for the difference between two population means is shown next. Because of the simplicity of the formula and its similarity to the large-sample result, we will not illustrate its use with an example.

SMALL-SAMPLE 95% CONFIDENCE INTERVAL FOR $\mu_1 - \mu_2$

$$(\bar{X}_1 - \bar{X}_2) \pm t_a s_p \sqrt{\frac{1}{n_1} + \frac{1}{n_2}}$$

where

$$s_p = \sqrt{\frac{(n_1 - 1)s_1^2 + (n_2 - 1)s_2^2}{n_1 + n_2 - 2}}$$

and t_a is the tabulated value of t (see Appendix Table 2) for $a = .025$ and d.f. $= n_1 + n_2 - 2$. (*Note:* The only change necessary to obtain either a 90% or 99% confidence interval is in the value of t_a. The appropriate tabulated values are obtained from Appendix Table 2 for $a = .05$ and $a = .005$, respectively. The degrees of freedom remain the same.)

[handwritten margin notes: "Estimate", "Always 2-tailed"]

EXERCISES

12. When utilizing the t distribution in making small-sample inferences about the difference in population means, what assumptions are made about the populations from which the independent random samples are selected?

13. Sixteen racially prejudiced, white, married couples were selected, with 8 randomly assigned to live in a highly integrated neighborhood and the other 8 in a highly segregated (black) neighborhood. After the first 12 months, the racial attitudes of the couples were compared, with the husband and wife treated as a unit. (See the accompanying table.) Assume that the data were interval level and that high scores reflect favorable attitudes towards minority group members. Do the data present sufficient evidence to indicate a difference in the mean racial attitude for the two types of neighborhoods? (Use $\alpha = .05$.)

EXERCISE 13

Racial attitudes

Segregated Neighborhood		Integrated Neighborhood	
1	2	4	1
3	1	2	2
2	3	3	3
1	2	3	3

14. Construct a 95% confidence interval for $\mu_1 - \mu_2$, using the data of Example 8.3. How would the interval change if the confidence coefficient were .90 rather than .95?

15. A study was conducted to investigate the effect of two diets on the weight gain of 14-year-old children suffering from malnutrition. Ten children were subjected to diet 1 and 9 to diet 2. The gains in weight over a nine-month period are shown in the accompanying table. Use the data to determine if there is evidence to indicate a difference between the mean gain in weight for children fed on the two diets. (Use $\alpha = .05$.)

EXERCISE 15

Weight gain

Diet 1		Diet 2	
14.0	11.2	14.4	11.6
12.5	15.0	18.2	12.8
10.2	22.0	19.5	13.1
9.8	13.0	21.2	11.3
10.5	9.6	15.3	

16. Refer to the previous exercise. Compare the results you obtained there to the accompanying computer-generated output for a two-sample t-test.

EXERCISE 16

```
MTB > twosamplet 'DIET1' 'DIET2';
SUBC> pooled.

TWOSAMPLE T FOR DIET1 VS DIET2
            N      MEAN     STDEV    SE MEAN
DIET1   10      12.78      3.73       1.2
DIET2    9      15.27      3.58       1.2

95 PCT CI FOR MU DIET1 - MU DIET2: (-6.0, 1.1)

TTEST MU DIET1 = MU DIET2 (VS NE): T= -1.48  P=0.16  DF=  17

POOLED STDEV =       3.66
```

17. The high school dropout rate in urban areas was studied. A random sample of 1645 schools was selected. Each school reported its dropout rate for the last semester. The results for the random sample of schools, broken down by racial

composition, are summarized in the accompanying table. Use the data to test the research hypothesis that the mean dropout rate in primarily black schools is different than in primarily white schools. (Use $\alpha = .05$.) Draw a practical conclusion.

EXERCISE 17

Dropout rate data

Schools	Sample Size	Mean	Standard Deviation
white	736	5.54	7.03
black	909	7.28	6.95

18. An educational researcher studied the mental abilities of Midwestern students enrolled in public and private secondary schools. Give the level of significance for the research hypothesis that the mean mental ability for students enrolled in private schools is higher than for students in public schools.

EXERCISE 18

Data for mental abilities of students

Characteristic	Private	Public
sample size	258	530
mean	71.26	49.31
standard deviation	392.44	240.43

19. The mean per capita school expenditure in five randomly selected Southern counties is $652 with a variance of $4727, and the mean per capita school expenditure in five randomly selected Northern counties is $726 with a variance of $14,615. Do the data indicate that Northern counties provide greater support for their schools than do Southern counties? (Use $\alpha = .05$.)

20. Refer to Exercise 19. Assume that you repeat the experiment but find that for a random sample of five Southern counties the mean is $565 with a variance of $4727, and for a random sample of five Northern counties the mean is $751 with a variance of $14,615.
    a. Is there evidence to indicate that your Southern sample differs from the original sample, where the mean equals $652?
    b. Is there evidence to indicate that your Northern sample differs from the original sample, where the mean equals $726?
    c. Using only your data, do you think they indicate that Northern counties provide greater support for their schools than do Southern counties? (Use $\alpha = .05$.)

21. Draw two additional random samples of 5 countries each from countries listed in Appendix Table 8, Database B: one sample of Latin American nations and one of African nations. Test the hypothesis that, on the average, life expectancy is higher for Latin American countries than for African countries. (Use $\alpha = .05$.) Compare and contrast your findings with the results shown in Example 8.3.

22. Demos (1990) counted the number of articles in the *Journal of Marriage and the Family* that focused on blacks. She wanted to know whether or not federal funds for research on blacks had increased over the years. From her data, you draw two random samples of five years each, one from journal issues before 1965 and the other from issues after 1965. The number of articles appearing in journals before 1965 is 3, 0, 1, 2, and 0. After 1965 the count is 20, 5, 10, 4, and 12. Test the hypothesis that there has been an increase in number of articles dealing with black families. (Set $\alpha = $ to .01.)

8.5   ANOTHER TWO-SAMPLE TEST: THE MANN-WHITNEY U-TEST

Some studies yield only ordinal-level data because of the crudeness of the measuring instruments employed by social researchers. (*Note:* This is no fault of the investigators but rather a problem in obtaining interval or ratio scores.) Although ordinal measurements are made in almost all fields of study, they are particularly common in social research. For example, when the variables of interest are anomie, social differentiation, prestige, power, social control, or alienation, they are often measured by crude scales, and researchers cannot assume ratio- or even interval-level data. In such cases the estimation and comparative test procedures presented thus far in this chapter are of little use. **Nonparametric statistical techniques** are appropriate, however, and they are very useful for analyzing such data. Nonparametric statistical methods are also appropriate for ratio data when the assumptions underlying the parametric test procedures (for example, the assumption of normal populations) fail to hold.

The word *nonparametric* evolves from the type of hypothesis usually tested when dealing with nominal or ordinal data. *Parametric* tests are statistical tests concerning one or more population parameters. Nonparametric tests are different. For example, instead of hypothesizing that two populations have the same mean (as in Section 8.3), we could hypothesize that the two populations of measurements are identical. Note that the practical implications of these two hypotheses are not equivalent, because the latter hypothesis is less clearly defined. Two distributions could be different and still have the same mean. We will now consider a nonparametric procedure that utilizes the ranks of measurements to test the hypothesis that two populations are identical.

In 1947 Mann and Whitney proposed a nonparametric test statistic for comparing two populations. Since the two populations are hypothesized to be identical, samples taken from the respective populations should be similar. One way to measure the similarity of these two samples is to count the number of observations in sample 1 (drawn from the first population) that are less than each observation in sample 2 (drawn from the second population). If this number, called U, is extremely large or extremely small, we would intuitively reject the hypothesis that the populations are identical.

A shortcut procedure for calculating U can be obtained by ranking the observations from the two samples as if they were one, letting the smallest observation from the two samples have a rank of 1, the next smallest a rank of 2, and so on. Then for samples of size n_1 and n_2, the number of observations from sample 1, less than each observation from sample 2 is

$$U = n_1 n_2 + \frac{n_1(n_1 + 1)}{2} - T_1$$

where T_1 is the sum of ranks for observations in sample 1.

It can be shown that when the two populations are identical and when n_1 and n_2 are both larger than 10, U is approximately normally distributed, with mean and standard deviation given by

$$\mu_U = \frac{n_1 n_2}{2} \quad \text{and} \quad \sigma_U = \sqrt{\frac{n_1 n_2(n_1 + n_2 + 1)}{12}}$$

We summarize the procedure for the **Mann-Whitney U-test** as follows.

MANN-WHITNEY U-TEST FOR IDENTICAL POPULATIONS

Research hypothesis for a one-tailed test

1. H_1: The distribution of measurements for population 1 is above (to the right of) the distribution of measurements for population 2.
2. H_1: The distribution of measurements for population 1 is below (to the left of) the distribution of measurements for population 2.

Research hypothesis for a two-tailed test

3. H_1: The distribution of measurements for the two populations are different.

Null hypothesis H_0: The distribution of measurements for the two populations are identical.

Test statistic

$$z = \frac{U - \mu_U}{\sigma_U}$$

Rejection region

1. R.R.: Reject H_0 if $z > z_\alpha$.
2. R.R.: Reject H_0 if $z < z_\alpha$.
3. R.R.: Reject H_0 if $z > z_{\alpha/2}$ or $z < -z_{\alpha/2}$.

Assumptions

1. The variables under study are measured on ordinal, interval, or ratio scales.
2. A random sample is selected from each of the two populations.
3. Both sample sizes are 10 or more.

We illustrate the test procedure with an example.

EXAMPLE 8.4

A sample of $n_1 = 25$ Catholic priests and a sample of $n_2 = 25$ Methodist ministers were randomly selected to determine if there is a difference between the two groups with respect to knowledge about the causes of mental illness. Each of the ministers and priests was administered a standard questionnaire scored from 0 to 40. The sample test score data, arranged in ascending order, appear in Table 8.6. Jointly rank the 50 test scores and use the Mann-Whitney test to check the hypothesis that there is no difference between Methodist ministers and Catholic priests with respect to their knowledge about the causes of mental illness. (Use $\alpha = .05$.)

TABLE 8.6

Mental health test scores

Methodist Ministers		Catholic Priests	
5	17	5	19
6	19	7	19
8	19	8	20
8	20	8	20
10	21	8	21
10	22	9	22
11	22	12	24
11	22	13	24
13	23	13	26
13	24	14	26
14	28	14	27
16	28	18	27
17		19	

SOLUTION

Recall that a test procedure developed for any one scale of measurement can be applied to data collected on a scale of higher quantitative sophistication.

Thus, although the test score data are measured on an interval scale, if we are uncomfortable with assuming normality of the test scores, we can apply the Mann-Whitney U-test, which was developed for ordinal data.

Before computing U, we must first jointly rank all 50 observations by assigning the lowest observation the rank of 1, the second lowest observation the rank of 2, and so on. **When two or more measurements are the same, we assign all of them a rank equal to the average of the ranks they occupy.**

The smallest observation from either sample is 5, but two clerics received a score of 5. These two measurements occupy ranks 1 and 2, so both individuals receive a rank equal to the average of the occupied ranks — namely, 1.5.

The next smallest score is a 6, and since there are no other scores of 6, we assign the rank of 3. Similarly, only one priest scored 7; he receives a rank of 4. There were five ministers or priests who received a score of 8, the next lowest measurement. The average of the occupied ranks is

$$\frac{5 + 6 + 7 + 8 + 9}{5} = 7$$

So all five observations receive a rank of 7. The remaining scores, ranked in the same way, appear in Table 8.7.

TABLE 8.7

Mental health test
scores and ranks

Methodist Ministers		Catholic Priests	
Score	Rank	Score	Rank
5	1.5	5	1.5
6	3	7	4
8	7	8	7
8	7	8	7
10	11.5	8	7
10	11.5	9	10
11	13.5	12	15
11	13.5	13	17.5
13	17.5	13	17.5
13	17.5	14	21
14	21	14	21
16	23	18	26
17	24.5	19	29
17	24.5	19	29
19	29	19	29
19	29	20	33

Methodist Ministers		Catholic Priests	
Score	Rank	Score	Rank
20	33	20	33
21	35.5	21	35.5
22	38.5	22	38.5
22	38.5	24	43
22	38.5	24	43
23	41	26	45.5
24	43	26	45.5
28	49.5	27	47.5
28	49.5	27	47.5
$T_1 = 621.5$		$T_2 = 653.5$	

The quantities μ and σ_U are computed for $n_1 = n_2 = 25$:

$$\mu_U = \frac{n_1 n_2}{2} = \frac{25(25)}{2} = 312.5$$

$$\sigma_U = \sqrt{\frac{n_1 n_2 (n_1 + n_2 + 1)}{12}} = \sqrt{\frac{25(25)(51)}{12}}$$

$$= \sqrt{2656.25} = 51.54$$

For a two-tailed test with $\alpha = .05$, we will reject the null hypothesis if the computed value of z is greater than $z_{\alpha/2} = 1.96$ or less than $-z_{\alpha/2} = -1.96$.

From Table 8.7 we see that the sum of the ranks for observations in sample 1 is $T_1 = 621.5$. Therefore we have

$$U = n_1 n_2 + \frac{n_1(n_1 + 1)}{2} - T_1$$

$$= 25(25) + \frac{25(26)}{2} - 621.5 = 328.5$$

The computed value of z is

$$z = \frac{U - \mu}{\sigma_U} = \frac{328.5 - 312.5}{51.54} = .31$$

Since this value does not exceed 1.96, we conclude that there is insufficient evidence to reject the hypothesis of no difference between Catholic priests and Methodist ministers with respect to their knowledge about causes of mental illness.

EXERCISES

23. What are the assumptions that should be met before performing a Mann-Whitney U-test?

24. A sample of $n_1 = 11$ groups of A students and a sample of $n_2 = 11$ groups of C students were randomly selected to determine if there is a difference between the two kinds of groups in the efficient use of time to complete the drafting of a student government constitution. Each group was rated on a 10-point scale, where a low score denotes efficient use of time. Test the null hypothesis of no difference between the two populations by using the Mann-Whitney U-test. (Use $\alpha = .05$.)

EXERCISE 24

Ratings of groups

Groups of A Students		Groups of C Students	
1	2	5	7
2	3	7	8
4	2	8	6
6	4	9	6
5	8	2	5
7		6	

25. A conference was held for all governmental personnel managers to make them aware of the inequities in government hiring practices towards several minority groups (including women). Random samples of $n_1 = 20$ women and $n_2 = 20$ men were selected from the conference participants, and each person sampled was asked to rate the success of the conference on a scale of 1 to 10 (high scores denote success). These data are recorded in the accompanying table. Use the Mann-Whitney U-test to test the null hypothesis of no difference in the perception of success for the population of male and female personnel managers. (Use $\alpha = .05$.)

EXERCISE 25

Success ratings of the conference

Females		Males	
1	4	7	5
3	4	9	10
4	6	8	6
3	3	5	1
6	0	10	2
8	1	9	3
9	6	10	9
7	4	6	7
8	5	5	4
1	6	2	2

26. Assume that the data in Table 8.3 on the reported rate of rapes are not normally distributed. Use the Mann-Whitney U-test and test the null hypothesis that the two distributions (North and West) are different. (Use $\alpha = .05$.)

27. Use the data in Table 5.6 and test the research hypothesis that the two distributions (South and West) are different. (Use $\alpha = .05$.)

8.6   COMPARISON OF TWO BINOMIAL PARAMETERS

Many practical research problems require the comparison of two binomial parameters. We might wish, for example, to compare the proportion of housewives who utilize prenatal health services before and after a campaign to publicize the services, the proportions of households in two states that are entirely supported by welfare, or the proportions of districts favoring candidate A located in the suburbs versus in rural areas.

We assume that independent random samples are drawn from two binomial populations with parameters p_1 and p_2. Further, we assume that the samples contain n_1 and n_2 observations, respectively. If X_1 represents the number of successes in n_1 trials and X_2 the number of successes in n_2 trials, then

$$\hat{p}_1 = \frac{X_1}{n_1} \quad \text{and} \quad \hat{p}_2 = \frac{X_2}{n_2}$$

which are the sample proportions of successes. These results are summarized in Table 8.8.

TABLE 8.8

Sampling from two binomial populations

Characteristic	Population 1	Population 2
population proportion	p_1	p_2
sample size	n_1	n_2
number of successes	X_1	X_2
sample proportion	$\hat{p}_1 = X_1/n_1$	$\hat{p}_2 = X_2/n_2$

The sampling distribution of $\hat{p}_1 - \hat{p}_2$ will be approximately normal for large values of n_1 and n_2 (see Figure 8.4), with mean and standard error given by

$$\mu_{\hat{p}_1 - \hat{p}_2} = p_1 - p_2 \quad \text{and} \quad \sigma_{\hat{p}_1 - \hat{p}_2} = \sqrt{\frac{p_1 q_1}{n_1} + \frac{p_2 q_2}{n_2}}$$

When large samples are involved, the sample size and value of p for each population should satisfy the requirement that *both np* and *nq* equal 10 or more.

Interval estimation of $p_1 - p_2$ is identical to that for $\mu_1 - \mu_2$, with $\bar{X}_1 - \bar{X}_2$ replaced by $\hat{p}_1 - \hat{p}_2$ and $\sigma_{\bar{X}_1 - \bar{X}_2}$ replaced by $\sigma_{\hat{p}_1 - \hat{p}_2}$. Since we don't know p_1 and p_2, we will substitute $\hat{p}_1$ and $\hat{p}_2$ into the formula for $\sigma_{\hat{p}_1 - \hat{p}_2}$.

95% CONFIDENCE INTERVAL FOR $p_1 - p_2$

$$(\hat{p}_1 - \hat{p}_2) \pm 1.96\sigma_{\hat{p}_1 - \hat{p}_2}$$

where we approximate $\sigma_{\hat{p}_1 - \hat{p}_2}$ by using

$$\sqrt{\frac{\hat{p}_1\hat{q}_1}{n_2} + \frac{\hat{p}_2\hat{q}_2}{n_2}} \quad \text{with} \quad \hat{q}_1 = 1 - \hat{p}_1 \quad \text{and} \quad \hat{q}_2 = 1 - \hat{p}_2$$

Also, for a 90% or 99% confidence interval, substitute 1.645 or 2.58, respectively, for the 1.96 that appears in the 95% confidence interval above.

FIGURE 8.4

Sampling distribution of $\hat{p}_1 - \hat{p}_2$

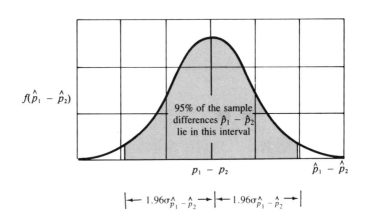

We illustrate these ideas with an example.

EXAMPLE 8.5

In a survey to analyze the cost of funeral expenditures for various social classes, a random sample of 162 families from the lower and working classes was interviewed to determine the funeral expenses for a recent family death. Of the 162 families contacted, 61 spent over $800 on the funeral. In a sample of 189 middle- and upper-class families experiencing a recent family death, 106 spent over $800 on the funeral. The proportions spending over $800 are .376 and .561, respectively. The difference between the proportions is .185. Estimate $p_1 - p_2$ using a 95% confidence interval.

SOLUTION   The interval estimate of $p_1 - p_2$ using the 95% confidence interval is

$$(\hat{p}_1 - \hat{p}_2) \pm 1.96\sigma_{\hat{p}_1 - \hat{p}_2}$$

where

$$\sigma_{\hat{p}_1 - \hat{p}_2} = \sqrt{\frac{\hat{p}_1 \hat{q}_1}{n_2} + \frac{\hat{p}_2 \hat{q}_2}{n_2}}$$

$$= \sqrt{\frac{(.376)(.624)}{162} + \frac{(.561)(.439)}{189}} = .052$$

Therefore

$$.185 \pm 1.96(.052) = .083 \text{ to } .287$$

That is, we are 95% confident that the true difference in the proportions of families that spend over \$800 per funeral for the middle and upper classes and for the lower and working classes lies somewhere between .083 and .287. Since this interval does not include 0, we are confident that the proportion p_1 of upper- and middle-class families spending more than \$800 per funeral is greater than p_2, the corresponding proportion for families in the lower and working classes.

We can readily formulate a statistical test to test the equality of two binomial parameters. A logical test statistic for this test is one that makes use of the difference in sample proportions, $\hat{p}_1 - \hat{p}_2$. The greater the difference between $\hat{p}_1$ and $\hat{p}_2$, the greater is the evidence to indicate that p_1 does not equal p_2.

The test statistic is

$$z = \frac{\hat{p}_1 - \hat{p}_2}{\sqrt{pq\left(\frac{1}{n_1} + \frac{1}{n_2}\right)}}$$

You will need to use the data to approximate p in the formula for $\sigma_{\hat{p}_1 - \hat{p}_2}$. The best estimate of p, the proportion of successes common to both populations, is

$$\hat{p} = \frac{\text{total number of successes}}{\text{total number of trials}} = \frac{X_1 + X_2}{n_1 + n_2} \qquad \text{with} \qquad \hat{q} = 1 - \hat{p}$$

We summarize the test procedure as follows.

LARGE-SAMPLE TEST FOR COMPARING TWO BINOMIAL PROPORTIONS

Research hypothesis for a one-tailed test

1. $H_1: p_1 - p_2 > 0$
2. $H_1: p_1 - p_2 < 0$

Research hypothesis for a two-tailed test

3. $H_1: p_1 - p_2 \neq 0$

Null hypothesis: $H_0 = p_1 - p_2 = 0$

Test statistic

$$z = \frac{\hat{p}_1 - \hat{p}_2}{\sqrt{\hat{p}\hat{q}\left(\dfrac{1}{n_1} + \dfrac{1}{n_2}\right)}} \qquad \text{where} \qquad \hat{p} = \frac{X_1 + X_2}{N_1 + N_2}$$

Rejection region for a one-tailed test with α specified

1. R.R.: Reject H_0 if $z > z_\alpha$.
2. R.R.: Reject H_0 if $z < -z_\alpha$.

Rejection region for a two-tailed test with α specified

3. R.R.: Reject H_0 if $z > z_{\alpha/2}$ or $z < -z_{\alpha/2}$.

Assumptions

1. $\hat{p}_1$ and $\hat{p}_2$ are sample estimates of two binomial parameters p_1 and p_2.
2. $n\hat{p}$ and $n\hat{q}$ are 10 or more for both binomial populations.

The comparison of two binomial proportions is illustrated by the following example.

EXAMPLE 8.6

Two sets of 60 ninth graders were taught high school algebra by two different methods. The experimental group used a programmed learning text with no formal lectures; the control group was given formal lectures by a teacher. At the conclusion of a four-month period, a comprehensive test was given to both groups to determine the proportion of students in each group that obtained a score of 85 (out of 100) or better. The results are shown in Table 8.9. Test the hypothesis that the two population proportions, p_1 and p_2, are equal. (Use a two-tailed test with $\alpha = .01$.)

TABLE 8.9

Data for Example 8.6

	Experimental Group	Control Group
	$n_1 = 60$	$n_2 = 60$
	$X_1 = 41$	$X_2 = 24$

SOLUTION

For all practical purposes, sampling from both populations satisfies the requirements of a binomial experiment. We wish to test the hypothesis that the proportions of students scoring 85 or better are the same for both teaching techniques. Thus the null hypothesis is that $p_1 = p_2$, or $p_1 - p_2 = 0$. We will reject the hypothesis if the z-score lies more than 2.58 away from zero. Then the rejection region for the test is as shown in Figure 8.5.

Recall that we must substitute an approximate value for p in the formula for computing a z-score. Substituting the values given in Table 8.9, the approximation for p is

$$\hat{p} = \frac{X_1 + X_2}{n_1 + n_2} = \frac{41 + 24}{60 + 60} = .54$$

Then the denominator of z is

$$\sqrt{(.54)(.46)\left(\frac{1}{60} + \frac{1}{60}\right)} = .091$$

Similarly, we compute the observed difference in sample proportions to

FIGURE 8.5

Rejection region for Example 8.6

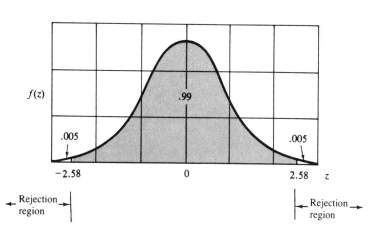

obtain the numerator for z:

$$\hat{p}_1 - \hat{p}_2 = \frac{X_1}{n_1} - \frac{X_2}{n_2} = \frac{41}{60} - \frac{24}{60} = .28$$

Thus

$$z = \frac{\hat{p}_1 - \hat{p}_2}{\sqrt{\hat{p}\hat{q}\left(\dfrac{1}{n_1} + \dfrac{1}{n_2}\right)}} = \frac{.28}{.091} = 3.08$$

Since this value falls in the rejection region (i.e., it exceeds 2.58), we reject the hypothesis that $p_1 = p_2$ and conclude that the two population proportions are different. Practically, we conclude that the programmed teaching technique produces a higher proportion of students scoring 85 or more than does the standard lecture teaching method.

EXERCISES

28. A law student believes that the proportion of Republicans in favor of the unrestricted right of executive privilege is greater than the proportion of Democrats in favor of the unrestricted right. He obtained independent random samples of 1000 Republicans and 1000 Democrats, respectively, and found 460 Republicans and 370 Democrats in favor of the unrestricted right. Does this evidence provide statistical support for the law student's belief? (Use $\alpha = .05$.)

29. A survey is conducted to determine whether a difference exists between the proportion of married and the proportion of single persons in the 20–29 age bracket who smoke. A sample of 200 persons from each group is polled, and 64 married and 80 single persons are found to smoke. Do the data provide sufficient evidence to indicate a difference in the proportion of smokers for the two populations? (Use $\alpha = .05$.)

30. Sixty of 87 Protestant housewives prefer a certain contraceptive technique A; 40 of 100 Catholic housewives prefer the same technique. Estimate the difference in the proportions of preferences by using a 95 % confidence interval.

31. Refer to Exercise 30. Test the null hypothesis that Protestant housewives and Catholic housewives do not differ in their preference for the contraceptive technique. (Use $\alpha = .01$.)

32. Independent random samples of 800 Republicans and 800 Democrats showed 40 % and 32 %, respectively, in favor of the death sentence for major crimes. Do these data provide sufficient evidence to indicate a difference in the population proportions favoring the death sentence? (Use $\alpha = .01$.)

33. Refer to Exercise 28. Estimate $p_1 - p_2$ using a 90% confidence interval for the difference in the proportions of Republicans and Democrats who favor the unrestricted right of executive privilege.

34. Refer to Exercise 33. Estimate $p_1 - p_2$ using a 99% confidence interval.

35. Refer to Exercise 29. Estimate $p_1 - p_2$ using a 90% and then a 99% confidence interval for the difference in proportion of smokers for the two populations.

36. Refer to Exercise 32. Estimate $p_1 - p_2$ using a 90% confidence interval for the difference in the proportion of Republicans and Democrats who favor the death penalty. Repeat the exercise using a 99% confidence interval.

8.7   THE PAIRED *t*-TEST

Suppose we wish to test the research hypothesis that on the average, the infant mortality rate for countries has changed from 1985 to 1990. One way to collect the sample data would be to select randomly 20 countries from 1985 records and 20 from 1990 records. Then the infant mortality rate would be recorded for each country.

You might detect a disadvantage to this sampling design. Because each country has a different mortality rate, the infant mortality rate could vary greatly from country to country, making the respective sample variances s_1^2 and s_2^2 large. Recall that when both samples are less than $n = 30$, the test statistic for the quality of two means μ_1 and μ_2 is

$$t = \frac{\bar{X}_1 - \bar{X}_2}{s_p \sqrt{\dfrac{1}{n_1} + \dfrac{1}{n_2}}}$$

where

$$s_p = \sqrt{\frac{(n_1 - 1)s_1^2 + (n_2 - 1)s_2^2}{n_1 + n_2 - 2}}$$

We reject H_0 if the observed value of t exceeds $t_{\alpha/2}$ or is less than $-t_{\alpha/2}$ based on d.f. $= n_1 + n_2 - 2$.

If the sample variances s_1^2 and s_2^2 are large, it takes large differences in the sample means $\bar{X}_1$ and $\bar{X}_2$ to reject the null hypothesis and declare a difference in the mean infant mortality rate. Hence the country-to-country variability, which inflates the sample variances, makes it difficult to detect a difference $\mu_1 - \mu_2$ in the mean infant mortality rates for 1985 and 1990 and thereby reduces the quantity of information in the experiment.

We can improve on the design just mentioned by reducing the variability in the sample data. To do this, we filter out the variability due to countries by making 1985-to-1990 comparisons within each country. That is, we select a country and obtain its infant mortality rates for 1985 and 1990. The process is repeated for each of 20 countries.

The infant mortality rates are given in Table 8.10. The 1985 and 1990 infant mortality rates (X_1 and X_2) for each country are shown in the second and third columns of the table. The difference in the infant mortality rates for each country, denoted by $d = X_1 - X_2$, is recorded in the fourth column. The sample averages for X_1, X_2, and d are shown at the bottom of the table. Note that $\bar{d} = \bar{X}_1 - \bar{X}_2$.

We would like to use these data to determine if there is sufficient evidence to indicate a difference in the mean infant mortality rates $\mu_1 - \mu_2$ for 20 countries from 1985 to 1990. At first glance we might be tempted to employ the method of comparing two means presented in Section 8.4. However, this

TABLE 8.10

Infant mortality rates for 20 countries, 1985 and 1990

Country	1985 X_1	1990 X_2	Difference $d = X_1 - X_2$
Algeria	109	74	35
Austria	12	8	4
Canada	9	7	2
Denmark	8	8	0
Egypt	80	90	-10
Greece	15	11	4
Ireland	11	10	1
Ivory Coast	122	96	26
Malaysia	29	30	-1
Morocco	99	82	17
Nigeria	105	121	-16
Pakistan	120	110	10
Poland	19	16	3
South Africa	92	55	37
Switzerland	8	7	1
Turkey	110	74	36
USSR	32	29	3
Uruguay	32	22	10
Yugoslavia	32	24	8
Zambia	101	80	21
	$\bar{X}_1 = 57.25$	$\bar{X}_2 = 47.7$	$\bar{d} = 9.55$

would not be the appropriate analysis, because one of the assumptions of the previous test procedure has been violated. **The two samples are not independent, because the pairs of observations are linked.** They read high or low, depending on the country being studied.

The analysis for an experiment must be dictated by the design used. If the design employed was to obtain a random sample of 20 countries for 1985 and another random sample of 20 countries for 1990, we would analyze the data by using the methods of Section 8.4. However, we realize that the infant mortality rates varied greatly from country to country and that we can filter out or eliminate the influence of this variability if we make a 1985-to-1990 comparison within each country. The restricted random assignment (Table 8.10) dictates that we must perform a different analysis to determine whether the mean infant mortality rates differ from 1985 and 1990. The appropriate method to compare the 20 different measurements in Table 8.10 is given here.

We summarize the procedures for this **paired *t*-test** as follows:

PAIRED *t*-TEST

Research hypothesis $H_1: \mu_d \neq 0$ (for a two-tailed test)   *Can do $> / <$; would make it a one-tailed test*

Null hypothesis $H_0: \mu_d = 0$ (i.e., $\mu_1 - \mu_2 = 0$)

Test statistic

$$t = \frac{\bar{d}}{s_d/\sqrt{n}}$$

Rejection region   R.R.: Reject H_0 if the absolute value of t is greater than the tabulated value of t for $a = \alpha/2$ and d.f. $= n - 1$.

Assumptions

1. n different pairs of measurements are obtained: one measurement in each pair from population 1, the other from population 2.
2. The sample differences are assumed to be selected from a normal population of differences.

The notation is slightly different from that used in Section 7.8, but the meaning is the same. We use the symbol $\bar{d}$ to denote the average of the sample differences. We observe differences $d_1, d_2, \ldots, d_n$ and compute

$$\bar{d} = \frac{\Sigma d}{n}$$

This is equivalent to observing n sample measurements $X_1, X_2, \ldots, X_n$ and computing

$$\bar{X} = \frac{\Sigma X}{n}$$

We state one word of warning: n refers to the number of sample differences (or number of pairs) rather than the total number of measurements, and s_d refers to the standard deviation of the differences:

$$s_d = \sqrt{\frac{\Sigma d^2 - [(\Sigma d)^2/n]}{n-1}}$$

Now we consider the data in Table 8.10 and test the null hypothesis that $\mu_d = 0$ against the research hypothesis that $\mu_d \neq 0$. (Use $\alpha = .05$.) We must first compute $\bar{d}$ and s_d. For these data we have

$$\Sigma d = 191 \qquad \text{and} \qquad \Sigma d^2 = 5973$$

Hence for $n = 20$ differences, we have

$$\bar{d} = \frac{\Sigma d}{n} = \frac{191}{20} = 9.55$$

$$s_d^2 = \frac{\Sigma d^2 - [(\Sigma d)^2/n]}{n-1} = \frac{5973 - [(191)^2/20]}{19}$$

$$= \frac{5973 - 1824.05}{19} = 218.37$$

$$s_d = \sqrt{218.37} = 14.78$$

Then

$$t = \frac{\bar{d}}{s_d/\sqrt{n}} = \frac{9.55}{14.78/\sqrt{20}} = \frac{9.55}{3.30} = 2.89$$

The crucial value of t for $a = .025$ and d.f. $= 19$ is 2.093. Since $t = 2.89$ exceeds 2.093, we reject the null hypothesis of equality of the mean infant mortality rates for 20 countries from 1985 to 1990. In fact, infant mortality rates, on the average, have decreased from 1985 to 1990 for 20 countries.

The statistical design employed in this experiment represents a simple example of a *randomized-block design*. As previously stated, the resulting test is often called a paired t-test. Several points should be emphasized. First, the measurements were paired when the study was planned. Comparisons of infant mortality rates for 1985 and 1990 were paired when the study was planned. Comparisons of infant mortality rates for 1985 and 1990 were then made within each country, to eliminate the variability among countries. Second, pairing does not always provide more information for testing the difference between two population means. If there were actually no differences between the infant mortality rates for countries, we would lose information, because instead of having 40 sample measurements (one on each of 20 different countries in both 1985 and 1990), we have only 20 differences. This makes it more difficult to detect a difference in means if no country-to-country variability is present. We therefore recommend pairing only if undesirable background variability can be eliminated.

This method can also be used to make before-and-after measurements on the same individuals. In this way a subject serves as his or her own control. For example, each of 30 overweight males could be weighed before treatment with a weight-reducing agent and again after one month of therapy. The measurements of interest would be 30 differences formed by subtracting the after-therapy reading for each subject from the before-therapy reading.

EXERCISES

37. In doing a paired t-test, can the pairing take place after the data are obtained? Explain.

38. Why would a researcher want to use the paired t-test?

39. Use the rate of reported rapes for Southern SMSAs (see Table 5.6). From your library, locate the *Uniform Crime Reports* for the more recent year. Test the null hypothesis that the mean difference between the data in Table 5.6 and the most recent issue is zero. (Use $\alpha = .05$.)

40. Refer to Table 8.10. Divide the 20 countries into two samples. Use the first 10 countries listed in alphabetical order and test the null hypothesis that there has been no change between 1985 and 1990. (Use $\alpha = .05$.)

41. Refer to Exercise 40. Use the second 10 countries listed in alphabetical order and test the null hypothesis that there has been no change between 1985 and 1990. (Use $\alpha = .05$.)

SUMMARY

In this chapter we presented statistical tests for comparing two population means (or two proportions) based on sample means (or proportions). This chapter was concerned with the following questions: If two sample means $\bar{X}_1$ and $\bar{X}_2$ differ, does this imply that the corresponding population means μ_1 and μ_2 differ? Similarly, if two sample proportions $\hat{p}_1$ and $\hat{p}_2$ differ, do we have sufficient evidence to indicate a difference in the corresponding population proportions? Rather than seek evidence of a difference in two population parameters, we might wish to estimate the difference by using a confidence interval.

In Sections 8.3 and 8.4 we discussed the large-sample and small-sample statistical tests for comparing two population means based on independent random samples from the populations of interest. A nonparametric test for comparing two populations, suitable for ordinal (as well as interval and ratio) data, utilized the Mann-Whitney U statistic of Section 8.5.

In Section 8.6 we discussed inferences concerning the difference between two population proportions based on independent random samples.

Finally, in Section 8.7 we discussed the paired t-test, which allows the researcher to analyze sample data when the same case is being measured at two points in time. It may also reduce variability in the sample data compared with the two-sample t-test in some research settings.

To summarize, we have learned how to make inferences about the differences in population means or proportions and how to measure the goodness of those inferences.

KEY WORDS

Mann-Whitney U-test   A nonparametric statistical test for comparing two population probability distributions based on independent random samples.

Nonparametric statistical techniques   Usually refers to statistical tests about population probability distributions but not about specific parameters of the distributions. Thus, instead of hypothesizing that two populations have the same mean, we could hypothesize that the two populations of measurements are identical.

Paired t-test   A parametric test for the difference between two means when the two samples are not independent because the pairs of observations are linked.

KEY FORMULAS

Mean and standard error for $\bar{X}_1 - \bar{X}_2$

$$\mu_{\bar{X}_1 - \bar{X}_2} = \mu_1 - \mu_2$$

$$\sigma_{\bar{X}_1 - \bar{X}_2} = \sqrt{\frac{\sigma_1^2}{n_1} + \frac{\sigma_2^2}{n_2}}$$

Mean and standard error for $\hat{p}_1 - \hat{p}_2$

$$\mu_{\hat{p}_1 - \hat{p}_2} = p_1 - p_2$$

$$\sigma_{\hat{p}_1 - \hat{p}_2} = \sqrt{\frac{p_1 q_1}{n_1} + \frac{p_2 q_2}{n_2}}$$

Large-sample 95 % confidence interval for $\mu_1 - \mu_2$

$$(\bar{X}_1 - \bar{X}_2) \pm 1.96\sigma_{\bar{X}_1 - \bar{X}_2}$$

Large-sample test for $\mu_1 - \mu_2$

$$H_0: \mu_1 - \mu_2 = 0$$

$$\text{T.S.}: z = \frac{\bar{X}_1 - \bar{X}_2}{\sigma_{\bar{X}_1 - \bar{X}_2}} \qquad \text{where} \qquad \sigma_{\bar{X}_1 - \bar{X}_2} = \sqrt{\frac{\sigma_1^2}{n_1} + \frac{\sigma_2^2}{n_2}}$$

Small-sample t-test for $\mu_1 - \mu_2$

$$H_0: \mu_1 - \mu_2 = 0$$

$$\text{T.S.}: t = \frac{\bar{X}_1 - \bar{X}_2}{s_p\sqrt{\frac{1}{n_1} + \frac{1}{n_2}}} \qquad \text{where} \qquad s_p = \sqrt{\frac{(n-1)s_1^2 + (n_2-1)s_2^2}{n_1 + n_2 - 2}}$$

Small-sample 95 % confidence interval for $\mu_1 - \mu_2$

$$(\bar{X}_1 - \bar{X}_2) + t_{.025}s_p\sqrt{\frac{1}{n_1} + \frac{1}{n_2}}$$

Mann-Whitney U-test

H_0: The two populations of measurements are identical.

$$\text{T.S.}: z = \frac{U - \mu_U}{\sigma_U}$$

where $$U = n_1 n_2 + \frac{n_1(n_1 + 1)}{2} - T_1$$

$$\mu_U = \frac{n_1 n_2}{2}$$

$$\sigma_U = \sqrt{\frac{n_1 n_2 (n_1 + n_2 + 1)}{12}}$$

95 % confidence interval for $p_1 - p_2$

$$(\hat{p}_1 - \hat{p}_2) \pm 1.96\sigma_{\hat{p}_1 - \hat{p}_2} \qquad \text{where} \qquad \sigma_{\hat{p}_1 - \hat{p}_2} = \sqrt{\frac{\hat{p}_1 \hat{q}_1}{n_1} + \frac{\hat{p}_2 \hat{q}_2}{n_2}}$$

Large-sample test for $p_1 - p_2$

$$H_0: p_1 - p_2 = 0$$

$$\text{T.S.: } z = \frac{\hat{p}_1 - \hat{p}_2}{\sqrt{\hat{p}\hat{q}\left(\frac{1}{n_1} + \frac{1}{n_2}\right)}} \qquad \text{where} \qquad \hat{p} = \frac{X_1 + X_2}{n_1 + n_2}$$

Paired t-test

$$H_0: \mu_d = 0$$

$$\text{T.S.: } t = \frac{\bar{d}}{s_d/\sqrt{n}}, \text{d.f.} = n - 1 \qquad \text{where } n \text{ is the number of pairs}$$

SUPPLEMENTARY EXERCISES FOR CHAPTER 8

42. Seventy-two college students enrolled in French 101 were randomly divided into two equal groups and subjected to one of two teaching techniques: class 1, in which the instructor spoke in both English and French to students, and class 2, in which the instructor spoke only in French to students. The mean and variances for the sample achievement test scores for the two groups are given in the accompanying table. State an appropriate research hypothesis that implies a two-tailed test. State the appropriate null hypothesis. Test the null hypothesis with $\alpha = .05$.

EXERCISE 42

Test score data

Group 1	Group 2
$n_1 = 36$	$n_2 = 36$
$\bar{X}_1 = 260$	$\bar{X}_2 = 294$
$s_1^2 = 3600$	$s_2^2 = 4300$

43. On the basis of two samples, each containing 1000 persons, a researcher reports that the average life expectancy (mean) is 65.8 for lower-class persons (sample A) and 69.4 for upper-class persons (sample B). If the standard deviations are 12.61 for sample A and 9.33 for sample B, would you accept the argument that upper-class people, in general, can expect to live longer? What evidence would you provide to support your argument?

44. The lengths of time (in hours) that it took to complete a work assignment were recorded for two samples of 30 persons, one sample drawn from those working in plants with high morale, the other from those working in plants with low morale. Do the data present sufficient evidence to indicate a difference in the mean time to complete the work assignment for groups in the two different environments? (Use $\alpha = .05$.)

EXERCISE 44

Length of time to
complete work
assignment

Characteristic	High Morale	Low Morale
mean	115	137
variance	595	420

45. Refer to Exercise 17. In this same study, the researchers examined the random
sample of 1645 schools (736 predominantly white, 909 predominantly black).
Each school reported its dropout rate for first-year students only. Use the data
to test the research hypothesis that the dropout rate for freshmen is higher in
black schools than in white schools. Give the level of significance for this test.

EXERCISE 45

Freshman dropout data

Characteristic	Black	White
sample mean	14.82	9.25
sample standard deviation	18.02	9.75

46. In two residential areas from different parts of a county, homes were randomly
selected for tax purposes. The mean prices were the same. One year later area
A had changed its composition so that it was now highly integrated, whereas
area B was basically all white. Two new random samples of 50 homes each
were selected for evaluation. The sample means and standard deviations for
prices are shown in the accompanying table. Do the data provide sufficient
evidence to indicate a difference in the mean market values of the homes in
these two areas? Explain. (Use $\alpha = .05$.)

EXERCISE 46

Data for market values
of homes

Characteristic	Area A	Area B
sample mean	$29,840	$27,520
sample standard deviation	$5,000	$4,404

47. A study was made of the prestige of occupations for women using the standard
International Occupational Prestige Scale. For Native American women in the
age range 30–44, the sample has been broken down by whether the women
have ever been married. Use the sample data to estimate the difference in mean
occupational prestige ratings for the two classifications of Native American
women.

EXERCISE 47

Data for occupational
prestige ratings by
Native American
women

Characteristic	Never Married	Married
sample size	50	500
sample mean	36	31
sample standard deviation	15	11

48. Refer to Exercise 47. In the same study the researcher also categorized each woman in a random sample of 1180 Japanese-American women by whether she had ever been married. Use the data to test the research hypothesis that the population means for the two groups are different. (Use $\alpha = .05$.)

EXERCISE 48

Data for occupational prestige ratings by Japanese-American women

Characteristic	Never Marrried	Married
sample size	100	900
sample mean	50	42
sample standard deviation	12	11

49. The percentage of D's and F's awarded by two college professors was noted by the student paper. Professor Smith achieved a rate of 43% as opposed to 30% for Professor Jones, based on 200 and 180 students, respectively. Do the data indicate a difference in the rate of awarding D's and F's? (Use $\alpha = .01$.) How confident are you in your conclusions? What are some of the explanations for your results?

50. The proportion of voters favoring Smith in the rural area of a county was 48% versus 35% around the university district, based on randomly selected samples of 300 voters from each area. Do the data indicate a difference in the proportion of voters favoring Smith in the two areas? (Use $\alpha = .01$.) How would you explain your findings?

51. When would you prefer to use the Mann-Whitney U-test as opposed to the z- or t-test?

52. Use the data in Exercise 15 and test the null hypothesis by using the Mann-Whitney U. Assume, for the sake of this example, that the distributions of weights are not normally distributed.

53. Female participation in higher education in 105 nations was studied. The variable of interest was the ratio of the percentage of females enrolled in school to the percentage of females in the country for individuals aged 15 through 24. These data are summarized in the accompanying table by Western and non-Western nations. Discuss the types of statistical inferences that can be made from this study.

EXERCISE 53

Data for female participation in higher education

Characteristic	Western Nations	Non-Western Nations
number	60	40
mean	.68	.35
standard deviation	.20	.15

54. A study was conducted to compare the average number of years of service at the age of retirement for military personnel retiring in 1970 and in 1990. A random sample of 100 career records for each of these two years showed average lengths of service of 30.3 and 25.2, respectively. If the population standard deviations are both approximately equal to 4, do the data present sufficient evidence to indicate a difference in the mean length of service for 1970 versus 1990? (Use $\alpha = .01$.)

55. A social scientist is interested in comparing social adjustment scores for prisoners of war who have participated in two rehabilitation programs. Fifteen returnees were randomly selected from each of two programs and were scored six months after the end of the program. Their social adjustment scores are provided in the accompanying table. Use the accompanying computer output to determine if the data present sufficient evidence to indicate a difference in mean scores for the two rehabilitative programs. (Use a Student's t-test with $\alpha = .05$.).

EXERCISE 55

Social adjustment scores

Program 1		Program 2	
65	50	67	80
87	65	88	80
94	37	76	80
74	46	94	91
52	30	31	74
42	63	48	94
55	82	99	42
91		98	

EXERCISE 55

```
MTB > TWOSAMPLE T 'PROG1' 'PROG2';
SUBC> POOLED.

TWOSAMPLE T FOR PROG1 VS PROG2
          N      MEAN     STDEV   SE MEAN
PROG1    15      62.2      20.1       5.2
PROG2    15      76.1      20.9       5.4

95 PCT CI FOR MU PROG1 - MU PROG2: (-29.3, 1.4)

TTEST MU PROG1 = MU PROG2 (VS NE): T= -1.86  P=0.073  DF=  28

POOLED STDEV =        20.5
```

56. Using the information in Database A, Appendix Table 7, determine the proportion of students in the social sciences who indicate "no religious preference." Repeat the same for students in business. Now test the research hypothesis that the proportion of social science students indicating no religious preference is larger than the proportion of business students indicating no religious preference. (Use $\alpha = .05$.)

57. Refer to Exercise 56. Compare the average age of students in the social sciences with that of students in the natural sciences. Test the hypothesis that there is no difference in average age. (Use $\alpha = .05$.)

58. Using the information in Database A, Appendix Table 7, determine the average number of acts defined as serious crimes first for the students in the humanities and then for the students in the natural sciences. Test the hypothesis of no difference between the two populations. What would be an appropriate level for α?

59. Refer to the clinical trials in Database C, Appendix Table 9. Use the HAM-D total score data to conduct a statistical test of $H_0: \mu_D - \mu_A = 0$ versus $H_1: \mu_D - \mu_A > 0$. That is, we want to know whether the placebo group (D) has a higher (worse) mean total depression score at the end of the study than the group receiving treatment A. Use $\alpha = .05$. What are your conclusions?

60. Refer to Exercise 59 and repeat this same comparison with the placebo group for treatment B and then for treatment C. Give the p-value for each of these tests. Which of the three treatment groups (A, B, or C) appears to have the lowest mean HAM-D total score?

61. Using the information in Database C, Appendix Table 9, construct a 95% confidence interval for $\mu_D - \mu_A$ based on the HAM-D anxiety score data. What can you conclude about $\mu_D - \mu_A$ based on this interval?

62. Using the information in Database C, Appendix Table 9, compare the mean ages for treatment groups B and D using a two-tailed statistical test. Set up all parts of the test using $\alpha = .05$; draw a conclusion. Why might it be important to have patients with similar ages in the different treatment groups when studying the effects of several drug products on the treatment of depression?

63. Refer to Exercise 62. What other variables should be comparable among the treatment groups in order to draw conclusions about the effectiveness of the drug products for treating depression?

64. A sample of 30 SMSAs was collected from both the North and South. These data are shown in the accompanying table. Computer output is also displayed.
  a. What test was run relative to the population means?
  b. What was the result and conclusion based on this test?

EXERCISE 64	North	Fertility Ratio	South	Fertility Ratio
Fertility ratios for 30 SMSAs from the North and South	Albany, NY	353	Atlanta, GA	346
	Allentown, PA	319	Augusta, GA	357
	Atlantic City, NJ	352	Baton Rouge, LA	347
	Canton, OH	352	Beaumont, TX	337
	Chicago, IL	356	Birmingham, AL	324
	Cincinnati, OH	372	Charlotte, NC	344
	Cleveland, OH	345	Chattanooga, TN	326
	Detroit, MI	369	Columbia, SC	334
	Evansville, IN	330	Corpus Christi, TX	395
	Grand Rapids, MI	382	Dallas, TX	365

North	Fertility Ratio	South	Fertility Ratio
Johnstown, PA	333	El Paso, TX	401
Kalamazoo, MI	318	Fort Lauderdale, FL	315
Kenosha, WI	384	Greensboro, NC	319
Lancaster, PA	356	Houston, TX	370
Lansing, MI	355	Jackson, MS	360
Lima, OH	400	Knoxville, TN	301
Madison, WI	321	Lexington, KY	319
Mansfield, OH	366	Lynchburg, VA	314
Milwaukee, WI	364	Macon, GA	352
Newark, NJ	337	Miami, FL	284
Paterson, NJ	311	Monroe, LA	386
Philadelphia, PA	344	Nashville, TN	313
Pittsfield, MA	358	Newport News, VA	356
Racine, WI	402	Orlando, FL	336
Rockford, IL	394	Richmond, VA	313
South Bend, IN	351	Roanoke, VA	310
Springfield, IL	344	Shreveport, LA	373
Syracuse, NY	377	Washington, DC	331
Vineland, NJ	377	Wichita Falls, TX	315
Youngstown, OH	339	Wilmington, DE	358

EXERCISE 64

```
MTB > TWOSAMPLE T 'NORTH' 'SOUTH';
SUBC> ALTERNATIVE 1;
SUBC> POOLED.

TWOSAMPLE T FOR NORTH VS SOUTH
          N     MEAN    STDEV   SE MEAN
NORTH    30    355.4    24.1      4.4
SOUTH    30    340.0    28.4      5.2

95 PCT CI FOR MU NORTH - MU SOUTH: (1.7, 28.9)

TTEST MU NORTH = MU SOUTH (VS GT): T= 2.26  P=0.014  DF=  58

POOLED STDEV =      26.3
```

65. In his study of the effects of labeling on sentencing of sex offenders, Walsh (1990) reported that psychiatrists recommended probation for 56.7% of the 210 cases, while probation officers recommended 38.6% of the 210 cases for probation. Test the hypothesis that psychiatrists are more likely to recommend convicted sex offenders for probation than are probation officers. (Use $\alpha = .05$.)

66. Walsh (1990) also collected information about sentencing patterns when a probation officer recommended probation ($n = 81$). In the same Ohio metropolitan area, Walsh reports that 81.5% of the cases were placed on probation and

18.5% were sent to prison. Again, you repeat the study in your home town and find that of 200 cases, 55% were placed on probation and 45% were sent to prison. Test the hypothesis that the pattern in your home town does not differ from the Ohio community. (Set $\alpha = .05$.)

67. Rosenfeld and Kalleberg (1990) studied women's labor force participation in the private sector in Canada, Norway, Sweden, and the United States. They report that on the average, women in Canada earn 59.0% as much as men, in Norway 70.9% as much as men, in Sweden 79.2% as much as men, and in the United States 55.7% as much as men. You repeat their study, basing your findings on samples of 1000 pairs of men and women for each nation. The average percentages you find are identical to the figures reported by Rosenfeld and Kalleberg. You also report the standard deviations: 5.8 for Canada, 4.2 for Norway, 2.9 for Sweden, and 3.6 for the United States. Test the following hypotheses. (Set $\alpha = .05$.)

a. The average percentage is greater in Canada than in the United States.

b. The average percentage is greater in Sweden than in Norway.

c. The average percentage differential is greater in Norway than it is in the United States.

68. Wong (1990) examines the popular belief that Asian high school seniors have unusual educational attainments. He compared whites with Chinese, Filipino, and Japanese students in the United States. He reports that 25.7% of white students spent 5 or more hours per week doing homework. The corresponding percentages of Chinese students was 50.5%; of Filipino students, 43.9%; and of Japanese students, 43.7%. Assume that each sample is based on the responses of 1000 high school students and test the following hypotheses:

a. More Filipino students spend 5 or more hours doing homework than white students. (Set $\alpha = .05$.)

b. More Chinese students spend 5 or more hours doing homework than white students. (Set $\alpha = .01$.)

c. More Chinese students spend 5 or more hours doing homework than Japanese students. (Set $\alpha = .05$.)

69. Hathaway and Pargament (1990) surveyed two samples of church members. One sample consisted of 40 members of the Assembly of God, and the other of 68 Presbyterians. Each person responded to a set of items designed to measure his or her degree of religiousness. The mean religiousness score for members of the Assembly of God was 39.6 ($s = 6.35$), and the mean score for Presbyterians was 32.8 ($s = 6.69$). Test the research hypothesis that Assembly of God members are more religious (as measured by the scale) than Presbyterians. (Set $\alpha = .01$.)

70. Nelsen (1990) studied interfaith marriages, based on a national sample. In the national sample there were 303 children born to couples in which the wife was Catholic and the husband Protestant. Of these children, 234 became Catholic as adults. Of 287 children born to couples in which the wife was Protestant and the husband Catholic, 136 became Catholic. Test the hypothesis that there is no difference in the percentage of children who become Catholic from these two types of interfaith marriages. (Set $\alpha = .01$.)

71. Weiss and Mendoza (1990) interviewed 132 males and 94 females who were members of the Hare Krishna movement. Subjects were divided into two groups, depending on their scores on an acculturation index (AI) measuring acculturation into the movement. Fifty subjects scored low, and 113 scored high. Sixty-three have intermediate scores. Subjects also responded to a mental health index and a life satisfaction scale. Subjects who are low on AI have a mean score of 74.7 on the mental health index with $s = 13.0$, and subjects who are high on the AI have a mean score of 80.1 with $s = 10.1$.

a. Test the significance of the difference between the two means. (Set $\alpha = .05$.) What conclusion would you draw and why?

b. The same subjects have a mean of 58.8 (for AI lows) with $s = 22.9$ and a mean of 69.3 (for AI highs) with $s = 18.8$. Again, test the significance of the difference between the two means.

CHAPTER 9

CROSS-CLASSIFICATION OF DATA

GENERAL OBJECTIVES

Just as univariate data (data on a single variable measured for each person, group, or organization sampled) can be classified in a one-way table (frequency table), bivariate data (data on two variables measured for each person, group, or organization sampled) can be classified in a two-way table called a *bivariate table*. A special kind of bivariate table is called a *contingency table*. This chapter introduces tables and shows you how to describe bivariate data displayed in two-way or bivariate tables by using percentage comparisons and how to make bivariate comparisons by using the chi-square test of independence or Fisher's exact test.

SPECIFIC OBJECTIVES

1. To define what we mean by independent and dependent variables.
2. To show how to set up a contingency table and the location of the independent and dependent variables.
3. To illustrate how to make percentage comparisons.
4. To demonstrate the utility of the chi-square test of independence and to indicate the properties of the chi-square distribution.
5. To provide an alternative to chi-square — Fisher's exact test — when the samples are small.
6. To introduce the McNemar test for analyzing changes over time.

9.1   INTRODUCTION

We learned in Chapter 2 that data can be grouped into classes for descriptive purposes. In Chapter 3 we described frequency distributions for a single variable, such as violent crime rates for 90 U.S. cities. However, much of social research is more interested in explaining than in describing a frequency distribution. For example, why do crime rates vary across cities? Why do some people consider themselves as politically conservative, while others think of themselves as politically liberal or moderate?

Answering questions like these builds on our discussion of hypothesis testing in Chapters 7 and 8. We learned, for example, that a researcher proposes a research hypothesis of differences between two groups and then tests the null hypothesis of no differences between the groups. If the null hypothesis is rejected, the researcher can conclude that there is a difference between the two groups; the data support the research hypothesis.

In this chapter the kind of research hypothesis proposed is somewhat different from that discussed in Chapters 7 and 8. Rather than hypothesizing differences between two groups, we are now concerned with proposing a research hypothesis of a relationship between two variables. For example, suppose we hypothesize that the geographical region in which cities are located causes or influences the violent crime rate in those cities. In this case we are suggesting that a particular kind of relationship exists between two variables: geographical region of a city and its violent crime rate. Proposing a research hypothesis such as this is the first step in attempting to answer the question, "Why do violent crime rates vary across cities?"

In this chapter we will examine ways to analyze a set of data on two variables by cross-classification. The cross-classification of two variables in a table provides a way to determine whether the variables are in fact related as a researcher has hypothesized. Such tables are called **contingency tables** when the research hypothesis is that a dependence (contingency) exists between the two variables. We will also test hypotheses of statistical independence based on data arranged in this fashion. For example, if we find that geographical region and a city's violent crime rate are statistically independent of each other, our research hypothesis is not supported by the data. If, on the other hand, the two variables are statistically dependent, we conclude that our research hypothesis is supported by the data; geographical location of a city does cause or influence a city's crime rate.

9.2   CROSS-CLASSIFICATION DATA: PERCENTAGE COMPARISONS

Before proceeding with a discussion of contingency tables, we need to define two terms: *independent variable* and *dependent variable*.

DEFINITION 9.1	An **independent variable** is the cause or antecedent of a dependent variable.

DEFINITION 9.2	A **dependent variable** is the effect or consequence of an independent variable.

For example, in the discussion above about the relationship between the geographical region of cities and their crime rates, "geographical region" is the independent variable and "crime rate" is the dependent variable. In preparing a contingency table, the researcher first identifies each of the two variables — one as the independent variable and one as the dependent variable.

A simple rule may be used to determine which variable is independent and which is dependent. The variable that occurs earliest in time or is determined earliest in time is the independent variable. In this example, the region of a city's location is determined earlier in time than is the city's crime rate. Similarly, gender of an individual is determined earlier in time than is the individual's income. Note that it would make little sense to say that a city's crime rate causes or influences a city's geographic location, or that an individual's income causes or influences an individual's gender. Rather, current conditions or experiences are caused by or influenced by earlier conditions or experiences.

Now let us consider examples involving two variables in which we cross-classify data according to independent and dependent variables. Table 9.1 shows a contingency table, the cross-classification of gender by intention of ever marrying among a sample of 150 people age 18 to 35 who have never been married. In this example, gender is the independent variable, and intention of marrying is the dependent variable. A cell entry indicates the number of persons classified in that particular combination of gender and intention of every marrying. For example, 45 men intend to marry in the future; 20 women never intend to marry.

In constructing a table for studying the relationship between two variables, the categories of one variable are used to label the rows of the table, and the categories of the other variable provide labels for the columns of the table. **The accepted practice is to use the independent variable as the column variable and the dependent variable as the row variable**. In Table 9.1, gender is the independent variable and is labeled along the columns.

In general, a bivariate frequency table should contain a title, headings for the row and column variables, category identification for the two variables, and row and column totals (called *marginals*). The marginals provide a

TABLE 9.1

Relationship between intention of ever marrying and gender

Intention of	Gender		
Ever Marrying	Male	Female	Total
yes	45	80	125
no	5	20	25
Total	50	100	150

univariate frequency distribution separately for the row variable (dependent variable) and the column variable (independent variable).

DEFINITION 9.3

A **univariate frequency table** portrays the tallies for each category of a single variable.

DEFINITION 9.4

A **bivariate frequency table** (also called a *contingency table*) portrays the tallies for two variables, based on cross-tabulations.

In studying the relationship between two variables it is useful to present the data as percentages. At this point we have a choice. We can present the cell frequencies as a percentage of either the row totals or the column totals. **The accepted practice is to base the percentages on the marginals of the independent (column) variable.** Then we can examine the percentage distribution in categories of the dependent variable for each category of the independent variable. Each column total provides a base sample size from which we can compute percentages, and percentages within a column must total 100%.

A percentage comparison of the data in Table 9.1 can be made using gender as the independent variable. In Table 9.2 we base all percentages on

TABLE 9.2

Percentage comparison of the data in Table 9.1

Intention of	Gender	
Ever Marrying	Male	Female
yes	90	80
no	10	20
Total %	100	100
Sample size (n)	50	100

the column totals. For example, 50 of the original sample are males. Of these 50, 45 (90%) intend to marry some day, and 5 (10%) intend never to marry. Percentages of females are computed in the same way.

The information in Table 9.2 can be reported in several equally meaningful ways. From this sample of 150 persons, we find that

1. Most males and females intended to marry eventually.
2. While most individuals intended to marry some day, men were slightly more likely than women to intend to marry.
3. Women were more likely than men to intend never to marry.
4. Women were twice as likely as men (20% compared to 10%) to intend never to marry.

When percentages in a table are calculated in the other direction (based on marginals of the dependent variable), the conclusions are usually questionable. If percentages in Table 9.1 were calculated across categories of the dependent variable, we might conclude, for example, that people who intend never to marry are likely to "become" females. In some instances we are unable to specify which variable is dependent and which is independent. In such circumstances it makes very little difference which way the percentages are calculated. However, when one variable is definitely the independent one, all percentages should be based on the marginals of the independent variable.

As noted previously, the accepted practice is to use the independent variable as the column variable and the dependent variable as the row variable. Sometimes, however, researchers will deviate from this practice and show the independent variable as the row variable and the dependent variable as the column variable. **This is why it is absolutely essential to know which variable in a table is the independent variable and which is the dependent variable.** Researchers may sometimes vary the position of the independent and dependent variables in a table, but meaningful percentage comparisons can be made *only* when percentages are based on the marginals of the independent variable. As an exercise, reconstruct Tables 9.1 and 9.2 using gender as the row variable and intention of ever marrying as the column variable.

Percentage comparisons are highly flexible with regard to the kinds of variables that can be compared. We could compare two nominal variables (Tables 9.1 and 9.2), one ordinal and one ratio variable, two ratio variables, and so on. For example, a researcher hypothesized that marital status (nominal variable) would cause or influence perceptions about the marital happiness of others (ordinal variable). Another way of stating the researcher's hypothesis is that the perception of others' marital happiness varies with (depends on) the individual's marital status. A random sample of 900 urban residents is selected for interviews, and each person is classified by marital status (separated, divorced, or married) and by his or her perception of others' marital happiness (low, medium, or high). These data are expressed as percentages in a bivariate table (Table 9.3). Note that 100 of the original sample are separated, 200 are divorced, and 600 are married.

TABLE 9.3

Relationship between marital status and perceptions of others' marital happiness, by percentage

Perception of Others' Marital Happiness	Marital Status		
	Separated	Divorced	Married
low	21	12	9
medium	23	20	9
high	56	68	82
Total (%)	100	100	100
Sample size (n)	100	200	600

By examining Table 9.3, we can conclude that marital status does appear to influence the perception of others' martial happiness. In particular, married people are the most likely to perceive the marital happiness of others as being high, followed by the divorced and then the separated. On the other hand, the separated are the most likely to perceive the marital happiness of others as low or medium, followed by the divorced and then the married. What these sample findings suggest is that those whose marital status is in transition (either to a reconciliation or to a divorce) are much less likely than those with a more stable marital status to perceive the marital happiness of others as being high. Among those with a more stable or permanent marital status, married people are more likely than divorced people to perceive the marital happiness of others as being high. Thus the researcher's hypothesis seems to be supported by these data; the perception of others' marital happiness varies with (depends on) the individual's marital status.

TABLE 9.4

Murder rates for 80 SMSAs classified by region

Murder Rate	Geographic Region		
	North	South	West
0–6	1	20	16
7–13	7	5	6
14–20	16	4	3
21–27	2	0	0
Total	26	29	25

Source: U.S. Bureau of the Census, *Statistical Abstract of the United States.*

A last example of percentage comparisons appears in Table 9.4. We have cross-classified a sample of 80 SMSAs according to region (North, South, and West) and murder rates. The variable, geographical region, is a nominal variable. Although the variable, murder rate, is a ratio variable, we have grouped the rates in Table 9.4 so that they form an ordinal variable.

Studies of murder rates usually compare the effect of different geographical regions on the distribution of percentages in the murder rate categories. A percentage comparison of the data, using geographical regions as the independent variable, will provide a means for comparing the rates across geographical areas. We can readily detect a trend in the percentages of Table 9.5. SMSAs from the North have a different percentage distribution of murder rates than either the South or the West. In particular, the percentage of SMSAs in the North with a murder rate between 14 and 27 is 61.5% + 7.7% = 69.2%, whereas the South and West have only 13.8% and 12.0%, respectively.

TABLE 9.5

Percentage comparison of the data in Table 9.4

Murder Rate	Geographic Region		
	North	**South**	**West**
0–6	3.8	69.0	64.0
7–13	26.9	17.2	24.0
14–20	61.5	13.8	12.0
21–27	7.7	0.0	0.0
Total %	99.9	100.0	100.0
Sample size (n)	26	29	25

Having illustrated percentage comparisons for describing bivariate (cross-classification) data, we offer the following guidelines for future use.

GUIDELINES FOR PERCENTAGE COMPARISONS OF BIVARIATE DATA

1. When dealing with qualitative variables, the categories should satisfy the principles of inclusiveness and exclusiveness (Section 3.2).
2. Always include the marginal totals that serve as the sample sizes for the independent variable. This practice protects the reader from identifying possible trends when in fact the sample sizes are so small as to render percentage differences meaningless. **Note also that in identifying trends, care should be taken to ensure that these trends are specified only for the data on which the percentage**

comparison was made. Percentage comparisons do not involve statistical inference where sample data are used to make inferences about the population from which the sample data were drawn.

3. The number and size of class intervals (especially for qualitative variables) are usually predetermined by the comparisons you wish to make. When you have a choice, keep the comparison as simple as possible without destroying the relationship between the variables.

4. For quantitative data, use the rules presented for frequency distributions in Section 3.6.

Not all percentage tables are easy to construct and read, especially if one variable cannot be considered to be the independent variable and the other the dependent variable. For example, a researcher sampled 100 individuals and asked them about their attitudes toward affirmative action (AA). The researcher asked individuals about their attitudes toward AA for women and also about their attitudes toward AA for racial and ethnic minorities. It is difficult to view one set of attitudes as the independent variable and the other as the dependent variable, since both sets of attitudes were determined at the same point in time. However, the researcher might be interested in whether people feel the same or differently about AA for different kinds of groups. Table 9.6 shows the cross-classification of attitudes toward affirmative action for the two different groups. (Note that although this is a bivariate table, it is not a contingency table, since one variable cannot be viewed as contingent or dependent on the other variable.)

TABLE 9.6

Attitudes toward AA for women and for racial and ethnic groups

Favor or Oppose Affirmative Action for Women	Favor or Oppose Affirmative Action for Racial and Ethnic Groups		Total
	Favor	Oppose	
favor	60	5	65
oppose	10	25	35
Total	70	30	100

By examining Table 9.6 we can see that 60 people favored AA for both groups. Since 100 individuals were sampled, the frequencies of Table 9.6 also represent percentages; hence it is clear that 60% of the individuals favored AA for both groups. (What percentage of the sample opposed AA for both groups?) We can also say that 65% of the sample favored AA for women and

70% favored AA for racial and ethnic groups. The researcher would probably conclude that, in general, people feel similarly about AA for various kinds of groups. That is, those who favor AA for one group tend to favor AA for other groups, and those who oppose AA for one group tend to oppose AA for other groups.

Since neither variable in Table 9.6 can be viewed as an independent or a dependent variable, we can express percentages in the table in either direction (across rows or down columns), depending on what we want to find out about the cross-classification of attitudes. For example, if we are interested in comparing attitudes toward AA for minorities for different categories of attitudes toward AA for women, we would express percentages in the table across rows (Table 9.7).

TABLE 9.7

Percentage comparison of the data in Table 9.6

Favor or Oppose AA for Women	Favor or Oppose AA for Racial and Ethnic Groups		Total %	Sample Size ($n = 100$)
	Favor	**Oppose**		
favor	92.3	7.7	100.0	65
oppose	28.6	71.4	100.0	35

Table 9.7 shows that among all those who favored AA for women, 92.3% also favored AA for racial and ethnic minorities. Among all those who opposed affirmative action for women, 71.4% also opposed it for racial and ethnic groups.

In this section we have presented a way for describing cross-classification data. **Although we tried to identify trends with our percentage comparisons, we did not draw specific statistical inferences. Identifying possible trends is useful for illustrative purposes but cannot replace a statistical test of significance for determining a trend.** In Section 9.3 we will present several tests of significance that are useful for making inferences from cross-classification data.

EXERCISES

1. How would the percentage comparisons in Table 9.3 differ if there did not appear to be a relationship between marital status and the perception of others' marital happiness? What would these results imply about the researcher's hypothesis?

2. What are the guidelines for percentage comparisons of cross-classified data?

3. Use the data in the accompanying table. Make a percentage comparison, with per capita spending on education as the independent variable.

EXERCISE 3

Per capita state and local taxes and per capita expenditure on education for the 50 states

Per Capita State and Local Taxes	Per Capita Spending on Education			Total
	Under $650	$650–$775	More than $775	
over $1200	2	8	8	18
$1000 to $1200	2	7	7	16
under $1000	13	2	1	16
Total	17	17	16	50

Source: U.S. Bureau of the Census, *Statistical Abstract of the United States.*

4. Refer to Exercise 3. Make a percentage comparison using per capita state and local taxes as the independent variable. Compare the results with those in Exercise 3.

5. Hughes and Hertel (1990) review results from a 1980 survey of over 2100 black Americans regarding the relationship between two variables, male skin color and job mobility. Based on the article by Hughes and Hertel, two race specialists wish to retest the hypothesis in 1990 that males with lighter skin color have greater job mobility than males with darker skin. Their sample of 500 black males is classified by mobility orientation (low, medium, or high) and skin color (light, medium, or dark), the same categories reported by Hughes and Hertel. The new results are presented in the accompanying table. A cell entry is the number of males classified in that particular category.
  a. What does the cell value of 112 mean?
  b. What does the cell value of 70 mean?
  c. What does the row marginal of 215 mean?

EXERCISE 5

Relationship between male skin color and job mobility

Job Mobility Orientation	Male Skin Color			Total
	Light	Medium	Dark	
high	50	120	73	243
medium	70	112	33	215
low	15	19	8	42
Total	135	251	114	500

6. Why is it important to identify the independent and dependent variables in a contingency table?

7. What happens to your analysis of a contingency table if you do not know which variable is dependent and which is independent?

8. Refer to Table 9.6. Calculate the percentages for the table using the column totals. When percentages are calculated in this way, what do they show? How do these findings compare to those in Table 9.7?

9.3 THE CHI-SQUARE TEST OF INDEPENDENCE

Most social researchers want to know whether the data on two variables in a cross-classification are independent of each other. For example, in trying to determine an advertising strategy for an upcoming election campaign, it would be useful to compare the proportion of voters favoring the incumbent council member in the three voting districts.

One method of comparison is to test for the independence of the qualitative variable, voter preference (favoring or not favoring the incumbent council member) and the qualitative variable, voting district. If the two variables are dependent, this would imply that the proportion of voters favoring the council member varies from one district to another. Detecting this dependence would help the campaign staff use its resources to obtain the best results.

Before we provide an illustration of the chi-square test of independence, let us reinforce the importance of not confusing a test of independence with dependent and independent variables. In the context of chi-square a test of independence has to do with whether one variable is connected or related to another variable. If the test is rejected, we conclude that the two variables are statistically related or connected, regardless of which variable is the independent variable and which is the dependent one. Thus we conclude that the two variables are related to each other in some fashion. It may be that one variable influences another, but chi-square does not call for specifying which, if either, is the dependent or independent variable. The test is used when the issue of which variable is independent and which is dependent is never considered (as in our example of attitudes toward affirmative action in Table 9.6), as well as when the social researcher is sure which specific variable is the dependent one and which is the independent one (as in our example of the relationship between gender and intention of marrying in Table 9.1).

We will illustrate a test of the independence of two variables with an example. A county social survey was conducted to compare the proportion of families with more than two children for different income categories. A

TABLE 9.8

Survey results relating annual income to number of children

Number of Children per Family	Annual Income			
	Less than $30,000	$30,000 to $40,000	More than $40,000	Total
two or fewer	11	13	21	45
more than two	68	28	9	105
Total	79	41	30	150

random sample of 150 families was questioned and each was classified into one of three income categories (under \$30,000, \$30,000 to \$40,000, and more than \$40,000). The number of children was also recorded for each family. Using the data in Table 9.8, determine if there is sufficient evidence to indicate that the proportion of families having more than two children differs among the three income categories. In other words, is the variable "number of children per family" dependent on the variable "annual income"? The results of the survey are presented in Table 9.8.

To answer the question of independence, we begin by defining two distributions of measurements. The first distribution corresponds to the variable "number of children per family." If we consider all families in the county, a certain proportion p_A have two children or fewer, and the remaining proportion of families p_B have more than two children. Since all families are classified into one of these two categories, $p_A + p_B = 1$.

The second distribution corresponds to the "annual income" variable. If we again consider all families in the sampled county, a certain proportion p_1 have annual incomes of less than \$30,000; a second proportion p_2 have incomes between \$30,000 and \$40,000; and the remaining proportion p_3 have annual incomes greater than \$40,000. Again, we have $p_1 + p_2 + p_3 = 1$.

It is interesting to note that the proportions for these distributions also represent the probabilities associated with each category in a classification. Thus the probability that a family chosen at random from the county will have an annual income of more than \$40,000 is p_3. These probabilities (proportions) are given in Table 9.9.

TABLE 9.9

Probabilities associated with variables in Table 9.8

Variable	Probability
Number of Children per Family	
two or fewer	p_A
more than two	p_B
Annual Income	
less than \$30,000	p_1
\$30,000 to \$40,000	p_2
more than \$40,000	p_3

Now consider a combination of the categories of the table, one category from each variable. **The two variables are independent if, for all combinations of categories, the probability that an item falls into a particular category combination is equal to the product of the respective category probabilities.** For our example, the variable "number of children per family" is independent of the variable "annual income" if the cell probabilities for the cross-classified data are as given in Table 9.10. Note that the probability associated with each cell is found by multiplying the probabilities for the categories combined in that cell. The probability that a family chosen at random has more than two children and an annual income of more than \$40,000 is the product $p_B p_3$, where p_B is the probability of having more than two children and p_3 is the probability of a family earning more than \$40,000.

TABLE 9.10

Cell probabilities for Table 9.8 if the variables are independent

	Annual Income		
Number of Children per Family	**Less than \$30,000** p_1	**\$30,000 to \$40,000** p_2	**More than \$40,000** p_3
two or fewer, p_A	$p_A p_1$	$p_A p_2$	$p_A p_3$
more than two, p_B	$p_B p_1$	$p_B p_2$	$p_B p_3$

A test of the null hypothesis of independence of "number of children per family" and "annual income" makes use of Table 9.11. The observed cell counts are shown in the table. In addition, we have given the **expected cell counts** in parentheses — that is, the cell counts expected if the null hypothesis of independence of the two variables is true. Without proof, we state that the expected cell count for any cell of Table 9.8 can be computed by multiplying the row total by the column total and dividing by the total number of sample measurements:

$$\text{expected cell count} = \frac{(\text{row total})(\text{column total})}{n}$$

Thus, for two children or fewer and an annual income of less than \$30,000, we get

$$\text{expected cell count} = \frac{45(79)}{150} = 23.7$$

For two children or fewer and an annual income between \$30,000 and \$40,000,

$$\text{expected cell count} = \frac{45(41)}{150} = 12.3$$

and for two children or fewer and an annual income of more than \$40,000,

$$\text{expected cell count} = \frac{45(30)}{150} = 9.0$$

For more than two children and an annual income of less than $30,000,

$$\text{expected cell count} = \frac{105(79)}{150} = 55.3$$

For more than two children and an annual income of $30,000 to $40,000,

$$\text{expected cell count} = \frac{105(41)}{150} = 28.7$$

and for more than two children and an annual income of more than $40,000,

$$\text{expected cell count} = \frac{105(30)}{150} = 21.0$$

Note in Table 9.11 that the expected cell counts in a given row may be added to get the corresponding row total. For example, in the first row of Table 9.11(a) $23.7 + 12.3 + 9.0 = 45$. Similarly, for any column the corresponding expected cell counts may be summed to obtain the appropriate column total. This additive property of the expected cell counts can reduce the computation necessary to obtain expected cell counts. Thus we would need to compute only the two expected cell counts shown in the following incomplete table, Table 9.11(b). The remaining cell counts could be obtained by subtracting from the appropriate row or column total.

TABLE 9.11

Observed and expected cell counts for the data of Table 9.8

| Number of Children per Family | (a) Annual Income | | | |
	Less than $30,000	$30,000 to $40,000	More than $40,000	Total
two or fewer	11(23.7)	13(12.3)	21(9.0)	45
more than two	68(55.3)	28(28.7)	9(21.0)	105
Total	79	41	30	150

| Number of Children per Family | (b) Annual Income | | | |
	Less than $30,000	$30,000 to $40,000	More than $40,000	Total
two or fewer	23.7	12.3	—	45
more than two	—	—	—	105
Total	79	41	30	150

We would suspect that the null hypothesis is false if the observed cell counts do not agree with the expected cell counts. To measure this agreement or disagreement, we compute the chi-square test statistic:

$$\chi^2 = \sum \frac{(O - E)^2}{E}$$

That is, we subtract the expected cell count E from each observed cell count O. The square of this difference is then divided by E. We do this for all cells and add our results.

Obviously, if the observed cell counts differed from the expected cell counts, the quantities $(O - E)^2$ would be large, and hence χ^2 would be large. Thus we would reject our hypothesis of independence of the two variables for large values of χ^2. How large is large? The answer to this question can be found by obtaining the distribution of χ^2 in many repetitions of an experiment or by examining the probability distribution of χ^2.

It can be shown that when n is large, χ^2 has a probability distribution in repeated sampling that is approximately a chi-square probability distribution. We will not give the formula for the chi-square probability function, but we will list its properties.

PROPERTIES OF THE CHI-SQUARE DISTRIBUTION

1. Chi-square is not a symmetrical distribution (see Figure 9.1).
2. There are many chi-square probability distributions. We obtain a particular one by specifying the degrees of freedom.

Recall that we showed that the expected cell counts in rows and columns add up to the corresponding marginal totals. For example, in a 2×2 table (two rows and two columns), if we compute the expected cell counts in the first row and the first column, then all other expected cell counts are fixed,

FIGURE 9.1

Chi-square probability distribution with d.f. = 4

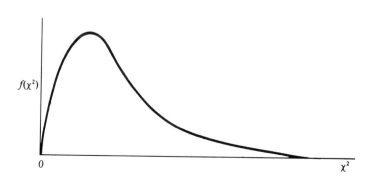

because expected cell counts for all rows and columns must add up to the corresponding marginal totals. In a similar way, for a 2 × 3 table (such as Table 9.11) we need only calculate the expected cell counts for the first two entries in row 1; all other expected cell counts are fixed and can be obtained by subtracting from the appropriate marginal total. The number of expected cell counts we need to calculate is related to the degrees of freedom for a chi-square distribution, as we will now show.

The **degrees of freedom** for a chi-square distribution correspond to the number of cells minus the number of restrictions we place on the expected cell counts. In other words, the degrees of freedom correspond to the number of expected cell counts we need to calculate before the remaining ones are fixed. In a 2 × 2 table, we have shown that d.f. = 1. Similarly, in a 2 × 3 table, we have seen that d.f. = 2.

There is a general formula for the degrees of freedom for a chi-square test of independence when the two-way contingency table has r rows and c columns. The formula is

$$d.f. = (r - 1)(c - 1)$$

We can verify that the formula gives the correct degrees of freedom. For example, in a 2 × 3 table, we have $r = 2$ and $c = 3$, and d.f. = 1(2) = 2. This is the number of expected cell counts we need to calculate before obtaining the rest by subtraction.

Upper-tail values for the test statistic

$$\chi^2 = \sum \frac{(O - E)^2}{E}$$

are shown in Appendix Table 3. Entries in the table are chi-square values such that an area of size a lies to the right under the curve. We specify the degrees of freedom (d.f.) in the left-hand column of the table, and the specified value of a in the top row of the table. Thus for d.f. = 14 and $a = .10$, the critical (tabulated) value of the chi-square distribution is 21.0642 (see Figure 9.2). The rejection region for this one-tailed test of independence can then be

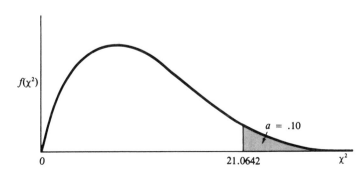

determined for a specified probability α of a type I error by use of Appendix Table 3. If the observed value of χ^2 falls beyond the critical value, we reject the null hypothesis of independence of the two variables.

We summarize the test procedure as follows.

CHI-SQUARE TEST OF INDEPENDENCE

Research hypothesis H_1: The two variables are dependent.
Null hypothesis H_0: The two variables are independent.
Test statistic

$$\chi^2 = \sum \frac{(O - E)^2}{E}$$

Rejection region   R.R.: Reject the null hypothesis if χ^2 exceeds the tabulated value of χ^2 for $a = \alpha$ and d.f. $= (r - 1)(c - 1)$ where

r = number of rows in the contingency table

c = number of columns in the contingency table

This will always be a one-tailed, upper-tail test.
Assumption   The expected cell counts satisfy the properties that no expected cell count is less than 1 and no more than 20% are less than 5.*

We illustrate the chi-square test with examples.

EXAMPLE 9.1

Use the sample count data in Table 9.11 to test the null hypothesis of independence of the two variables "number of children per family" and "annual income." (Use $\alpha = .05$.)

SOLUTION

The observed and expected cell counts are presented in Table 9.11. The value of the test statistic χ^2 will be computed and compared with the critical value

---

* Recall that we said that the distribution of $\Sigma(O - E)^2/E$ could be approximated by a chi-square distribution provided n is large. Some researchers (see, for example, Siegel, *Nonparametric Statistics for the Behavioral Sciences*, 1956) recommend that the sample size be large enough that all expected cell counts are five or more. This requirement is perhaps too stringent. Cochran ("Some Methods for Strengthening the Common χ^2 Tests," *Biometrics* 10 (1954), pp. 417–451) indicated that the approximation should be quite good if no expected cell count is less than 1 and no more than 20% are less than 5. We will follow the more lenient requirements of Cochran for the chi-square test of independence.

$(a = .05)$ of the chi-square distribution having d.f. $= (r - 1)(c - 1) = 1(2) = 2$. To find the value of the test statistic, we use the formula

$$\chi^2 = \sum \frac{(O - E)^2}{E}$$

Substituting, we obtain

$$\chi^2 = \frac{(11 - 23.7)^2}{23.7} + \frac{(13 - 12.3)^2}{12.3} + \frac{(21 - 9.0)^2}{9.0}$$
$$+ \frac{(68 - 55.3)^2}{55.3} + \frac{(28 - 28.7)^2}{28.7} + \frac{(9 - 21.0)^2}{21.0}$$
$$= 6.80 + .04 + 16.0 + 2.92 + .02 + 6.86 = 32.64$$

The rejection region for this test can be obtained from Appendix Table 3 for d.f. $= 2$ and $a = .05$. This value is 5.99. Since the observed value 32.64 of χ^2 exceeds the critical value 5.99, we conclude that the variables "number of children per family" and "annual income" are dependent. That is, the distribution of families in the categories "two or fewer" and "more than two" depends on the income category of interest.

EXAMPLE 9.2

A study was reported in which college students were classified according to political preference and their support for student rights. The results of 116 student responses are summarized in Table 9.12. Perform a chi-square test of independence and draw a practical conclusion. (Use $\alpha = .05$.)

TABLE 9.12

Survey results of 200 college students

	Political Preference		
Student Rights	**Democratic**	**Republican**	**Total**
low priority	20	24	44
moderate priority	26	33	59
high priority	76	21	97
Total	122	78	200

SOLUTION

For this 3 × 2 table we need to compute the expected cell counts in columns 1 and 2 of row 1. Using the formula

$$\text{expected cell count} = \frac{(\text{row total})(\text{column total})}{n}$$

these two expected cell counts are, respectively,

$$\frac{44(122)}{200} = 26.8 \text{ and } \frac{59(122)}{200} = 36.0$$

The remaining expected cell counts are obtained by subtraction (see Table 9.13). Since none of the expected cell counts is small, we can perform the chi-square test of independence.

TABLE 9.13

Expected cell counts for the data of Table 9.12

	Political Preference		
Student Rights	**Democratic**	**Republican**	**Total**
low priority	26.8	17.2	44
moderate priority	36.0	23.0	59
high priority	59.2	37.8	97
Total	122	78	200

H_1: The two variables "political preference" and "student rights" are dependent.
H_0: The two variables are independent.
T.S.:

$$\chi^2 = \sum \frac{(O - E)^2}{E}$$

$$= \frac{(20 - 26.8)^2}{26.8} + \frac{(26 - 36.0)^2}{36.0} + \cdots + \frac{(21 - 37.8)^2}{37.8}$$

$$= 1.72 + 2.78 + \cdots + 7.47 = 23.78$$

R.R.: From Appendix Table 3, with $a = .05$ and d.f. $= (3 - 1)(2 - 1)$ $= 2$, the critical value of chi-square is 5.99. Since the computed value 23.78 of chi-square is greater than 5.99, we reject the null hypothesis and conclude that the two variables are dependent. In particular, the Democratic Party is preferred by a higher proportion of students who place a high priority on student rights than of students who place a moderate or low priority on student rights.

EXAMPLE 9.3   Table 9.14 contains the results of a study conducted to determine if there is a relationship between the variables "ethnicity" and "degree of religiosity." These results are reported in a bivariate contingency table. Test the null hypothesis that the two variables are independent. (Use $\alpha = .05$.)

Degree of Religiosity	Ethnicity			Total
	Black	Mexican-American	Anglo-American	
low	21	23	55	99
medium	23	38	51	112
high	56	139	494	689
Total	100	200	600	900

SOLUTION

Before computing chi-square we must obtain the expected cell counts. Recall from previous work that we need to determine the degrees of freedom. In this problem d.f. = 4. Thus we will determine the expected cell count for the first and second cells in the top row and the first and second cells in the second row:

$$\frac{99(100)}{900} = 11.0 \qquad \frac{99(200)}{900} = 22.0$$

$$\frac{112(100)}{900} = 12.4 \qquad \frac{112(200)}{900} = 24.9$$

The remaining expected cell counts can then be found by subtracting from the appropriate marginals. These expected cell counts are listed in Table 9.15.

Degree of Religiosity	Ethnicity			Total
	Black	Mexican-American	Anglo-American	
low	11.0	22.0	66.0	99
medium	12.4	24.9	74.7	112
high	76.6	153.1	459.3	689
Total	100	200	600	900

The expected cell counts are large enough to allow us to perform the test of independence. The elements of the test are given next.

H_1: The two variables "degree of religiosity" and "ethnicity" are dependent.

H_0: The two variables are independent.

T.S.:

$$\chi^2 = \sum \frac{(O - E)^2}{E}$$

$$= \frac{(21 - 11)^2}{11} + \frac{(23 - 22)^2}{22} + \frac{(55 - 66)^2}{66}$$

$$+ \frac{(23 - 12.4)^2}{12.4} + \frac{(38 - 24.9)^2}{24.9} + \frac{(51 - 74.7)^2}{74.7}$$

$$+ \frac{(56 - 76.6)^2}{76.6} + \frac{(139 - 153.1)^2}{153.1} + \frac{(494 - 459.3)^2}{459.3}$$

$$= 9.09 + .04 + 1.83 + 9.06 + 6.89 + 7.52 + 5.54 + 1.30 + 2.62$$

$$= 43.89$$

R.R.: Using Appendix Table 3 with $a = .05$ and d.f. $= 4$, the critical value of χ^2 is 9.49. Since the observed value 43.89 of χ^2 is greater than 9.49, we reject H_0 and conclude that the two variables are dependent.

The use of the chi-square probability distribution in analyzing cross-classification data can present a problem. **Researchers have long recognized that the chi-square distribution may poorly approximate the actual distribution of χ^2 where some or all of the expected cell frequencies are small. One attempt at improving the approximation was offered by Yates in 1934 for the 2 × 2 table and has become known as *Yates's correction for continuity*, or simply *Yates's correction*.** The test suggested by Yates is identical to the chi-square test of independence just discussed, with the exception that we use the test statistic

$$\chi_c^2 = \sum \frac{(|O - E| - .5)^2}{E}$$

Note that in using χ_c^2 we take the absolute value of all differences $(O - E)$ and subtract .5. Each of these quantities is then squared and divided by the appropriate expected value E.

EXERCISES

9. A preelection survey was conducted in three different districts to compare the proportion of voters favoring the incumbent governor. Random samples of 50 registered voters were polled in each district. These results are presented in the

accompanying table. Do these data present sufficient evidence to indicate that the proportions favoring the incumbent governor differ in the three districts? (Use $\alpha = .05$.)

EXERCISE 9

Opinion toward incumbent governor by voters in three districts

Opinion toward Incumbent Governor	District		
	1	**2**	**3**
favor	19	14	26
do not favor	31	36	24

10. Two anthropologists compared the duration of the postpartum taboo restricting coitus with the presence or absence of initiation ceremonies at puberty in 60 societies. Use their data in the accompanying table to test the null hypothesis of independence of the two variables. (Use $\alpha = .05$.)

EXERCISE 10

Categorization of 60 societies according to initiation ceremonies and the duration of postpartum taboo

Initiation Ceremonies	Duration of Postpartum Taboo		Total
	Up to a Year	**One Year or More**	
absent	21	11	32
present	9	19	28
Total	30	30	60

11. A poll of 100 members of Congress was taken to determine their opinions toward a bill to raise the ceiling on the national debt. Each congressperson was then classified according to political party affiliation and opinion. The survey results are listed in the accompanying table. At this point neither the opponents nor the proponents can claim victory. Test the null hypothesis that these two variables are independent of one another against the research hypothesis that a congressperson's opinion on the national debt bill is related to his or her party affiliation. Give the level of significance for this test.

EXERCISE 11

Relationship between party affiliation and approval of a bill to raise the ceiling on the national debt

χ^2 calculated: 6.11

Opinion toward Bill	Party Affiliation		Total
	Republican	**Democrat**	
approve	28	19	47
do not approve	14	28	42
no opinion	5	6	11
Total	47	53	100

12. Social researchers surveyed 400 white voters in the South and categorized each one by party affiliation and socioeconomic status (SES). The data are given in the accompanying table.

EXERCISE 12

Relationship between political and socioeconomic status in the South

Party Affiliation	Socioeconomic Status			
	High	Medium	Low	Total
Democratic	50	79	67	196
Republican	84	77	43	204
Total	134	156	110	400

a. Construct a percentage comparison for this bivariate table, by using party affiliation as the dependent variable.
b. Do the two variables appear to be related?
c. Test the null hypothesis that these two variables are independent of one another against the research hypothesis that a voter's party affiliation in the South is related to his or her SES.

9.4   FISHER'S EXACT TEST

In Chapter 8 we presented a two-sample test for comparing two proportions for which the sample sizes were both 30 or more. In each sample we observed the number of successes in a fixed number of trials. The sample results could then be displayed in the form of Table 9.16. Note that in sample 1 we observed X_1 successes (and $n_1 - X_1$ failures) in n_1 trials. Similarly, in sample 2 we observed X_2 successes in the n_2 trials (we assume that n_1 and n_2 are both 30 or more).

What happens when the sample sizes are less than 30? We will consider this problem now.

The data of Table 9.16 represent a cross-classification of data by sample and by outcome. **Fisher's exact test** provides a nonparametric test for

TABLE 9.16

Summary of data for two samples

Outcome	Sample		Total
	1	2	
success	X_1	X_2	$X_1 + X_2$
failure	$n_1 - X_1$	$n_2 - X_2$	$n_1 + n_2 - X_1 - X_2$
Total	n_1	n_2	$n_1 + n_2$

analyzing count (nominal or ordinal) data when the sample sizes are small. We assume that there are two independent random samples and that each observation can be classified into one of two categories, which we will call *success* and *failure.*

We can compute the exact probability of observing X_1 successes in the first sample and X_2 successes in the second by using Fisher's exact distribution. The exact probability of observing X_1 and X_2 successes from independent random samples of sizes n_1 and n_2, respectively, is given by

$$P(X_1, X_2) = \frac{n_1! n_2! (X_1 + X_2)! (n_1 + n_2 - X_1 - X_2)!}{(n_1 + n_2)! X_1! X_2! (n_1 - X_1)! (n_2 - X_2)!}$$

If we use the marginal totals of Table 9.16, we see that $P(X_1, X_2)$ is computed by taking the ratio of the products of the factorials for the four marginal totals to the product of the factorials of the individual cell frequencies and the total sample size $n_1 + n_2$.

To illustrate Fisher's exact test, we consider the next example.

EXAMPLE 9.4

Eleven professors teaching fine arts in church-related colleges and 11 fine arts teachers in state-supported colleges were asked to classify their perceptions of departmental pressures to publish. The sample data are summarized in Table 9.17. Determine the probability of observing 0 and 4 successes in the samples of size 11 and 11, respectively.

TABLE 9.17

Faculty perceptions of
the pressure to publish

Amount of Pressure to Publish	Type of College		Total
	Church-Related	**State-Supported**	**Total**
quite a lot/some	0	4	4
very little/none	11	7	18
Total	11	11	22

SOLUTION

Utilizing the marginal totals and cell frequencies, we have

$$P(0, 4) = \frac{11!\, 11!\, 4!\, 18!}{22!\, 0!\, 4!\, 11!\, 7!}$$

(Recall that $0! = 1$.) After much simplification and cancellation of terms, we obtain

$$P(0, 4) = \frac{11 \cdot 10 \cdot 9 \cdot 8}{22 \cdot 21 \cdot 20 \cdot 19} = .045$$

That is, given that we have two samples of size 11 each and a total of 4 professors who feel that there is quite a lot or some pressure to publish, the probability of obtaining a split of 0 and 4 ($X_1 = 0$, $X_2 = 4$) between the two samples is .045.

Example 9.4 could have been stated as a statistical test of a hypothesis. It may be important to test the null hypothesis that the proportion of successes in population 1 is identical to the proportion of successes in population 2 against the one-sided research hypothesis that one population has a higher proportion of successes. We illustrate this idea with an example.

EXAMPLE 9.5

Suppose that the sample data of Example 9.4 were those given in Table 9.18. Test the hypothesis that the proportions of professors who feel that quite a bit of departmental pressure is brought to bear on publishing for the two types of colleges are identical against the one-sided alternative that there is a higher proportion of professors who feel this way in state-supported colleges. (Use $\alpha = .05$.)

TABLE 9.18

Sample data for Example 9.5

| Amount of | Type of College | | |
Pressure to Publish	Church-Related	State-Supported	Total
quite a lot/some	1	3	4
very little/none	10	8	18
Total	11	11	22

SOLUTION

Observed values of X_2 greater than those of X_1 will indicate possible rejection of the null hypothesis. Hence we must compute the probability of observing the sample values for X_1 and X_2. In addition, however, we must compute values of X_1 and X_2 that are more extreme (more unlikely) while maintaining the same marginal total, $X_1 + X_2$. In our example we have $X_1 = 1$, $X_2 = 3$, and $X_1 + X_2 = 4$, for which

$$P(1, 3) = \frac{11!\,11!\,4!\,18!}{22!\,1!\,3!\,10!\,8!} = .248$$

A more extreme set of values for X_1 and X_2 with the same marginal total $X_1 + X_2 = 4$ would be $X_1 = 0$ and $X_2 = 4$. From Example 9.4 we have

$$P(0, 4) = .045$$

The probability of observing $X_1 = 1$ and $X_2 = 3$ or worse is $P(1, 3) + P(0, 4) = .293$. Since this value is greater than $\alpha = .05$, we have insufficient evidence to reject the null hypothesis that these proportions differ for church-supported and state-supported colleges.

SUMMARY OF FISHER'S EXACT TEST

Research hypothesis H_1: The proportion of successes in population 2 is greater than that in population 1 (a one-sided test).

Null hypothesis H_0: The proportions of successes in the two populations are identical.

Test statistic For the marginal total $X_1 + X_2$ equal to some value k, compute $P(X_1, X_2)$ for the observed number of successes and other more extreme results for which $X_1 + X_2 = k$.

Rejection region R.R.: Reject the null hypothesis if the sum of the probabilities computed in the previous step is less than the specified value of α. (*Note*: Either population can be labeled as 1.)

Assumption n_1 and n_2 are less than 30.

Fisher's exact test is not always easy to apply, especially if we must compute several of the probabilities $P(X_1, X_2)$. There are tables of critical values that can be helpful in applying this test, but since they are so cumbersome, we omit them from our presentation. If you are faced with a problem requiring several difficult calculations of $P(X_1, X_2)$, you can make use of any of several electronic calculators that compute factorials, or you can refer to Siegel, *Nonparametric Statistics for the Behavioral Sciences* (1956), for the necessary critical values.

EXERCISES

13. Discuss the situation in which the social researcher is most likely to use Fisher's exact test.

14. A sports sociologist examines the recruiting practices of college athletic departments. The researcher hypothesizes that programs in major conferences are less likely to recruit marginal student-athletes than programs in marginal conferences. SAT scores are used to measure student quality, and sports revenue is used to measure success. Compute Fisher's exact test on the information contained in the accompanying table.

EXERCISE 14

SAT scores for stu-
dent-athletes and
membership in a suc-
cessful conference

	Degree of Conference Success	
SAT Scores	**High**	**Low**
900 and lower	2	10
910 and higher	20	12

9.5   THE McNEMAR TEST

Many times cross-classification data arise from studies in which several
individuals are sampled at two different times to determine if an attitude,
preference, viewpoint, philosophy, or whatever has changed between the two
test periods. For example, an advertising firm in charge of the promotional
work for a political candidate may sample 100 voters in a precinct to estimate
the proportion of voters in favor of its candidate. After an extensive
advertising campaign, the firm might recontact the same 100 voters to
determine their preference and, in particular, to see if a change in preference
(for better or worse) has taken place.

To determine if a significant change has taken place over time, we
construct a two-way table in which we classify an individual's response at
each test period into one of two categories (see Table 9.19). For lack of better
words, we will call these categories "success" or "failure."

TABLE 9.19

Summary of McNemar
data

	After	
Before	**Success**	**Failure**
failure	cell 1 (n_1)	cell 2
success	cell 3	cell 4 (n_4)

**If we let n_1 be the number of observations in cell 1 and n_4 be the number of
observations in cell 4, the total for cells 1 and 4, $n_1 + n_4$, represents the total
number of persons whose responses have changed in either direction.** Under the
null hypothesis that changes from failure to success (cell 1) or from success to
failure (cell 4) are equally likely, we would expect $(n_1 + n_4)/2$ changes to
occur in the two directions. We can utilize this information in testing the
significance of any observed changes.

The test statistic for this test makes use of this information and again
involves the quantities $(O - E)^2/E$. Unlike the chi-square test of independence, however, we only sum the terms for cells 1 and 4. Also, the expected

cell count for both cells 1 and 4 is $(n_1 + n_4)/2$. When the null hypothesis of no change is true, the quantity

$$\chi_M^2 = \sum_{\substack{\text{cells 1} \\ \text{and 4}}} \frac{(O - E)^2}{E}$$

follows a chi-square distribution with d.f. = 1.

A convenient shortcut formula for χ_M^2, which incorporates the expected cell counts $(n_1 + n_4)/2$, is

$$\chi_M^2 = \frac{(n_1 - n_4)^2}{n_1 + n_4}$$

We summarize the test procedure as follows.

McNEMAR TEST OF CHANGE

Research hypothesis H_1: Changes in attitudes from failure to success or from success to failure are not equally likely.

Null hypothesis H_0: Changes in attitudes from failure to success or from success to failure are equally likely.

Test statistic

$$\chi_M^2 = \sum_{\substack{\text{cells 1} \\ \text{and 4}}} \frac{(O - E)^2}{E} = \frac{(n_1 - n_4)^2}{n_1 + n_4}$$

Rejection region   R.R.: Reject H_0 if χ_M^2 exceeds the critical chi-square value, with d.f. = 1 and $a = \alpha$.

EXAMPLE 9.6

A random sample of 50 delegates was drawn from the party delegates at a national convention. Prior to the convention 15 of these delegates favored a policy of detente with the Soviet Union and 35 were opposed. After several hours of heated debate the convention delegates adopted a plank for the party platform supporting detente. The same 50 delegates were polled again after the convention. Use the data of Table 9.20 to test for a significant change in opinion from the pre- to postconvention polls. (Use $\alpha = .05$.)

SOLUTION

The observed frequencies are given in Table 9.20. We can compute the value of our test statistic by using the shortcut formula with $n_1 = 0$ and $n_4 = 15$. The quantity χ_M^2 is then

$$\chi_M^2 = \sum_{\substack{\text{cells 1} \\ \text{and 4}}} \frac{(O - E)^2}{E} = \frac{(n_1 - n_4)^2}{n_1 + n_4} = \frac{(0 - 15)^2}{0 + 15} = \frac{225}{15} = 15$$

TABLE 9.20

Pre- and postconvention attitudes of delegates toward detente

| | Postconvention | | |
Preconvention	Against	For	Total
for	0	15	15
against	20	15	35
Total	20	30	50

The critical chi-square value with $a = .05$ and d.f. $= 1$ is 3.84 (see Appendix Table 3). Since χ^2_M exceeds 3.84, we reject the null hypothesis and conclude that a significant change of opinion has occurred during the party's convention.

EXERCISE

15. Describe the context in which a social researcher is most likely to use the McNemar test. What are the primary limitations with this test?

SUMMARY

This chapter is concerned with the cross-classification of data, percentage comparisons, and several statistical tests of the relationship between two variables measured on nominal and ordinal scales.

In cross-classifying bivariate data into a contingency table, we learned that one variable is labeled the independent variable and the other the dependent variable. We then made percentage comparisons of the two variables, where percentages are based on the marginal totals of the independent variable. Although percentage comparisons are meaningful in showing whether two variables are related, we cannot draw specific statistical inferences from these comparisons.

In order to make statistical inferences, we presented several statistical tests of the relationship between two variables. The first test discussed was the chi-square test of independence. Provided the expected cell counts are large enough, we can test the null hypothesis that two variables are independent against the research hypothesis that they are dependent.

It is essential not to confuse a test of independence with dependent and independent variables. In the context of a chi-square test, a test of independence has to do with whether one variable is connected or related to another variable.

The other two tests presented are Fisher's exact test and the McNemar test. Both tests are applied to a 2×2 bivariate frequency table. Fisher's exact test provides a small-sample alternative to the large-sample test presented in Chapter 8 for comparing two populations. On the other hand, the McNemar test is useful for analyzing whether a change in attitude, preference, philosophy, or the like has occurred over a period of time. For the McNemar test each person in the sample is interviewed at two distinct times and classified by his or her responses at the two interviews. A chi-square test is constructed utilizing the number of persons whose responses have changed from the first to the second sampling times.

In this chapter we have presented the first step in examining the relationship between two variables that are measured on nominal or ordinal scales by trying to answer the question, "Are the two variables statistically related?" Chapters 10 and 11 will carry this examination further. Chapter 10 is concerned with quantifying the strength of the relationship between two nominal or two ordinal variables by using measures of association. Chapter 11 examines how the strength of a bivariate relationship between nominal or ordinal variables is affected when controlling for a third variable.

KEY WORDS

Bivariate frequency table A table (also called a contingency table) that portrays the tallies for two variables, based on cross-tabulations.

Chi-square test of independence A test of the null hypothesis of independence for two variables of a contingency table.

Contingency table A two-way table constructed for classifying bivariate data. The entries in the table show the number of observations falling in each cell.

Degrees of freedom A parameter of the chi-square distribution. For a chi-square test of independence, the degrees of freedom equal the number of rows minus 1 times the number of columns minus 1, or $(r - 1)(c - 1)$.

Dependent variable The effect or consequence of an independent variable.

Expected cell counts The cell counts expected if the null hypothesis is true in a chi-square test of independence.

Fisher's exact test A nonparametric test for comparing two proportions based on independent random samples. Used when samples are small.

Independent variable The cause or antecedent of a dependent variable.

McNemar test A nonparametric test for determining change with regard to some variable in cases sampled at two different times.

Univariate frequency table A table that portrays the tallies for each category of a single variable.

Yates's correction   A technique used to improve the chi-square distribution where some or all of the expected cell frequencies are small in a 2×2 table.

KEY FORMULAS

Chi-square test of independence H_0: The two variables are independent.

$$\text{T.S.:} \chi^2 = \sum \frac{(O - E)^2}{E}$$

where $E = \dfrac{(\text{row total})(\text{column total})}{n}$

Fisher's exact test H_0: The proportions of successes in the two populations are identical.

T.S.: $\Sigma\, P(X_1, X_2)$ for the observed values of X_1 and X_2 and more extreme results for which $X_1 + X_2 = k$

McNemar test H_0: Changes from failure to success or from success to failure are equally likely.

$$\text{T.S.:} \chi_M^2 = \sum_{\substack{\text{cells 1} \\ \text{and 4}}} \frac{(O - E)^2}{E} = \frac{(n_1 - n_4)^2}{n_1 + n_4}$$

SUPPLEMENTARY EXERCISES FOR CHAPTER 9

16. What are the objectives in cross-classifying two variables?

17. State the rules for constructing contingency tables.

18. The governor of each state was polled to determine his or her opinion concerning a particular domestic policy issue. At the same time the governor's party affiliation was recorded. The data are given in the accompanying table. If we assume that the 50 governors represent a random sample of political leaders throughout the nation, do the data present sufficient evidence to indicate a dependence between party affiliation and the opinion expressed on the domestic policy issue? (Use $\alpha = .05$.)

EXERCISE 18

Categorization of party affiliation and opinion on a domestic policy issue

Opinion	Party Affiliation	
	Republican	Democrat
approve	18	8
do not approve	5	8
no opinion	5	6

19. Margaret Eichler (1975) reported results of a study of the relationship between male circumcision and rules of lineage. Suppose you replicate her study and report your findings. Use your data (in the accompanying table) to perform a chi-square test of independence. Give the level of significance for your test.

EXERCISE 19

Categorization of 100 societies according to male circumcision and rules of lineage

	Rules of Lineage	
Male Circumcision	**Male Line**	**Female Line**
present	27	3
absent	42	28

20. When is Yates's correction for continuity appropriate?

21. Discuss the kinds of problems appropriate for using each of the following statistical tests:
a. chi-square test of independence
b. Fisher's exact test

22. Use the data from 50 physicians given in the accompanying table to determine whether concern for the need to communicate with lower-class people changes after the physician spends four weeks in a general hospital. Comment.

EXERCISE 22

Before and after concerns of physicians to communicate with lower-class people

Concern before	Concern after Hospital Experience		
Hospital Experience	**High**	**Low**	**Total**
low	27	5	32
high	9	9	18

23. In a study of small groups, a researcher reported the results in the accompanying table. Do the data provide sufficient evidence to indicate that completion or noncompletion of a task is related to type of leadership? Test a hypothesis of no relationship using $\alpha = .05$.

EXERCISE 23

Categorization of leadership style and task completion for small groups

Completion	Group Leadership Style	
of Task	**Democratic**	**Authoritarian**
yes	6	2
no	1	4
Total	7	6

24. In a recent national party convention, pro-lifers were against a pro-abortion plank for the party platform. In a poll of 150 delegates, each was classified by religious background and attitude toward abortion. Use these data to examine the relationship between the two variables. Are they independent?

EXERCISE 24

Categorization of religious background and attitude toward abortion for 100 delegates

Attitude toward Abortion	Religious Background	
	Catholic	Protestant
pro	10	40
con	70	30

25. If a researcher wished to test the null hypothesis that social class is independent of sex (Exercise 19, Chapter 2), would he or she have any difficulties in meeting the assumptions underlying the use of the chi-square test of independence? If so, which assumption(s)?

26. See Exercise 19, Chapter 2. Combine the lower- and lower-middle-class groups and test whether the distribution of people by social class is independent of sex. (Use the chi-square test with $\alpha = .05$.)

27. In a study to determine the effectiveness of a drug for arthritis, two groups, each consisting of 200 arthritic patients, were compared. One group was inoculated with the serum; the other received a placebo (an inoculation that appears to contain serum but actually is nonactive). After a period of time, each person in the study was asked to state whether his or her arthritic condition had improved. The results are given in the accompanying table. Do these data present sufficient evidence to indicate that the serum was effective in improving the condition of arthritic patients? Test by using chi-square and $\alpha = .05$.

EXERCISE 27

Categorization of mode of treatment and arthritic condition for 100 arthritic patients

Arthritic Condition	Treatment	
	Treated	Untreated
improved	117	74
not improved	83	126

28. Convert the raw frequencies in Exercise 27 to proportions and perform the z-test for the difference between two proportions. Are the conclusions comparable to those in Exercise 27 if we use $\alpha = .05$? Explain your findings.

29. In a study of a midwestern city, a sample of 242 individuals studied the evidence presented at a trial involving a rape charge against a husband who had demanded marital relations with his wife. Use the data summarized in the accompanying table to determine whether guilty judgments are independent of sex. Give the level of significance for your test.

EXERCISE 29

Relationship between sex and judgment of guilt

	Judgment	
Sex	**Guilty**	**Not Guilty**
female	97	24
male	30	91

30. A group of 306 people were interviewed to determine opinions on a current American foreign policy issue. At the same time the person's political affiliation was recorded. The data are given in the accompanying table. Do the data present sufficient evidence to indicate a dependence between party affiliation and the opinion expressed for the sampled population? Explain.

EXERCISE 30

Categorization of party affiliation and opinion about a current American foreign policy issue for 306 persons interviewed

	Party Affiliation	
Opinion	**Republican**	**Democrat**
approve	114	87
disapprove	53	27
no opinion	17	8

31. Student opinion on a resolution presented to the student council was surveyed to determine whether opinion was independent of fraternity and sorority affiliation. Two hundred students were interviewed, with the results as shown in the accompanying table. In a chi-square test of independence, how many degrees of freedom are there? Determine if there is sufficient evidence to indicate that student opinion on the resolution is independent of status (i.e., fraternity, sorority, or unaffiliated). (Use $\alpha = .05$.)

EXERCISE 31

Student opinion and fraternity-sorority affiliation for 200 students surveyed

Student Opinion	Status of Affiliation		
	Fraternity	**Sorority**	**Unaffiliated**
in favor	40	35	27
opposed	18	25	55
Total	58	60	82

32. Researchers interviewed a sample of 350 white urban males in Detroit and categorized each individual according to occupational prestige (as measured by the Occupational Prestige Scale) and religious affiliation. Use the data in the accompanying table to test the research hypothesis that the two variables "religious affiliation" and "occupational prestige" are related. Give the level of significance for your test.

EXERCISE 32

Categorization of religious affiliation and occupational prestige for 350 males

Occupational Prestige	Religious Affiliation				
	Pentecostal	**Lutheran**	**Catholic**	**Episcopalian**	**Total**
0–25	25	30	30	5	90
26–50	15	20	40	15	90
51–75	10	15	40	30	95
76–96	0	5	30	40	75
Total	50	70	140	90	350

33. A study of changes in belief toward the permissibility of abortion at the discretion of the pregnant woman was reported. It involved 100 Catholics who had extensively studied the moral and ethical ramifications of abortion. Use the McNemar test to determine if beliefs changed during the extensive study.

EXERCISE 33

Change in abortion attitudes after extensive study of relevant issues

Before Study	After Study	
	No	**Yes**
yes	0	20
no	50	30

34. Two counselors at a state university interviewed 100 entering first-year students. Students were asked how frequently they attended church. Four years later, at the time of graduation, these students were interviewed again. The data are shown in the accompanying table. Use the McNemar test to determine if church attendance changed over the four-year period.

EXERCISE 34

Change in church attendance after four years of college

Before	After	
	At Least Once a Month	**Less than Once a Month**
at least once a month	20	60
less than once a month	0	20

35. Refer to Table 9.6. Do these data offer sufficient evidence to indicate that attitude toward affirmative action for women is independent of attitude toward affirmative action for racial and ethnic groups? (Use $\alpha = .05$.)

36. Refer to Exercise 35. Recalculate the chi-square using Yates's correction. Does the correction cause you to draw a different conclusion? Explain.

37. Refer to Table 9.5. Combine murder rates 0 to 13 into a single category and 14 to 27 into another category. Use these new categories and test the null hypothesis of independence of the two variables. (Use $\alpha = .05$.)

38. Refer to Exercise 37. Recalculate the chi-square using Yates's correction. Does the correction cause you to draw a different conclusion? Explain.

39. Refer to Exercise 3. Test the null hypothesis of independence. How confident are you in your conclusion? Explain.

40. Refer to Exercise 5. Use these data and set up an appropriate statistical test. What is your hypothesis? Is it supported? Explain.

41. Refer to Database A, Appendix Table 7. Assume that the samples of social science and humanities majors are random. Do the data present sufficient evidence to indicate that religious preference is dependent of major? (Use $\alpha = .05$.)

42. Using the information in Database A, Appendix Table 7, test the hypothesis that religious preference is independent of parents' income for majors in the social sciences and humanities. (Use $\alpha = .05$.) Interpret your findings. (Use 150 cases, excluding Jews; $n = 146$.)

43. Use the information in Database B, Appendix Table 8. Set up a contingency table using "level of technology" and "denial of civil liberties" as your two variables. Divide technology scores into two categories (high = 50 to 100; low = 6 to 49) and then divide civil liberties scores into three categories (minimal denial = 2–4; medium denial = 5–9; maximum denial = 10–14).
a. Use "level of technology" as the independent variable and compute percentages. What conclusion might you draw?
b. Use "denial of civil liberties" as the independent variable and compute percentages. What conclusion might you draw? Would it differ from the conclusion based on (a)? How?
c. Test the hypothesis of independence. (Use $\alpha = .05$.)
d. Recalculate the chi-square using Yates's correction. Is your conclusion still the same?

44. Refer to Database C, Appendix Table 9.
a. Construct a 4 × 5 contingency table to categorize patients by treatment group and therapeutic effect.
b. Compute expected cell counts. Do the expected cell counts satisfy the criteria for running a chi-square test of independence?
c. Run a chi-square test of independence on your table in (a), if appropriate, or on a "collapsed" 4 × 2 table, as shown.

Treatment Group	Therapeutic Effect	
	Marked/Moderate	Minimal/Unchanged/Worse
A		
B		
C		
D		

45. Refer to Exercise 44(c). If the table is collapsed as suggested, what information may be lost?

46. The accompanying computer output gives the results of a statistical test based on the data of Table 9.12.
   a. Identify the test used.
   b. State the null hypothesis.
   c. Draw a conclusion based on the results of this test.

EXERCISE 46

```
MTB > chisquare 'DEM' 'REP'

Expected counts are printed below observed counts

            DEM      REP     Total
     1       20       24        44
          26.84    17.16

     2       26       33        59
          35.99    23.01

     3       76       21        97
          59.17    37.83

  Total     122       78       200

ChiSq =  1.743 +  2.726 +
         2.773 +  4.337 +
         4.787 +  7.487 = 23.854
  df = 2
```

47. Wong (1990) examined the popular belief that Asian high school seniors have unusual educational aspirations. He compared whites with Chinese, Filipino, and Japanese students in the United States. He reports that 31.4% of white students plan to attend a four-year college. The corresponding figures for Chinese students was 56.2%; for Filipino students, 42.6%; and for Japanese students, 39.8%. Assume that each of his samples is based on the responses of 1000 high school students. Use the accompanying table to perform a chi-square test of independence. (Set $\alpha = .01$.)

EXERCISE 47

Plans to attend a four-year college, by race

College plans	Ethnic group			
	White	Chinese	Filipino	Japanese
yes	314	562	426	398
no	686	438	574	602
Total	1000	1000	1000	1000

48. Refer to Exercise 47. Perform a chi-square test of independence for each of the following: (Set $\alpha = .05$.)

a. College plans for white and Chinese students

b. College plans for white and Filipino students

c. College plans for white and Japanese students

d. College plans for Chinese and Filipino students

e. College plans for Chinese and Japanese students

f. College plans for Filipino and Japanese students

49. Wong's (1990) study reports on the number of white, Chinese, Filipino, and Japanese students who participate in varsity sports. For every 1000 white students, 354 participate in varsity sports; 281 of every 1000 Chinese students, 319 of every 1000 Filipino students, and 353 of every 1000 Japanese students participate in varsity sports. Use the chi-square test of independence to determine if varsity participation is independent of ethnic background. (Set $\alpha = .05$.)

50. Danziger and Radin (1990) report on the living arrangements of 173 white teen mothers and 111 black teen mothers. Of the 173 white teen mothers, 91 live alone, 34 live with their mothers, and 48 live with both parents. Of the 111 black teen mothers, 53 live alone, 41 live with their mothers, and 17 live with both parents. Using chi-square, test the independence of living arrangements and race of teen mothers. (Set $\alpha = .05$.) Interpret your results.

51. Andrews and Brewin (1990) studied a sample of 70 women who have experienced marital violence. The research team examined the patterns of attribution of blame for the violence. Of these 70 women, 51 are no longer in a violent relationship, and 44 blame their partners and 7 blame themselves. Nineteen are still in violent relationships; of these, 10 blame themselves for the violence and 9 blame their partners. Use chi-square to test the independence of current violent relationship and type of blame. (Set $\alpha = .05$.) Use Yates's correction.

52. Nelson and Henry (1990) report on the results of several surveys, involving over 17,000 respondents. The investigators studied the subjects' attitudes on women's rights and their church attendance rates. Based on reported patterns, about 34% of Roman Catholic weekly church attenders score high on women's rights, compared to 36% of intermittent attenders and 38% of rare attenders. For Baptists, corresponding figures are about 28%, 35%, and 39%; and for Pentecostals, the figures are 20%, 30%, and 38%. Assume that these patterns are representative of these religious groupings in the United States and that you have 9 samples of 100 people each. Use a chi-square test of independence and answer each of the following questions.

a. Does church attendance for Catholics influence their views on women's rights?

b. Does church attendance for Baptists influence their views on women's rights?

c. Does church attendance for Pentecostals influence their views on women's rights?

d. Disregarding attendance, is attitude toward women's rights independent of religious affiliation? (Set $\alpha = .01$.)

CHAPTER 10

MEASURES OF ASSOCIATION: NOMINAL AND ORDINAL DATA

GENERAL OBJECTIVES

In Chapter 9 we saw how social researchers deal with bivariate data that have been cross-classified. In this chapter we explore other ways of handling such data. In particular, we explore measures of association for nominal and ordinal data. If two variables are dependent based on a chi-square test, we are likely to want to know the degree of association or dependence. This chapter will examine a variety of measures of association and their interpretation.

SPECIFIC OBJECTIVES

1. To introduce two simple measures of association for nominal data: the contingency coefficient C and Cramer's V.
2. To show you one of the major differences among measures of association: Some measures of association take on values in a fixed interval, and others do not.
3. To illustrate some of the problems with C and to offer an alternative, lambda.
4. To introduce the concept of proportional-reduction-in-error (PRE) measures of association and to show you their advantage over non-PRE measures of association.
5. To introduce measures of association for ordinal data: gamma and rho.
6. To introduce a measure of association for a 2×2 table: Yule's Q.

10.1   INTRODUCTION

Cross-classification of data, presented in Chapter 9, is performed by social researchers to determine whether two variables, representing two systems of classification, are related. Hence Chapter 9 dealt solely with the question of whether the two variables are dependent and presented statistical tests for the null hypothesis that the two variables are independent. Our objective was to collect evidence to support the research hypothesis that the two variables are dependent and therefore related. In this chapter we carry the study of the relationship between two variables one step further. It is not sufficient to know only that two variables are related; we also want measures of the strength of the relationship or association, because many times the ultimate goal in a social science investigation is to predict the value of one variable based on knowledge of a second.

This chapter presents measures of association for nominal and ordinal data. For each measure of association presented, we discuss when it is to be used and its interpretation. A statistical test of no association between two variables is presented for several of the measures of association.

10.2   NOMINAL MEASURES OF ASSOCIATION: THE CONTINGENCY COEFFICIENT AND CRAMER'S *V*

We discussed the use of the chi-square test of independence for contingency tables in Chapter 9. After we have performed a chi-square test for independence and found the variables to be dependent, we may be interested in the strength of the dependence between the two variables.

One difference in the various measures of association is in the scale of measurement used for the two variables being studied. Some measures of association are specifically for nominal variables, others for ordinal variables, and still others for interval or ratio variables.

Another distinction relates to how measures of association are standardized, or normed. A measure of association that takes on values in a fixed interval is called a *normed*, or *standardized*, measure of association. Most normed measures of association fall into one of two categories, **type A** or **type B**, as shown in Figure 10.1.

The **contingency coefficient** is a measure of association for cross-classification data when the two variables are measured at the nominal level or higher. The contingency coefficient is computed as follows.

FIGURE 10.1

Two types of normed measures of association

TYPE A: Values between 0 and 1

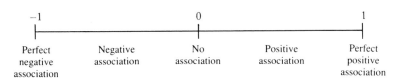

TYPE B: Values between -1 and 1

CONTINGENCY COEFFICIENT

$$C = \sqrt{\frac{\chi^2}{n + \chi^2}}$$

where

$$\chi^2 = \sum \frac{(O - E)^2}{E} \quad \text{and} \quad n = \text{total sample size}$$

The contingency coefficient is relatively easy to compute and satisfies the condition that it equals zero when there is no association between the variables. However, it does have some disadvantages as a measure of association. *First*, the contingency coefficient is always less than 1, even when the two variables are completely dependent on one another. *Second*, C provides only an intuitive measure of the degree of association between two variables. It is used after a chi-square test of independence and hence is most frequently employed for data that satisfy the conditions required of a chi-square test. *Third*, contingency coefficients for two different sets of data can be compared only if the two-way tables are of the same size (the same number of rows and columns). This restriction is due to the fact that C can attain larger values for larger tables, so the range of possible values of C changes with the size of the table involved. *Finally*, it is difficult to compare the contingency coefficient with any of the other measures of association that will be presented later in this chapter.

Before we further discuss the contingency coefficient, we illustrate its use with an example.

EXAMPLE 10.1

A study of migrants and their family relations was conducted to determine whether the variable "degree of kinship participation" in the extended family was independent of a family's socioeconomic status. Use the data in Table 10.1 to run a chi-square test of independence, and then compute the contingency coefficient C. Expected cell counts have been computed and are given in parentheses in the table.

TABLE 10.1

Study of newcomer adaptations

Socioeconomic Status	Degree of Kinship Participation			Total
	Low	**Medium**	**High**	**Total**
low	75 (88.69)	98 (102.48)	75 (56.83)	248
medium	182 (184.53)	211 (213.23)	123 (118.24)	516
high	116 (99.78)	122 (115.29)	41 (63.93)	279
Total	373	431	239	1043

Source: Felix M. Berardo, "Internal Migrants and Extended Family Relations — A Study of Newcomer Adaptation" (Ph.D diss., Florida State University, 1965), p. 122; by permission.

SOLUTION

Before computing C we should first run a test of independence to see if the data provide sufficient evidence to show that the two variables "socioeconomic status" and "degree of kinship participation" are dependent. Using the observed and expected cell frequencies from Table 10.1, we have

$$\chi^2 = \sum \frac{(O - E)^2}{E}$$

$$= \frac{(-13.69)^2}{88.69} + \frac{(-4.48)^2}{102.48} + \frac{(18.17)^2}{56.83} + \frac{(-2.53)^2}{184.53} + \frac{(-2.23)^2}{213.23}$$

$$+ \frac{(4.76)^2}{118.24} + \frac{(16.22)^2}{99.78} + \frac{(6.71)^2}{115.29} + \frac{(-22.93)^2}{63.93}$$

$$= 19.62$$

Since the boundary of the rejection region for $\alpha = .05$ (and hence $a = .05$) with d.f. $= (r - 1)(c - 1) = 2(2) = 4$ is 9.49, we conclude that the classifications are dependent. That is, socioeconomic status influences (is related to) the degree of kinship participation.

Now let us compute a measure of the strength of this dependence, the contingency coefficient. Using $\chi^2 = 19.62$, we find the contingency coefficient to be

$$C = \sqrt{\frac{\chi^2}{n + \chi^2}} = \sqrt{\frac{19.62}{1043 + 19.62}} = \sqrt{.0185} = .136$$

Unfortunately, very little can be said concerning the magnitude of C. However, we know from the chi-square test that socioeconomic status influences the degree of kinship participation, and C gives us a measure of the strength of this relationship.

Some of the disadvantages of C can be alleviated by adjusting the computed value of C according to the maximum value C may attain. It can be shown that for any square two-way table (i.e., a table with the same number of rows and columns), the maximum value of C obtainable under perfect association is

$$C_{\max} = \sqrt{\frac{r-1}{r}}$$

where r is the number of rows in the table. For $r = 2$, we have

$$C_{\max} = \sqrt{\frac{1}{2}} = .707$$

If we now form a modified (adjusted) version of the contingency coefficient,

$$C_{\mathrm{adj}} = \frac{C}{C_{\max}}$$

the largest value that C_{adj} can assume is 1.0, which occurs under perfect association when $C = C_{\max}$. Applying this result to the data in Table 10.1, we see that with $r = 3$ rows, we have

$$C_{\max} = \sqrt{\frac{2}{3}} = .816$$

Hence the adjusted value of C is

$$C_{\mathrm{adj}} = \frac{C}{C_{\max}} = \frac{.136}{.816} = .17$$

Using C_{adj}, we now have a type A normed measure of association (which equals 0 under no association and 1 when the two variables are perfectly associated). C_{adj} should be used in place of C for square two-way tables.

In spite of the fact that C_{adj} is a type A normed measure of association for square two-way tables, C_{adj} is still difficult to compare for two tables with different numbers of rows. **Cramer's** V is a second measure of association for comparing two nominal variables; it avoids some of the problems associated with C. For a two-way table with r rows and c columns, we define V as follows.

CRAMER'S V: NOMINAL MEASURE OF ASSOCIATION (TYPE A)

$$V = \sqrt{\frac{\chi^2}{nt}}$$

where n is the total sample size and t is the smaller of the two numbers $r - 1$ and $c - 1$; r and c are the number of rows and columns, respectively, for the two-way table.

It can be shown that V is a type A normed measure of association and hence lies in the interval from 0 to 1.

EXAMPLE 10.2   Compute Cramer's V for the data of Example 10.1.

SOLUTION   For $\chi^2 = 19.62$, $r = c = 3$, and $n = 1043$, we have

$$V = \sqrt{\frac{\chi^2}{nt}} = \sqrt{\frac{19.62}{1043(2)}} = .097$$

We know from the chi-square test that the variables are related. V gives us another measure of the magnitude of this association.

Previously we indicated that measures of association are distinguished by the scales of measurement for the two variables being studied and the way the measures of association are normed. A third distinction between measures of association for two variables relates to their interpretations. The nominal measures of association discussed so far have been based on the chi-square statistic and provide only a vague measure of the association between the two variables of interest. In succeeding sections we will turn to some measures of association based on a concept called *reduction in error*. All the procedures based on this concept will be presented in a similar manner and have a common method of interpretation. First, however, we must discuss the concept of reduction in error.

EXERCISES

1. Using the data in Exercise 27, Chapter 9, compute C and C_{adj}.

2. Refer to Table 9.12. In Example 9.2 we ran a chi-square test of independence between "student rights" and "political preference" and found $\chi^2 = 23.78$.
   a. Give the level of significance for the test of independence.
   b. Compute Cramer's V to measure the strength of the association between the two variables.

3. Refer to Exercise 2.
   a. Would C be an appropriate measure of association?
   b. Compute C.

4. Two social researchers conducted a study on the relationship between the type of book publisher for scholars and the type of college represented. Using the data in the accompanying table, run a chi-square test of independence and compute both C and C_{max} to measure the strength of the association between the two variables.

EXERCISE 4

Relationship between type of publisher and type of college for 55 professors

	Type of Publisher		
Type of College	**Secular**	**Religious**	**Total**
bible college	15	15	30
state college	25	0	25
Total	40	15	55

5. Compute Cramer's V for the data of Exercise 4.

6. Refer to Table 9.1, which compares the variables "gender" and "intention of ever marrying." Compute C and V for the data.

7. Would C_{adj} be more appropriate than C in Exercise 6? Explain.

10.3 PROPORTIONAL REDUCTION IN ERROR FOR MEASURES OF ASSOCIATION

The concept of reduction in error is based on the premise that we can predict the dependent variable more accurately if we have information on the independent variable. If the two variables are related, then information on the independent variable should help us in predicting the dependent variable.

Specifically, we assume that we can classify objects (people, relationships, beliefs, types of government, etc.) in a two-way table according to two variables. Knowing that an object is in a particular category for one variable (the *independent variable*), we wish to predict the category in which the object will fall for the second variable (*the dependent variable*). For example, suppose that married couples are categorized according to the two variables "religious affiliation of husband" and "religious affiliation of wife," as shown in Table 10.2. If we wish to predict the religious affiliation of the wife when we know the religious affiliation of the husband, then "religious affiliation of husband" is the independent variable and "religious affiliation of wife" is the dependent variable. Hence the objective of the classification is to predict the dependent variable, assuming that the value of the independent variable is known.

TABLE 10.2	Religious Affiliation of Wife	Religious Affiliation of Husband	
Two directions of classification		**Protestant**	**Catholic**
	Protestant		
	Catholic		

The reasoning behind the reduction in error is based on two rules of association. The first is a rule of *no association* between the variables (implying that the independent variable contributes no information for predicting the dependent variable). The second rule is a rule of *perfect association* between the two variables. Then, given a set of elements classified in a two-way contingency table, we calculate the number of elements misclassified (called the number of errors of classification) for the no-association rule and again for the perfect-association rule. If the two variables in the two-way table are really associated, the number of errors for the perfect-association rule should be less than for the no-association rule. The difference between these two numbers is called the *reduction in error*.

The perfect-association rule is easy to define. **Perfect association, meaning no prediction error, implies that given a particular column, all the elements fall in one (and only one) row.** If the religious affiliation of husbands and wives were perfectly associated, the religious affiliations for a sample of 100 married couples might appear as shown in one of the tables in Table 10.3. Table 10.3a might result if husbands and wives always had the same religious affiliation. The data would fall as shown in Table 10.3(b) if husbands and wives always possessed different religious affiliations. For either case, know-

TABLE 10.3

Data for Table 10.2
showing perfect
association

(a)

Religious Affiliation of Wife	Religious Affiliation of Husband		
	Protestant	Catholic	Total
Protestant	50	0	50
Catholic	0	50	50
Total	50	50	100

(b)

Religious Affiliation of Wife	Religious Affiliation of Husband		
	Protestant	Catholic	Total
Protestant	0	50	50
Catholic	50	0	50
Total	50	50	100

ing the husband's religious affiliation (column), you could correctly predict the affiliation of the wife (row).

Similarly, perfect association for a 3 × 3 table (three rows and three columns) might yield data as shown in Table 10.4. Note that for any given column in the tables, all the couples fall in one (and only one) row.

TABLE 10.4

Data showing perfect
association in a 3 × 3
table

(a)

Religious Affiliation of Wife	Religious Affiliation of Husband			
	Protestant	Catholic	Other	Total
Protestant	40	0	0	40
Catholic	0	35	0	35
Other	0	0	25	25
Total	40	35	25	100

(b)

Religious Affiliation of Wife	Religious Affiliation of Husband			
	Protestant	Catholic	Other	Total
Protestant	25	0	0	25
Catholic	0	0	25	25
Other	0	50	0	50
Total	25	50	25	100

A rule for classification that implies no association is more difficult to define. In fact, the definition of the no-association rule is the major source of difference among the various measures of association based on reduction in error.

In real life we know that perfect association between the two variables "religious affiliation of husband" and "religious affiliation of wife" does not exist. Hence it is more likely that the sample data would appear as shown in Table 10.5. Here we can no longer infer a wife's religious affiliation by merely examining her husband's (or vice versa). We can state this more formally as follows: If our objective is to infer the religious affiliation of a wife, the perfect-association rule that a wife's religious affiliation matches that of her husband would work only for the case where there is a perfect association between the two variables. If the association is less than perfect, applying this rule would introduce some error in assigning the religious affiliation of the wives.

TABLE 10.5	Religious Affiliation of Wife	Religious Affiliation of Husband		
Data for Table 10.2 showing less-than-perfect association		Protestant	Catholic	Total
	Protestant	35	15	50
	Catholic	15	35	50
	Total	50	50	100

Applying the perfect-association rule to the data of Table 10.5, we would classify all 50 wives of the 50 Protestant husbands as Protestant. Note, however, that only 35 of these wives are Protestant; hence we have 15 errors of classification. Similarly, by classifying all 50 wives of the 50 Catholic husbands as Catholic, we would make an additional 15 errors. The total number of misclassifications (errors) using the perfect-association rule would be 30.

In spite of the errors, knowing the husband's religious affiliation does give some information about a wife's religious affiliation. For example, if we ignore the husband's affiliation and try to infer a wife's affiliation, we could use the no-association rule that all wives are Protestant. If we were to assume that the row totals of Table 10.5 were fixed, with 50 Catholic wives and 50 Protestant wives, use of this rule would result in the misclassification of 50 wives. Hence in determining the degree of association between the classification of religious affiliations of husband and wife, it seems reasonable to compare the number of errors (misclassifications) resulting from inferring a wife's affiliation with and without the information concerning the husband's religious affiliation. Thus we could also choose the no-association rule that all wives are Catholic. For this example (since the numbers of

Catholic and Protestant wives are equal), the number of misclassifications would again be 50.

For the data of Table 10.5, the number of errors resulting from the no-association rule (that all wives are Protestant) is 50, while using the perfect-association rule (that a wife's religious affiliation is the same as her husband's) results in 30 errors. The reduction in error obtained by incorporating information on the husband's religious affiliation is $50 - 30 = 20$. The *proportional reduction in error* (PRE) in going from the first rule to the second is

$$\frac{50 - 30}{50} = \frac{20}{50} = .4$$

In other words, knowing the husband's religious affiliation reduces by 40% the error in predicting the wife's religious affiliation. The higher the PRE, the higher the degree of association between the two variables (or classifications).

PROPORTIONAL REDUCTION IN ERROR (PRE)

$$\text{PRE} = \frac{\text{number of errors for no-association rule} - \text{number of errors for perfect-association rule}}{\text{number of errors for no-association rule}}$$

If we applied this procedure to the data of Table 10.3a, there would again be 50 errors in classifying wives by the rule "all wives are Protestant." However, in using the rule "a wife's affiliation is the same as her husband's religious affiliation," we incur no errors. Hence the reduction in errors is 50 and the PRE is

$$\frac{50 - 0}{50} = 1.00$$

In cases such as Table 10.3 where there is a perfect association between two variables, the *percentage* reduction in error going from a rule that ignores a second variable (e.g., husband's religious affiliation) to one that utilizes this information is 100. Knowing the husband's religious affiliation predicts the wife's religious affiliation.

It is important at this point to summarize the procedures involved in using any of the PRE measures of association. Two rules and two errors are defined.

SUMMARY OF THE GENERAL CONCEPT OF REDUCTION IN ERROR

Rule 1 (no-association rule)   A rule for classifying data according to one variable with knowledge only of the marginal totals for that variable. Information on a second variable is ignored.

E_1 = number of errors of classification obtained using Rule 1

Rule 2 (perfect association rule)   A rule for classifying data according to one variable that utilizes information on a second variable.

E_2 = number of errors of classification obtained using Rule 2

The **proportional reduction in error** (PRE), obtained by using Rule 2, is then

$$\text{PRE} = \frac{E_1 - E_2}{E_1}$$

Although rules for classifying data differ for various measures of association, the concept of the PRE is the same. We proceed in the next section with specific reduction-in-error measures of association.

EXERCISES

8. Explain the concept of reduction in error as applied to measures of association.

9. State the rule of no association.

10. State the rule of perfect association.

11. In symbolic form, express the formulas for any PRE statistic.

10.4   A PRE NOMINAL MEASURE OF ASSOCIATION: LAMBDA

For any contingency table involving two variables measured on a nominal scale, we can compute two numbers, one designated by the symbol λ_r (when the row variable is the dependent variable) and the other designated by λ_c (when the column variable is the dependent variable). Both λ_r and λ_c are type A normed measures of association with a PRE interpretation.

It should be noted that λ_r and λ_c calculated from the same set of data are not necessarily identical or even similar in numerical value. However, the nature of the problem will usually dictate which variable is being predicted (which is the dependent variable). If this is not the case and it is impossible to designate an independent and a dependent variable, then we can calculate $(\lambda_r + \lambda_c)/2$, which provides a measure of mutual predictability between two variables.

The calculation of λ_r requires that we define Rules 1 and 2, corresponding to no association and perfect association, and the two errors of classification associated with these rules. In Section 10.3 we actually computed λ_r for the religious affiliation data to illustrate the concept of PRE. We can formulate the general rule for computing λ_r (when the row variable is the dependent variable) as follows.

RULES AND ERRORS FOR COMPUTING λ_r (TYPE A)

Rule 1 (no-association rule)   Place all observations in the row with the largest row total.

$$E_1 = n - \text{largest row total}$$

Rule 2 (perfect-association rule)   Place all observations of column 1 in the row with the largest cell frequency. Compute the number of errors for column 1 as the column 1 total minus the largest cell frequency of column 1. Place all observations of column 2 in the row with the largest cell frequency. Compute the number of errors for column 2 as the column 2 total minus the largest cell frequency of column 2, and so on.

$$E_2 = \text{sum of the errors for each column}$$

The reduction in errors obtained by using information on the column variable to predict the row variable is $E_1 - E_2$, and the **PRE** is

$$\lambda_r = \frac{E_1 - E_2}{E_1}$$

It should be noted that the procedure for computing λ_c (when the column variable is the dependent variable) is identical to that for computing λ_r, with the roles of rows and columns reversed. Thus Rule 1 would specify that all observations be placed in the column with the largest column total. Because of the similarity of λ_r and λ_c, we omit a formal restatement of the rules and errors.

EXAMPLE 10.3

A family specialist conducted a study to determine whether kinship lineage is predictive of which spouse will dominate family decision making. Two societies, one matrilineal and one patrilineal, were included in the study, and families were classified as to which spouse dominated family decision making. Use the data of Table 10.6 to compute λ_r to measure the degree of association between the sex of the decision maker and kinship lineage.

TABLE 10.6

Kinship and decision making among couples

| Decision Maker | Kinship Lineage | | Total |
	Matrilineal (Iroquois)	Patrilineal (Hindu)	
husband	22	103	125
wife	58	17	75
Total	80	120	200

SOLUTION

Since we are trying to predict the sex of the decision maker within the family based on kinship lineage, the row variable is the dependent variable.

Rule 1 (no-association rule) Place all families in the row with the largest row total (namely, row 1):

$$E_1 = 200 - 125 = 75$$

Rule 2 (perfect-association rule) Place all 80 families of column 1 in the row with the largest cell frequency (namely, row 2). The number of errors incurred in column 1 is $80 - 58 = 22$. Place all 120 families of column 2 in the row with the largest cell frequency (namely, row 1). The number of errors incurred in column 2 is $120 - 103 = 17$.

$$E_2 = 22 + 17 = 39$$

The **PRE** λ_r due to the independent variable "kinship lineage" is

$$\lambda_r = \frac{E_1 - E_2}{E_1} = \frac{75 - 39}{75} = \frac{36}{75} = .48$$

Thus there is a 48 % reduction in error attributed to using information on the independent or column variable (kinship lineage) to predict the dependent or row variable (which spouse will dominate family decision making). In other words, knowing kinship lineage of a couple reduces by 48 % the error in predicting which spouse dominates family decision making.

To compute λ_c for our example (the data in Table 10.6), Rule 1, the no-association rule, places all observations in the column with the largest column total (namely, column 1). The number of errors incurred is

$$E_1 = 200 - 120 = 80$$

Rule 2, the perfect-association rule, places all 125 families of row 1 in the column with the largest cell frequency (namely, column 2) and the 75 families of row 2 in the column with the largest cell frequency (namely, column 1). The number of errors incurred in row 1 is 22. Similarly, the number of errors in row 2 is 17. Hence we have

$$E_2 = 22 + 17 = 39$$

and

$$\lambda_c = \frac{E_1 - E_2}{E_1} = \frac{80 - 39}{80} = \frac{41}{80} = .51$$

There is a 51% reduction in error using the row variable to predict the column variable. For these data, λ_c gives us a larger PRE than does λ_r.

Several additional comments should be made about λ_r and λ_c. First, both λ_r and λ_c are type A measures of association. The closer λ_r (or λ_c) is to 1, the more relative reduction in error is achieved by shifting from Rule 1 to Rule 2. Since Rule 2 uses a second variable for prediction purposes, the larger λ_r (or λ_c) is, the greater is the degree of association between the two variables (or classifications). Second, λ_r (or λ_c) can be used for any two-way tables with two or more rows and two or more columns. Third, as stated previously, some researchers use the average of λ_r and λ_c when it is not clear which variable is the dependent variable and which is the independent variable. In such cases, $(\lambda_r + \lambda_c)/2$ provides a combined measure of association between the two variables, which lies between 0 and 1. **However, $(\lambda_r + \lambda_c)/2$ cannot be interpreted as a PRE statistic, unlike the separate components λ_r and λ_c.** For our example, a combined measure of association is

$$\frac{\lambda_r + \lambda_c}{2} = \frac{.48 + .51}{2} = .495$$

Many social researchers compute chi-square on the same table for which they have just computed lambda. If the observed value of chi-square is significant, they will conclude that the association is significant (see Section 9.3). Although the formula for lambda itself does not contain χ^2, as does the contingency coefficient, knowing that chi-square is significant does enhance our confidence in the relevance of lambda.

In the next section we turn to several ordinal measures of association that are PRE measures.

EXERCISES

12. What is the distinction between λ_c and λ_r?

13. Use the data of Exercise 23, Chapter 9, to compute λ_r. Interpret your results.

14. Use the data of Exercise 23, Chapter 9, to compute λ_c. Interpret your results.

15. Compute a measure of mutual predictability for the data in Exercises 13 and 14, assuming no independent variable.

16. What is the advantage of λ_r (or λ_c) over C_{adj}?

17. Compute λ_r for the data in Exercise 2. State the no-association rule and the perfect-association rule.

18. Compute λ_c for the data in Exercise 2. State the no-association rule and the perfect-association rule.

19. Compute λ_r for the data in Exercise 4. State the no-association rule and the perfect-association rule.

20. Compute λ_c for the data in Exercise 4. State the no-association rule and the perfect-association rule.

21. Refer to Exercise 10, Chapter 9. Specify the independent variable. Compute lambda based on the independent variable that you specify.

22. Compute λ_r for the data in Exercise 11, Chapter 9. State the no-association rule and the perfect-association rule.

10.5   A PRE ORDINAL MEASURE OF ASSOCIATION: GAMMA

Gamma is a type B normed measure of association between two variables measured on ordinal scales. To understand the meaning of gamma, we must consider *pairs of observations* rather than single observations (as with lambda). If we know the rank of one individual of the pair relative to the other individual on one variable, can we also predict the rank of one individual relative to the other individual for the second variable? For example, if we know that person A has been with a company longer than person B (i.e., person A has a higher rank than person B on the variable "years of service"), can we also predict the order of ranks for persons A and B on a second variable, such as "job satisfaction"? Gamma attempts to measure our ability to do this. We will explain the no-association and perfect-association rules for gamma, as well as its computation, by means of an example.

Seventy-seven individuals sampled in a community were ranked according to their annual income (low, medium, or high) and the prestige of their occupation (low, medium, or high). These data are recorded in Table 10.7. The objective is to make inferences about the rankings for a dependent variable ("annual income") based on knowledge of an independent variable ("occupational prestige").

TABLE 10.7

Income and occupa-
tional ranks

Annual Income	Occupational Prestige		
	Low	**Medium**	**High**
low	6	4	2
medium	10	12	8
high	8	12	15

If we know the order of ranks on the variable "occupational prestige" for a pair of individuals, can we predict the order of ranks for that pair on a second variable, "annual income"? For example, if individual 1 has an occupational prestige rank of "medium" and individual 2 has an occupational prestige rank of "low," can we predict that individual 1 will have a higher ranking on annual income? **Note that we are not trying to predict the actual rank. Rather, we are trying to predict the rank of one individual on the dependent variable "annual income" relative to that of another individual.** The no-association rule is used to predict the order of ranks for pairs of observations on one variable (the dependent variable) without reference to a second variable (the independent variable). The perfect-association rule uses information about the order of ranks for pairs of observations on the independent variable to predict the order of ranks for pairs of observations on the dependent variable.

The definition of error is different from that used for the nominal measures of association. **An error is incurred if the predicted order of ranks of the dependent variable for a pair of observations differs from the actual order of ranks.** For example, if we predict that individual 1 will have a higher annual income rank than individual 2 when, in fact, the reverse is true, we have incurred an error. **Thus, for gamma, the term *error* denotes an incorrectly predicted order of ranks for a pair of observations rather than a misclassification of a single observation.**

We now consider the no-association rule for our example. If we have no information about the independent variable for a pair of observations that would be useful in predicting which individual of the pair has a higher annual income rank, we have no basis for a prediction rule. We resort to a random assignment of orderings of annual income ranks for pairs of individuals. For our example we could form all possible pairs of individuals from the 77 persons sampled. (Since a mathematician could show that there would be 2926 such pairs, we will not actually list the pairs.) We could then randomly label one individual within each pair as A and the other as B. Our no-association rule could then be stated as follows.

RULE 1: NO-ASSOCIATION RULE FOR GAMMA

For each pair of individuals A and B, we predict that person A has a higher rank than person B on the dependent variable. (*Note*: The roles of A and B are arbitrary and can be switched.)

In our case the no-association rule would be that for each pair, person A has a higher annual income rank than person B.

If we ignore pairs where the ranks of the two observations are the same, it seems reasonable to assume that our random assignment of A and B within a pair of individuals would lead to errors in 50% of the orderings (i.e., we would expect to predict the wrong order of ranks for 50% of the pairs). Indeed, this is true.

Now, if we ignore tied ranks on both variables and let N_s be the number of pairs of individuals where the ordering is the *same* on both variables and let N_r be the number of pairs where the ordering is *reversed* for the two variables, then $N_s + N_r$ is the total number of pairs without ties on either variable. The quantities N_s and N_r are frequently referred to as the number of *concordant* and the number of *discordant pairs*, respectively. The number of errors incurred using Rule 1 is

$$E_1 = .5(N_s + N_r)$$

The computation of gamma (from the Greek letter gamma, γ) can be illustrated by using the data for Table 10.7. For convenience we have relisted these data in Table 10.8. Starting from the upper-left-hand corner of Table 10.8, if any of the 6 persons classified as low income and low prestige (i.e., low, low) is paired with any of the other 6 persons in the first row of Table 10.8, the two individuals of a pair would have the same income ranking, and hence none of these pairs would go into the computation of N_s or N_r. Similarly, if any of the 6 persons classified (low, low) is paired with any of the remaining 18 individuals in the first column of Table 10.8, the two individuals would have a tied rank for the variable "occupational prestige." Again, none of these pairs would go into the calculation of N_s or N_r. However, if any of the 6 individuals classified as (low, low) is paired with any of the other $12 + 8 + 12 + 15 = 47$ individuals not in either row 1 or column 1, the order of ranks for both variables "occupational prestige" and "annual income" would be the same. For example, if a person classified (low, low) is paired with one classified (medium, high), the second individual has a higher rank on both variables and hence the order of ranks is the same for both variables. There are

$$6(12 + 8 + 12 + 15) = 282$$

pairs that could be formed by using one individual from the upper-left-hand cell of Table 10.8 and another from the 47 individuals that **fall below and to the right of that cell.**

TABLE 10.8

Data of Table 10.7

Annual	Occupational Prestige		
Income	Low	Medium	High
low	6	4	2
medium	10	12	8
high	8	12	15

Consider now the 4 individuals in the first row and second column of Table 10.8. If any of these 4 individuals, classified as (low, medium), is paired with one of the $8 + 15 = 23$ individuals that fall below and to the right of the first row and second column of Table 10.8, we would obtain the same ordering of ranks for both variables. There are

$$4(8 + 15) = 92$$

pairs formed in this way.

Moving across the first row of Table 10.8 to the (low, high) category, there are no cells to the right and below, so we could not pair an individual in this cell with any other to form a pair with the same ordering of ranks in both variables.

Moving to the second row and first column of Table 10.8, we could form

$$10(12 + 15) = 270$$

pairs with one individual categorized (medium, low) and another from the categories to the right and below this cell. Each of these pairs would have the same ordering of ranks on both variables. Similarly, pairing any of the 12 individuals in the second row and second column with an individual from a cell to the right and below, we obtain

$$12(15) = 180$$

more pairs with the same ordering of ranks on the two variables. Proceeding to the remaining cell in row 2 and the three cells in row 3, there are no more pairs that can be formed such that the ordering of ranks is the same for both variables.

We have now determined N_s, the number of pairs of observations where the ordering is the same on both variables:

$$N_s = 282 + 92 + 270 + 180 = 824$$

FIGURE 10.2

Illustration of the
computation of N_s

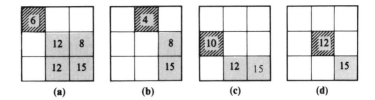

The computation of N_s for the data of Table 10.8 is shown graphically in Figure 10.2. Thus for each table in Figure 10.2, you can compute the product of the number in the crosshatched square and the sum of the numbers in the shaded squares below and to the right. Notice how you **start with the crosshatched square in the upper-left-hand corner and move to the right across the first row, stopping at the next-to-last square**. This is because there are no cells below and to the right of the last square in the first row. This operation yields the products in Figures 10.2a and 10.2b. Then you select the first element to the left in the second row and repeat the process to obtain Figures 10.2c and 10.2d. The operation is stopped at the next-to-last row, because no cells lie below the last row.

In a similar way, N_r, **the number of pairs where the ordering of ranks is reversed for the two variables, can be computed by starting at the upper-right-hand corner of Table 10.8 and working to the left and below**. For example, if any of the 2 individuals classified as (low, high) is paired with any of the other $10 + 12 + 8 + 12 = 42$ individuals not in either row 1 or column 3, the order of ranks on the first variable would be the reverse of the order of ranks on the second variable. We might pair an individual classified (low, high) with one classified (medium, medium). Note here that ranking for the first individual is lower on the first variable but higher on the second variable. Hence the order of ranks is reversed.

Beginning at the upper-right-hand corner of Table 10.8 and working to the left and below, we have the following computations:

$$2(10 + 12 + 8 + 12) = 84$$
$$4(10 + 8) = 72$$
$$8(8 + 12) = 160$$
$$12(8) = 96$$

Hence we have

$$N_r = 84 + 72 + 160 + 96 = 412$$

The number of errors using the no-association rule is

$$E_1 = .5(N_s + N_r) = .5(824 + 412) = .5(1236) = 618$$

FIGURE 10.3

Illustration of the computation of N_r

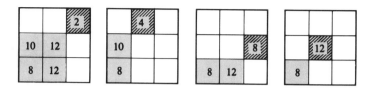

The illustration of the computation of N_r for the same data produces figures with the shaded area diminishing as you move from top right to bottom left (see Figure 10.3). You can see that the computational procedure for N_r is the same as for N_s except that you move from right to left.

The procedure for computing N_s and N_r is summarized as follows.

PROCEDURE FOR COMPUTING N_s AND N_r

1. Arrange the categories for both variables from the lowest to the highest order in the cross-classification of the data.
2. The number of pairs with the same ordering of ranks for the two variables, N_s, can be computed by beginning in the upper-left-hand corner of the table and moving across the rows, multiplying the number of entries in a cell by the number of entries in the cells to the right and below. The sum of all these multiplications equals N_s.
3. Reverse the procedure of step 2 to compute N_r. Beginning in the upper-right-hand corner of the table and moving across the rows, multiply the number of entries in each cell by the number of entries in all cells to the left and below. The sum of all these is N_r, the number of pairs having the reverse ordering of ranks for the two variables.

We can now state the perfect-association rule, which utilizes information on the orders of ranks for pairs for one variable (the independent variable) to predict the orders of ranks for pairs of observations on a second variable (the dependent variable).

RULE 2: PERFECT-ASSOCIATION RULE FOR GAMMA

For $N_s \geq N_r$ predict the *same* order for a pair of ranks on the dependent variable as was observed for the same pair on the independent variable. When $N_s > N_r$ there is a *positive* association between the two variables. For $N_s < N_r$ predict the *reverse* order for a pair of ranks on the dependent variable as was observed for the same pair on the independent variable. There is a *negative* association between the two variables.

The number of errors incurred using Rule 2 will be either N_s or N_r, whichever is smaller. We designate the number of errors by

$$E_2 = \text{minimum}(N_s, N_r)$$

For our example we have

$$E_2 = \text{minimum }(824, 412) = 412$$

The PRE is

$$\text{PRE} = \frac{E_1 - E_2}{E_1} = \frac{.5(N_s + N_r) - \text{minimum}(N_s, N_r)}{.5(N_s + N_r)}$$

The three situations that can arise are illustrated next. The calculations of PRE for these situations are easily verified.

VALUES OF PRE FOR GAMMA

1. $N_s = N_r$ (no association)

$$\text{PRE} = 0$$

2. $N_s > N_r$ (positive association)

$$\text{PRE} = \frac{N_s - N_r}{N_s + N_r}$$

3. $N_s < N_r$ (negative association)

$$\text{PRE} = \frac{N_r - N_s}{N_s + N_r}$$

We will be consistent with most textbooks and journals by defining gamma as follows.

→ *ordinal / ordinal*

ORDINAL MEASURE OF ASSOCIATION GAMMA (TYPE B)

$$\gamma = \frac{N_s - N_r}{N_s + N_r}$$

where N_s is the number of concordant pairs and N_r is the number of discordant pairs.

For this definition, we have the following relationships for N_s, N_r, γ, and PRE.

RELATIONSHIP BETWEEN GAMMA AND PRE

1. $N_s = N_r$ (no association)

$$\gamma = 0 \quad \text{and} \quad \text{PRE} = 0$$

2. $N_s > N_r$ (positive association)

$$\gamma = \frac{N_s - N_r}{N_s + N_r} \quad \text{and} \quad \text{PRE} = \frac{N_s - N_r}{N_s + N_r} = \gamma$$

3. $N_s < N_r$ (negative association)

$$\gamma = \frac{N_s - N_r}{N_s + N_r} \quad \text{and} \quad \text{PRE} = \frac{N_r - N_s}{N_s + N_r} = -\gamma$$

The interpretation of gamma is quite simple. Gamma is a type B normed ordinal measure of association with a PRE interpretation. When the number of concordant pairs equals the number of discordant pairs (i.e., $N_s = N_r$), $\gamma = 0$ and PRE $= 0$. No information is gained by examining the information on the order of ranks for pairs on the independent variable. If $N_s > N_r$, gamma is positive and PRE $= \gamma$. Perfect positive association ($\gamma = 1$) is achieved when $N_r = 0$ (i.e., there are no discordant pairs). When $N_s < N_r$, gamma is negative and PRE $= -\gamma$. Perfect negative association ($\gamma = -1$) is achieved when $N_s = 0$ (i.e., there are no concordant pairs).

For the data of Table 10.8, with $N_s = 824$ and $N_r = 412$, we have

$$\gamma = \frac{N_s - N_r}{N_s + N_r} = \frac{412}{1236} = .33$$

Thus we know that there is a positive association between the two variables, annual income and occupational prestige, for the data of Table 10.8; the higher an individual's occupational prestige, the higher the individual's annual income. We also know that the PRE due to the independent variable (occupational prestige) is .33. Thus the error of prediction can be reduced by 33% if we use the order of ranks on the independent variable (occupational prestige) to predict the order of ranks for the dependent variable.

EXAMPLE 10.4   A total of 500 women, married and working full-time outside the home, were surveyed. Researchers were interested in whether these women varied in their degree of marital satisfaction according to their level of formal education. Use the data in Table 10.9 to compute gamma, a measure of association between pairs of ranks for the variables "level of education" and "degree of marital satisfaction."

TABLE 10.9

Educational level and degree of marital satisfaction for working women

Degree of Marital Satisfaction	Level of Education				
	High School	1-3 Years College	4 Years College	Graduate Level	Total
above average	47	65	125	50	287
average and below	53	60	75	25	213
Total	100	125	200	75	500

SOLUTION

The tables needed to compute N_s, the number of concordant pairs, are shown in Figure 10.4. From Figure 10.4, multiplying the number in the crosshatched cell by the sum of the numbers in the shaded cells gives us

$$N_s = 47(60 + 75 + 25) + 65(75 + 25) + 125(25) = 17,145$$

The tables needed to compute N_r, the number of discordant pairs, are shown in Figure 10.5. Then we have

$$N_r = 50(53 + 60 + 75) + 125(53 + 60) + 65(53) = 26,970$$

Substituting these values into the formula for gamma, we have

$$\gamma = \frac{N_s - N_r}{N_s + N_r} = \frac{17,145 - 26,970}{17,145 + 26,970} = -.22$$

Since γ is negative ($N_s < N_r$), the ordering of ranks for pairs of individuals on the two variables is negatively correlated. This means that wives with more education are less satisfied with their marriages than are wives with less

FIGURE 10.4

Tables for computation of N_s in Example 10.4

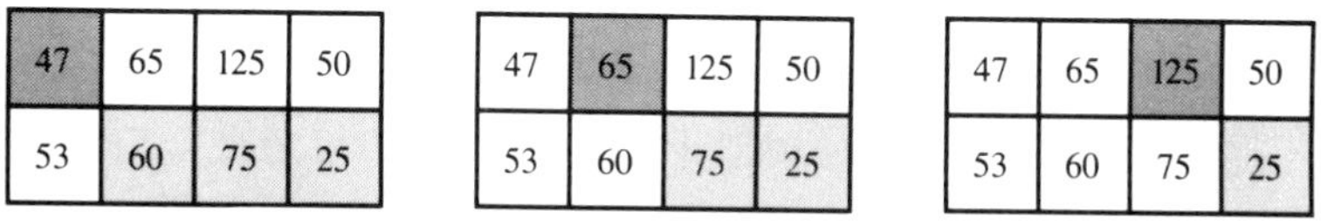

FIGURE 10.5

Tables for computation of N_r in Example 10.4

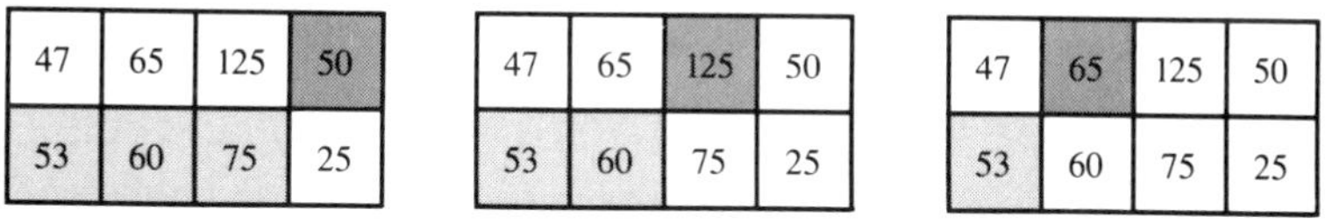

education. The magnitude of gamma indicates that the error of prediction can be reduced by 22% if we use the orders of ranks on the independent variable (level of education) to predict the orders of ranks for the dependent variable.

Besides being able to give gamma a PRE interpretation, we can add further meaning to the magnitude of a computed value of gamma by conducting a statistical test. When the data presented in a two-way table are sample data, and we are interested in making an inference about the association between the two variables for the population of data, we will designate the computed measure of association for the two-way table as $\hat{\gamma}$. For this situation gamma (γ) will designate the unknown population value. We can test the null hypothesis that $\gamma = 0$; that is, the orders of ranks on the independent variable give us no information concerning the orders of ranks on the dependent variable. A summary of the test procedure follows.

STATISTICAL TEST FOR GAMMA

Research hypothesis for a one-tailed test

    1. $H_1: \gamma > 0$
    2. $H_1: \gamma < 0$

Research hypothesis for a two-tailed test

    3. $H_1: \gamma \neq 0$

Null hypothesis $H_0: \gamma = 0$

Test statistic $z = \hat{\gamma} \sqrt{\dfrac{N_s + N_r}{n(1 - \hat{\gamma}^2)}}$

where N_s is the number of concordant pairs, N_r is the number of discordant pairs, and n is the total sample size.

Rejection region for a one-tailed test and specified value of α

    1. R.R.: Reject H_0 if $z > z_\alpha$.
    2. R.R.: Reject H_0 if $z < -z_\alpha$.

Rejection region for a two-tailed test and specified value of α

    3. R.R.: Reject H_0 if $z > z_{\alpha/2}$ or $z < -z_{\alpha/2}$.

Assumptions

    1. Both variables are measured on an ordinal scale or higher.
    2. The sample data that are cross-classified in a two-way table represent a random sample from the population of interest.

3. Although no specific requirement for sample size is generally given, we should never use this test when $n < 10$.

EXAMPLE 10.5

Refer to the data of Example 10.4. Suppose that the 500 married women who responded in the survey represented a random sample selected from the national registry of full-time working women. Use the sample to test the research hypothesis that $\gamma < 0$ (there is a negative relationship between order of ranks on the independent and dependent variables). (Use $\alpha = .05$.)

SOLUTION

Recall that $N_s = 17{,}145$, $N_r = 26{,}970$, and $\hat{\gamma} = -.22$. For our test we have

$$H_1 : \gamma < 0 \quad \text{and} \quad H_0 : \gamma = 0$$

The test statistic is

$$z = \hat{\gamma}\sqrt{\frac{N_s + N_r}{n(1 - \hat{\gamma}^2)}} = -.22\sqrt{\frac{17{,}145 + 26{,}970}{500[1 - (-.22)^2]}} = -2.12$$

For $\alpha = .05$ we reject the null hypothesis when $z < -1.645$. Since the observed value of z is less than -1.645, we reject H_0 and conclude that $\gamma < 0$. We have shown that there is a significant negative relationship between the order of ranks on the independent and the dependent variables. We interpret this to mean that wives with more education are significantly less satisfied with their marriages than are wives with less education.

EXERCISES

23. State the no-association rule for γ. How does the no-association rule for λ_r (or λ_c) differ from that for gamma?

24. State the perfect-association rule for gamma.

25. Compute gamma for the data in Exercise 9, Chapter 3. Interpret your results.

26. When would you use gamma in preference to lambda?

27. A researcher was interested in testing the hypothesis that the relationship between feuding and marriage between cousins is positive. The data for 50 societies are presented in the accompanying table.

| | Marriage between Cousins | |
Feuding	Absent	Present
absent	15	10
infrequent	8	5
frequent	2	10

a. If we identify the variable "marriage between cousins" as an ordinal variable, compute and interpret gamma.

b. Assuming that the 50 societies represent a random sample from a much larger population of possible societies, use the sample data to test the research hypothesis posed by the researcher. (Use $\alpha = .05$.)

28. Refer to Exercise 27. The researcher also investigated the relationship between feuding and another independent variable, "exogamy." Test the research hypothesis that there is a positive association between "exogamy" and "feuding." (Use $\alpha = .05$.)

| | Exogamy | |
Feuding	Absent	Present
absent	20	5
infrequent	5	10
frequent	5	5

29. If we assume that the data of Example 9.2 represent a random sample from a population of possible students, test the null hypothesis that $\gamma = 0$ using a two-sided research hypothesis. Give the level of significance for your test.

10.6 ANOTHER PRE ORDINAL MEASURE OF ASSOCIATION: SPEARMAN'S RHO

Many times in social research the same individuals (or items) are ranked on each of two variables. Since we are dealing with two sets of ranks, we are concerned with two ordinal variables, and, as is often the case, it may be important to measure the strength of the relationship between the two ordinal variables. **Spearman's rank-order correlation coefficient**, designated by the Greek letter ρ (rho), is a type B normed ordinal measure of association between the ranks of items on each of two variables.

Spearman's rho measures a different kind of association than the other type B normed measures for ordinal data that we have presented. Rather than being concerned with the *order of ranks* of two variables for pairs of items (or individuals), we are concerned with the *actual ranks* associated with two variables for each individual. For example, if one item is ranked high on one variable, can we also predict that it will be ranked high (or low) on the second variable? Spearman's rho attempts to answer this question.

To illustrate, consider the data in Table 10.10. The 1990 life expectancy and per capita income are ranked (from lowest to highest) for 10 different countries. One measure of the strength of the relationship between the sets of ranks for the two variables is given by Spearman's rank-order correlation coefficient.

SPEARMAN'S RANK-ORDER CORRELATION COEFFICIENT RHO

$$\rho = 1 - \frac{6 \, \Sigma \, d^2}{n(n^2 - 1)}$$

where d is the difference between pairs of ranks and n is the total number of pairs of ranks.

TABLE 10.10

Life expectancy and per capita income in 1990

Country	Rank on Life Expectancy	Rank on Per Capita Income
Bolivia	9	8
Colombia	4	5
Egypt	6	6
Hungary	2	2
India	7	10
Malaysia	3	4
Senegal	10	7
South Africa	5	3
Togo	8	9
United States	1	1

The formula for Spearman's rho is correct if there are no ties in the ranks on either one of the variables. The formula is a good approximation to rho if the number of ties is small relative to n, the number of pairs of ranks.

EXAMPLE 10.6   Use the data of Table 10.10 to compute rho.

SOLUTION   Before computing rho from Table 10.10, we need two additional columns for the differences and the squares of those differences in the pairs of ranks. These columns are given in Table 10.11. For $n = 10$ pairs of ranks, the computed value of ρ is

$$\rho = 1 - \frac{6 \, \Sigma \, d^2}{n(n^2 - 1)} = 1 - \frac{6(26)}{10(100 - 1)} = 1 - .16 = .84$$

TABLE 10.11

Differences in pairs of ranks for data in Table 10.10

Country	Rank on Life Expectancy	Rank on Per Capita Income	Difference d	d^2
Bolivia	9	8	1	1
Colombia	4	5	-1	1
Egypt	6	6	0	0
Hungary	2	2	0	0
India	7	10	-3	9
Malaysia	3	4	-1	1
Senegal	10	7	3	9
South Africa	5	3	2	4
Togo	8	9	-1	1
United States	1	1	0	0
				$\Sigma \, d^2 = 26$

How do we interpret rho as a measure of the strength of the association of the ranking for two variables? Spearman's rank-order correlation coefficient varies between -1.0 and 1.0. A value of $\rho = 1.0$ indicates a perfect positive association between rankings for the two variables. For our example, ρ would equal 1.0 if all the differences were zero — that is, if the ranks on life expectancies agreed perfectly with the ranks for per capita income. A value of $\rho = -1.0$ also indicates a perfect relationship between the ranks, but in this case the relationship is negative. For example, if a rank of 1 on life expectancy was associated with a rank of 10 for per capita income, a rank of 2 with a 9, and so on, ρ would equal -1.0.

Spearman's rho also has a PRE interpretation. We define the rules as follows.

RULES FOR SPEARMAN'S RHO

Rule 1 (no-association rule)   Assign each observation of the dependent variable a rank of $(n + 1)/2$, the average of the ranks for n pairs.

Rule 2 (perfect-association rule)   If r_I is the rank of the independent variable for an observation, then we predict r_D, the rank of the dependent variable, as

$$r_D = r_I(\rho) + \frac{n + 1}{2}(1 - \rho)$$

It can then be shown (see Mueller, Schuessler, and Costner, *Statistical Reasoning in Sociology*, 1977) that the PRE realized by using Rule 2 rather than Rule 1 is ρ^2, the square of the Spearman rank-order correlation coefficient.

As with gamma, we can do more than merely quantify the degree of association using rho. We can use the rank-order correlation coefficient computed for sample data as the test statistic in a statistical test of a hypothesis of no association between ranks of paired observations from two populations. For this situation, ρ will designate the unknown population correlation coefficient, and $\hat{\rho}$ will denote the correlation coefficient computed from the sample data. When the sample size n is 10 or more, the quantity

$$t = \hat{\rho}\sqrt{\frac{n - 2}{1 - \hat{\rho}^2}}$$

follows a Student's t distribution. A summary of the rank-order correlation test for rho follows.

STATISTICAL TEST FOR RHO

Research hypothesis for a one-tailed test

    1. $H_1: \rho > 0$
    2. $H_1: \rho < 0$

Research hypothesis for a two-tailed test

    3. $H_1: \rho \neq 0$

Null hypothesis $H_0: \rho = 0$

Test statistic $t = \hat{\rho}\sqrt{\dfrac{n - 2}{1 - \hat{\rho}^2}}$

Rejection region for a one-tailed test and specified value of α

1. R.R.: Reject H_0 if $t > t_\alpha$.
2. R.R.: Reject H_0 if $t < -t_\alpha$.

Rejection region for a two-tailed test and specified value of α

3. R.R.: Reject H_0 if $t > t_{\alpha/2}$ or $t < -t_{\alpha/2}$.

(*Note*: Use Appendix Table 2, d.f. $= n - 2$.)
Assumptions

1. n items are ranked on each of two variables.
2. There are very few tied ranks on either variable.
3. The sample size is 10 or more.
4. For the sample data

$$\hat{\rho} = 1 - \frac{6 \, \Sigma \, d^2}{n(n^2 - 1)}$$

EXAMPLE 10.7   Treat the countries of Example 10.6 as a random sample of 10 countries. Test the null hypothesis that the correlation between the rank order of observations on life expectancy and the rank order of per capita income is zero (i.e., $\rho = 0$) against the research hypothesis that there is a positive correlation between these two sets of ranks.

SOLUTION   The research hypothesis and null hypothesis are

$$H_1: \rho > 0 \qquad \text{and} \qquad H_0: \rho = 0$$

From a sample of $n = 10$ different countries, we obtain the corresponding ranks for life expectancy and per capita income (see Table 10.11). The sample rank-order correlation coefficient is, then, $\hat{\rho} = .84$, as we calculated it to be in Example 10.6. The test statistic for our test is

$$t = \hat{\rho} \sqrt{\frac{n-2}{1-\hat{\rho}^2}} = (.84) \sqrt{\frac{10-2}{1-(.84)^2}} = .84(5.21) = 4.376$$

For $\alpha = .05$ and d.f. $= n - 2 = 8$, the critical t (with $\alpha = .05$ and d.f. $= 8$) is 1.86. Since the observed value of $t = 4.376$ exceeds 1.86, we reject the null hypothesis and conclude that ranks on life expectancy and per capita income are positively correlated for countries. That is, countries with high per capita income have significantly higher life expectancy than do countries with lower per capita income.

EXERCISES

30. Under what circumstances is Spearman's rank-order correlation coefficient an appropriate statistic to use?

31. What are the assumptions that should be met before testing a hypothesis in which ρ is used?

32. Assume that two judges have ranked 15 cities as places in which to live with Spearman's $\rho = .75$. Test the hypothesis that $\rho \neq 0$.

33. For Spearman's rho, state the no-association rule.

34. For Spearman's rho, state the perfect-association rule.

35. The accompanying table shows the relative ranks of ten nations on "level of technology" and "crude birth rate." Compute $\hat{\rho}$ and test the hypothesis that $\rho \neq 0$.

EXERCISE 35

Crude birth rate and
level of technology for
10 countries

Country	Crude Birth Rate	Level of Technology
Bolivia	2.5	9
Colombia	6	5
Egypt	2.5	8
Ireland	8	4
Malaysia	4	6.5
Netherlands	10	1
Nigeria	1	10
Norway	9	2
Poland	7	3
Turkey	5	6.5

10.7 MEASURE OF ASSOCIATION FOR A 2 × 2 TABLE: YULE'S *Q*

Sometimes nominal or ordinal variables of interest naturally include only two categories, such as the variable "gender" (male, female). In other cases the researcher may wish to collapse observations on a variable into two categories such as an individual's earnings (high, low) or degree of marital satisfaction (above average, average, or below). A nominal or ordinal variable that has only two categories is called a **dichotomous variable**.

When social researchers are interested in the relationship between two dichotomous variables, there are several measures of association that can determine the strength of the relationship. **Yule's Q**, which has enjoyed wide use in social science research, is one measure of association for two dichotomous variables. Indeed, Yule's Q is suitable *only* for 2×2 tables. Yule's Q makes use of cross-products in a 2×2 table — that is, the two products of cell frequencies that are diagonal to each other. We will explain cross-products, as well as the computation of Yule's Q, by means of an example.

One hundred teens sampled in a community were asked their level of sexual activity. Their responses are cross-classified by age group in Table 10.12. The objective is to determine whether there is a bivariate association between age group and level of sexual activity — that is, whether older teens have a higher level of sexual activity than younger teens do.

TABLE 10.12

Age and level of sexual activity among teens

Level of Sexual Activity	Age 17–19	13–16	Total
high	35	15	50
low	20	30	50
Total	55	45	100

In Table 10.12, multiplying 35 by 30 is one product of two cell frequencies that are diagonal to each other, and multiplying 15 by 20 yields the product of the other two cell frequencies that are diagonal to each other. We now provide the formula for calculating Yule's Q:

$$Q = \frac{ad - bc}{ad + bc}$$

where conventionally, a is the upper-left-hand cell frequency, b is the upper-right-hand cell frequency, c is the lower-left-hand cell frequency, and d is the lower-right-hand cell frequency. According to the data in Table 10.12, $a = 35$, $b = 15$, $c = 20$, and $d = 30$. Thus

$$Q = \frac{(35)(30) - (15)(20)}{(35)(30) + (15)(20)} = \frac{1050 - 300}{1050 + 300} = \frac{750}{1350} = .555$$

Yule's Q is a type B normed measure of association with a PRE interpretation. $Q = .555$ suggests that there is a positive association between age and level of sexual activity; older teens have higher levels of sexual activity than younger teens do.

Note that if one of the four cells in a 2×2 table is 0, the value of Q must be either -1.00 or $+1.00$. For example, if $a = 0$, then the cross-product ad is 0 in both the numerator and the denominator of Q. This leaves only the cross-product bc in both the numerator and denominator of Q, and $bc/bc = 1.00$. It is also important to note that **if only one cell frequency is 0, this does not reflect a perfect association, even though the value of Q would be $+1.00$ or -1.00.** A "perfect" association would mean that all cases fall into only one set of diagonal cells. That is, either all observations would be in cells a and d, or all observations would be in cells b and c.

The discussion above clearly indicates that Q can give misleading information when one cell has 0 observations. This is shown in Table 10.13, where we have rearranged the data of Table 10.12 in three different ways.

TABLE 10.13

Rearranged data from Table 10.12

(a)

Level of Sexual Activity	Age 17–19	13–16	Total
high	50	0	50
low	0	50	50
Total	50	50	100

$Q = 1.00$

(b)

Level of Sexual Activity	Age 17–19	13–16	Total
high	10	70	80
low	0	20	20
Total	10	90	100

$Q = 1.00$

(c)

Level of Sexual Activity	Age 17–19	13–16	Total
high	9	70	79
low	1	20	21
Total	10	90	100

$Q = .440$

In Table 10.13a, a maximum positive relationship is shown, with all 100 observations located in cells a and d. Q attains its maximum value of $+1.00$, which indicates that knowing a teen's age perfectly predicts the teen's level of sexual activity. If we know that a teen is 18, for example, we can perfectly predict that the teen has a high level of sexual activity. In Table 10.13b, Q also has a value of $+1.00$, even though the cell frequencies show that the majority of teens with a high level of sexual activity are the 13–16-year-olds rather than 17–19 year olds. We can see, then, just how misleading Q can be when only one cell frequency is 0.

Additionally, Table 10.13c shows what the cross-classification of data of Table 10.13b would look like if one older teen were shifted from cell a to cell c. The value of Yule's Q would drop substantially, to $+.440$, if just one older teen had a low level of sexual activity.

These tables emphasize one of the major drawbacks of Yule's Q as a measure of association: It is extremely sensitive to distortion when a cell has 0 observations. The problem is most serious when the sample size is small or when the number of observations in some variable categories is small. For these reasons, the cell frequencies of a 2×2 table should be carefully examined before using Yule's Q as a measure of association.

Using the original data in Table 10.12, we can show that Q is actually a special case of gamma (γ). Remember that

$$\gamma = \frac{N_s - N_r}{N_s + N_r}$$

where N_s is the number of concordant pairs and N_r is the number of discordant pairs. If we compute N_s for a 2×2 table, it contains a single term, ad. The cross-product ad gives the pairs that have the same order on both variables, and the cross-product bc gives the number of pairs having reverse orders on the two variables. However, the statistical test for Yule's Q differs from that of gamma. A summary of the test procedure for Q follows.

STATISTICAL TEST FOR YULE'S Q

Research hypothesis for a one-tailed test

    1. $H_1: Q > 0$
    2. $H_1: Q < 0$

Research hypothesis for a two-tailed test

    3. $H_1: Q \neq 0$

Null hypothesis $H_0: Q = 0$

Test statistic $z = \dfrac{Q}{\hat{\sigma}_Q}$

where $\hat{\sigma}_Q$ is the standard error of the sampling distribution of Q, and

$$\hat{\sigma}_Q = \sqrt{\frac{1}{4}(1 - Q^2)^2 \left(\frac{1}{a} + \frac{1}{b} + \frac{1}{c} + \frac{1}{d}\right)}$$

where a, b, c, and d are cell frequencies in a 2×2 table.

Rejection region for a one-tailed test and specified value of α

    1. R.R.: Reject H_0 if $z > z_\alpha$.

    2. R.R.: Reject H_0 if $z < z_\alpha$.

Rejection region for a two-tailed test and specified value of α

    3. R.R.: Reject H_0 if $z > z_{\alpha/2}$ or $z < -z_{\alpha/2}$.

Assumptions

    1. The sample data that are cross-classified in a two-way table represent a random sample from the population of interest.

    2. Although no specified requirement for sample size is generally given, we should never use this test when $n < 10$.

EXAMPLE 10.8

Refer to the data of Table 10.12. Use the data to test the null hypothesis that $Q = 0$ against the research hypothesis that $Q > 0$ (there is a positive relationship between age of teens and their level of sexual activity). (Use $\alpha = .05$.)

SOLUTION

If we consider these data to be a random sample of teens, we have $a = 35$, $b = 15$, $c = 20$, and $d = 30$. We also have $Q = .555$. The statistical test procedure is as follows:

$$H_1 : Q > 0$$
$$H_0 : Q = 0$$

$$\text{T.S.: } z = \frac{.555}{\sqrt{\frac{1}{4}(1 - .555^2)^2(\frac{1}{35} + \frac{1}{15} + \frac{1}{20} + \frac{1}{30})}}$$

$$= \frac{.555}{\sqrt{\frac{1}{4}(.479)(.178)}}$$

$$= \frac{.555}{.146}$$

$$= 3.80$$

R.R.: For $\alpha = .05$, we will reject H_0 if $z > 1.645$.

Since the observed value of Z is > 1.645, we reject H_0 and conclude that $Q > 0$. Practically speaking, we have evidence that a positive association exists between age and level of sexual activity for teens; older teens have significantly higher levels of sexual activity than younger teens do.

While an assumption of the statistical test for gamma was that variables are measured on an ordinal scale or higher, this rule is generally relaxed for Yule's Q to allow its use for nominal variables. In the case of nominal variables, however, the sign of Q depends solely on how the categories of the independent and dependent variables appear in a table. For example, if gender is the independent variable of interest, the category "male" could appear either in the left-hand column or the right-hand column of the table.

To illustrate, let us cross-classify the 100 teens in the preceding example by gender and level of sexual activity. Table 10.14a shows the category "male" in the left-hand column, and Table 10.14b shows the category "female" in the left-hand column.

TABLE 10.14

Gender and level of sexual activity among teens

(a)

Level of Sexual Activity	Gender		Total
	Male	Female	
high	45	15	60
low	10	30	40
Total	55	45	100

$Q = .800$

(b)

Level of Sexual Activity	Gender		Total
	Female	Male	
high	45	15	60
low	10	30	40
Total	55	45	100

$Q = -.800$

For Table 10.14a, $Q = .800$, and for Table 10.14b, $Q = -.800$. The strength or magnitude of the association between gender and level of sexual activity is identical for both tables, as it should be: The cell values for the respective categories of the independent variable are the same in both tables. However, the sign (direction) of the association is positive in Table 10.14a and negative in Table 10.14b. This is because the data show that males are more likely than females to have high levels of sexual activity, and similarly, that females are less likely than males to have high levels of sexual involvement. As a rule of thumb, the sign of Yule's Q indicates the direction of the association between the first category of the independent variable (gender) and the first category of the dependent variable (level of sexual activity). Thus when the category "male" appears in the upper-left-hand column, the relationship between gender and level of sexual involvement is positive. Alternatively, when the category "female" appears in the upper-left-hand column, the relationship between gender and level of sexual involvement is negative.

EXERCISES

36. How does Yule's Q differ from gamma?

37. Refer to Exercise 27. Combine response categories "infrequent" and "frequent" into a single category. Compute Q. Is Q significantly different from zero? How confident are you?

38. Assuming that the 50 societies of Exercise 28 represent a random sample from a much larger population, first combine response categories "infrequent" and "frequent" into a single category and then use the sample data to test the research hypothesis $H_1: Q > 0$. (Use $\alpha = .05$.)

SUMMARY

This chapter has presented measures of association for both nominal and ordinal data. It is a natural extension of Chapter 9, where we discussed the chi-square test of independence for determining whether two variables are related. In this chapter we discussed how to measure the strength of a relationship between two variables. Measures of association for nominal data include the contingency coefficient C and lambda. Measures of association for ordinal data include gamma and Spearman's rho.

We also discussed Yule's Q, which is a measure of association for a 2×2 table. Yule's Q is a special case of gamma, and it can be used for both nominal and ordinal variables. In Chapter 11, we extend our measures of association to multivariate data. We examine how the strength of a bivariate relationship between nominal or ordinal variables is affected when controlling for a third variable.

KEY WORDS

Contingency coefficient (C) A measure of association for square tables. Used primarily with nominal data. Requires the calculation of chi-square and must be adjusted in order for a perfect association to equal 1.

Cramer's V A type A measure of association for two-way tables. Used primarily with nominal data.

Dichotomous variable A variable with only two categories.

Gamma (γ) A type B measure of association used with ordinal data that has a PRE interpretation.

Lambda (λ_r or λ_c) A type A measure of association used with nominal data that has a PRE interpretation.

Proportional reduction in error (PRE) The number of errors for no-association rule minus the number of errors for perfect-association rule divided by the number of errors for no-association rule.

Spearman's rank-order correlation coefficient (ρ) A type B measure of association for $k = 2$ sets of ranks that has a PRE interpretation.

Type A measure of association A measure of association that assumes values between 0 and 1.

Type B measure of association A measure of association that assumes values between -1 and $+1$.

Yule's Q A type B measure of association for a 2×2 table that has a PRE interpretation. It is a special case of gamma.

KEY FORMULAS

Nominal measures

$$C = \sqrt{\frac{\chi^2}{n + \chi^2}}$$

$$V = \sqrt{\frac{\chi^2}{nt}}$$

$$\lambda_r = \frac{E_1 - E_2}{E_1}$$

Ordinal measures

$$\gamma = \frac{N_s - N_r}{N_s + N_r}$$

$$\rho = 1 - \frac{6\Sigma d^2}{n(n^2 - 1)}$$

$$Q = \frac{ad - bc}{ad + bc}$$

SUPPLEMENTARY EXERCISES FOR CHAPTER 10

39. As a measure of association, how does the contingency coefficient differ from lambda?

40. Using the data given in the accompanying table, compute the contingency coefficient C. What is the value of C_{max} for these data? Of C_{adj}? Interpret your results.

EXERCISE 40

Type of publisher by type of college for faculty publications

	Type of Publisher	
Type of College	**Secular**	**Religious**
church supported	75	24
state supported	80	1

41. In dealing with measures of association for nominal data, why might a social scientist prefer λ over other measures?

42. Compute the value for C_{max} for 2×2, 3×3, 4×4, 5×5, and 6×6 tables. What do these values suggest about the nature of the contingency coefficient?

43. In general, and without reference to any specific measure of association, describe what is meant by the term "proportional-reduction-in-error measure of association."

44. In computing λ_r, what is the no-association rule? The perfect-association rule?

45. How does λ_r differ from λ_c? Why would a social scientist usually be more interested in one than in the other?

46. Compute and interpret λ_r for the data in the accompanying table. They come from a study about the relationship between occupations and orientation to modern life for South Americans.

EXERCISE 46

Study of modernity among 623 South Americans

Occupation	Orientation to Modern Life			
	High	**Medium**	**Low**	**Total**
mental	148	27	8	183
physical	253	105	82	440
Total	401	132	90	623

Source: David A. Ward, "A Study of Modernity and Occupation in Candelaria, Colombia," unpublished paper; by permission.

47. How does ρ differ from γ?

48. A large corporation selects ten college graduates for employment on the basis of both an interview and an achievement test. The paired scores are as shown. Calculate the Spearman rank-order correlation coefficient $\hat{\rho}$. Rank 1 is assigned to the candidate judged to be the best.

EXERCISE 48

Ranks and test scores

Subject	Interview Rank	Test Score
1	8	74
2	5	81
3	10	66
4	3	83
5	6	66
6	1	94
7	4	96
8	7	70
9	9	61
10	2	86

49. Refer to Exercise 48. Do the data present sufficient evidence to indicate that the correlation between interview rankings and test scores is greater than zero? If so, can you say that tests could be used to reduce the number of interviews?

50. A political scientist wished to examine the relationship of the voter image of a conservative political candidate and the distance (in miles) between the residences of the voter and the candidate. Each of 12 voters rated the candidate on a scale of 1 to 20. The data are as shown, in the accompanying table. Calculate the Spearman rank-correlation coefficient $\hat{\rho}$.

EXERCISE 50

Voter image of candidate and distance from candidate

Voter	Rating	Distance
1	12	75
2	7	165
3	5	300
4	19	15
5	17	180
6	12	240
7	9	120
8	18	60
9	3	230
10	8	200
11	15	130
12	4	130

51. Refer to Exercise 50. Do these data provide sufficient evidence to indicate a negative correlation between rating and distance?

52. Compute and interpret γ for the data given in the accompanying table.

EXERCISE 52

Perceived career satisfaction and self-esteem among career officers

	Degree of Perceived Career Satisfaction			
Self-Esteem	High	Medium	Low	Total
high	90	55	5	150
medium	100	100	25	225
low	10	45	20	75
Total	200	200	50	450

53. Use the data of Exercise 52 to test $H_0: \gamma = 0$. (Use $\alpha = .05$ for a two-tailed test.)

54. Consider the data in the accompanying table. Which statistical measure of association, λ_r or γ, is more appropriate? Compute and interpret the appropriate measure.

EXERCISE 54

Social status of father and subject's religiosity

	Social Status of Father	
Religiosity	White Collar	Blue Collar
nonpracticing	10	50
semipracticing	50	100
practicing	40	40

55. Refer to Exercise 54. Can Yule's Q be calculated for this table? Why or why not?

56. Criminologists investigated the reactions of urban and rural adults to 20 criminal acts, ranging from drunk driving to second-degree murder. The crimes and their relative ranks, based on people's reaction to seriousness, are given in the accompanying table. Compute rho, the rank-order correlation coefficient. Test a hypothesis of no correlation between the crime rankings for the two groupings of people.

EXERCISE 56

Rank order of crimes
by urban and rural
adults

Crime	Urban	Rural
sexual abuse of children	1	3
forcible rape	2	1
armed robbery	3	2
arson	4	5
burglary	5	4
automobile theft	6	6
vandalism	7	7
aggravated assault	8	8
embezzlement	9	14
treason	10	10
shoplifting	11	11
drug addiction	12	13
sexual discrimination	13	9
payola (kickbacks)	14	12
price fixing	15	15
strip mining	16	18
homosexuality	17	17
prostitution	18	16
masturbation	19	19
gambling	20	20

57. Compute and interpret Yule's Q for the data given in the accompanying table. Is the value of Q statistically significant? (Use $\alpha = .05$ for a two-tailed test.)

EXERCISE 57

Occupational prestige
and income among
375 workers

	Occupational Prestige		
Income	**High**	**Low**	**Total**
high	95	55	150
low	80	145	225
Total	175	200	375

58. A social researcher sampled 288 individuals in order to examine the relationship between race and attitudes toward busing to achieve school integration. The researcher hypothesized that blacks would be more favorable than whites toward busing. Use the data in the accompanying table to compute Yule's Q.

Is the relationship between race and attitudes toward busing statistically significant? (Use $\alpha = .05$ for a one-tailed test.) Is the researcher's hypothesis confirmed?

Attitudes toward School Busing	Race		
	Black	White	Total
favor	90	58	148
oppose	32	108	140
Total	122	166	288

59. Use the accompanying computer output to answer the following questions for the data of Table 10.10:

a. What correlation coefficient was computed here?

b. What computational formula could be used to obtain this correlation coefficient?

c. What test statistic would you use to test H_0: correlation coefficient $= 0$?

```
MTB > NOTE THAT 'LIFE' and 'INCOME' ARE IN RANK FORM
MTB > correlate 'LIFE' 'INCOME'

Correlation of LIFE and INCOME = 0.842

MTB > let k1=(0.842)*sqrt(8/(1-(0.842)**2))
MTB > print k1
K1       4.41452
MTB > NOTE k1=t
```

60. Reconstruct the table in Exercise 58 so that "white" is the first category and "black" is the second category of the independent variable "race." Compute and interpret Yule's Q.

61. Using information in Database A, Appendix Table 7, set up a contingency table with "income of parents" as the independent variable and "religious preference" as the dependent variable for all 200 students. Because there are only five Jewish students, combine Jewish students with "other" so as not to violate the assumption concerning expected cell count.

a. Compute C and interpret your results.

b. Perform a chi-square test of independence. (Use $\alpha = .05$.)

c. Which measures of association other than C would be appropriate for these data? Comment.

62. Refer to Exercise 61 and Database A, Appendix Table 7. Now set up a contingency table with "income of parents" as the independent variable and "number of acts defined as serious crimes" as the dependent variable. For this exercise, group the number of crimes as follows: 8 to 13, 14 to 19, and 20 to 25.

a. Compute both C and chi-square. Interpret.

b. Compute and interpret gamma.

c. Would the procedure in part (a) or in part (b) be most appropriate for analyzing the data? Explain.

63. Use the contingency table set up for Exercise 43, Chapter 9, which deals with Database B, Appendix Table 8.
   a. Compute the contingency coefficient C.
   b. Compute gamma. Interpret.

64. Refer to Exercise 14 in Chapter 9. Would you compute the contingency coefficient, C, as your measure of association? Explain your position. Which measures of association would be appropriate? Explain your position for each measure that you indicate is an appropriate one.

65. Refer to Exercise 18 in Chapter 9. Combine the "do not approve" category with the "no opinion" category and compute the contingency coefficient and Yule's Q.

66. Refer to Exercise 19 in Chapter 9. Compute the contingency coefficient, C, and Yule's Q. How would you determine if C and Q are significant?

67. Refer to Exercise 24 in Chapter 9. Compute Yule's Q, using $\alpha = .05$.

68. Refer to Exercise 27 in Chapter 9. Compute Yule's Q, using $\alpha = .05$.

69. Refer to Exercise 46 and combine the categories "medium" and "low" into a single category. Compute Yule's Q and test the hypothesis that $Q > 0$, setting $\alpha = .05$.

70. Refer to Exercise 52 and combine "low" and "medium" into a single category, first for career satisfaction and then for self-esteem. Compute Q, lambda, and gamma. Test the significance of each correlation coefficient. Which of the three measures would you most likely use in a research paper? Explain your answer.

71. Refer to Exercise 57. Compute both lambda and gamma.

72. Refer to Exercise 58. Compute both lambda and gamma.

CHAPTER 11

CONTINGENCY ANALYSIS: MULTIVARIATE EXTENSIONS

GENERAL OBJECTIVES

In Chapter 10 we showed a variety of measures of association for bivariate analysis of nominal and ordinal variables. In this chapter we extend our discussion to multivariate analysis. In particular, we examine how the strength and direction of association between two nominal or ordinal variables are affected when controlling for a third variable. This chapter explores several possible ways in which a third variable may affect a bivariate relationship.

SPECIFIC OBJECTIVES

1. To extend our measures of association to multivariate data. It is important that social researchers know more than just whether or not there is an association and how strong it is.
2. To introduce the idea of controlling for the effect of a third variable on a bivariate relationship involving nominal or ordinal data.
3. To explore the four possible outcomes for a bivariate relationship when controlling for a third variable—replication, spuriousness, interpretation, and specification (or interaction).
4. To show that statistics as a tool for the social sciences is insufficient by itself; statistics must be used in a context of theory and prior research.

11.1   INTRODUCTION

We learned in Chapter 9 that one variable is often dependent (contingent) on another variable, and therefore the two variables are related. In Chapter 10 we presented several measures of association that show the strength of the relationship between two nominal or ordinal variables. We also determined whether the relationship was statistically significant.

Many measures of the strength of a relationship are based on PRE statistics, such as lambda, gamma, rho, and Yule's *Q*. Our goal was to establish the extent to which knowledge of a case's classification in a category of an independent variable reduces the error in predicting its classification in a category of the dependent variable. In this chapter we carry the study of bivariate relationships between nominal or ordinal variables one step further.

In social science research it is usually not sufficient to know only how strongly two variables are related based on PRE statistics; we also need to know whether the relationship between the two variables is true—that is, not affected by some third variable.

This chapter examines the ways in which a third variable can influence a bivariate relationship involving nominal or ordinal variables. The purpose of controlling for a third variable is to eliminate, or at least understand, any effect this third variable has on a bivariate association between the independent and dependent variables. In this way we can clarify the true relationship between the two original variables. In other words, we are exploring multivariate extensions of the bivariate contingency tables that were discussed in Chapter 9.

11.2   CONTROLLING FOR THE EFFECT OF A THIRD VARIABLE WITH ONLY TWO CATEGORIES

As we noted in Chapter 9, the most simple bivariate relationship can be examined by the cross-classification of dichotomous variables in a 2 × 2 contingency table. Similarly, the basic principle of examining a bivariate association for the influence of a third variable uses a trivariate (three-variable) cross-classification where each of the three variables is dichotomous. We begin our discussion with an example of a simple bivariate relationship.

Suppose we are interested in the relationship between income and attitude toward busing to achieve racial balance in a public school system. Based on theory and prior research, we hypothesize a negative association between income and attitude toward busing; that is, individuals with high income are less likely to favor school busing than individuals with low income. In this example, then, income level is the independent variable, and attitude toward busing is the dependent variable. The cross-classification of the two variables for a hypothetical sample of 500 adults appears in Table 11.1.

TABLE 11.1

Income level and attitude toward school busing

School Busing	Income Level					
	High		Low		Total	
	n	(%)	*n*	(%)	*n*	(%)
favor	55	(26.8)	200	(67.8)	255	(51.0)
oppose	150	(73.2)	95	(32.3)	245	(49.0)
Total	205	(100.0)	295	(100.0)	500	(100.0)
$Q = -.703$						

Note that we have included percentages in Table 11.1. Percentages are very useful for initially examining the relationship between two variables. Recall from Chapter 9 that we calculated percentages in the direction of the independent variable. In this example, income level is the independent variable, and it appears as the column variable in Table 11.1. Thus we calculated percentages based on the column totals. In examining these percentages, we see that individuals with a high income are much more likely to oppose busing (73.2%) than they are to favor busing (26.8%). In contrast, low-income individuals are much more likely to favor busing than to oppose it. Based on our comparison of these percentages, we would tentatively conclude that there is a relationship between income level and attitude toward school busing.

Although comparing percentages helps show whether two variables appear to be related to each other, percentages cannot tell us how strongly two variables are related or whether the association is statistically significant. Thus we now determine the strength of the association between income level and attitude toward busing, and then test whether the association is statistically significant—that is, whether or not we can reject the null hypothesis of no relationship between the two variables.

Since both variables in Table 11.1 are dichotomous, we can use Yule's Q as our measure of association. Recall from Chapter 10 that the calculation of Yule's Q utilizes cell frequencies, and that

$$Q = \frac{ad - bc}{ad + bc}$$

In Table 11.1, $a = 55$, $b = 200$, $c = 150$, and $d = 95$. Thus

$$Q = \frac{(55)(95) - (200)(150)}{(55)(95) + (200)(150)} = \frac{5225 - 30,000}{5225 + 30,000} = -.703$$

We will set $\alpha = .05$ for a one-tailed test, since our research hypothesis is that $Q < 0$. The test statistic is

$$z = \frac{Q}{\hat{\sigma}_Q} = \frac{-.703}{\sqrt{\frac{1}{4}(1 - .703^2)^2(\frac{1}{55} + \frac{1}{200} + \frac{1}{150} + \frac{1}{95})}}$$

$$= \frac{-.703}{\sqrt{\frac{1}{4}[.2560(.0182 + .0050 + .0067 + .0105)]}}$$

$$= \frac{-.703}{\sqrt{\frac{1}{4}[.2560(.0182 + .0050 + .0067 + .0105)]}}$$

$$= \frac{-.703}{.0026}$$

$$= \frac{-.703}{.051}$$

$$= -13.78$$

For $\alpha = .05$, we reject the null hypothesis when $z < -1.645$. Since the observed value of z is less than -1.645, we reject H_0 and conclude that $Q < 0$. There is a significant relationship between income level and attitude toward school busing; that is, high-income individuals are less likely to favor busing than low-income individuals. However, we also want to determine whether the observed relationship is true between income level and attitude toward busing or whether it is due to the influence of some other variable.

The selection of control variables reflects the importance of theory and prior research. For example, in studying the influence of age at first marriage on the number of children couples have, we would be guided by theory and prior research to control for education, employment status of wife, and social class background. We would not, however, control for the influence of food preferences or shopping habits. For our example involving income level and attitude toward busing, we would probably control for racial background, but not for the influence of leisure-time activities.

In controlling for the influence of race, we are asking whether the strength and the statistical significance of the relationship is the same or different for blacks and whites. If the relationship is the same, we can say that race does not influence the original association. However, if the relationship differs for blacks and whites, then race *is* influencing the original bivariate association.

To determine if race is a factor, we first partition the sample of 500 individuals by race (Table 11.2), and then examine the relationship between income and attitude for blacks and whites separately. Essentially, we are creating two **partial tables**, one for whites (Table 11.2a) and one for blacks (Table 11.2b).

TABLE 11.2

Income level and attitude toward school busing, by race

(a) Whites

School Busing	High		Low		Total	
	n	(%)	*n*	(%)	*n*	(%)
favor	27	(26.5)	100	(67.6)	127	(50.8)
oppose	75	(73.5)	48	(32.4)	123	(49.2)
Total	102	(100.0)	148	(100.0)	250	(100.0)

Income Level

$Q = -.705$

(b) Blacks

School Busing	High		Low		Total	
	n	(%)	*n*	(%)	*n*	(%)
favor	28	(27.2)	100	(68.0)	128	(51.2)
oppose	75	(72.8)	47	(32.0)	122	(48.8)
Total	103	(100.0)	147	(100.0)	250	(100.0)

Income Level

$Q = -.701$

Table 11.2 is a multivariate contingency table that consists of three variables, and each variable contains two categories. In other words, Table 11.2 is a trivariate ($2 \times 2 \times 2$) table.

Table 11.2 shows that there are 250 blacks and 250 whites in the sample. Note that it is necessary to ensure that the number of blacks plus the number of whites is equal to the original sample size. This is also true for the relative cell frequencies and the marginals. For example, adding cell *a* (upper-left) in Table 11.2a to cell *a* in Table 11.2b should equal the value of cell *a* in Table 11.1: $27 + 28 = 55$, which is the value of cell *a* in Table 11.1.

The number of categories of the control variable, or third variable, determines how many partial tables we create. For example, Table 11.2 consists of two partial tables because there are two categories of race in the sample.

Our next step is to determine whether race is influencing the relationship between income and attitude toward school busing. To do this, we calculate a measure of association for each partial table in Table 11.2. We can use Yule's Q to compute the strength and statistical significance of this relationship for blacks and then for whites. The steps we have taken in our example use the principles listed below.

GUIDELINES TO SHOW THE EFFECT OF A THIRD VARIABLE ON A BIVARIATE RELATIONSHIP

1. Measure the strength and statistical significance of a bivariate relationship.
2. Based on theory and/or prior research, determine which control variable(s) could influence the bivariate relationship.
3. Partition the sample into partial tables, where the number of partial tables is equal to the number of categories of the third variable.
4. Make certain that the sum of partial table totals and the sums of relevant cell frequencies and marginals are equal, respectively, to those in the original bivariate table.
5. Compute the strength and statistical significance of the bivariate association for each partial table.

With a Yule's Q for each partial table, we can determine if the third variable is influencing the original bivariate relationship. If it is a factor, we can also determine *how* the original relationship is being affected.

There are four possible outcomes for a bivariate relationship when controlling for a third variable: **replication**, **spuriousness**, **interpretation**, and **specification (interaction)**. We will discuss each of these outcomes in turn.

11.3   REPLICATION

Suppose that Table 11.2 describes the trivariate relationship among race, income level, and attitude toward busing. For Table 11.2a, $Q = -.705$, and for Table 11.2b, $Q = -.701$. Each value of Q is statistically significant (using a one-tail test and $\alpha = .05$). Note that the sign and the strength of these Q values are nearly identical to each other and to the value of Q reported for Table 11.1. These findings indicate that race, as a third variable, does not influence the bivariate relationship between income and attitude. For both blacks and whites, people with high income are less likely to favor school busing than those with low income.

If bivariate associations in the partial tables are of the same strength and sign and are about equal to the original bivariate association, we conclude that the third variable does not influence the original relationship. In this case we say that the original association is *replicated* when controlling for the third variable. **Replication occurs when an original bivariate relationship is the same for each category of the control variable.**

EXAMPLE 11.1

A social researcher hypothesizes that highly religious teens are less sexually active than are teens who are not religious. The researcher studies a sample of 400 teens and determines their level of religiosity and sexual activity. Results are shown in Table 11.3. They indicate a negative association between religiosity and sexual activity; that is, highly religious teens are less likely to be sexually active than are teens who are not religious.

TABLE 11.3

Level of sexual activity by level of religiosity for teens

	Religiosity					
	High		Low		Total	
Level of Sexual Activity	*n*	(%)	*n*	(%)	*n*	(%)
sexually active	36	(17.3)	76	(39.6)	112	(28.0)
not sexually active	172	(82.7)	116	(60.4)	288	(72.0)
Total	208	(100.0)	192	(100.0)	400	(100.0)

$Q = -.516$

Based on prior research, the investigator thinks that a teen's gender (male or female) may influence the relationship between religiosity and sexual activity. The researcher then divides the sample into males and females and recalculates Yule's Q for each group. Two questions are pertinent. First, what values of Q would the data show if gender had no influence on the relationship between religiosity and sexual activity? Second, why?

SOLUTION

If gender had no influence on the relationship between religiosity and sexual activity, the strength of this relationship for both males and females would be approximately $-.516$. If gender is not a factor, the sign and the strength of the relationship should be replicated for both groups; that is, the relationship between religiosity and sexual activity should not vary by gender of the teens.

In some cases a third variable is not a factor. In others, a third variable does influence the bivariate relationship. The remaining outcomes—

spuriousness, interpretation, and specification—when controlling for a third variable reflect the different ways in which a third variable can influence a bivariate relationship between two other variables.

EXERCISES

1. Define replication. Write a brief essay in which you spell out the logic behind replication as an outcome when controlling for a third variable.

2. Why is Yule's Q used in the analysis of bivariate data when the variables have only two categories each?

3. As a sociologist employed by your community's Department of Public Health, you are asked to study whether school children who are inoculated for measles are also inoculated for polio. You draw a random sample of 500 student records for your study and find that $Q = .805$. However, you suspect that the bivariate relationship could be affected by students' grade level in school (elementary, junior high, high school). How will you determine if grade level affects the bivariate relationship? If grade level does not affect the relationship, what results would you obtain from controlling for this variable?

11.4   SPURIOUSNESS

In social science research it is not usually sufficient to know only the strength and direction of a relationship between two variables. We also need to be certain that the observed relationship is true and is not unknowingly affected by some other variable. We need to know if *spuriousness* is producing the bivariate relationship. **Spuriousness occurs in a bivariate relationship when the only reason for the observed relationship is that both variables are influenced by one or more other variables**.

A spurious relationship is illustrated by the observation that people are more likely to wear shorts and sundresses all year in an environment with many palm trees than they are in an environment with few or no palm trees. A naive researcher might hypothesize that the presence and number of palm trees (the independent variable) influences people's mode of dress (the dependent variable), but social researchers are not likely to conclude that this is a true relationship, because the possibility of spuriousness has not been considered. Clearly, there are other variables that are simultaneously affecting both the presence and number of palm trees and the way people dress year round. We know that the presence of palm trees and the wearing of shorts year round are more prevalent in areas with a warm climate, near an ocean, where the soil consists largely of sand. Thus climate and geography may combine to create a spurious relationship between the two variables.

Most spurious situations are not this obvious. Both a review of the relevant literature and an awareness of relevant theoretical propositions help the social researcher spot possible spurious relationships. In the final analysis, however, social researchers must subject the possibility of spuriousness to appropriate tests.

As another example of a spurious relationship, we refer again to Table 11.1, where $Q = -.703$ for the association between income level and attitude toward school busing. Suppose that when we control for the third variable, race, $Q = -.016$ for whites and $Q = .004$ for blacks. These Q values for whites and blacks would show that there is no association between income and attitude toward busing. High-income blacks and whites are as likely to favor busing as low-income blacks and whites. Findings like these suggest that the original relationship between income level and attitude toward busing is spurious, in that race influences both income and attitude.

To confirm a spurious association, we would examine first the relationship between race and income level, and second the relationship between race and attitude toward busing. Tables 11.4 and 11.5 depict the bivariate representations of race and income and race and attitude toward busing, respectively, for the 500 adults sampled. In calculating Yule's Q for Table

TABLE 11.4

Race and income

	Race					
	Whites		**Blacks**		**Total**	
Income Level	**n**	**(%)**	**n**	**(%)**	**n**	**(%)**
high	130	(52.0)	75	(30.0)	205	(41.0)
low	120	(48.0)	175	(70.0)	295	(59.0)
Total	250	(100.0)	250	(100.0)	500	(100.0)

$Q = .433$

TABLE 11.5

Race and attitude

	Race					
	Whites		**Blacks**		**Total**	
School Busing	**n**	**(%)**	**n**	**(%)**	**n**	**(%)**
favor	90	(36.0)	165	(66.0)	255	(51.0)
oppose	160	(64.0)	85	(34.0)	245	(49.0)
Total	250	(100.0)	250	(100.0)	500	(100.0)

$Q = -.551$

11.4, we find that $Q = .433$, and for Table 11.5 $Q = -.551$. These values show that whites are much more likely than blacks to have high income and that whites are much less likely than blacks to favor busing. Consequently, the original association between income level and attitude toward busing (Table 11.1) could have occurred largely because of the influence of race on each variable. Race "explains away" the relationship between income and attitude.

Since the original bivariate association disappears when we control for race, we would conclude that the relationship is not a true one. The variables *appeared* to be related only because each variable was influenced by the third variable, race.

EXAMPLE 11.2

A health researcher hypothesized that individuals who drink coffee daily made more visits to a physician for health problems during the last year than individuals who do not drink coffee regularly. The researcher obtained a sample of 300 adults and then determined whether they were daily coffee drinkers or not and how many visits they made last year to see a physician for health problems. The data in Table 11.6 show a positive association ($Q = .763$) between coffee consumption and the frequency of visits to a physician.

TABLE 11.6

Coffee consumption and visits to a physician

	Daily Coffee Drinker					
	Yes		**No**		**Total**	
Number of Visits	**n**	**(%)**	**n**	**(%)**	**n**	**(%)**
three or more	80	(53.3)	20	(13.3)	100	(33.3)
less than three	70	(46.7)	130	(86.7)	200	(66.7)
Total	150	(100.0)	150	(100.0)	300	(100.0)

$Q = .763$, $p < .05$, using a one-tail test.

The health researcher then reasoned that the stress experienced by individuals could be producing the observed relationship between coffee consumption and physician visits; that is, stress might contribute to becoming a coffee drinker. Moreover, stress might create symptoms that lead to physician visits.

The researcher divides the sample into those who experienced high stress and those who experienced low stress. What values of Q would the data show if level of stress is producing a spurious association between coffee consumption and physician visits? Why?

SOLUTION   If stress were producing a spurious relationship between coffee consumption and physician visits, the strength of the coffee-physician relationship would be near 0 for individuals experiencing high stress as well as for individuals experiencing low stress. That is, neither value of Q would be statistically significant. In addition, there would be a relatively strong association between level of stress and coffee consumption and between level of stress and physician visits. If the original bivariate relationship were spurious due to stress, that relationship would disappear when the level of stress is controlled. That is, the number of physician visits would not depend on (be contingent on) coffee consumption once we controlled for stress. Rather, there would *appear* to be a relationship between coffee consumption and physician visits *only because* each variable was influenced by the third variable, stress level. Individuals with high stress drink more coffee than do individuals with low stress, and individuals with high stress visit a physician more often than do individuals with low stress.

Research studies are seriously flawed when researchers do not attempt to make certain that observed bivariate relationships are true. The variables researchers choose to control must be based on theory and/or prior research so that they qualify as potential causes of a spurious association.

EXERCISES

4. Define spuriousness. Write a brief essay in which you spell out the logic behind spuriousness as an outcome when controlling for a third variable.

5. A social researcher sampled 200 communities and found that the level of ice cream consumption (high or low) was positively associated with level of crime (high or low). The Q value of .628 suggests that the amount of ice cream consumed influences a community's crime rate. The researcher then controlled for outdoor temperature (high or low) and found that $Q = .014$ for communities with high temperatures and $Q = .010$ for communities with low temperatures. What do these findings suggest about the relationship between ice cream consumption and crime? Explain your answer.

11.5   INTERPRETATION

Thus far we have examined examples of replication, in which controlling for a third variable did not change the original bivariate relationship. We also examined examples of spuriousness, in which two variables appeared to be related but in actuality were not.

A third possibility is that one variable is dependent on (contingent on) another variable, but the nature of the dependency is more complex than the basic bivariate relationship would indicate. Specifically, the observed association between two variables is due to a third, **intervening variable**. In this case, we say that the original relationship is **interpreted** by the variable we are controlling. **Interpretation occurs in a bivariate relationship when the relationship is due to a third, intervening variable.** Thus the relationship between the control variable and the two original variables represents a process in which the control variable connects the original independent variable to the original dependent variable.

For example, family sociologists report that a negative association exists between educational attainment and the probability of divorce; that is, people who complete more years of schooling are less likely to divorce than are people who complete fewer years of schooling. A possible intervening variable is age at first marriage. Continued educational enrollment often delays the age at first marriage, because people want to complete their schooling and get established in a job before they marry. It is difficult to be in school and be married at the same time. The older individuals are when they first marry, the less likely it is that their marriage will end in divorce, because older people tend to be more mature emotionally and to be better established financially.

In this example, age at first marriage is an intervening variable that connects educational attainment (the independent variable) to the probability of divorce (the dependent variable). The relationship among the three variables represents a process in which more schooling increases the age at first marriage, which in turn lowers the likelihood of divorce. We illustrate with an example.

A family sociologist interviewed 400 individuals, determining their educational attainment and whether their first marriage ended in divorce. Table 11.7 shows the cross-classification of education and divorce status. The value of Q shows a negative association; that is, people who graduate from college are less likely to have their first marriage end in divorce than people

TABLE 11.7

Educational attainment and divorce status

| First Marriage Ended in Divorce | College Graduate | | | | | |
| | Yes | | No | | Total | |
	n	(%)	n	(%)	n	(%)
yes	78	(36.8)	110	(58.5)	188	(47.0)
no	134	(63.2)	78	(41.5)	212	(53.0)
Total	212	(100.0)	188	(100.0)	400	(100.0)

$Q = -.416$, $p < .05$, using a one-tail test.

with fewer years of education. Since the family sociologist had hypothesized that age at first marriage was an intervening variable between education and divorce state, the sociologist then controlled for age at first marriage and reexamined the relationship between the independent and dependent variables. The results are shown in Table 11.8.

TABLE 11.8

Educational attainment and divorce by age at first marriage

(a) Under 25 Years Old at First Marriage						
	College Graduate					
	Yes		No		Total	
First Marriage Ended in Divorce	n	(%)	n	(%)	n	(%)
yes	31	(19.9)	16	(20.3)	47	(20.0)
no	125	(80.1)	63	(79.7)	188	(80.0)
Total	156	(100.0)	79	(100.0)	235	(100.0)

$Q = -.012$

(b) 25 Years or Older at First Marriage						
	College Graduate					
	Yes		No		Total	
First Marriage Ended in Divorce	n	(%)	n	(%)	n	(%)
yes	47	(83.9)	94	(86.2)	141	(85.5)
no	9	(16.1)	15	(13.8)	24	(14.5)
Total	56	(100.0)	109	(100.0)	165	(100.0)

$Q = -.091$

Table 11.8 shows that when age at first marriage is controlled, the bivariate association between education and divorce status disappears. When age at first marriage is controlled, individuals 25 years or older with a college degree are as likely to be divorced (19.9%) as others with less education (20.3%). Age at first marriage is associated with both educational attainment and divorce status. Yule's Q is .587 between age at first marriage and educational attainment, and .918 between age at first marriage and divorce status. This suggests that individuals with a college degree tend to be older when they first marry than individuals with less education. In turn, individuals who are older at first marriage are less likely to divorce than people who are younger at first marriage.

The results in Table 11.8 do not imply that the relationship between education and divorce status is spurious. Rather, their association is interpreted by the intervening variable, age at first marriage.

Statistically, spuriousness and interpretation are similar, in that controlling for a third variable eliminates or reduces the original bivariate association. Theoretically and substantively, however, spuriousness and interpretation are very different. If we conclude that the original bivariate relationship is spurious, we are saying that the relationship is *not* true — that is, the independent variable does not influence the dependent variable. They only appear to be related because each is influenced by the third variable. However, if we conclude that the original association is mediated by the third variable, we accept the association but recognize that the control variable intervenes between the independent and dependent variables and thereby interprets the association.

Figure 11.1 shows the theoretical difference between spuriousness and interpretation in the relationship among an independent variable, a dependent variable, and a third variable. In this figure, X is the independent variable, Y is the dependent variable, and Z is the third variable (control variable). The association between the independent and dependent variables shown in Figure 11.1a is spurious, since the control variable, Z, is causing or influencing each of these variables. However, the association between the independent and dependent variables shown in Figure 11.1b is interpreted by the control variable, Z, since Z is the intervening variable that connects the independent and dependent variables.

FIGURE 11.1

Conceptual difference between spuriousness and interpretation

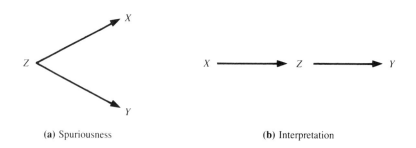

(a) Spuriousness   **(b)** Interpretation

It is the researcher's knowledge of theory and prior research that determines whether the relationship between two variables is spurious because of a third variable or whether the relationship is mediated by the third variable.

EXAMPLE 11.3   A sociologist is interested in the relationship between the geographic region in which people live and how soon after marriage they buy a home. The sociologist hypothesizes that couples who live in the South are more likely than couples in the North to buy a home within three years of marriage. The results from surveying a sample of 200 couples appear in Table 11.9.

TABLE 11.9

Region of residence
and home purchase
after marriage

Home Purchased Within Three Years	Region					
	South		North		Total	
	n	(%)	*n*	(%)	*n*	(%)
yes	60	(60.0)	30	(30.0)	90	(45.0)
no	40	(40.0)	70	(70.0)	110	(55.0)
Total	100	(100.0)	100	(100.0)	200	(100.0)

$Q = .555$, $p < .05$, using a one-tail test.

Yule's $Q = .555$ is our measure of the strength of the bivariate relationship. This finding suggests that couples in the South are more likely than couples in the North to buy a home within three years of marriage.

The sociologist is interested in explaining why region might be associated with the ability to buy a home. Based on previous research, the investigator hypothesizes that the cost of local housing is generally lower in the South than in the North. A third variable, cost of housing, is hypothesized to mediate or interpret the bivariate association between region and home buying within three years of marriage.

What would the sociologist do first to determine if cost of housing is the intervening variable? What statistical results would the social researcher find if cost of housing is the intervening variable? Suppose that when cost of housing is controlled, the original association between region and home buying disappears! How would the sociologist determine whether spuriousness or interpretation describes the original bivariate association?

SOLUTION

Since cost of housing is the variable that is being controlled, the sociologist would first partition the sample into high-cost housing areas and low-cost housing areas. The sociologist would then determine the strength and the significance of the relationship between region and home buying for the two categories of the variable, "cost of local housing."

The original association between region and home buying would disappear when cost of local housing is controlled. Housing cost is an intervening variable between region and home buying. The Q values would be near 0 for both high- and low-cost housing areas.

In a statistical sense, either spuriousness or interpretation could account for the disappearance of the original association. In a theoretical sense, however, the sociologist would conclude that local housing costs explain or mediate the relationship between region and home buying within three years of marriage.

It is doubtful that the original association is spurious. While housing costs could realistically influence whether a couple purchased a home, it makes little sense to say that housing costs cause or influence geographic region. However, it is possible that some couples might change geographic region in response to housing costs, although more important factors, such as better employment opportunities and the geographic residence of family and friends, are likely to cause couples to move from one area to another.

Our discussion of interpretation should reinforce the idea that statistical techniques are useful tools, but they are no substitute for sound conceptual thinking.

EXERCISES

6. Define interpretation. Write a brief essay in which you spell out the logic behind interpretation as an outcome when controlling for a third variable.

7. In what ways are spuriousness and interpretation similar when controlling for a third variable? In what ways are they dissimilar?

8. An industrial sociologist employed by the United Nations sampled 300 nations and found that life expectancy (high or low) was positively associated with the level of technological development (high or low). Which variable is the independent variable and which is the dependent variable? Explain your answer.

9. Refer to Exercise 8. Now assume that the researcher found that $Q = .716$ for the relationship between life expectancy and level of technological development. The researcher also thought that the percentage of the population that lives in urban areas (high or low) could influence the bivariate relationship. The researcher decided to control for this variable. In introducing the control variable, the values of Yule's Q suggest that the variable "percent urban" interprets the relationship between life expectancy and level of technological development. What does this imply about the Q values? How would you decide that interpretation and not spuriousness explained the researcher's findings?

11.6   SPECIFICATION (INTERACTION)

In our discussion so far, the values of Q in the partial tables are very similar in sign and magnitude. For example, $Q = -.705$ for Table 11.2a and $Q = -.701$ for Table 11.2b. Thus the relationship between income and attitude toward busing is the same for blacks and whites (a case of replication). Table 11.8 shows that the values for both partial tables are nearly equal to 0 when age at first marriage is controlled (a case of interpretation).

Sometimes when we control for a third variable, however, the original bivariate association differs in magnitude or sign or both for each of the two categories of the third variable. For example, the association may disappear in one partial table but not in the other. Or the association may be large in one partial table and small in the other. It is even possible that the bivariate association is positive in one partial table and negative in the other. Whenever the relationships in partial tables are not the same, we conclude that the original bivariate association is **specified by** the third variable. In other words, the control variable **interacts with** the independent variable to influence the dependent variable. **Specification or interaction occurs when the control for a third variable produces different associations between the two original variables for each partial table.**

Specification is the fourth possible outcome for a bivariate relationship when a third variable is controlled. In one way, specification is similar to interpretation, in that the nature of the contingent or dependent relationship is more complex than the basic bivariate association indicates. However, with specification (interaction) the observed association between two variables differs for *each* category of the third variable.

As an illustration of specification, we refer again to the original association between income level and attitude toward busing. The cross-classification of these two variables is repeated here in Table 11.10.

TABLE 11.10

Income level and attitude toward school busing

School Busing	Income Level					
	High		Low		Total	
	n	(%)	n	(%)	n	(%)
in favor	55	(26.8)	200	(67.8)	255	(51.0)
opposed	150	(73.2)	95	(32.2)	245	(49.0)
Total	205	(100.0)	295	(100.0)	500	(100.0)

$Q = -.703$

Table 11.10 shows a negative association between income level and attitude toward busing; that is, high-income individuals are not as likely to favor busing as low-income individuals. Now suppose that when race is introduced, $Q = -.949$ for whites and $Q = -.222$ for blacks (see Table 11.11). These findings show that high-income whites are much less likely to favor busing than low-income whites. However, for blacks, there is only a small association between income and attitude. High-income blacks are almost as likely as low-income blacks to favor busing. In this case, the researcher concludes that race **specifies** the relationship between income level and attitude toward school busing. Race **interacts** with income to influence attitude toward busing.

TABLE 11.11

Income level and attitude toward school busing, by race

(a) Whites

School Busing	High n	High (%)	Low n	Low (%)	Total n	Total (%)
in favor	20	(17.4)	120	(88.9)	140	(56.0)
opposed	95	(82.6)	15	(11.1)	110	(44.0)
Total	115	(100.0)	135	(100.0)	250	(100.0)

$Q = -.949$

(b) Blacks

School Busing	High n	High (%)	Low n	Low (%)	Total n	Total (%)
in favor	35	(38.9)	80	(50.0)	115	(46.0)
opposed	55	(61.1)	80	(50.0)	135	(54.0)
Total	90	(100.0)	160	(100.0)	250	(100.0)

$Q = -.222$

In the preceding example, the magnitude of the bivariate association drops considerably for one category, but increases for the other category. You will also find situations where controlling for a third variable produces a positive association for one category of the control variable and a negative association for the other category.

EXAMPLE 11.4

A criminologist hypothesizes that adults living in the North are more likely to favor gun control than adults living in the South. The criminologist also hypothesizes that income level (high or low) will specify the relationship between region of residence (North or South) and attitude toward gun control (in favor or opposed). Samples of 200 adults are selected from both the North and the South. Subjects are interviewed. For the relationship between region and gun control, $Q = .637$.

If income level interacts with region of residence to influence attitudes toward gun control, will the bivariate associations in the two partial tables be the same? Suppose that for high-income individuals, $Q = .031$, but for low-income individuals, $Q = .767$. How would you interpret these findings? Furthermore, suppose that for high-income individuals, $Q = .625$, and for low-income individuals, $Q = .641$. Would you conclude that income level specifies the relationship between region and gun control attitude? Based on your answer, what outcome does controlling for a third variable have on the original bivariate relationship?

SOLUTION

If income level interacts with region in influencing attitudes, then the bivariate associations in the two partial tables will be different. If $Q = .031$ for high-income individuals and $Q = .767$ for low-income individuals, income level specifies the relationship between region and attitude toward gun control. This is because for high-income individuals, the bivariate relationship disappears; Northerners are as likely as Southerners to favor gun control. For people with low income, however, those in the North are much more likely than those in the South to favor gun control.

If the bivariate association for high-income individuals ($Q = .625$) is about the same as that for low-income individuals ($Q = .641$), you would conclude that income level does *not* specify the relationship between region and attitude. Rather, controlling for income level **replicates** the original bivariate association between region of residence and attitude toward gun control. The bivariate relationship between region and attitude is about the same magnitude and sign for high-income people as it is for low-income people, and these associations are also nearly equal to the original bivariate association.

In the preceding illustrations, we showed two possible ways in which specification describes the outcome for a bivariate association when controlling for a third variable. In Example 11.4 the original bivariate association of $Q = .637$ disappears for one category of the control variable ($Q = .031$), but not for the other category ($Q = .767$). For Table 11.10, the original bivariate association of $Q = -.703$ is still negative but increases for one category ($Q = -.949$), while it remains negative and decreases for the other category of the control variable ($Q = -.222$). It is also possible that a bivariate relationship is positive for one category of the control variable but negative for the other category. The important thing to remember about specification is that when a third variable is controlled, the bivariate association differs in magnitude or sign or both for the two categories of the third variable.

Our discussion of specification should reinforce in your mind the idea that a social researcher's knowledge of theory and/or prior research is central to explaining how and why a control variable interacts with the independent variable to influence the dependent variable. For example, a sociologist might hypothesize that the relationship between earnings (independent variable) and job satisfaction (dependent variable) for mothers with young children is specified by the control variable, "level of work commitment." It is important for the sociologist to draw on theory and previous research to explain how and why the mothers' work commitment interacts with their earnings to influence their job satisfaction.

In examining multivariate contingency tables in this chapter, we have not yet introduced any new statistical techniques. One reason is that for nominal and ordinal data, the possible outcomes for a bivariate association when a third variable is controlled are most easily illustrated with three dichotomous variables. We have already learned in Chapter 10 that Yule's Q is the most appropriate measure of association for dichotomous variables. A more important reason is that conceptual reasoning and previous research are the important factors in hypothesizing about and interpreting the results of a bivariate association when a third variable is controlled.

Although statistics are useful for determining the strength and significance of bivariate relationships, they cannot determine the theoretical relationship among three or more variables. It is the researcher's knowledge of theory and/or prior research that gives insights into which variables should be controlled and how and why the variables are interconnected.

Although our discussion of replication, spuriousness, interpretation, and specification (interaction) has focused on three dichotomous variables, multivariate contingency tables are not limited to dichotomous variables, nor to the consideration of only three variables at a time.

In the next section we will take a brief look at the situation in which one or more variables has more than two categories.

EXERCISES

10. Define specification (interaction). Write a brief essay in which you spell out the logic behind specification as an outcome when controlling for a third variable.

11. A social researcher interested in the relationship between job seniority (high or low) and annual income (high or low) samples 350 employed adults. The researcher finds that $Q = .673$, which suggests that workers with more job seniority have higher annual incomes than workers with less job seniority. The researcher then reasons that educational attainment should be controlled. She classifies workers into three groups: those with fewer than 12 years of schooling, those who are high school graduates, and those who have completed one or more years of college. If educational attainment specifies the relationship between job seniority and annual income, what will the values of Q be like

when education is controlled? Suppose that for those with fewer than 12 years of schooling, $Q = .883$, for those with a high school education, $Q = .695$, and for those with some college, $Q = .118$. Interpret these findings.

11.7 CONTROLLING FOR THE EFFECT OF A THIRD VARIABLE FOR NOMINAL VARIABLES WITH THREE OR MORE CATEGORIES

When we examine a trivariate relationship among nominal variables, and one or more of the variables has three or more categories, we can no longer use Yule's Q as our measure of association. In this section we present techniques for controlling for a third variable when one or more of the nominal variables consists of three or more categories. We begin our discussion with an example.

The data presented in Table 11.12 arose from a study of drug-related complaints at a hospital emergency ward. Each person in a sample of 2100 was classified by gender and marital status (divorced, widowed, or married) and by the drug-related complaint (overdose, suicide, psychiatric, or addiction). We first hypothesized that gender influences the individual's drug-related complaint. We also reasoned that the bivariate relationship is influenced by a third variable, marital status. Therefore we decided to examine this relationship for each category of marital status.

The data have been arranged in three partial tables, corresponding to the levels of the control variable, in Table 11.12. In examining the relationship between two variables in the presence of a control variable, we could first run separate chi-square tests of independence for each of the partial tables. These results would indicate whether the two variables of interest are independent at each of the indicated levels of the control variable. A combined test of independence of the two variables could be obtained by adding the values of chi-square computed for each of the partial tables. Here we would be testing the independence of the two variables while controlling for the influence of a third variable on the two variables being studied. The degrees of freedom of the overall test would be the sum of the degrees of freedom for each of the partial tables. We illustrate these ideas with some examples.

EXAMPLE 11.5   Use the data of Table 11.12 to test the independence of the two variables "complaint" and "gender" for each of the partial tables. Use $\alpha = .05$ for all tables and interpret your results.

TABLE 11.12

Partial tables for the comparison of drug-related complaints and gender in the presence of the control variable "marital status"

(a) Divorced

| | Gender | | | | | |
| | Male | | Female | | Total | |
Complaint	n	(%)	n	(%)	n	(%)
overdose	96	(48.0)	208	(52.0)	304	(50.7)
suicide	14	(7.0)	100	(25.0)	114	(19.0)
psychiatric	38	(19.0)	24	(6.0)	62	(10.3)
addiction	52	(26.0)	68	(17.0)	120	(20.0)
Total	200	(100.0)	400	(100.0)	600	(100.0)

(b) Widowed

| | Gender | | | | | |
| | Male | | Female | | Total | |
Complaint	n	(%)	n	(%)	n	(%)
overdose	46	(46.0)	82	(41.0)	128	(42.7)
suicide	18	(18.0)	96	(48.0)	114	(38.0)
psychiatric	22	(22.0)	10	(5.0)	32	(10.7)
addiction	14	(14.0)	12	(6.0)	26	(8.7)
Total	100	(100.0)	200	(100.0)	300	(100.0)

(c) Married

| | Gender | | | | | |
| | Male | | Female | | Total | |
Complaint	n	(%)	n	(%)	n	(%)
overdose	266	(44.3)	330	(55.0)	596	(49.7)
suicide	72	(12.0)	156	(26.0)	228	(19.0)
psychiatric	116	(19.3)	36	(6.0)	152	(12.7)
addiction	146	(24.3)	78	(13.0)	224	(18.7)
Total	600	(99.9)	600	(100.0)	1200	(100.1)

SOLUTION   Since we already know how to compute expected cell counts by using the formula

$$\frac{(\text{row total}) (\text{column total})}{n}$$

TABLE 11.13

Expected cell counts
for the partial tables in
Table 11.12

(a) Divorced

	Gender		
Complaint	Male	Female	Total
overdose	101.3	202.7	304
suicide	38.0	76.0	114
psychiatric	20.7	41.3	62
addiction	40.0	80.0	120
Total	200.0	400.0	600

(b) Widowed

	Gender		
Complaint	Male	Female	Total
overdose	42.7	85.3	128
suicide	38.0	76.0	114
psychiatric	10.7	21.3	32
addiction	8.6	17.4	26
Total	100.0	200.0	300

(c) Married

	Gender		
Complaint	Male	Female	Total
overdose	298	298	596
suicide	114	114	228
psychiatric	76	76	152
addiction	112	112	224
Total	600	600	1200

we have listed the expected cell counts for each of the partial tables in Table 11.13. You should check a few of the cell entries to convince yourself that these are correct.

Using Table 11.12a, we have the test procedure shown next.

H_1: For the divorced, the two variables "complaint" and "gender" are dependent.

H_0: For the divorced, the two variables are independent.

T.S.:

$$\chi^2 = \sum \frac{(O - E)^2}{E}$$

$$= \frac{(96 - 101.3)^2}{101.3} + \frac{(208 - 202.7)^2}{202.7} + \cdots + \frac{(68 - 80)^2}{80}$$

$$= .2773 + .1386 + \cdots + 1.8000 = 50.2579$$

R.R.: Based on the chi-square value of 7.81 from Appendix Table 3 with $a = .05$ and d.f. $= 3$, we reject the null hypothesis and conclude that for divorced people the variables "drug-related complaint" and "gender" are dependent. It appears that a higher percentage of females than males are classified in the suicide category. A clear picture of this trend is seen in Table 11.14, giving a percentage comparison of Table 11.12a.

TABLE 11.14

Percentage comparison of drug-related complaints by gender for the divorced

	Gender	
Complaint	**Male**	**Female**
overdose	48	52
suicide	7	25
psychiatric	19	6
addiction	26	17
Total %	100	100
Sample size	200	400

We can form the same research and null hypotheses for widowed people. The computed value of the test statistic is $\chi^2 = 39.1672$. Again, comparing the computed value to 7.81 ($a = .05$, d.f. $= 3$) we reject the null hypothesis of independence of the two variables for widowed people. As was seen for divorced people, a higher percentage of females than males have the drug-related complaint categorized as suicide. (See the percentage comparison in Table 11.15.) Note, however, that suicide percentages for the widowed are much higher for both males and females than for divorced people. In contrast, the divorced have higher percentages for the addiction complaint.

Finally, for married people the computed value of chi-square is $\chi^2 = 100.5678$. Again, this result is highly significant. From the percentage comparison in Table 11.16 and the chi-square test of independence, we see that married females have higher percentages associated with the overdose and suicide complaints than do married males. Also note that the married percentages for males and females are very similar to the corresponding

TABLE 11.15

Percentage compar-
ison of drug-related
complaints by gender
for the widowed

Complaint	Gender	
	Male	**Female**
overdose	46	41
suicide	18	48
psychiatric	22	5
addiction	14	6
Total %	100	100
Sample size	100	200

percentages for the divorced, but the widowed percentages appear to be quite different from the percentages for divorced and married people.

In summary, we have seen that gender and drug-related complaints at the hospital emergency room are related at each level of the control variable "marital status."

EXAMPLE 11.6 Combine the separate chi-square tests for the partial tables in Table 11.13 to compute a pooled chi-square. List the parts of the statistical test and draw conclusions. Give the level of significance of the test.

TABLE 11.16

Percentage compar-
ison of drug-related
complaints by gender
for married people

Complaint	Gender	
	Male	**Female**
overdose	44	55
suicide	12	26
psychiatric	19	6
addiction	24	13
Total %	99	100
Sample size	600	600

SOLUTION The four parts of the pooled test of independence are given here:

H_1: When controlling for marital status, the two variables "complaint" and "gender" are dependent.

H_0: When controlling for marital status, the two variables are independent.

T.S.: $\chi^2 =$ sum of the computed chi-square test statistics for the partial tables.

R.R.: Since we are asked to give the level of significance for our test, we do not specify a rejection region. The chi-square test statistic has d.f. $= 9$, the sum of the degrees of freedom for the separate partial tables. Since $\chi^2 = 189.9929$ exceeds the $a = .005$ value of 23.589 in Appendix Table 3 for d.f. $= 9$, the test is significant at the $p < .005$ level. Indeed, the data indicate a dependence of the two variables while controlling for marital status.

A word of caution should be noted here. The pooled chi-square test just performed is *not* equivalent to, and will not necessarily lead to the same conclusion as, the chi-square test of independence between "gender" and "complaint" *that ignores* the control variable "marital status." The results for these two separate tests may lead to quite different conclusions. The pooled chi-square gives us a test of independence between two variables while controlling the influence of a third variable. In contrast, to construct the chi-square test of independence that ignores the influence of a third variable, we form a two-way table (by summing over the cells of the third variable) and perform the chi-square test in the usual way.

Note also that although we have established independence between two nominal variables (which have three or more categories) while controlling for a third variable, we have not determined the strength of the association. In order to determine the strength of an association, we first establish independence between two nominal variables for each of the partial tables and then use a PRE nominal measure of association, such as lambda (discussed in Chapter 10), for each partial table. We proceed in this way because there is no statistical technique for computing a combined measure of association on nominal-level variables in a multivariate contingency table analysis. Although we perform a combined test of independence on the two variables, we are not able to relate the results to a combined measure of association if the variables were measured on a nominal scale.

When we calculate a measure of association for nominal variables with three or more categories, controlling for a third variable indicates if the control variable affects the bivariate relationship. If the control variable does affect the relationship, we can determine how the association is being influenced.

As in our treatment of dichotomous variables, we can determine whether replication, spuriousness, interpretation, or specification (interaction) describes the outcome for a bivariate association when we control for a third variable *and* one or more of the variables has three or more categories. However, rather than selecting Yule's Q as our measure of association, we use a measure, such as lambda, which can be used for variables with three or more categories.

EXAMPLE 11.7

A family sociologist hypothesizes that the presence of preschool children at home influences the couple's division of household labor. The sociologist also reasons that the wife's employment status affects the relationship between the presence of young children and who was likely to do most of the household chores. Six hundred and ninety (690) couples are interviewed for the study. The data appear in Table 11.17. Calculate lambda for each partial table.

TABLE 11.17

Division of household labor by presence of preschool children and employment status of wife

(a) Housewife

Majority of Household Tasks Performed by	Preschool Children				Total	
	Yes		No			
	n	(%)	n	(%)	n	(%)
husband	10	(7.1)	25	(22.7)	35	(14.0)
wife	110	(78.6)	15	(13.6)	125	(50.0)
both	20	(14.3)	70	(63.6)	90	(36.0)
Total	140	(100.0)	110	(99.9)	250	(100.0)

χ^2 is significant for $\alpha = .05$.

(b) Wife Employed Part-time

Majority of Household Tasks Performed by	Preschool Children				Total	
	Yes		No			
	n	(%)	n	(%)	n	(%)
husband	10	(9.5)	30	(31.6)	40	(20.0)
wife	85	(80.9)	15	(15.8)	100	(50.0)
both	10	(9.5)	50	(52.6)	60	(30.0)
Total	105	(99.9)	95	(100.0)	200	(100.0)

χ^2 is significant for $\alpha = .05$.

(c) Wife Employed Full-time

Majority of Household Tasks Performed by	Preschool Children				Total	
	Yes		No			
	n	(%)	n	(%)	n	(%)
husband	15	(14.3)	35	(25.9)	50	(20 8)
wife	60	(57.1)	20	(14.8)	80	(33.3)
both	30	(28.6)	80	(59.3)	110	(45.8)
Total	105	(100.0)	135	(100.0)	240	(99.9)

χ^2 is significant for $\alpha = .05$.

Which term best describes the outcome from controlling for wife's employment status? Explain your answer. (*Hint*: λ_r for the relationship between having preschool children and the household division of labor is .415 when the wife's employment status is not controlled.)

SOLUTION

Recall from Chapter 10 that

$$\lambda_r = \frac{E_1 - E_2}{E_1}$$

where E_1 refers to the number of errors of classification obtained by using Rule 1 (no-association rule), and E_2 refers to the number of errors of classification obtained by using Rule 2 (perfect-association rule). (You may wish to refer back to Section 10.4 in Chapter 10 for our in-depth discussion of lambda as a PRE measure.) To compute λ_r for the data in Table 11.17a, we first calculate E_1 and E_2:

$$E_1 = 250 - 125 = 125$$

and

$$E_2 = (140 - 110) + (110 - 70) = 70$$

The PRE λ_r due to the independent variable "preschool children" is

$$\lambda_r = \frac{E_1 - E_2}{E_1} = \frac{125 - 70}{125} = \frac{55}{125} = .44$$

Thus there is a 44% reduction in error by using presence of preschool children to predict the household division of labor for couples in which the wife is not employed outside the home. In other words, knowledge about preschool children in the home reduces by 44% the error in predicting who will perform the majority of household tasks.

Since the row variable (household division of labor) is the dependent variable in our example, we do not calculate λ_c. Recall from Chapter 10 that λ_c assumes that the column variable in a table is the dependent variable. In our research example, it makes no sense to hypothesize that knowledge about household task performer predicts or influences the presence of preschool children.

To calculate λ_r for Table 11.17b,

$$E_1 = 200 - 100 = 100$$

and

$$E_2 = (105 - 85) + (95 - 50) = 65$$

The PRE λ_r due to preschool aged children is

$$\lambda_r = \frac{E_1 - E_2}{E_1} = \frac{100 - 65}{100} = \frac{35}{100} = .35$$

Knowing if preschool children are present reduces by 35% the error in predicting who performs the majority of household work for couples when the wife is employed part-time.

Finally, in calculating λ_r for Table 11.17c,

$$E_1 = 240 - 110 = 130$$

and

$$E_2 = (105 - 60) + (135 - 80) = 100$$

The PRE λ_r is

$$\lambda_r = \frac{E_1 - E_2}{E_1} = \frac{130 - 100}{130} = \frac{30}{130} = .231$$

Thus knowing if preschool children are present reduces by 23.1% the error in predicting who performs the majority of household work when the wife is employed full-time.

Table 11.17 shows that the relationship between presence of preschool children and the household division of labor *is specified by* the third variable, wife's employment status. This is because the values of λ_r for the partial tables are not of the same magnitude. That is, λ_r is much lower for Table 11.17c than it is for the other two partial tables.

What these findings suggest is that the presence of preschool children is more closely associated with the division of household labor for couples when the wife is not employed or when she works part-time. The presence of young children in the home is less predictive of the couple's division of household labor when the wife is employed full-time. Thus wife's employment status interacts with the presence of preschool children to influence the division of household labor.

EXERCISES

12. Refer to Table 11.12.

   a. Perform a chi-square test of independence to determine whether the two variables "complaint" and "gender" are related. Ignore the presence of the third variable "marital status." (*Hint*: Sum the appropriate cell values across the partial tables for your bivariate comparison. Use $\alpha = .05$.)

b. Compare your conclusions in part a to those for the pooled chi-square test of Example 11.6.

13. Refer to Table 11.12. Calculate lambda for the relationship between "complaint" and "marital status." Ignore the presence of the third variable "gender." (*Hint:* Use the final column of each partial table for your bivariate comparison. Use $\alpha = .05$.)

14. Refer to Table 11.12. Rearrange the data to construct partial tables for comparing the two variables "complaint" and "marital status," while controlling for "gender." Use the partial tables to test the independence of the two variables.

15. Refer to Exercise 14. Calculate lambda for each partial table. Which outcome — replication, spuriousness, interpretation, or specification — does your analysis suggest? Justify your answer.

16. Compare the results of Exercise 13 to those of Exercise 15.

11.8 CONTROLLING FOR THE EFFECT OF A THIRD VARIABLE FOR VARIABLES MEASURED ON AN ORDINAL SCALE

In this section we present techniques for controlling the effect of a third variable when we have ordinal data. Just as in our previous discussion of nominal variables, replication, spuriousness, interpretation, or specification (interaction) are used to describe the outcome for a bivariate association between ordinal variables when controlling for a third variable. However, the measure of association is different. We will now use an extension of gamma (Chapter 10) called **partial gamma,** denoted by the symbol γ_p.

Recall from our initial discussion of a trivariate relationship between nominal variables with three or more categories (Section 11.7) that we made the following computations:

1. We ran chi-square tests of independence for each partial table. These results indicated whether the two variables were independent for each of the indicated categories of the control variable.

2. We performed a combined test of independence by adding the separate chi-square values for each of the partial tables. In this situation we were testing the independence of the two variables while controlling for the third.

3. Finally, we conducted a test of independence that ignored the presence of the control variable by summing frequencies over categories of the control variable.

Just as we ran separate chi-square tests of independence between two variables for each category of a control variable, we can compute gamma to measure the strength of association between two ordinal variables for each partial table corresponding to a category of the control variable. The control variable need not be ordinal. **Partial gamma is a measure of association that combines information from each of the partial tables** and is analogous to the combined chi-square test mentioned earlier. Similarly, a value of gamma that is used to measure the association between the two ordinal variables and that ignores the control variable is analogous to an overall chi-square test of independence that ignores the presence of a control variable. We will illustrate with an example.

To form partial gamma, we simply compute N_s and N_r, the number of concordant and discordant pairs for each partial table, and combine the results as shown below.

PARTIAL GAMMA

$$\gamma_p = \frac{\Sigma N_s - \Sigma N_r}{\Sigma N_s + \Sigma N_r}$$

(*Note*: Summations are over all partial tables.)

EXAMPLE 11.8 William Form (1975) studied workers' job satisfaction in countries that differ in extent of technological development (Argentina, India, Italy, and the United States). In light of the political upheavals of the early 1990s, you and your colleague updated the original findings for the United States and India, but replaced Argentina with Hungary and Italy with Yugolsavia. You surveyed 400 workers in Hungary, 400 in India, 400 in the United States, and 400 in Yugoslavia. Each worker surveyed was classified into one of three categories of job satisfaction (low, moderate, or high) and labor status (unskilled, semiskilled, or skilled). Using an index of technology, the United States had the highest index score, 100; Hungary, 49; Yugoslavia, 23; and India, 6, the lowest.

The data in Table 11.18 can be used to examine the association, or predictability, of orders of ranks on job satisfaction for pairs of individuals

TABLE 11.18

Four-nation study of industrial workers and their job satisfaction

(a) United States (Technology score of 100)

| | Labor Status | | | | | | Total | |
| | Unskilled | | Semiskilled | | Skilled | | | |
Job Satisfaction	n	(%)	n	(%)	n	(%)	n	(%)
low	25	(21.4)	49	(19.9)	64	(46.7)	138	(27.6)
moderate	36	(30.8)	173	(70.3)	65	(47.4)	274	(54.8)
high	56	(47.9)	24	(9.8)	8	(5.8)	88	(17.6)
Total	117	(100.1)	246	(100.0)	137	(99.9)	500	(100.0)

(b) Hungary (Technology score of 49)

| | Labor Status | | | | | | Total | |
| | Unskilled | | Semiskilled | | Skilled | | | |
Job Satisfaction	n	(%)	n	(%)	n	(%)	n	(%)
low	40	(25.8)	99	(39.0)	40	(43.9)	179	(35.8)
moderate	50	(32.3)	80	(31.5)	30	(33.0)	160	(32.0)
high	65	(41.9)	75	(29.5)	21	(23.1)	161	(32.2)
Total	155	(100.0)	254	(100.0)	91	(100.0)	500	(100.0)

(c) Yugoslavia (Technology score of 23)

| | Labor Status | | | | | | Total | |
| | Unskilled | | Semiskilled | | Skilled | | | |
Job Satisfaction	n	(%)	n	(%)	n	(%)	n	(%)
low	52	(28.6)	62	(32.0)	37	(29.8)	151	(30.2)
moderate	60	(33.0)	65	(33.5)	40	(32.3)	165	(33.0)
high	70	(38.5)	67	(34.5)	47	(37.9)	184	(36.8)
Total	182	(100.1)	194	(100.0)	124	(100.0)	500	(100.0)

(d) India (Technology score of 6)

| | Labor Status | | | | | | Total | |
| | Unskilled | | Semiskilled | | Skilled | | | |
Job Satisfaction	n	(%)	n	(%)	n	(%)	n	(%)
low	80	(37.5)	66	(37.5)	21	(18.9)	167	(33.4)
moderate	70	(32.9)	60	(34.1)	40	(36.0)	170	(34.0)
high	63	(29.6)	50	(28.4)	50	(45.0)	163	(32.6)
Total	213	(100.0)	176	(100.0)	111	(99.9)	500	(100.0)

from the order of ranks associated with the variable "labor status." Since a partial table is shown for each category of the control variable "level of technology," you can compute gamma for each partial table and then combine your results to form partial gamma.

SOLUTION

Computations for N_s, N_r, and γ are shown for each of the partial tables. United States:

$$N_s = 25(173 + 65 + 24 + 8) + 49(65 + 8) + 36(24 + 8) + 173(8)$$
$$= 12,863$$
$$N_r = 64(36 + 173 + 56 + 24) + 49(36 + 56) + 65(24 + 56) + 173(56)$$
$$= 37,892$$
$$\gamma = \frac{N_s - N_r}{N_s + N_r} = -.49$$

Hungary:

$$N_s = 40(80 + 30 + 75 + 21) + 99(30 + 21) + 50(75 + 21) + 80(21)$$
$$= 19,769$$
$$N_r = 40(50 + 80 + 65 + 75) + 99(50 + 65) + 30(65 + 75) + 80(65)$$
$$= 31,585$$
$$\gamma = \frac{N_s - N_r}{N_s + N_r} = -.23$$

Yugoslavia:

$$N_s = 52(65 + 40 + 67 + 47) + 62(40 + 47) + 60(67 + 47) + 65(47)$$
$$= 26,677$$
$$N_r = 37(60 + 65 + 70 + 67) + 62(60 + 70) + 40(70 + 67) + 65(70)$$
$$= 27,784$$
$$\gamma = \frac{N_s - N_r}{N_s + N_r} = -.02$$

India:

$$N_s = 80(60 + 40 + 50 + 50) + 66(40 + 50) + 70(50 + 50) + 60(50)$$
$$= 31,940$$
$$N_r = 21(70 + 60 + 63 + 50) + 66(70 + 63) + 40(63 + 50) + 60(63)$$
$$= 22,181$$
$$\gamma = \frac{N_s - N_r}{N_s + N_r} = +.18$$

From the values of gamma for the partial tables, there appears to be a difference in the relationship between the ordinal variables "labor status" and "job satisfaction." In the United States, there is a negative gamma of $-.49$. Thus for the U.S., the error of predicting job satisfaction can be reduced by 49% if we use the order of ranks on labor status to predict the order of ranks on job satisfaction. The negative value of gamma indicates that U.S. workers with higher skill levels tend to have lower levels of job satisfaction than workers with lower skill levels. The value of gamma drops for Hungary to $-.23$. Although the relationship between labor status and job satisfaction is still negative, labor status has lower predictive power for job satisfaction in Hungary compared to the U.S. For Yugoslavia, gamma is nearly 0 ($-.02$), which suggests that labor status has little effect on job satisfaction for workers in Yugoslavia. Finally, gamma is $+.18$ for India. Although the predictive power of labor status is relatively small, the positive value of gamma indicates that workers who have higher levels of skill tend to be more satisfied with their jobs than workers with lower levels of skill.

This value of partial gamma indicates that the predictability of the order of ranks for the variables "job satisfaction" and "labor status" is slightly negative when we control for a third variable, "level of technology" by country. That is, countries in which workers have higher skill levels tend to have workers who are less satisfied with their jobs, controlling for the countries' level of technology.

EXAMPLE 11.9

Refer again to the data of Table 11.18 and the computations of gamma for each of the partial tables. What do the values of gamma indicate regarding the outcome for the association between labor status and job satisfaction when the countries' level of technology is controlled?

Suppose that the value of gamma for the association between labor status and job satisfaction is $-.35$ when level of technology is not controlled. If replication describes the outcome from controlling for the third variable, what would be the approximate value of the partial gamma?

If the value of gamma for the association between labor status and job satisfaction is $-.35$, and the values of gamma for each of the partial tables are nearly 0, what would this suggest about the outcome from controlling for level of technology?

SOLUTION

Since the magnitude and/or sign of the gammas is different for each partial table, the level of technology interacts with labor status to influence job satisfaction. That is, the countries' level of technology specifies the relationship between labor status and job satisfaction.

The value of partial gamma would be approximately $-.35$ if replication describes the outcome from controlling for level of technology. The values of gamma for each partial table would also be approximately −.35. If level of technology does not influence the relationship between labor status and job satisfaction, the value of the association between the latter two variables would be nearly zero for the different categories of the control variable, level of technology.

This suggests that either spuriousness or interpretation describes the association between labor status and job satisfaction. If spuriousness describes the outcome from controlling for the third variable, level of technology would be influencing both labor status and job satisfaction. The variables would appear to be related because of their common association with level of technology. If interpretation describes the outcome from controlling for level of technology, level of technology would be an intervening variable that connects labor status to job satisfaction. In other words, level of technology would mediate the influence of labor status on job satisfaction. The researcher's knowledge of theory and/or past research would determine whether spuriousness or interpretation actually describes the influence of technology on the association between labor status and job satisfaction.

EXERCISES

17. Dillman and his colleagues (1976) conducted a public opinion survey to examine response rates of individuals surveyed under two different conditions. Their research design was replicated, and interviews were conducted with 800 adults. Four hundred of the interviews were conducted using a personal approach; that is, the interviewer identified herself. The remaining interviews were conducted under a blind approach, where the interviewer did not identify herself. One-half of the interviews using each approach contained two sentences of introduction that emphasized the importance of the survey and offered a $20 reward for those who would take the time to respond. The results of the survey are listed in the accompanying table.

EXERCISE 17

Comparison of personal versus blind approach in securing completed questionnaires

Questionnaire Status	Personal Approach		Blind Approach	
	Introduction	No Introduction	Introduction	No Introduction
completed	164	160	155	180
partially completed	4	2	3	2
not completed	32	38	42	18
Total	200	200	200	200

    a. Compute gamma for the two partial tables presented.

    b. Combine the results from part a to compute partial gamma.

18. Refer to the data of Exercise 17. Combine the data for the two partial tables to form one table (three rows and two columns). Compute gamma for this table, which ignores the contribution of the control variable "interview approach." Compare your answer here to the value of partial gamma you obtained in part b of Exercise 17.

19. When you control for interview approach, which outcome do you think best applies to the association between the dependent and independent variables? Explain your selection.

SUMMARY

This chapter is concerned with the outcome for a bivariate association between nominal and ordinal variables when controlling for a third variable. It is a natural extension of Chapter 10, where we discussed measures of association for bivariate data. The first outcome discussed is replication, where the bivariate association does not change in magnitude or sign when a third variable is controlled. The other three outcomes presented — spuriousness, interpretation, and specification (interaction) — reflect different ways in which a third variable can influence the relationship between two other variables.

Spuriousness is an outcome if the bivariate association disappears when a third variable is controlled. The bivariate relationship also disappears if interpretation is the outcome. We discussed how spuriousness and interpretation are very different theoretically, even though they are similar statistically. Specification is the outcome if the bivariate association varies in magnitude and/or sign for categories of the control variable. These various outcomes show the importance of theory and/or past research in proposing research hypotheses and in interpreting statistical results.

We also considered how to examine the effect of a third variable when one or more of the variables consists of several categories. We introduced two measures of association for these variables: the pooled chi-square test and partial gamma.

KEY WORDS

Control variable   A third variable used in studying the relationship between two variables of interest.

Interpretation   An outcome for a bivariate association when a third variable is controlled. The association disappears for all categories of the control variable, because the third variable connects the independent variable to the dependent variable.

Intervening variable   A third variable that connects an independent variable to a dependent variable. Exists when interpretation is the outcome for a bivariate association when a third variable is controlled.

Partial gamma   A type B measure of association used with ordinal data in which one or more variables are controlled.

Partial table   A contingency table for data involving two variables of interest corresponding to a category of a control variable.

Replication   An outcome for a bivariate association when a third variable is controlled. The bivariate association is of the same magnitude and sign for each category of the control variable. The third variable has no effect.

Specification (interaction)   An outcome for a bivariate association when a third variable is controlled. The association differs in magnitude and/or sign for categories of the third variable.

Spuriousness   An outcome for a bivariate association when controlling for a third variable. The association disappears in all categories of the control variable, because the third variable is the cause of both the independent and dependent variables.

KEY FORMULAS

$$\gamma_p = \frac{\Sigma N_s - \Sigma N_r}{\Sigma N_s + \Sigma N_r}$$

SUPPLEMENTARY EXERCISES FOR CHAPTER 11

20. What are the objectives in controlling for the influence of a third variable on a bivariate relationship?

21. State the guidelines for showing the influence of a third variable on a bivariate relationship.

22. Name the possible outcomes for a bivariate association when a third variable is controlled.

23. A family sociologist investigated reasons that urban and rural adults consider sufficient for a couple to divorce. The researcher categorized the 250 adults into those who primarily cited reasons that were emotional in orientation (e.g., fell out of love, lack of communication) and those who primarily cited reasons that were behavioral in orientation (e.g., infidelity, serious drinking problem). See the accompanying table.

EXERCISE 23

Reasons for a divorce and residence

Sufficient Reasons for a Divorce			
Residence	**Emotional**	**Behavioral**	**Total**
urban	80	20	100
rural	60	90	150
Total	140	110	250

a. Use the accompanying data to calculate Yule's Q.

b. The family sociologist was interested in whether the extent of church attendance influences the relationship between urban/rural residence and sufficient reasons for a divorce. For those who attend church regularly, $Q = .717$. For those who attend church irregularly, $Q = .712$. Does church attendance influence the bivariate relationship? Explain.

24. Compare specification and interpretation as two of the possible outcomes for a bivariate association when a third variable is controlled.

25. A sociologist surveys the 300 students in his class concerning their attitudes toward the death penalty. The class consists of social science majors and business majors. The sociologist hypothesizes that a student's major affects his or her attitude toward the death penalty. The data are presented in the accompanying table.

EXERCISE 25

Attitude toward the death penalty and college major

Attitude Toward the Death Penalty			
Major in College	**Favor**	**Oppose**	**Total**
business	100	80	180
social science	40	80	120
Total	140	160	300

a. Use the accompanying data to calculate Yule's Q.

b. The sociologist divides the 300 students into males and females and calculates Yule's Q for each partial table. For males, $Q = .647$. For females, $Q = .202$. Does gender influence the relationship between major in college and attitude toward the death penalty? Explain.

26. Refer to Exercise 25. Suppose that $Q = .011$ for males and $Q = .004$ for females. What would you conclude about the influence of gender on the relationship between major in college and attitude toward the death penalty? Explain.

27. Mary Ann Burg and her colleagues (1990) examined the variables associated with whether women aged 50 to 75 had obtained a mammogram in the past year. They surveyed over 3000 women on Long Island, New York, and found that women with higher family incomes were more likely than women with lower family incomes to have obtained a mammogram. You sample 1000 women of comparable age in your home state and report the data in the accompanying table.

EXERCISE 27

Income and whether women aged 50 to 75 had a mammogram in past year

Had Mammogram	Income Level		
in Past Year	High	Low	Total
yes	228	148	376
no	262	362	624
Total	490	510	1000

a. What percentage of the total number of women aged 50 to 75 obtained a mammogram in the past year?

b. Compute Yule's Q and interpret your answer.

c. You decide that age might be influencing the relationship between income level and having had a mammogram. You partition your data into five age groups: 50–54, 55–59, 60–64, 65–69, and 70–75. For women age 55–59, $Q = .244$, and for women age 60–64, $Q = .486$. Would you conclude that age is influencing the bivariate relationship? Explain.

28. Refer to Exercise 27c. Suppose that for each age group, $Q = 0$. What would this indicate about the influence of age on the bivariate relationship?

29. Refer to Exercise 27c. What variables other than age might influence the relationship between income level and having had a mammogram?

30. Refer to Example 11.1. Suppose that, when the social researcher partitions the data into males and females and recalculates Yule's Q for each group, $Q = .731$ for males and $Q = .352$ for females. What would you conclude about the influence of gender on the relationship between religiosity and sexual activity among teens? Explain.

31. Refer to Exercise 3. When you control for students' grade level in school, $Q = .005$ for elementary students, $Q = .002$ for junior high students, and $Q = .004$ for high school students. What would you conclude about the influence of grade level on the relationship between religion and sexual activity? Explain.

32. Refer to Example 11.2. When the health researcher controls for the influence of stress level, she finds that $Q = .760$ for those who experienced high stress and $Q = .764$ for those who experienced low stress. What should the health researcher conclude about the influence of stress level on the relationship between coffee consumption and physician visits? Explain.

33. Refer to Exercise 31 in Chapter 9. Suppose we introduce a control variable, socioeconomic status of parents (families with incomes of $35,000 or more and with incomes below $35,000). The partial tables for the data are given in the accompanying table. Run separate chi-square tests of independence to determine whether the variable "student opinion" is independent of status (fraternity, sorority, unaffiliated), while controlling for socioeconomic status. Interpret your results. (Use $\alpha = .05$.)

	Status of Affiliation		
Student Opinion	**Fraternity**	**Sorority**	**Unaffiliated**
in favor	26	21	11
opposed	8	15	39
Total	34	36	50

	Status of Affiliation		
Student Opinion	**Fraternity**	**Sorority**	**Unaffiliated**
in favor	14	14	16
opposed	10	10	16
Total	24	24	32

34. Use the results of Exercise 33 to conduct a pooled chi-square test of independence while controlling for the socioeconomic status of a student's family. What is the difference between the research hypothesis for this exercise and that for Exercise 31 in Chapter 9?

35. You have performed a combined test of independence between two nominal variables that have three categories each, while controlling for a third variable with four categories. Can you determine the strength of the bivariate association while controlling for the third variable? Explain.

36. Refer to Example 11.7.
   a. Use the partial tables to calculate a pooled chi-square for the independence of the variables "division of household labor" and "presence of preschool children" while controlling for the wife's employment status.
   b. Rearrange the data in Table 11.7 to ignore the wife's employment status, and calculate the overall chi-square test.
   c. Compare the results of parts a and b.

37. Danziger and Radin (1990) studied white teen mothers and black teen mothers. They reported that black teen mothers were more likely to live with their mothers and less likely to live with both parents, compared to white teen mothers. You replicate their study in your home state, sampling 260 white teen mothers and 170 black teen mothers. You are particularly interested in whether the relationship between age at first birth and living arrangement varies by the race of teen mothers. You report your results in the accompanying table.

EXERCISE 37

Age at first birth and living arrangements of (a) white teen mothers and (b) black teen mothers

(a) White Teen Mothers

Living Arrangement	Age at First Birth		Total
	13–15	**16–18**	
alone	33	104	137
mother only	32	20	52
both parents	45	26	71
Total	110	150	260

(b) Black Teen Mothers

Living Arrangement	Age at First Birth		Total
	13–15	**16–18**	
alone	30	51	81
mother only	29	34	63
both parents	11	15	26
Total	70	100	170

    a. State the independent and dependent variables for each partial table.

    b. Calculate a pooled chi-square test of independence. Interpret your answer.

38. Refer to the data in Exercise 37.

    a. Is it more appropriate to calculate λ_r or λ_c for each partial table? Explain.

    b. Calculate the appropriate lambda for each partial table.

    c. Combine the partial tables so that the third variable is ignored, and calculate lambda.

    d. Is the relationship between age at first birth and living arrangement influenced by the third variable, race? Explain.

39. A political sociologist examines people's attitudes toward mothers who receive welfare. The researcher hypothesizes that these attitudes are related to the political party with which people identify. She samples 600 adults and asks them whether mothers with one or more children under the age of 3 should be required to work if they receive welfare benefits. Use the accompanying table to calculate lambda. Do attitudes toward mothers who receive welfare seem to be related to political party identification for this sample of adults?

EXERCISE 39

Political party identification and attitudes toward requiring mothers with children under age 3 to work in exchange for welfare benefits

Require mothers	Party Identification			
to work	Independent	Democrat	Republican	Total
yes	60	150	75	285
no	40	150	125	315
Total	100	300	200	600

40. Refer to Exercise 39. The political sociologist then partitions the data by race and creates partial tables for blacks and whites. If λ_r for whites is 0 and λ_r for blacks is also 0, what would you conclude about the influence of race on the bivariate relationship? Explain.

41. Walsh (1990) studied the sentencing patterns by judges of felony assault cases in an Ohio metropolitan area. He found that cases were more likely to be placed on probation if a probation officer recommended probation (81.5%) than if a psychiatrist recommended probation (58.8%). You repeat the study in your home state and report data as shown in the accompanying table.

EXERCISE 41

Who recommends probation and sentence for felony assault cases

Actual Sentence	Probation Officer Recommends Probation	Psychiatrist Recommends Probation	Both Recommend Probation	Total
probation	75	103	44	222
prison	15	67	16	98
Total	90	170	60	320

a. Calculate λ_r.

b. You partition your sample into two groups: cases that are a first offense and cases that are not a first offense. You calculate λ_r for each partial table. For cases that are a first offense, λ_r is about the same magnitude as your answer in a. For cases that are not a first offense, $\lambda_r = 0$. What would you conclude about the influence of whether or not the case is a first offense on the relationship between who recommends probation and the judge's sentence? Explain.

42. Wong (1990) examined the popular belief that Asian high school seniors have unusual educational aspirations. He compared whites with various groups of Asian students in the United States. He reported that white students were less likely than Asian students to spend 5 or more hours per week doing homework and that white students were less likely than Asian students to plan to attend a

four-year college. You replicate his research procedures and obtain a sample of 1000 high school seniors across the United States. Your findings are in the accompanying table.

Plan to Attend 4-Year College	Race				Total
	White	Chinese	Filipino	Japanese	
yes	157	141	64	40	402
no	343	109	86	60	598
Total	500	250	150	100	1000

a. Calculate λ_r and interpret your answer.

b. You partition the data into those who spend 5 or more hours per week doing homework and those who do not. You find that $\lambda_r = 0$ for each group. What would you conclude about the influence of time spent doing homework on the relationship between race and college plans? Explain.

43. Refer to the data in Exercise 42. Combine Asian students into one category and create a 2×2 table.

    a. Calculate Yule's Q and interpret your answer.

    b. You partition the data as in Exercise 42b and find that $Q = -.012$ for those who spend 5 or more hours per week doing homework and $Q = -.589$ for those who spend less than 5 hours per week doing homework. Does time spent doing homework influence the relationship between race and college plans? Explain.

44. Refer to Exercise 43a. You partition the data into two groups — students who live with both parents and students who live with only one parent — and calculate Yule's Q for each group. What values of Q would you obtain if living arrangement does not influence the relationship between race and college plans? Explain.

45. We know that for partial tables of ordinal variables, we can compute partial gamma as a measure of association that controls for a third variable. Is this the most appropriate way to determine whether a third variable influences a bivariate relationship between ordinal variables? Explain.

46. Two criminologists at a large Southern university surveyed 500 students on whether each of 25 different behaviors should be regarded as crimes. Students' positive responses ranged in numbers from 8 to 25. The criminologists grouped the number of crimes into three categories: 8 to 13, 14 to 19, and 20 to 25. They also classified the income level of parents as low, medium, or high.

    a. What measure of association is most appropriate to determine the strength of the relationship between number of crimes and parental income? Explain.

    b. How would you determine whether the third variable "year in college" influences the relationship between number of crimes and parental income?

47. The accompanying tables come from a study of career officers.

EXERCISE 47

Perceived degree of
career satisfaction and
self-esteem for
(a) whites, (b) blacks,
and (c) other races

(a) Whites

| Self-Esteem | Perceived Degree of Career Satisfaction | | | |
	High	Medium	Low	Total
high	205	100	15	320
medium	169	152	39	360
low	26	73	21	120
Total	400	325	75	800

(b) Blacks

| Self-Esteem | Perceived Degree of Career Satisfaction | | | |
	High	Medium	Low	Total
high	80	125	27	232
medium	70	116	75	261
low	15	60	12	87
Total	165	301	114	580

(c) Other

| Self-Esteem | Perceived Degree of Career Satisfaction | | | |
	High	Medium	Low	Total
high	92	56	7	155
medium	104	106	26	236
low	15	44	10	69
Total	211	206	43	460

a. Compute gamma for each partial table.

b. Combine the results in part a to form partial gamma. Interpret your answer.

c. Ignore the third variable, race, and calculate gamma for the entire sample of career officers combined. Interpret your answer.

48. Refer to Exercise 47. Based on your answers in parts a and c, does race influence the relationship between self-esteem and degree of perceived career satisfaction? Explain.

49. Refer to Exercise 47. Compare the results of parts b and c.

CHAPTER 12

BIVARIATE REGRESSION AND CORRELATION

GENERAL OBJECTIVES

This chapter introduces an interval or ratio measure of association, Pearson's *r*, and explores the basic concept of regression. It also extends your knowledge of measures of association to interval and ratio data. The problems that it considers are parallel to those in Chapter 10. This chapter also lays the foundation for many procedures involved in more advanced courses in statistics.

SPECIFIC OBJECTIVES

1. To look at measures of association appropriate for interval and ratio data.
2. To illustrate the use of the scatter diagram as a technique for presenting interval or ratio bivariate data.
3. To explain several of the key concepts in regression and correlation analysis: linear relationship, regression equation, method of least squares, and coefficient of determination.
4. To show you how to compute and interpret the Pearson product-moment correlation coefficient *r*.
5. To present and interpret a test of significance for *r*.
6. To look at some important assumptions underlying the use of bivariate regression and correlation as inferential statistics.

12.1   INTRODUCTION

In this chapter we extend our study of the relationship between two variables measured on nominal or ordinal scales to that between variables on interval or ratio scales. The chi-square test discussed in Chapter 9 was used to determine dependency and, by implication, the strength of the relationship between the two variables. Measures of the strength of a relationship based on various PRE statistics, such as lambda, gamma, and rho, were presented in Chapter 10. Our objective was to establish whether two variables, measured on an appropriate scale — nominal or ordinal — were related and to measure the strength of the relationship. In social research our ultimate goal in many cases is to predict one variable based on information about another. This chapter considers exactly the same problems with the same objectives and goals as in Chapters 9 and 10, except that we now assume that the data for both variables have been measured on an interval or ratio scale.

For example, suppose that we wish to determine whether the crude birth rate (X) for a nation is related to that nation's infant mortality rate (Y), for a sample of nations. If we collect data on X and Y for a sample of nations, we will want to know whether the data provide sufficient evidence to indicate a relationship. We also want to know how strong the relationship is and to be able to predict infant mortality rates. If we think the crude birth rate in a nation is increasing, we might wish to predict an increase in the infant mortality rate.

Social researchers routinely measure the relationship between two variables, such as per capita income and support for public education, IQ and academic grades, and level of knowledge and health care practices.

This chapter focuses our attention on a study of a straight-line (linear) relationship between two variables. We will begin our discussion of measures of relationships by looking at an example involving bivariate data, the scatter diagram, and the freehand regression line.

12.2   THE SCATTER DIAGRAM

Suppose we have bivariate data that have been measured on a ratio scale. Furthermore, suppose we are interested in examining the relationship between level of technology and average life expectancy of babies born in 1990 for a sample of nations. We draw a sample of 10 nations from Appendix Table 8 and determine the values for the two variables. We will introduce the idea of the scatter diagram by examining the values of these two variables for the 10 sampled nations.

TABLE 12.1

Level of technology
and life expectancy in
10 nations

Nation	Level of Technology Development (0–100)	Life Expectancy (in years)
Algeria	17	60
Bolivia	10	53
Chile	22	71
Colombia	15	66
Egypt	13	60
Ireland	48	74
Japan	53	79
Malawi	12	49
Peru	12	65
Romania	33	71

Source: Population Reference Bureau, 1990
World Population Data Sheet (Washington,
D.C.: Population Reference Bureau, Inc.,
1990).

We can calculate the means for each of the two variables for the data in
Table 12.1. The mean level of technology is 23.5, and the mean life expectancy
for infants born in 1990 is 64.8. These averages tell us nothing about the
relationship between the two variables. To help us understand the relationship, we will plot the data contained in Table 12.1 in a **scatter diagram** (see
Figure 12.1). In developing a scatter diagram we label one of the variables as

FIGURE 12.1

Scatter diagram of lev-
el of technology and
life expectancy (circled
dot represents datum
for Ireland)

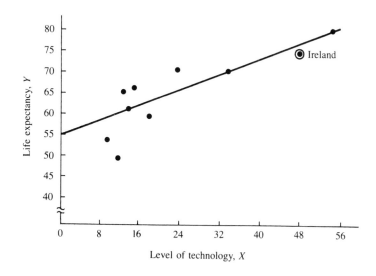

independent and the other as dependent. As with cross-classification, the independent variable (X) is labeled across the horizontal axis and the dependent variable (Y) along the vertical axis.

Having labeled the axes, we then draw scales along the axes in such a way that all scores can be easily plotted along the appropriate axis. For our example, the level of technology ranges from 10 to 53 and life expectancy from 49 to 79. Note that the values for each of the variables fall within the scales chosen in Figure 12.1.

Having drawn, labeled, and scaled the axes of the scatter diagram, we plot the data from Table 12.1. Each dot on the scatter diagram represents our information concerning one nation and can be obtained by plotting the level of technology X versus the corresponding life expectancy Y. For example, the dot circled in Figure 12.1 corresponds to Ireland ($X = 48$, $Y = 74$). It is clear from Figure 12.1 that life expectancy increases as the level of technology of a nation increases. In fact, many dots of the scatter diagram seem to lie on a straight line. We call a line running through the data of a scatter diagram a *line of best fit*.

When the line of best fit is a straight line, we say that there is a **linear relationship** between X and Y (see Figures 12.2a and 12.2b). However, not all bivariate relationships are linear. In some cases the line of best fit is curved;

FIGURE 12.2

Different types of lines of best fit for a bivariate relationship

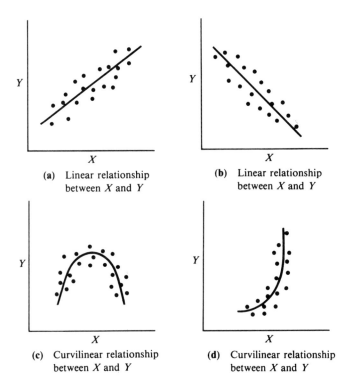

(a) Linear relationship between X and Y

(b) Linear relationship between X and Y

(c) Curvilinear relationship between X and Y

(d) Curvilinear relationship between X and Y

then we say that there is a *curvilinear* relationship between X and Y (see Figures 12.2c and 12.2d).

There are various ways to obtain a regression line relating Y to X. The first is called an *eyeball fit*, or **freehand regression line**, which can be obtained by placing a ruler on the graph (Figure 12.1) and moving it about until it seems to pass through or close to as many of the dots as possible (see Figure 12.3). The resulting line can be used to predict life expectancy based on a nation's level of technology. To predict Y when $X = 20$, refer to the graph and note that the coordinate for the point corresponding to $X = 20$ is $Y = 63$ (see the arrows in Figure 12.3). We can predict Y from X by using our regression line.

FIGURE 12.3

Freehand regression line for the data of Table 12.1

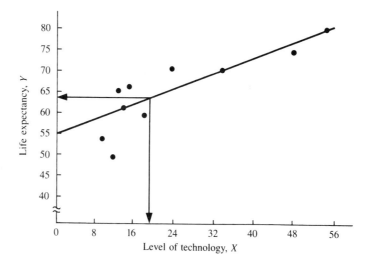

The **freehand regression line in Figure 12.3 can be represented by an equation of the form**

$$Y = a + bX$$

The two constants a and b in the equation determine the location and slope of the line. **The constant a is the Y intercept — that is, the value of Y at the point where the line crosses the Y axis ($X = 0$); b is the slope of the regression line — that is, the unit of change in Y that corresponds to 1 unit change in X** (see Figure 12.4).

Looking at Figure 12.4 it appears that the Y intercept is approximately 55, so $a = 55$. Thus, when a nation's level of technology equals 0, life expectancy is 55. The change in Y for a 8-unit increase in X appears to be 4. The slope is approximately $4/8 = .50$, which suggests that if the level of technology increases by 1, life expectancy will increase by .5 year, on average. The equation corresponding to the freehand regression line of Figure 12.3 is $Y = 55 + .50X$. To predict Y when $X = 20$, we substitute $X = 20$ into the equation to obtain $Y = 55 + .50(20) = 65.0$. We see that we can predict Y

FIGURE 12.4

Slope *b* and intercept
a for the equation *Y* =
a + *bX*

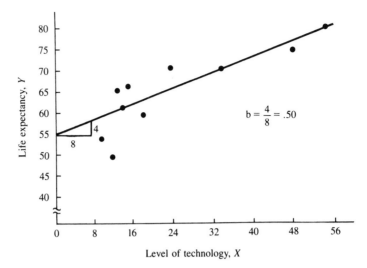

using either the graph in Figure 12.3 or the equivalent prediction equation, *Y* = 55 + .50*X*. The difference between our prediction *Y* = 63 using the graph and *Y* = 65.0 using the equation is due to our guessed values for the intercept *a* and slope *b* of the equation *Y* = *a* + *bX*.

Although the freehand regression line provides us with a prediction equation, it is a subjective procedure, since there could be many different prediction equations from different eyeball fits to the same data. What we seek is a precise procedure for determining the constants *a* and *b* in our prediction equation *Y* = *a* + *bX*. The procedure that we use for determining *a* and *b* is called the *method of least squares*; anyone using this procedure will obtain the same values for *a* and *b* and hence obtain the same prediction equation. We will discuss this method in the next section.

EXERCISES

1. What is meant by line of best fit?
2. What is meant by a scatter diagram?
3. Does a freehand regression line have any utility? Explain.
4. Plot the data shown here in a scatter diagram.

X	5	10	12	15	18	24
Y	10	19	21	28	34	40

5. Refer to Exercise 4.
   a. Use an eyeball fit to construct a freehand regression line.
   b. Identify the intercept and slope for your regression line.
   c. Predict *Y* when *X* = 20.

6. Plot a scatter diagram and draw a freehand regression line for the data in the accompanying table.

EXERCISE 6

Life expectancy and per capita gross national product for 6 nations

Nation	Life Expectancy	Per Capita Gross National Product
Malawi	49	160
Bolivia	53	520
Egypt	60	650
Peru	65	1440
Chile	71	1510
Yugoslavia	71	2680

Source: Source: Population Reference Bureau, *1990 World Population Data Sheet* (Washington, D.C.: Population Reference Bureau, Inc., 1990).

7. What is meant by the Y intercept of a regression line?
8. Can you construct a scatter diagram for ordinal data? Explain.
9. Use the data for average teacher's income and public education expenditure per student by state, shown in the accompanying table, to plot a scatter diagram and draw a freehand regression line.

EXERCISE 9

Average teacher's income and public education expenditure per student

State	Average Teacher's Income X	Public Education Expenditure per Student Y
Arkansas	$25,200	$2,698
Connecticut	$37,300	$7,199
Kansas	$27,400	$4,404
Maryland	$33,700	$5,391
Michigan	$34,400	$4,576
Mississippi	$22,000	$2,846
Nebraska	$24,200	$3,732
New Jersey	$32,900	$7,571
Washington	$29,200	$4,744
Wisconsin	$31,000	$5,117

Source: U.S. Bureau of the Census, *Statistical Abstract of the United States.*

10. Refer to Exercise 9 to identify the slope and intercept for your regression line. Write the equation corresponding to your regression line and use it to predict the public education expenditure per student for a state with the following average teacher's income: **a.** $18,500   **b.** $41,500.

11. The GPAs for high school and for college are shown for 11 different students in the accompanying table. Use these data to construct a scatter diagram. Draw a freehand regression line for the data and use it to predict the college GPA for a student with a high school GPA of 2.5 (on a 4.0 system).

EXERCISE 11

High school and college GPAs for 11 students

Student	High School GPA	College GPA
1	2.00	1.60
2	2.25	2.00
3	2.60	1.80
4	2.65	2.80
5	2.80	2.10
6	3.10	2.00
7	2.90	2.65
8	3.25	2.25
9	3.30	2.60
10	3.60	3.00
11	3.25	3.10

12. Refer to Exercise 11.
    a. Write the equation for your regression line and use it to predict a student's college GPA base on a high school GPA of 2.50.
    b. Compare your prediction to the one in Exercise 11.

12.3   METHOD OF LEAST SQUARES

The statistical procedure for finding the best prediction equation is, in many respects, an objective way to obtain an eyeball fit to the points. For example, when we eyeball a line to a set of points, we move the ruler until we think that we have minimized the distances from the points to the fitted line. For a given value of X the fitted line provides a predicted value of Y, which we denote by $\hat{Y}$. The prediction equation is

$$\hat{Y} = a + bX$$

The vertical distance from an observed point to the prediction line represents the deviation of a point from the predicted value of Y (see Figure 12.5). The deviation of a point from the predicted value of Y reflects how much error there is between the actual value of Y and the predicted value ($\hat{Y}$) that we would obtain from using X to predict Y. Symbolically, this deviation is $Y - \hat{Y}$. To find the best prediction equation (regression line), we work with deviations from the prediction line. The **method of least squares** chooses the prediction line that minimizes the sum of the squares of the deviations of the observed values from the predicted values of Y. In other words, the best prediction equation is the regression line that minimizes the amount of difference that there is between the actual values and the predicted values of Y.

FIGURE 12.5

Least-squares fit to the data in Table 12.1.

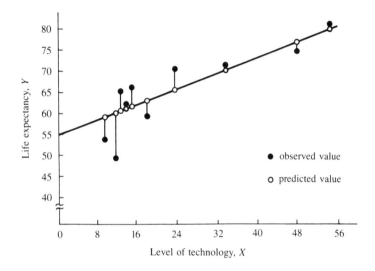

The sum of the squares of deviations, which is also referred to as the **sum of squares for error** and denoted by SSE, can be written as

$$SSE = \Sigma (Y - \hat{Y})^2$$

where

$$\hat{Y} = a + bX$$

Substituting for $\hat{Y}$, we have

$$SSE = \Sigma [Y - (a + bX)]^2$$

Thus the method of least squares chooses values for a and b that minimize the SSE. Stated differently, the method of least squares chooses the regression line that describes a bivariate relationship with the least amount of error.

Derivation of the formulas for obtaining these values is beyond the scope of this text; they are presented as follows.

LEAST-SQUARES FORMULA FOR COMPUTING a AND b

$$b = \frac{S_{xy}}{S_{xx}} \quad \text{and} \quad a = \bar{Y} - b\bar{X}$$

where

$$S_{xy} = \Sigma XY - \frac{(\Sigma X)(\Sigma Y)}{n} \quad \text{and} \quad S_{xx} = \Sigma X^2 - \frac{(\Sigma X)^2}{n}$$

The use of these formulas for finding a and b and the least-squares line will be illustrated by an example.

EXAMPLE 12.1

Obtain the best-fitting prediction line for the data in Table 12.1 by using the method of least squares. Predict Y when $X = 30$.

SOLUTION

The calculation of a and b with the method of least squares is greatly simplified by using Table 12.2:

$$S_{xx} = \Sigma X^2 - \frac{(\Sigma X)^2}{n} = 7757 - \frac{(235)^2}{10} = 2234.5$$

$$S_{xy} = \Sigma XY - \frac{(\Sigma X)(\Sigma Y)}{n} = 16{,}332 - \frac{(235)(648)}{10} = 1104$$

$$\bar{Y} = \frac{\Sigma Y}{n} = \frac{648}{10} = 64.8$$

$$\bar{X} = \frac{\Sigma X}{n} = \frac{235}{10} = 23.5$$

Hence we have

$$b = \frac{S_{xy}}{S_{xx}} = \frac{1104}{2234.5} = .494$$

$$a = \bar{Y} - b\bar{X} = 64.8 - .494(23.5) = 53.19$$

This value for a suggests that when a nation's level of technology is 0, life expectancy is 53.19. Similarly, life expectancy increases by 1 year, on average,

	X	Y	X²	XY	Y²
TABLE 12.2	17	60	289	1,020	3,600
Calculations based on	10	53	100	530	2,809
the data of Table 12.1	22	71	484	1,562	5,041
for applying the meth-	15	66	225	990	4,356
od of least squares	13	60	169	780	3,600
	48	74	2,304	3,552	5,476
	53	79	2,809	4,187	6,241
	12	49	144	588	2,401
	12	65	144	780	4,225
	33	71	1,089	2,343	5,041
Totals	235	648	7,757	16,332	42,790

when the nation's level of technology increases by .494. The least-squares prediction equation relating life expectancy Y to a nation's level of technology X is then

$$\hat{Y} = 53.19 + .494X$$

This equation is the best prediction equation of Y, since 53.19 and .494 are the values of a and b that reflect the least amount of error in using X to predict Y. Thus, if a nation has a level of technology of 30, we predict life expectancy to be

$$\hat{Y} = 53.19 + .494(30) = 68.01$$

Likewise, if a nation has a level of technology of 16, we predict life expectancy to be

$$\hat{Y} = 53.19 + .494(16) = 61.09$$

EXERCISES

13. Use the accompanying data to determine the least-squares prediction equation.

X	1	2	3	4	5
Y	2	4	6	7	9

14. Use the accompanying data.
   a. Determine the least-squares prediction equation.
   b. Use the prediction equation to predict Y when $X = 6$.

X	1	3	5	7	9
Y	1	4	8	9	12

15. Data on annual income and annual savings are displayed in the accompanying table for a sample of nine families. Graph the data and draw a freehand regression line.

EXERCISE 15

Annual savings and annual income for 9 families

Family	Y **Annual Savings** (× $1000)	X **Annual Income** (× $1000)
1	1	36
2	2	39
3	2	42
4	5	45
5	5	48
6	6	51
7	7	54
8	8	56
9	7	59

16. Refer to Exercise 15. Compute the least-squares prediction equation.

17. Use the data in Exercise 6 to compute a and b.

18. Use the data in Exercise 17 to compute all the predicted $\hat{Y}$-values based on $a + bX$. Plot the actual regression line.

19. Find the least-squares estimates a and b for the regression $Y = a + bX$ for the data of Exercise 11.

20. Plot the regression line for the data in the previous exercise. Compare the observed values of Y with the predicted values (points on the regression line).

21. Refer to the accompanying computer output for the data of Exercise 9.
   a. Identify the least-squares prediction equation.
   b. Predict the public education expenditure per student for a state with an average teacher's income of $25,000, and then for $18,000. Is there any problem with the latter prediction? If so, what?

EXERCISE 21   `MTB > plot 'STUDENT' 'TEACHER'`

```
        -                                                 *
STUDENT -
        -                                                      *
        -
  6400+
        -
        -
        -                                          *
        -                                  *
  4800+                            *
        -                  *                              *
        -
        -        *
        -
  3200+
        -   *
        -            *
         +---------+---------+---------+---------+---------+------TEACHER
        21000     24000     27000     30000     33000     36000
```

```
MTB > regress 'STUDENT' 1 'TEACHER';
SUBC> predict 25000;
SUBC> predict 18000.
```

The regression equation is
STUDENT = - 3185 + 0.270 TEACHER

Predictor	Coef	Stdev	t-ratio	p
Constant	-3185	1919	-1.66	0.136
TEACHER	0.26953	0.06376	4.23	0.003

s = 952.3   R-sq = 69.1%   R-sq(adj) = 65.2%

Analysis of Variance

SOURCE	DF	SS	MS	F	p
Regression	1	16207353	16207353	17.87	0.003
Error	8	7255602	906950		
Total	9	23462956			

Unusual Observations

Obs.	TEACHER	STUDENT	Fit	Stdev.Fit	Residual	St.Resid
8	32900	7571	5682	363	1889	2.14R

R denotes an obs. with a large st. resid.

Fit	Stdev.Fit	95% C.I.		95% P.I.	
3553	426	(2570,	4536)	(1146,	5960)
1666	806	(-193,	3526)	(-1212,	4544) X

X   denotes a row with X values away from the center

12.4   THE COEFFICIENT OF DETERMINATION r^2

In the previous section we showed how to obtain the least-squares regression line

$$\hat{Y} = a + bX$$

for two variables X and Y. The values for a and b in the regression line were chosen to minimize

$$SSE = \Sigma(Y - \hat{Y})^2$$

Now we want to examine the strength of the linear relationship between X and Y. In other words, we want to examine the usefulness of the regression line $\hat{Y} = a + bX$ for predicting Y from X.

Suppose, for the moment, that X and Y are not linearly related and that X contributes no information for predicting Y. Then we would drop the term bX out of the prediction equation and predict Y to equal the sample mean.

$$\hat{Y} = \bar{Y}$$

This prediction line is shown in Figure 12.6b, along with the vertical lines representing the errors of prediction. Compare the magnitude of the deviations of the data points from the line $\hat{Y} = a + bX$ for Figure 12.6a with those about the line $\hat{Y} = \bar{Y}$ of Figure 12.6b. This subjective comparison can be expressed in a more objective way by comparing the sums of squares for error for the two prediction equations.

FIGURE 12.6

Two models fit to the same data

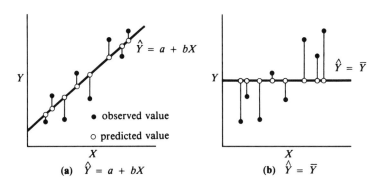

(a) $\hat{Y} = a + bX$ (b) $\hat{Y} = \bar{Y}$

observed value

predicted value

The sum of squares of deviations about the prediction equation $\hat{Y} = \bar{Y}$ is often called the *total variation* and is expressed by

$$\Sigma(Y - \hat{Y})^2 = \Sigma(Y - \bar{Y})^2 = S_{yy}$$

The reduction in the sum of squares for error obtained by using the information on the independent variable X is then

$$S_{yy} - SSE$$

This quantity is called the **explained variation**—that is, the amount of the total variation in the Y values that is explained by the X values. The **unexplained variation** is SSE, the variation in the Y values that cannot be explained by the X values. Thus the total variation equals the explained plus the unexplained variation:

$$S_{yy} = (S_{yy} - \text{SSE}) + \text{SSE}$$

The ratio of the explained variation to the total variation is called the **coefficient of determination r^2**:

$$r^2 = \frac{\text{explained variation}}{\text{total variation}} = \frac{S_{yy} - \text{SSE}}{S_{yy}}$$

We can think of r^2 as being analogous to the PRE statistics discussed in Chapters 10 and 11. The difference here is that we compare the sum of the squared errors for the two prediction rules, whereas in Chapters 10 and 11 we compared the number of errors for two prediction rules. The no-association rule for r^2 is

$$\hat{Y} = \bar{Y} \qquad \text{and} \qquad E_1 = \Sigma(Y - \bar{Y})^2 = S_{yy}$$

(i.e., X contributes no information for the prediction of Y). The corresponding perfect-association rule is

$$\hat{Y} = a + bX \qquad \text{and} \qquad E_2 = \Sigma(Y - \hat{Y})^2 = \text{SSE}$$

Substituting into the formula for r^2, one can obtain the following computational formula for r^2:

COEFFICIENT OF DETERMINATION

$$r^2 = \frac{E_1 - E_2}{E_1} = \frac{S_{xy}^2}{S_{xx}S_{yy}}$$

where

$$S_{xy} = \Sigma XY - \frac{(\Sigma X)(\Sigma Y)}{n}$$

$$S_{xx} = \Sigma X^2 - \frac{(\Sigma X)^2}{n} \qquad \text{and} \qquad S_{yy} = \Sigma Y^2 - \frac{(\Sigma Y)^2}{n}$$

EXAMPLE 12.2   Use the data of Table 12.1 and the computational formula to compute r^2.

SOLUTION   Recall that in Example 12.1 we calculated S_{xy} and S_{xx} to be

$$S_{xy} = 1104 \qquad \text{and} \qquad S_{xx} = 2234.5$$

Substituting the values in Table 12.2 into the formula for S_{xx}, we have

$$S_{yy} = \Sigma Y^2 - \frac{(\Sigma Y)^2}{n} = 42,790 - \frac{(684)^2}{10} = 799.6$$

Substituting these values into the formula for r^2, we have

$$r^2 = \frac{S_{xy}^2}{S_{xx}S_{yy}} = \frac{(1104)^2}{(2234.5)(799.6)} = .682$$

By incorporating the information on level of technology X into our prediction model, we achieve a 68% reduction in the sum of squares for error. That is, 68% of the variability in the Y values (life expectancy) can be explained by the X values (level of technology). Stated differently, the regression line, $\hat{Y} = 53.19 + .494X$, predicts life expectancy with 68% less prediction error than using the overall mean of life expectancy, 64.8, to predict the mean life expectancy of infants born in 1990.

As we have seen, the coefficient of determination is a PRE statistic that identifies the proportional drop in the sum of squares for error obtained by using the model $\hat{Y} = a + bX$ rather than the model $\hat{Y} = \bar{Y}$. If the independent variable X contributes no information toward the prediction of Y, the coefficient of determination $r^2 = 0$. Similarly, if the incorporation of X into our model allows us to predict Y perfectly (with no error), then $r^2 = 1$.

We turn in the next section to a measure of the strength of the linear relationship between two interval or ratio variables.

EXERCISES

22. What is the value of r^2 for the following data? Interpret your result.

X	Y	X	Y
14.3	2.3	16.8	3.0
16.0	2.8	14.8	3.1
17.1	4.1	18.8	5.2
19.7	3.4	18.0	3.4
13.2	2.2	16.4	3.8

23. State the perfect-association rule for r^2.

24. Is r^2 meaningful if one of the variables is measured on an ordinal scale and the other on a ratio scale?

25. Compute the coefficient of determination for the data of Exercise 6. Interpret your result.

26. Refer to Exercise 11 and compute r^2. Interpret your result.

27. Refer to Exercise 13 and compute r^2. Interpret your result.

28. Refer to Exercise 14 and compute r^2. Interpret your result.

12.5 THE PEARSON PRODUCT-MOMENT CORRELATION COEFFICIENT r

There are numerous studies of the relationship(s) between two or more variables measured on an interval or ratio scale. Social researchers have studied relationships among almost all the social, psychological, economic, political, and geographical variables imaginable. They have reported correlation coefficients ranging from the high 90s to zero. What do these measures mean, and how are they calculated? In Chapter 10 we discussed Spearman's rank-order correlation coefficient, which was appropriate for ordinal data. In this section we present the **Pearson product-moment correlation coefficient** r, which measures the strength of the linear relationship between two variables measured on an interval or ratio scale. The formula for r is shown next. Note that r is the square root of the coefficient of determination r^2.

PEARSON PRODUCT-MOMENT CORRELATION COEFFICIENT r

$$r = \frac{S_{xy}}{\sqrt{S_{xx}S_{yy}}}$$

where

$$S_{xy} = \Sigma XY - \frac{(\Sigma X)(\Sigma Y)}{n}$$

$$S_{xx} = \Sigma X^2 - \frac{(\Sigma X)^2}{n} \quad \text{and} \quad S_{yy} = \Sigma Y^2 - \frac{(\Sigma Y)^2}{n}$$

The Pearson product-moment correlation coefficient is a type B normed measure of association with a PRE interpretation. You will note a similarity between r and the slope b of the least-squares prediction equation $\hat{Y} = a + bX$. That is, we have

$$b = \frac{S_{xy}}{S_{xx}} \quad \text{and} \quad r = \frac{S_{xy}}{\sqrt{S_{xx}S_{yy}}}$$

and r can be rewritten as

$$r = b \sqrt{\frac{S_{xx}}{S_{yy}}}$$

For experimental situations where not all X-values and Y-values are the same, both S_{xx} and S_{yy} are positive. Then r and b have the same sign. Because of the relationship between r and b, the Pearson product-moment correlation coefficient measures the strength of the linear relationship between two interval or ratio variables X and Y. (See Figures 12.7 and 12.8.)

FIGURE 12.7

Implications of possible values for r, the Pearson product-moment correlation coefficient

-1.0 ———————— 0 ———————— 1.0

| Some negative correlation between X and Y | Some positive correlation between X and Y |

Perfect negative correlation between X and Y No correlation between X and Y Perfect positive correlation between X and Y

FIGURE 12.8

Interpretations of r

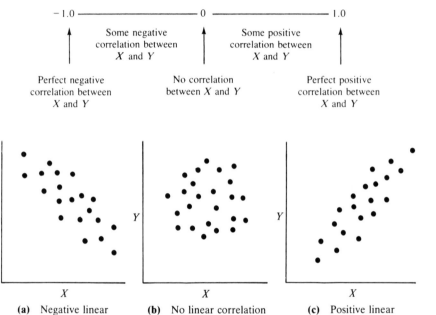

(a) Negative linear correlation   (b) No linear correlation   (c) Positive linear correlation

---

EXAMPLE 12.3   Compute the Pearson product-moment correlation coefficient for the data in Table 12.1.

SOLUTION   Recall that in Example 12.1, we computed S_{xx} and b to be

$$S_{xx} = 2234.5 \quad \text{and} \quad b = .494$$

From Example 12.2, we computed S_{yy} to be

$$S_{yy} = 799.6$$

Substituting these values into the formula for r, we have

$$r = .494 \sqrt{\frac{2234.5}{799.6}} = .494(1.672) = .826$$

Alternatively, we know that r is the square root of r^2. We computed r^2 in Example 12.2 to be $r^2 = .682$. Hence

$$r = \sqrt{.682} = .826$$

Although r is the square root of r^2, these two measures focus on two different but interrelated aspects of correlation. Before we can clarify this distinction, we need to show that r is the slope of the *standardized* least-squares prediction equation.

To explain this idea, we must note that the slope b of the least-squares line depends on the magnitude of the units of X and Y. Hence we cannot compare slopes of different regression lines unless the Xs and Ys are recorded in the same units (such as inches, feet, meters, or miles). To avoid this difficulty, we work in *standardized units,* or *z-scores*:

$$z_x = \frac{X - \bar{X}}{\sigma_x} \quad \text{and} \quad z_y = \frac{Y - \bar{Y}}{\sigma_y}$$

where

$$\sigma_x = \sqrt{\frac{S_{xx}}{n}} \quad \text{and} \quad \sigma_y = \sqrt{\frac{S_{yy}}{n}}$$

and

$$S_{xx} = \Sigma X^2 - \frac{(\Sigma X)^2}{n} \quad \text{and} \quad S_{yy} = \Sigma Y^2 - \frac{(\Sigma Y)^2}{n}$$

Rewriting our regression line $\hat{Y} = a + bX$ in terms of z-scores, we have

$$\hat{z}_y = a_s + b_s z_x$$

where a_s is the intercept and b_s the slope of the regression line computed from standardized measurements z_x and z_y. **Without proof, we simply state that the least-squares value of a_s will always equal zero.** Hence our regression line for standardized units is

$$\hat{z}_y = b_s z_x$$

where b_s is computed as it was previously, with X replaced by z_x and Y replaced by $\hat{z}_y$. Thus we have

$$b_s = \frac{S_{z_x z_y}}{S_{z_x z_x}}$$

This formula simplifies to

$$b_s = \frac{\Sigma\, z_x z_y}{n}$$

which is equal to r.

EXAMPLE 12.4   Use the data of Table 12.1 to find the least-squares prediction equation.

$$z_y = b_s z_x$$

Verify that the computed value of the slope b_x is identical to the value of r computed in Example 12.3.

SOLUTION   The first step in solving this problem is to transform the X and Y data to z-scores. Recall from Example 12.1 that we computed S_{xx}, $\bar{X}$, and $\bar{Y}$ to be

$$S_{xx} = 2234.5 \qquad \bar{X} = 23.5 \qquad \bar{Y} = 64.8$$

Similarly, we computed S_{yy} in Example 12.2 to be

$$S_{yy} = 799.6$$

The quantities σ_x and σ_y are then

$$\sigma_x = \sqrt{\frac{S_{xx}}{n}} = \sqrt{\frac{2234.5}{10}} = 14.95$$

$$\sigma_y = \sqrt{\frac{S_{yy}}{n}} = \sqrt{\frac{799.6}{10}} = 8.94$$

We can now compute z-scores for the X and Y data of Table 12.1 by using the formulas

$$z_x = \frac{X - \bar{X}}{\sigma_x} = \frac{X - 23.5}{14.95}$$

$$z_y = \frac{Y - \bar{Y}}{\sigma_y} = \frac{Y - 64.8}{8.94}$$

Substituting each value of X and Y into the appropriate z formula, we obtain the z-scores listed in Table 12.3. Using the data of Table 12.3, we can proceed to compute b_s, the slope of the standardized least-squares regression line. Recall that

$$b_s = \frac{\Sigma\, z_x z_y}{n}$$

Substituting, we have

$$b_s = \sum \frac{z_x z_y}{n} = \frac{8.26}{10} = .826$$

which is identical to the value of *r* computed in Example 12.3.

TABLE 12.3

Raw scores, z-scores, and cross-products for the data of Table 12.1

X	z_x	Y	z_y	$z_x z_y$
17	−.435	60	−.537	.233
10	−.903	53	−1.320	1.192
22	−.100	71	.694	−.070
15	−.569	66	.134	−.076
13	−.702	60	−.537	.377
48	1.639	74	1.029	1.686
53	1.973	79	1.588	3.134
12	−.769	49	−1.767	1.359
12	−.769	65	.022	−.017
33	.635	71	.694	.441
Totals 235	0	648	0	8.260

We return to our discussion of the important distinction between *r* and r^2. Although *r* and r^2 are interdependent, they focus on different aspects of correlation. On the one hand, r^2 measures the proportion of the total variation in *Y* that is predicted by *X*. That is, r^2 is a PRE statistic that reflects the reduction in prediction error. On the other hand, *r* measures the rate of change in *Y* relative to *X*, where both *X* and *Y* have been represented in standardized form. In other words, *r* is a standardized regression slope. Because of this difference, *r* is primarily useful as a predictive statistic, whereas r^2 measures the relative accuracy of the prediction (i.e., the reduction in error from using *X* rather than $\overline{Y}$ to predict *Y*).

EXERCISES

29. Compute *r* for the accompanying data.

X	1	2	3	4	6	9	10
Y	2	4	5	7	8	12	13

30. Refer to Exercise 29. Suppose the first three Y-values are 16, 12, and 10 instead of 2, 4, and 5, respectively.
    a. Plot the data.
    b. Compute r.
    c. Why do the values of r differ for these two exercises?

31. Use the data in the accompanying table.
    a. Compute σ_x.
    b. Compute σ_y.
    c. Convert each X to z_x.
    d. Convert each Y to z_y.
    e. Compute b_s. Interpret your result.

EXERCISE 31

Average personal income and average state and local taxes, by state

State	Average Personal Income per Capita (per $1000)	Average State and Local Taxes per Capita (per $1000)
Arkansas	$12.219	$1.037
California	$18.753	$1.926
Connecticut	$23.059	$2.216
Illinois	$17.525	$1.650
Louisiana	$12.292	$1.227
Mississippi	$11.116	$ .990
New Jersey	$21.994	$2.099
North Dakota	$12.833	$1.276
Oklahoma	$13.323	$1.218
Oregon	$14.885	$1.926

Source: U.S. Bureau of the Census, *Statistical Abstract of the United States.*

12.6 A TEST OF SIGNIFICANCE FOR r

In the material presented thus far in this chapter, we have used r (and r^2) in a strictly descriptive sense, under the assumption that we were *not* sampling from a larger body of data. In situations where our data represent a random sample from a larger body of data (the population), the Pearson product-moment correlation $\hat{r}$ will be a sample correlation coefficient — that is, an estimate of the unknown population correlation coefficient r. We may be interested in a test of the null hypothesis $H_0: r = 0$ (i.e., there is no linear correlation between X and Y). This test is summarized as follows.

TEST OF A HYPOTHESIS CONCERNING *r*, THE POPULATION
CORRELATION COEFFICIENT

Research hypothesis for a one-tailed test

    1. $H_1: r > 0$ (positive relationship)

    2. $H_1: r < 0$ (negative ")

Research hypothesis for a two-tailed test

    3. $H_1: r \neq 0$

Null hypothesis $H_0: r = 0$ (no relationship)

Test statistic $t = \hat{r}\sqrt{\dfrac{n-2}{1-\hat{r}^2}}$

Rejection region for a one-tailed test with α specified

    1. R.R.: Reject H_0 if $z > z_\alpha$.

    2. R.R.: Reject H_0 if $z < -z_\alpha$.

Rejection region for a two-tailed test with α specified

    3. R.R.: Reject H_0 if $z > z_{\alpha/2}$ or $z < -z_{\alpha/2}$.

(*Note*: d.f. $= n - 2$.)

EXAMPLE 12.5

Suppose that the data on level of technology and life expectancy in Table 12.1 represent a random sample of 10 nations drawn from the population of world nations. The research hypothesis for this study is that an increase in life expectancy (*Y*) accompanies an increase in the level of technology (*X*). Use the sample data to test the null hypothesis $r = 0$.

SOLUTION

The research hypothesis for our test is $H_1: r > 0$, since we expect that there is a positive correlation between level of technology and life expectancy. The null hypothesis is then $H_0: r = 0$.

    In Example 12.3 we computed the sample correlation coefficient to be $r = .826$. Hence the test statistic is

$$t = \hat{r}\sqrt{\frac{n-2}{1-r^2}} = .826\sqrt{\frac{8}{1-(.826)^2}}$$

$$= .826\sqrt{25.181} = .826(5.02) = 4.14$$

For $n = 10$ and $\alpha = .05$, we will reject H_0 if the observed value of *t* is greater than the tabulated value with d.f. $= n - 2$ and $\alpha = .05$. From Appendix Table 2, the critical value of *t* is 1.860. Since the observed value of *t*, 4.14, is greater than 1.860, we reject the null hypothesis and conclude that r is greater than zero. Thus, as the level of technology increases, we predict a longer life expectancy.

EXERCISES

32. State a hypothesis involving Pearson's r in which you would use a two-tailed test.

33. If $\hat{r} = +.80$ and $n = 100$, is r significantly different from zero? (Use $\alpha = .01$.)

34. Compute $\hat{r}$ for the data in the accompanying table on 12 high school students.

EXERCISE 34

Grade point average and IQ scores for 12 students

Grade Point Average	IQ	Grade Point Average	IQ
2.1	116	2.9	126
2.2	129	2.7	122
3.1	123	2.1	114
2.3	121	1.7	109
3.4	131	3.3	132
2.9	134	3.5	140

35. Refer to Exercise 34. Is r significantly different from zero? (Use $\alpha = .05$.)

36. Refer to Exercise 34. Find the coefficient of determination and interpret it for this set of data.

37. What are some of the factors that might account for the fact that $\hat{r}$ is not 1 for Exercise 34?

38. Use the data of Exercise 9 to compute the sample correlation coefficient $\hat{r}$. Test the research hypothesis $H_1 : r > 0$. (Use $\alpha = .05$.)

39. Use the data of Exercise 11 to compute the sample correlation coefficient $\hat{r}$. Test the research hypothesis $H_1 : r \neq 0$. (Use $\alpha = .05$.)

40. Refer to Exercise 15. Compute $\hat{r}$ and test the research hypothesis $H_1 : r \neq 0$. (Use $\alpha = .01$.)

41. Refer to Exercise 31. Compute $\hat{r}$ and test the research hypothesis $H_1 : r > 0$. (Use $\alpha = .05$.)

42. An equal number of families from a random sample of eight different cities of varying size were questioned on how much money they spend on food, clothing, and housing per year. The city sizes and average family expenditures are summarized in the accompanying table. Plot the data.

	City Size (000)	Expenditure (000)
EXERCISE 42	30	$65
Expenditures for food,	50	77
clothing, and housing	75	79
per year by city size	100	80
	120	81
	150	82
	175	84
	200	90

12.7 INTERPRETATIONS OF *r*

Having discussed the calculation of *r* and an appropriate test of significance, we can now discuss some interpretations of the Pearson product-moment correlation coefficient. A value of *r* equal to .5 does *not* mean that the strength of the linear relationship between *Y* and *X* is halfway between no correlation and perfect correlation. As we have stated, the proportion of the total variation in the *Y* values that is attributable to *X* is equal to r^2. If $r = .5$, the independent variable *X* is accounting for $r^2 = .25$ of the total variation in *Y*.

Also note that we cannot add correlations. If the simple linear correlations between *Y* and X_1, *Y* and X_2, and *Y* and X_3 are .10, .30, and .20, respectively, it does not follow that X_1, X_2, and X_3 account for $(.10)^2 + (.30)^2 + (.20)^2$ of the variability. In actuality these variables may be highly correlated and contribute the same information for the prediction of *Y*. The relationship between *Y* and several independent variables cannot always be studied by computing simple correlation coefficients for each of the independent variables. Rather, we should relate *Y* to X_1, X_2, and X_3 by using a single multivariable model. This topic is discussed in Chapter 13.

Finally, we illustrate the theoretical importance of interpreting the value of *r* with an example. Based on theory and prior research, a medical sociologist hypothesizes that number of social supports (friends, relatives, etc.) is negatively related to depression. That is, the more social supports individuals have, the lower their score on a scale measuring depression. The sociologist calculates the strength of the association for a sample of individuals and finds that $r = -.11$ and that it is not statistically significant (i.e., *r* does not differ significantly from 0). Should we conclude that there is no relationship between social support and depression?

Even though the test itself shows that there is insufficient evidence to indicate an association between *X* and *Y* (as measured by *r*), we should examine the plot of values on a scatter diagram. Figure 12.9 shows three examples of what the relationship between social supports and depression might look like when r is 0 or near 0. One possibility is that there is no relationship between number of social supports and depression scores (Figure 12.9a). However, it may also be that there is a relationship between the two variables, but that the relationship is not linear.

An example of a perfect curvilinear relationship between social support and depression scores is shown in Figure 12.9b. As the number of social supports increases from 1 to 7, depression scores decline. However, as the number of social supports increases beyond 7, depression scores increase. Thus when r is calculated for the entire sample of individuals, its value is 0.

A curvilinear relationship is also evident in Figure 12.9c. In this case the figure shows that there is no relationship between the variables for individuals who have 9 or fewer social supports, but as the number of social supports increases above 9, depression scores drop sharply. That is, as the number of social supports increases beyond 9, there is a strong negative relationship between social support and depression scores. As a result of these differences, r for the whole sample is small and statistically insignificant.

FIGURE 12.9

Various shapes for
scatter diagrams when
$r \approx 0$

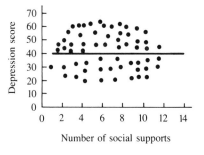
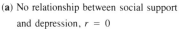

(**a**) No relationship between social support
and depression, $r = 0$

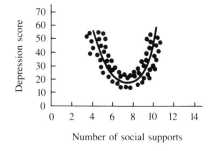

(**b** Curvilinear relationship between social
support and depression, $r = 0$

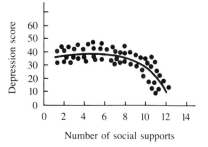

(**c**) Curvilinear relationship between social
support and depression, $r = -.11$

Although the latter two examples in Figure 12.9 show a relationship between the number of social supports and scores on a depression scale, the relationship is not linear. In this situation a statistical technique other than linear regression and correlation should be used, since the predictive equation, $\hat{Y} = a + bX$, does not accurately reflect the relationship between social support and depression. One assumption of bivariate regression and correlation is that a linear relationship exists between two variables. We discuss this and other assumptions underlying bivariate regression and correlation in the following section.

12.8 SOME ASSUMPTIONS UNDERLYING BIVARIATE REGRESSION AND CORRELATION

Technically, the method of least squares can be used with any data, and there are no underlying assumptions regarding its use. We just obtain the best-fitting equation to the data. However, as discussed in Chapter 1, the major contribution of statistics to the social sciences is that it enables us to make inferences about a population of interest by analyzing data obtained from a sample that is drawn from the population. In other words, we use statistics to measure the quality or "goodness" of an inference (e.g., regression slope) that is obtained from sample data. Thus, although we can apply bivariate regression and correlation to any data, the results are of little use to most social scientists if certain assumptions about the data are not met. We now discuss four of the most important assumptions that determine how accurate our inferences will be.

First, the scatter of Y values for corresponding X values, known as the *scedasticity*, should be uniform across values of X (see Figure 12.10a). That is,

FIGURE 12.10

Various shapes for scatter diagrams

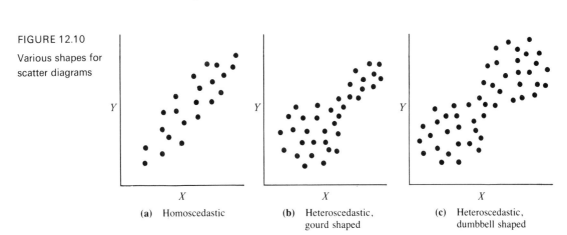

(a) Homoscedastic   (b) Heteroscedastic, gourd shaped   (c) Heteroscedastic, dumbbell shaped

the points should be grouped in a band of equal width above and below the regression line. In this case, we can see that the Y values are homoscedastic. Figure 12.10a shows that homoscedasticity is present.

If, however, the points fan out from the regression line for different values of X, the Y values are heteroscedastic. Two kinds of heteroscedasticity are illustrated in Figures 12.10b and 12.10c. Figure 12.10b shows that Y values are much farther from the regression line when the X values are small than when the X values are larger. Figure 12.10c shows that when X values are small and when X values are large, the Y values are much farther from the regression line than when the X values are neither very small nor very large.

If the assumption of homoscedasticity is violated and heteroscedasticity is present, the significance test for r will be invalid. Looking at a scatter diagram will help indicate whether or not the Y values are homoscedastic. The problem of heteroscedasticity can be solved, but the solution is beyond the scope of this text (see, for example, Lewis-Beck, 1990).

A second assumption of correlation is that we regard each pair of values (X, Y) as representing a random sample from a bivariate population. This is unlike the regression situation, where we assume that the X values are fixed and observe the corresponding Y values. When the X values are predetermined, as is the case in regression problems, we can systematically increase or decrease the magnitude of r by varying the choices of X values. If there is a linear relationship between variable X and variable Y, the wider the range of X values included, the larger the value of r. This concept is illustrated in Figure 12.11.

If all the (X, Y) values are included in the sample in Figure 12.11, there is an obvious strong correlation between X and Y. On the other hand, if we include only the X values between the dotted vertical lines, the sample correlation, though still positive, is much weaker. Here it is clear than when X values are preselected, the magnitude of the sample correlation can be affected.

FIGURE 12.11

The effect of predetermined X values on the sample correlation coeffient (see text)

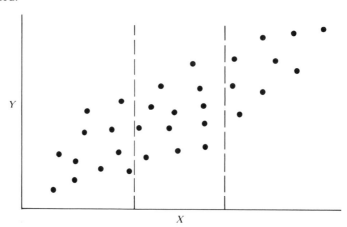

EXAMPLE 12.6

A company has the following data on productivity (Y) and aptitude test score (X) for 12 data entry personnel:

productivity (Y)	41 39 47 51 43 40 57 46 50 59 61 52
aptitude test score (X)	24 30 33 35 36 36 37 37 38 40 43 49

a. Compute the sample correlation coefficient assuming all 12 data points are included in the sample.

b. Compute the sample correlation assuming that only the highest six X values are included in the sample. Compare your result to part a.

SOLUTION

a. For $n = 12$, we have the following results:

$$\Sigma X = 438 \qquad \Sigma Y = 586$$

$$\Sigma X^2 = 16{,}414 \qquad \Sigma Y^2 = 29{,}232$$

$$\Sigma XY = 21{,}720$$

Therefore

$$S_{xx} = 16{,}414 - \frac{(438)^2}{12} = 426$$

$$S_{yy} = 29{,}232 - \frac{(586)^2}{12} = 615.67$$

$$S_{xy} = 21{,}720 - \frac{(438)(586)}{12} = 331$$

and

$$\hat{r} = \frac{331}{\sqrt{427(615.67)}} = .646$$

b. For the six highest X values:

$$\Sigma X = 244 \qquad \Sigma Y = 325$$

$$\Sigma X^2 = 10{,}032 \qquad \Sigma Y^2 = 17{,}771$$

$$\Sigma XY = 13{,}242$$

Therefore

$$S_{xx} = 10{,}032 - \frac{(244)^2}{6} = 109.33$$

$$S_{yy} = 17{,}771 - \frac{(325)^2}{6} = 166.83$$

$$S_{xy} = 13{,}242 - \frac{(244)(325)}{6} = 25.33$$

and

$$\hat{r} = \frac{25.33}{\sqrt{109.33(166.93)}} = .188$$

Note that the sample correlation coefficient is drastically reduced when 6 rather than 12 X values are used.

The third assumption underlying regression is especially critical, because it concerns the relationship of theory to research. The predictive equation is actually the statistical representation of the proposed theoretical relationship between variables. Thus the third assumption is that the theoretical model represented by the predictive equation is valid. For the theoretical relationship between variables to be validly represented by a linear regression equation, certain conditions must be met. We now state these conditions.

CONDITIONS IN WHICH THE THEORETICAL RELATIONSHIP BETWEEN TWO VARIABLES IS CORRECTLY REPRESENTED BY A LEAST-SQUARES EQUATION

1. The form of the relationship is linear (a straight line).
2. No important independent variable has been excluded from the predictive equation.
3. No unimportant variable has been included in the predictive equation.

We use our sample data of the relationship between level of technology and life expectancy (Table 12.1) to illustrate each of these conditions.

To determine whether the relationship between level of technology and life expectancy is linear, we examine both the scatter diagram and the coefficient of determination. Figure 12.4 should help convince you that a straight line describes the relationship between level of technology and life expectancy. Also the value of r^2 (equal to .682) we obtained in Example 12.2 is further indication that the relationship is essentially linear.

If the theoretical model that is reflected in the predictive equation is valid, no important independent variable has been excluded from the equation. However, relevant variables may have been excluded from the predictive equation for life expectancy, since other factors, such as the percentage of the population that lives in urban areas, are also likely to influence life expectancy for infants born in 1990. If so, the other variables should be identified and then included in the equation, to provide a more complete explanation of life expectancy. The relationship between a dependent variable and more than one independent variable is discussed in Chapter 13.

Finally, if the theoretical relationship between variables that is represented by the least-squares predictive equation is accurate, unimportant independent variables will not be included in the equation. For our sample data in Table 12.1, this condition asserts that level of technology does influence life expectancy, and that the variable is properly included in the predictive equation. Indeed, this was shown to be the case in Example 12.5, when we determined that r, the correlation coefficient between the level of technology and life expectancy, was statistically significant.

The fourth assumption underlying regression and correlation is that the independent variable, X, is not correlated with the error that results from using X to predict the dependent variable, Y. If the error in predicting life expectancy, for example, is related to level of technology, this could easily mean that other important independent variables that are related to level of technology are missing from the predictive equation. For example, assume that technology is correlated with percentage of the population that is urban and that the latter variable also helps predict life expectancy. If the percentage that is urban is not included in the predictive equation, the slope of the line, b, will tend to be biased; that is, b will tend to over- or underestimate the value of the "true" slope for the population.

The level of technology may not only be correlated with the percentage that is urban, but may also appear to account for some of the variation in life expectancy that is actually due to the percentage that is urban. In this case, the value of b equal to .494, which we obtained in Example 12.1, will be too large. This is because the level of technology (X) will be accounting for some of the variation in life expectancy (Y) that should be attributed to the percentage that is urban.

As noted in Section 12.7, we cannot add bivariate correlations (e.g., the correlations between Y and X_1 and between Y and X_2), because the independent variables may be highly correlated and contribute the same information for the prediction of Y. This topic is discussed in Chapter 13.

You may have observed that the fourth assumption has something in common with one of the conditions for asserting that the theoretical relationship represented by the predictive equation is valid: the condition that all important independent variables have been included in the predictive equation. Our discussion in the preceding paragraphs suggests that the theoretical model reflected in the equation would not accurately represent the relationship between level of technology and life expectancy if percentage that is urban is not included in the equation.

However, it is important to keep in mind that even if an independent variable is not related to the error that results from using X to predict Y, this does not mean that all important independent variables have been included in the predictive equation. It is still possible that a variable that is unrelated to the independent variable has been excluded from the predictive equation.

We can now summarize the assumptions underlying bivariate regression and correlation.

ASSUMPTIONS UNDERLYING BIVARIATE REGRESSION AND CORRELATION

1. The scatter of Y values for corresponding X values, known as the *scedasticity*, should be uniform across values of X.
2. The sample data of X values and Y values represent a random sample from the population of interest.
3. The theoretical relationship between variables X and Y, represented by the predictive equation, is valid.
4. The independent variable (X) is not correlated with the error that results from using X to predict the independent variable (Y).

EXERCISES

43. Explain the concept of homoscedasticity.
44. Explain the concept of heteroscedasticity.
45. State the three assumptions necessary for a theoretical relationship between the dependent and independent variables to be represented by a least-squares prediction equation.
46. Why are theory and prior research so important in doing research that involves the use of a least-squares prediction equation?

SUMMARY

This chapter presents techniques for studying the relationship between two variables measured on an interval or ratio scale. A scatter diagram provides a graphical method for examining the relationship between two variables. A regression line, computed from sample data and graphed on the scatter diagram, yields further graphical evidence of this relationship and permits the prediction of the dependent variable Y from knowledge of the independent variable X.

A numerical measure of the association between Y and X is provided by the Pearson product-moment correlation coefficient r, which is, in fact, the slope of the computed regression line when using standardized scores for the variables X and Y. We noted that r ranges between -1 and 1, with values near 0 implying little or no relationship between Y and X. Values near -1 or 1 indicate a strong relationship. The sign of r is also significant: Positive values imply that Y increases as X increases; negative values indicate that Y decreases as X increases. A test of the hypothesis of no correlation was presented in Section 12.6.

The coefficient of determination r^2, a PRE statistic, provides another (perhaps more meaningful) measure of the strength of the relationship between Y and X. Based on the notion of prediction and the PRE computed from no-association and perfect-association models, r^2 gives the proportion of the total variability in the Y values that can be attributed to a linear relationship between Y and X. The logical basis for the interpretation of r^2 is identical to that encountered in Chapter 10, except that the magnitudes as well as the numbers of errors are taken into account when dealing with interval and ratio data.

In this chapter we have presented the first step in examining the relationship between an independent and a dependent variable measured on an interval or ratio scale. However, as we illustrated in Section 12.8, it is likely that more than one independent variable influences a dependent variable. In Chapter 13 we extend our discussion of the linear relationship between interval and ratio variables to the multivariable model.

KEY WORDS

Coefficient of determination   The explained variation divided by total variation.

Explained variation   The amount of the total variation in the Y values that can be explained by the X values.

Freehand regression line   A regression line that *appears* to be the line of best fit but is drawn without exact values of a and b.

Heteroscedasticity   The scatter of Y values for corresponding X values is not uniform across values of X; data points are grouped in a band of unequal width above and below the regression line.

Homoscedasticity   The scatter of Y values for corresponding X values is uniform across values of X; data points are grouped in a band of equal width above and below the regression line.

Linear relationship   The regression line is a straight line.

Method of least squares   The method of curve fitting that selects the best-fitting curve — namely, the one that minimizes the sum of the squares of deviations of the data points from the fitted curve.

Pearson product-moment correlation coefficient   The measure of linear dependence between two variables measured on an interval or ratio scale that has a PRE interpretation when squared.

Regression line   A line fit to data points by using the method of least squares.

Scatter diagram   A plot of bivariate data in which each dot represents a pair of values: one for the dependent variable and one for the independent variable.

Sum of squares for error   A sum of squares of deviations $\Sigma(Y - \hat{Y})^2$ about the regression line.

Trend line   A line fit to data points by using the method of least squares.

Unexplained variation   An amount of the total variation in the Y values that cannot be explained by the X values.

KEY FORMULAS

Least-squares formulas for a and b in $\hat{Y} = a + bX$

$$b = \frac{S_{xy}}{S_{xx}} \quad \text{and} \quad a = \overline{Y} - b\overline{X}$$

where

$$S_{xy} = \Sigma XY - \frac{(\Sigma X)(\Sigma Y)}{n} \quad \text{and} \quad S_{xx} = \Sigma X^2 - \frac{(\Sigma X)^2}{n}$$

Sum of squares for error, SSE

$$SSE = \Sigma (Y - \hat{Y})^2$$

Coefficient of determination, r^2

$$r^2 = \frac{S_{xy}^2}{S_{xx}S_{yy}} \quad \text{where} \quad S_{yy} = \Sigma Y^2 - \frac{(\Sigma Y)^2}{n}$$

Correlation coefficient, r

$$r = \frac{S_{xy}}{\sqrt{S_{xx}S_{yy}}}$$

Statistical test for r

$$H_0: r = 0$$
$$\text{T.S.: } t = \hat{r}\sqrt{\frac{n-2}{1-\hat{r}^2}}$$

SUPPLEMENTARY EXERCISES FOR CHAPTER 12

47. Why is it useful to construct a scatter diagram before computing Pearson's r?

48. What is a regression line?

49. Refer to the data of Example 12.6. Compute the standardized regression coefficient b_s.

50. Use the results of Exercise 49 to compute the coefficient of determination r^2. Interpret your findings.

51. What do we know about the limits on r?

52. What do we mean by the expression "b is the slope of the regression line"?

53. What is the method of least squares?

54. How does r as the slope of the regression line differ from b as the slope of the regression line?

55. Why is a researcher more likely to be interested in r than in b?

56. What is the distinction between an r of $-.80$ and an r of $+.80$?

57. What is the coefficient of determination?

58. Social adjustment and perceived self-image tests were administered to $n = 6$ ex-drug addicts. Compute the least-squares regression line for the data in the accompanying table. Predict the social adjustment score for an ex-addict who scores 29 on the perceived self-image test.

EXERCISE 58

Perceived self-image and social adjustment scores for 6 ex-drug addicts

Perceived Self-Image Score X	Social Adjustment Score Y
35	55
23	37
42	61
18	28
31	52
45	70

59. Refer to Exercise 58. Compute r and r^2. Interpret your results.

60. To compute r, the data should be homoscedastic, linear, and normal. What do these three assumptions involve?

61. For every 100,000 U.S. citizens, there were 149 physicians and 249 nurses in 1950. The corresponding figures were 150 and 259 in 1955, 151 and 293 in 1960, 155 and 321 in 1965, 168 and 368 in 1970, 187 and 446 in 1975, 211 and 560 in 1980, 237 and 647 in 1985, and 275 and 698 in 1990. Let X denote the number of physicians and Y the number of nurses. Plot the data on a scatter diagram and draw a freehand regression line.

62. Write the equation of the line obtained from your freehand regression line in Exercise 61. Compare your results to those of Exercise 58.

63. Use the method of least squares to obtain a prediction equation relating the actual number of physicians to the number of nurses Y (by year) for the data in Exercise 61.

64. Compute r for the data in Exercise 63.

65. Compute r^2 for the data in Exercise 64.

66. An experiment was conducted to measure the strength of the linear relationship between two variables: a student's emotional stability (as measured by a guidance counselor's subjective judgment after an encounter session) and the student's score on an achievement test administered to children entering the first grade. The variable of emotional stability was measured on a scale of 0 to 40 (from low to high), and the achievement test was also measured from 0 to 40. Use the accompanying data from a random sample of 15 children to calculate the correlation coefficient. (*Note:* $S_{xx} = 485.33$, $S_{yy} = 522.93$, and $S_{xy} = 316.67$.)

EXERCISE 66

Emotional stability and achievement scores of 15 students

Student	Emotional Stability X	Achievement Y
1	23	31
2	21	23
3	31	34
4	34	29
5	26	29
6	22	27
7	14	21
8	18	17
9	32	33
10	29	35
11	16	21
12	29	22
13	23	24
14	27	28
15	25	15

67. Refer to the previous exercise and the accompanying computer output.
   a. Identify the least-squares prediction equation.

b. Show the relationship between $\hat{\rho}$ and B. (Hint: Compute $\hat{\rho}$ from the least-squares values for b.) Compare.

c. Based on the scatter diagram, does the value of $\hat{\rho}$ seem about right? Is it too high or low? What does $\hat{\rho}$ measure?

EXERCISE 67

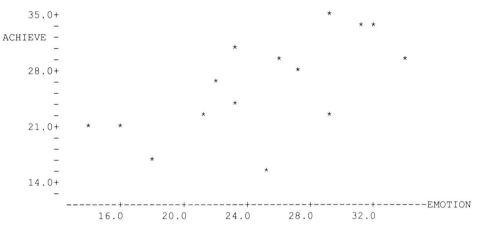

```
MTB > PLOT 'ACHIEVE' 'EMOTION'

   35.0+                                                    *
       -                                                         *   *
ACHIEVE -
       -                                        *
       -                                             *              *
   28.0+                                                  *
       -                                   *
       -
       -                              *
   21.0+      *       *
       -
       -              *
       -                                        *
   14.0+
       -
         --------+---------+---------+---------+---------+--------EMOTION
              16.0      20.0      24.0      28.0      32.0
```

MTB > REGRESS 'ACHIEVE' 1 'EMOTION'

The regression equation is
ACHIEVE = 9.84 + 0.652 EMOTION

Predictor	Coef	Stdev	t-ratio	p
Constant	9.839	5.668	1.74	0.106
EMOTION	0.6525	0.2239	2.91	0.012

s = 4.933   R-sq = 39.5%   R-sq(adj) = 34.9%

Analysis of Variance

SOURCE	DF	SS	MS	F	p
Regression	1	206.62	206.62	8.49	0.012
Error	13	316.32	24.33		
Total	14	522.93			

Unusual Observations

Obs.	EMOTION	ACHIEVE	Fit	Stdev.Fit	Residual	St.Resid
15	25.0	15.00	26.15	1.28	-11.15	-2.34R

R denotes an obs. with a large st. resid.
MTB > CORRELATE 'ACHIEVE' 'EMOTION'

Correlation of ACHIEVE and EMOTION = 0.629

68. Conduct a study to determine whether there is a correlation between a social science major's performance in a math (or a statistics) course and in a social science course. For example, you may wish to visit the department of sociology in your school to obtain a random sample of 30 senior majors. Contact these students to determine their (numerical) grades in a specific sociology course (such as one on contemporary theory) and a mathematics (or statistics) course required for graduation. Let X denote a student's sociology grade and Y his or her mathematics grade.

a. Identify the population from which the sample was drawn.

b. Find the least-squares prediction equation, $Y = a + bX$.

c. Calculate the coefficient of linear correlation.

d. Describe the strength of the relationship between the two sets of scores.

69. We are given the accompanying scatter diagrams:

a. Which of the following relationships best describes diagram 1?

strong positive relationship   little or no relationship

strong negative relationship   perfect positive relationship

rather weak positive relationship   perfect negative relationship

rather weak negative relationship

b. Which relationship best describes diagram 2?

c. Which best describes diagram 3?

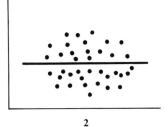

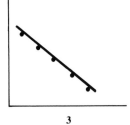

     1   2   3

70. A study was conducted in a poverty region to determine the effects that level of education had on family income. For ten families in the region, information was collected on the number of grades of school completed by the head of each family and the annual income of the family. Family income is thought to be linearly related to the amount of schooling. The data are given in the accompanying table.

Summary of data:

$$\Sigma X = 80 \qquad \Sigma Y = 260 \qquad \Sigma(X - \bar{X})^2 = 113$$

$$\Sigma X^2 = 684 \qquad\qquad\qquad \Sigma(Y - \bar{Y})^2 = 250$$

a. Compute b.

b. Explain in plain English the meaning of a and b. (Use a sketch if that would help.)

EXERCISE 70

Relationship between
family income and
grade of school com-
pleted by head of
family

Family	Grades of School Completed X	Family Income (× $100) Y
1	6	21
2	5	19
3	10	31
4	7	25
5	8	28
6	12	33
7	5	20
8	9	29
9	7	22
10	11	32

71. Refer to Database A, Appendix Table 7.
   a. Compute r between "age" and "number of acts defined as crimes."
   b. Compute r between "number of acts defined as crimes" and "income of
   parents." (*Note*: Treat "income of parents" as if measured on an interval scale.)
   c. Compute r between "income of parents" and "age."
   d. Compute the partial r between "income of parents" and "number of acts
   defined as crimes," controlling for "age."

72. Refer to Database A, Appendix Table 7, and test the following research hypotheses:
   a. $r < 0$ between "age" and "number of acts defined as crimes." (Use $\alpha = .05$.)
   b. r > 0 between "income of parents" and "number of acts defined as crimes."
   (Use $\alpha = .05$.)

73. Refer to Database B, Appendix Table 8. Compute a and b, the regression line
   between "level of technology" (Y) and "infant mortality rate" (X).

74. Refer to Exercise 73. What is the value of r? r^2? Is the value of r significant?
   Explain.

75. Refer to Database C, Appendix Table 9. Determine the correlation coefficient
   between HAM-D total score and the HAM-D anxiety score.

76. Refer to Database C, Appendix Table 9. Determine the correlation coefficient
   between the HAM-D total score and the HOPKINS OBRIST cluster total.

77. Refer to Database C, Appendix Table 9. Determine the correlation coefficient
   between "age" and "coffee/tea consumption."

78. Refer to Database D, Appendix Table 10.
   a. Compute r between poverty (percent of persons living below the poverty
   level) and suicide rate (cause of death per 100,000 deaths) for the 30 states.

Assume that the 30 states constitute a sample of all political units, and test the hypothesis that $r > 0$. (Set $\alpha = .05$.)

b. Compute r between abortion rate (number of abortions per 1000 women age 15–44) and births to unmarried women (percent of births to unmarried women) for the 30 states. Assume that the 30 states constitute a sample of all political units, and test the hypothesis that $r < 0$. (Set $\alpha = .05$.)

79. Eisinga, Felling, and Peters (1990) studied the relationships among religious beliefs, church involvement, and ethnocentrism for 1190 Dutch citizens. They report that Christian belief was correlated with positive attitudes toward the national ingroup ($r = .65$), with authoritarianism ($r = .63$), and with localism ($r = .47$). Determine whether each Pearson r is significantly different from 0. (Set $\alpha = .01$.)

80. Refer to Exercise 79. Assume that you replicated the study in the Netherlands. You sample 100 people who are 60 years of age or over and find Christian belief correlated with positive attitudes toward the national ingroup ($r = .85$), with authoritarianism ($r = .79$), and with localism ($r = .72$).

a. Test $H_0: r = 0$ for correlation between Christian belief and positive attitude toward the national ingroup. (Set $\alpha = .05$.)

b. Test $H_0: r = 0$ for correlation between Christian belief and authoritarianism. (Set $\alpha = .05$.)

c. Test $H_0: r = 0$ for correlation between Christian belief and localism. (Set $\alpha = .05$.)

81. Refer to Database D, Appendix Table 10.

a. Compute r between births to unmarried women (percentage of births to unmarried women) and poverty rate (percentage of persons living below the poverty level) for the 30 states. Assume that the 30 states constitute a sample of all political units, and test the hypothesis that $r > 0$. (Set $\alpha = .05$.)

b. Compute r between births to unmarried women and population density (average number of persons per square mile) for the 30 states. Assume that the 30 states constitute a sample of all political units, and test the hypothesis that $r > 0$. (Set $\alpha = .05$.)

c. Compute r between poverty rate and population density for the 30 states. Assume that the 30 states constitute a sample of all political units, and test the hypothesis that $r > 0$. (Set $\alpha = .05$.)

CHAPTER 13

REGRESSION AND CORRELATION: MULTIVARIATE EXTENSIONS

GENERAL OBJECTIVES

In Chapter 12 we examined linear (bivariate) regression and correlation for variables measured on interval and ratio scales. In this chapter we extend our discussion to multivariate analysis. We also discuss the application of assumptions underlying bivariate regression and correlation for the multivariate case. For example, we show what can happen to the relationship between an independent variable (X) and a dependent variable (Y) when a second (and relevant) independent variable is introduced into the least-squares prediction equation. Thus many of the issues this chapter considers are parallel to those in Chapter 11 for nominal and ordinal data.

SPECIFIC OBJECTIVES

1. To look at multiple regression, especially the logic behind it and how it builds on linear (bivariate) regression.
2. To show how to compute and interpret partial correlation coefficients and the coefficient of determination for multiple regression.
3. To explore some of the possible outcomes for the relationship between X and Y when the prediction equation includes a second independent variable.
4. To introduce the problem of multicollinearity, a condition that results when two independent variables in a multiple regression equation are highly correlated.

503

13.1   INTRODUCTION

In Chapter 12 we examined methods for using an independent variable (X) to predict a dependent variable (Y) when the variables are measured on interval or ratio scales. Social researchers routinely use knowledge of the values of one variable to predict values of another variable. Often, however, we seek a more sophisticated model to predict one variable based on knowledge of the values of two or more independent variables. A multivariate model is useful in two ways.

First, including several independent variables in the prediction equation usually offers a fuller explanation of the dependent variable than using only one independent variable. For example, prediction of public support for education per child per year is likely to be more accurate if we use per capita income, knowledge of the assessed valuation of property throughout a state, the rate of economic inflation, the rate of growth of public school attendance, and many other relevant variables. This multivariate equation should be able to predict per-child expenditures better than an equation that includes only (for instance) per capita income.

Second, we can be more confident of the true relationship between an independent variable and a dependent variable once other relevant independent variables are controlled — that is, when other variables are included in the prediction equation. We discussed this issue in Section 12.8, which presented the assumptions underlying regression and correlation.

This chapter, which focuses our attention on the study of the linear relationship between a dependent variable and more than one independent variable, examines some of the possible outcomes for the relationship between X and Y when a second independent variable is included in the least-squares prediction equation. We will also illustrate a potential problem with multiple regression and correlation called *multicollinearity*.

We begin our discussion by presenting the general least-squares prediction equation and the appropriate notation for multiple regression.

13.2   METHOD OF LEAST SQUARES FOR MULTIPLE REGRESSION

In Chapter 12 we examined methods for obtaining the least-squares prediction equation $\hat{Y} = a + bX$ based on values for two variables, X and Y. The methods for multiple regression are a straightforward extension of those for bivariate regression, in that the dependent variable is seen as linearly related to more than one independent variable. We will use the method of least squares to obtain the **multiple regression prediction equation**

$$\hat{Y} = a + b_1 X_1 + b_2 X_2 + \cdots + b_k X_k$$

where the subscript identifies a particular independent variable.

For example, suppose a group of sociologists used census tract data from a random sample of 100 neighborhoods to collect information on the following variables: median income, median number of rooms per housing unit, median value of housing unit, and median number of persons per household. If they were interested in obtaining a prediction equation relating median income to the other three variables, then the dependent variable would be median income, and the other three variables would be independent variables. Before we illustrate the actual computation of the coefficients for a multiple regression prediction equation, we need some additional notation.

NOTATION FOR MULTIPLE REGRESSION

Y: dependent variable

X_k: independent variable k

$\overline{Y}$: sample mean for Y

$\overline{X}_i$: sample mean for variable X_i ($i = 1, 2, \ldots, k$)

s_y: standard deviation for Y values

s_i: standard deviation for values of X_i ($i = 1, 2, \ldots, k$)

r_{yi}: Pearson product-moment correlation coefficient between the variables Y and X_i ($i = 1, 2, \ldots, k$)

r_{ij}: Pearson product-moment correlation coefficient between the variables X_i and X_j

---

Using this notation, we will illustrate the basic concepts of developing a multiple regression prediction equation with two independent variables, X_1 and X_2, where

$$\hat{Y} = a + b_1 X_1 + b_2 X_2$$

As with bivariate regression, the least-squares values for the intercept and slopes (a, b_1, b_2) produce less prediction error than any other possible combinations of values. In other words, the least-squares equation fits the data collected for a sample better than any other equation of the form $\hat{Y} = a + b_1 X_1 + b_2 X_2$.

Recall that in relating a dependent variable Y to an independent variable X (Chapter 12), we used a two-dimensional plot of corresponding values for X and Y. We could then draw a freehand regression line (or the actual least-squares regression line) through the scatter of data points. For the three-variable prediction equation, we must imagine a three-dimensional scatter of data points. To help you visualize the difference between a two-dimensional scatter of points and a three-dimensional scatter, consider the difference between a wall map of the world and a globe. Rather than fitting a regression line through the display of data points, we must fit a **regression plane** to a three-dimensional scatter of points. We illustrate with an example.

Suppose we have trivariate data (three variables Y, X_1, and X_2) that have been measured on a ratio scale. Furthermore, suppose we are interested in examining the relationship between the dependent variable, annual income, and two independent variables, educational attainment and number of children at home, for a sample of employed wives. To help us understand the graphical representation of the relationship between the three variables, we will plot the data contained in Table 13.1 in a regression plane (see Figure 13.1). In developing a regression plane, we label one axis to correspond with education, a second axis to correspond with number of children, and a third axis to correspond to annual income. For the data in Table 13.1, the dependent and independent variables are

Y: annual income
X_1:   education
X_2:   number of children

TABLE 13.1

Annual income, education, and number of children for a sample of five employed wives

Case	X_1 Education (in years)	X_2 Number of Children	Y Annual Income (in dollars)
1	11	2	$20,000
2	12	6	15,000
3	14	3	25,000
4	16	1	35,000
5	18	4	30,000

$r_{12} = -.145$; $r_{y1} = .828$; $r_{y2} = -.658$

If we look at the edge of the regression plane that goes along the X_1 axis in Figure 13.1, we see that the edge slopes upward as education increases. This suggests a positive relationship between education and annual income. However, when we examine the edge of the regression plane for the X_2 axis, we see that the edge slopes downward as the number of children increases. This suggests that a negative relationship exists between number of children and annual income. By now you may have determined that it is very difficult to draw a regression plane through a scatter of data points. Indeed, it is far more difficult to draw a regression plane than to draw a regression line.

However, we have shown you how to visualize a scatter of data points that represents a three-variable regression equation so that you might see an example of what a regression plane looks like.

Like the location of the regression line in a scatter diagram, the location of the regression plane in a three-dimensional scatter of data points is determined by the values of a, b_1, and b_2. We will now give the formulas for the least-squares estimates a, b_1, and b_2 for the general three-variable relationship.

FIGURE 13.1

Least-squares fit to the data in Table 13.1 (circled dot represents data for case 3)

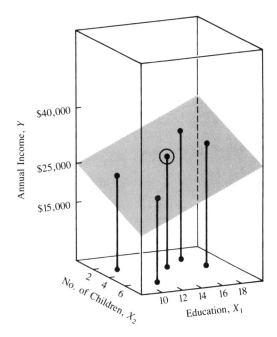

LEAST-SQUARES ESTIMATES FOR THE MULTIPLE REGRESSION PREDICTION EQUATION $\hat{Y} = a + b_1X_1 + b_2X_2$

$$b_1 = \frac{s_y}{s_1}\left(\frac{r_{y1} - r_{y2}r_{12}}{1 - r_{12}^2}\right)$$

$$b_2 = \frac{s_y}{s_2}\left(\frac{r_{y2} - r_{y1}r_{12}}{1 - r_{12}^2}\right)$$

$$a = \bar{Y} - b_1\bar{X}_1 - b_2\bar{X}_2$$

Note that the least-squares estimates can all be obtained if we know the means, standard deviations, and Pearson product-moment correlation coefficients for each combination of pairs for the three variables of interest. These statistics should always be reported in a summary table when doing a multiple regression analysis. We now illustrate how to obtain the least-squares estimates for the three-variable prediction equation with an example.

EXAMPLE 13.1

A sociologist hypothesizes that life expectancy of a nation is positively associated both with level of technology development and with proportion of the population living in urbanized areas. In other words, level of technology and percentage urban population are hypothesized to predict life expectancy. Using the data from a sample of ten nations (Table 13.2), develop the multiple regression equation $\hat{Y} = a + b_1 X_1 + b_2 X_2$, where the dependent and independent variables are

Y: life expectancy
X_1: level of technology
X_2: percentage of population that is urban

TABLE 13.2

Three demographic characteristics of ten nations

Nation	Life Expectancy (in years)	Level of Technology Development (0–100)	Percentage of Population that is Urban
Algeria	60	17	43
Bolivia	53	10	49
Chile	71	22	84
Colombia	66	15	68
Egypt	60	13	45
Ireland	74	48	56
Japan	79	53	77
Malawi	49	12	14
Peru	65	12	69
Romania	71	33	61

Source: Population Reference Bureau, *1990 World Population Data Sheet* (Washington, D.C.: Population Reference Bureau, Inc., 1990).

SOLUTION

For these data, you can verify the following calculations:

$$\bar{Y} = 64.80 \quad s_y = 9.426 \quad r_{y1} = .826$$
$$\bar{X}_1 = 23.50 \quad s_1 = 15.757 \quad r_{y2} = .807$$
$$\bar{X}_2 = 56.60 \quad s_2 = 20.173 \quad r_{12} = .402$$

Substituting these values into the formulas for b_1 and b_2, we have

$$b_1 = \frac{9.426}{15.757}\left[\frac{.826 - (.807)(.402)}{1 - (.402)^2}\right] = .358$$

$$b_2 = \frac{9.426}{20.173}\left[\frac{.807 - (.826)(.402)}{1 - (.402)^2}\right] = .265$$

The intercept for the multiple regression equation is

$$a = 64.80 - (.358)(23.50) - (.265)(56.60)$$
$$= 41.388$$

The prediction equation is thus

$$\hat{Y} = 41.388 + .358X_1 + .265X_2$$

This equation is the best prediction equation of Y because the values 41.388, .358, and .265 are the values of a, b_1, and b_2 that produce the least amount of error in using X_1 and X_2 to predict Y. We discuss how to interpret the values of a, b_1, and b_2 in the following section.

13.3 INTERPRETATIONS OF MULTIPLE REGRESSION ESTIMATES

The value of a in the multiple regression prediction equation $\hat{Y} = a + b_1X_1 + b_2X_2$ can be given an interpretation very similar to a in the bivariate regression prediction equation $\hat{Y} = a + bX$. The intercept, a, is the average value of Y when each independent variable equals zero. The interpretations of b_1 and b_2 are similar to the interpretation of b in bivariate regression, but they require more explanation.

Recall that in bivariate regression, b is interpreted as the average change in Y associated with a unit change in X. However, with the three-variable multiple regression equation, the coefficient b_1 is interpreted as the average change in Y associated with a unit change in X_1, **when the other independent variable, X_2, is controlled**. We must control for the effect of X_2 so that the actual relationship between Y and X_1 can be determined. By controlling for X_2, we are able to separate out the effect of the variable so that it does not influence the relationship between Y and X_1. What we essentially do when we control for X_2, then, is to **hold X_2 constant**.

Similarly, we must control for X_1 (hold X_1 constant) to determine the relationship between Y and X_2 without the influence of X_1. Thus the coefficient b_2 is interpreted as the average change in Y associated with a unit change in X_2, when the other independent variable X_1 is held constant.

The term we apply to b_1 or b_2 differs from the term we use for b in bivariate regression. Recall that in bivariate regression, b is called a *regression coefficient* or *slope*. In multiple regression, b_1 and b_2 are called **partial regression coefficients** or **partial slopes**. The interpretations of the coefficients in bivariate and multiple regression are compared in Table 13.3.

TABLE 13.3	$\hat{Y} = a + bX$	$\hat{Y} = a + b_1X_1 + b_2X_2$
Interpretations of coefficients in the regression prediction equation	a: Y intercept, predicted value of Y when $X = 0$	a: Y intercept, predicted value of Y when $X_1 = 0$ and $X_2 = 0$
	b: change in Y for a 1-unit increase in X	b_1: change in Y for a 1-unit increase in X_1 when X_2 is held constant
		b_2: change in Y for a 1-unit increase in X_2 when X_1 is held constant

We illustrate the interpretation of the coefficients a, b_1, and b_2 with an example.

Recall from Example 13.1 that the prediction equation

$$\hat{Y} = 41.388 + .358X_1 + .265X_2$$

shows the relationship between life expectancy (Y), level of technology (X_1), and percent of the population that is urban (X_2) for a sample of 10 nations. The value of 41.388 reflects the average life expectancy of a nation when both level of technology and percentage urban population are equal to zero. It is very unlikely today, however, that a nation has not begun to develop technologically and that none of the nation's population lives in urban areas. As we discussed in Chapter 12, the intercept is a statistical projection; it must always be added to the slope components, b_1X_1 and b_2X_2 in this example, for Y to be properly estimated.

The value of the partial regression coefficient b_1 is .358. As a multiple regression estimate, this value shows that a one-point increase in level of technology is associated with an average increase in life expectancy of .358 year, when the percent of the population that is urban is held constant. The value of the coefficient b_2, .265, suggests that an increase of one percentage point in the proportion of the population that is urban is associated with an average increase in life expectancy of .265 year, when the level of technology is held constant.

We now illustrate how to calculate the predicted life expectancy of a nation using the derived values of a, b_1, and b_2. If a nation's level of technology is 30 and the nation's percentage of urban population is 50, we predict the nation's life expectancy to be

$$\hat{Y} = 41.388 + .358(30) + .265(50) = 65.378$$

Likewise, if a nation's level of technology is 15 and the nation's urban population percentage is 25, we predict the nation's life expectancy to be

$$\hat{Y} = 41.388 + .358(15) + .265(25) = 53.383$$

EXERCISES

✱ **1.** What is the multiple regression equation? *& what do the terms mean.*

2. Define a and b_1, in the three-variable multiple regression equation $\hat{Y} = a + bX_1 + bX_2$.

3. A statistical software package was used to fit the multiple regression equation $\hat{Y} = a + b_1X_1 + b_2X_2$ to the data of Table 13.2. The output is shown in the accompanying printout.
   a. Locate the least-squares prediction equation. → *AKA: regression equation*
   b. Compare the computer-generated equation to the one obtained in Example 13.1.
   c. Locate and identify other "familiar" quantities from the output.

EXERCISE 3

```
MTB > REGRESS 'LIFE' 2 'TECH' 'URBAN'

The regression equation is
LIFE = 41.4 + 0.358 TECH + 0.265 URBAN

Predictor       Coef        Stdev      t-ratio        p
Constant       41.411       2.353       17.60      0.000
TECH           0.35772      0.05459      6.55      0.000
URBAN          0.26471      0.04264      6.21      0.000

s = 2.362       R-sq = 95.1%       R-sq(adj) = 93.7%

Analysis of Variance

SOURCE        DF          SS          MS          F         p
Regression     2       760.54      380.27      68.14     0.000
Error          7        39.06        5.58
Total          9       799.60

SOURCE        DF       SEQ SS
TECH           1       545.45
URBAN          1       215.08

Unusual Observations
Obs.    TECH       LIFE       Fit  Stdev.Fit  Residual   St.Resid
  2     10.0     53.000    57.959     1.007    -4.959      -2.32R

R denotes an obs. with a large st. resid.
```

13.4   MEASURING THE STRENGTH OF ASSOCIATIONS IN MULTIPLE REGRESSION

In many multiple regression situations the social scientist may also wish to measure the strength of the relationship between the dependent variable Y and a single independent variable while controlling for another independent variable. For example, suppose we are investigating the effects of two independent variables

X_1: academic effort
X_2: academic ability

on the dependent variable Y, academic achievement. If we already know the strength of the relationship between each of these independent variables and the dependent variable, we will want to determine if each relationship holds when we include the other independent variable. In this case we would measure the strength of the relationship between Y and X_1 (or X_2) while controlling for the other independent variable. One such measure is the **partial correlation coefficient**. For example, $r_{y1.2}$ is the partial correlation of Y and X_1 controlling for X_2, and $r_{y2.1}$ is the partial correlation of Y and X_2 controlling for X_1. We let r_{y1} denote the Pearson product-moment correlation coefficient between Y and X_1 (which ignores values of X_2); similarly, r_{y2} and r_{12} represent the Pearson product-moment correlation coefficients between Y and X_2 and between X_1 and X_2, respectively. The partial correlation coefficients can be computed as follows.

COMPUTATION OF PARTIAL CORRELATION COEFFICIENTS

$$r_{y1.2} = \frac{r_{y1} - r_{y2}r_{12}}{\sqrt{(1 - r_{y2}^2)(1 - r_{12}^2)}}$$

$$r_{y2.1} = \frac{r_{y2} - r_{y1}r_{12}}{\sqrt{(1 - r_{y1}^2)(1 - r_{12}^2)}}$$

Partial correlation coefficients, like Pearson product-moment correlation coefficients, are type B normed measures of association for interval and ratio data.

EXAMPLE 13.2   A sociologist obtains data from a random sample of students who have just completed their first year of college. The sociologist determines that academic effort (measured as the average number of hours studied per week) and academic ability (measured as SAT scores) predict academic achievement (measured as grade point average, or GPA, for the year) where

Y: GPA for the first year of college
X_1: average number of hours studied per week
X_2: SAT scores

The researcher is interested in the strength of the relationship between GPA and each independent variable when the other independent variable is controlled. The data collected show that $r_{y1} = .65$, $r_{y2} = .50$, and $r_{12} = .25$. Determine the partial correlation coefficients $r_{y1.2}$ and $r_{y2.1}$. Interpret your findings.

SOLUTION

Using the computation formulas, we have

$$r_{y1.2} = \frac{r_{y1} - r_{y2}r_{12}}{\sqrt{(1 - r_{y2}^2)(1 - r_{12}^2)}} = \frac{.65 - (.50)(.25)}{\sqrt{(1 - (.50)^2)(1 - (.25)^2)}}$$

$$= \frac{.525}{\sqrt{(.75)(.9375)}} = .63$$

$$r_{y2.1} = \frac{r_{y2} - r_{y1}r_{12}}{\sqrt{(1 - r_{y1}^2)(1 - r_{12}^2)}} = \frac{.50 - (.65)(.25)}{\sqrt{(1 - (.65)^2)(1 - (.25)^2)}}$$

$$= \frac{.3375}{\sqrt{(.5775)(.9375)}} = .46$$

For these data the strength of the relationship between study time and GPA is .63 when SAT scores are controlled. Similarly, the strength of the association between SAT scores and GPA is .46 when study time is controlled.

Note that controlling for the influence of the other independent variable in multiple regression is analogous to controlling for the effects of a third variable when examining the association between nominal and ordinal variables. Recall that in Chapter 11 we created partial tables, each representing a category of the third variable we were controlling. We then determined the relationship between an independent variable and a dependent variable for each partial table. The interpretation of the partial correlation coefficients is comparable to the interpretation of the results of partial tables: the strength of the relationship between a dependent and an independent variable when a third variable is controlled.

As r^2 gives a PRE interpretation to r in bivariate correlation, the squared partial correlation coefficients give a PRE interpretation to the partial correlation coefficients in multiple regression. That is, the squared partial correlation coefficient indicates the amount of variance in Y that is explained by X_1 (or X_2) when X_2 (or X_1) is controlled. For Example 13.2, then, $r^2_{y1.2} = .3969$ and $r^2_{y2.1} = .2116$. Thus study time explains about 39.7% of the variance in GPA when SAT scores are held constant; SAT scores explain about 21.2% of the variance in GPA when study time is held constant. These findings suggest that although both academic effort and academic ability are related to academic achievement, academic effort is the more important variable.

As is the case with values of r^2, we observe that values of squared partial correlations cannot be added. If the partial correlation coefficients between Y and X_1 and between Y and X_2 are .30 and .50, it does not follow that X_1 and X_2 account for $(.30)^2 + (.50)^2$ of the variability in Y. In actuality these variables may be correlated and contribute some of the same information for the prediction of Y. We will explore this issue more fully when we present the coefficient of determination for multiple regression. We now turn our attention to how the interpretation of the partial correlation coefficient is related to the multiple regression prediction equation.

13.5 DETERMINING THE RELATIVE IMPORTANCE OF THE INDEPENDENT VARIABLES IN MULTIPLE REGRESSION

We sometimes want to evaluate the relative importance of the independent variables as predictors of Y. One way might be to compare the magnitudes of the partial regression coefficients. However, this could prove difficult if the independent variables are measured in different units (e.g., years, dollars, test scores). For example, suppose that the following multiple regression equation predicts the amount of money given annually to a college alumni association by former students:

$$\hat{Y} = 8.34 + 2.53X_1 + .010X_2$$

where Y is the annual contribution to the association (in dollars), X_1 is age (in years), and X_2 is annual income (in dollars). The relative effects of income and age on monetary contributions to the alumni association are difficult to assess, because the measurement units are not comparable. That is, contributions and income are measured in dollars, but age is measured in years.

One solution is to standardize the variables so that Y, X_1, and X_2 are converted to standardized units z_y, z_{x1}, and z_{x2}. (You may wish to refer to Section 12.5 for a detailed discussion of standardized regression variables.)

The regression equation can then be written as

$$\hat{z}_y = b_{s1}z_{x1} + b_{s2}z_{x2}$$

Once we have standardized the multiple regression equation, we can easily compare the strength of the relationship of each independent variable to the dependent variable. This is because the standardized partial slopes (b_{s1}, b_{s2}) are partial slopes expressed as units of standard deviation (z-scores). In other words, standardized partial slopes are partial slopes that have been multiplied by the ratio of the standard deviation of the independent variable to the standard deviation of the dependent variable. Thus,

$$b_{s1} = b_1\left(\frac{s_1}{s_y}\right) \quad \text{and} \quad b_{s2} = b_2\left(\frac{s_2}{s_y}\right)$$

The standardized partial slope indicates, then, the average standard deviation change in Y associated with a standard deviation change in an independent variable when the other independent variable is held constant.

Suppose the standardized equation for our example of alumni contributions is

$$\hat{Y} = .22z_{x1} + .66z_{x2}$$

The value for b_{s1} of .22 means that an increase of one standard deviation in age is associated with an increase of .22 standard deviation in alumni contributions, on average, when income is controlled. Similarly, b_{s2} of .66 means that an increase of one standard deviation in income is associated with an increase of .66 standard deviation in alumni contributions, on average, when age is controlled. The values of the standardized partial slopes show that the impact of income on alumni contributions is much greater than the influence of age, when the variables are measured in standard deviation units (z-scores). In fact, we can say that the influence of income on contributions is three times as great as the influence of age ($.66/.22 = 3$).

We present without proof the equivalent formulas for calculating b_{s1} and b_{s2}.

$$b_{s1} = b_1\left(\frac{s_1}{s_y}\right) = \frac{r_{y1} - r_{y2}r_{12}}{1 - r_{12}^2}$$

$$b_{s2} = b_2\left(\frac{s_2}{s_y}\right) = \frac{r_{y2} - r_{y1}r_{12}}{1 - r_{12}^2}$$

With these formulas it is relatively easy to compute b_{s1} and b_{s2}, because they utilize the Pearson product-moment correlation coefficients.

EXAMPLE 13.3

Refer to Example 13.2. Suppose we are interested in the relative importance of academic effort and academic ability in predicting the academic achievement of college students who have just completed their freshman year. Calculate b_{s1} and b_{s2}. Show the standardized regression equation. Interpret the findings.

SOLUTION

For the data of Example 13.2, $r_{y1} = .65$, $r_{y2} = .50$, and $r_{12} = .25$. Using these Pearson product-moment correlation coefficients, we find that

$$b_{s1} = \frac{r_{y1} - (r_{y2})(r_{12})}{1 - r_{12}^2} = \frac{.65 - (.50)(.25)}{1 - (.25)^2}$$

$$= \frac{.525}{.9375} = .56$$

$$b_{s2} = \frac{r_{y2} - (r_{y1})(r_{12})}{1 - r_{12}^2} = \frac{.50 - (.65)(.25)}{1 - (.25)^2}$$

$$= \frac{.3375}{.9375} = .36$$

Thus the standardized regression equation can be written

$$\hat{z}_y = .56z_{x1} + .36z_{x2}$$

The value for $b_{s1} = .56$ means that for an average of one standard deviation increase in study time, GPA increases by .56 standard deviation, on average, when SAT scores are controlled. Similarly, $b_{s2} = .36$ means that for an average of one standard deviation increase in SAT score, GPA increases by .36 standard deviation, on average, when study time is controlled. These values for the standardized partial slopes suggest that the impact of study time on GPA is somewhat larger than the influence of SAT scores, when the variables are measured in standard deviation units. We can say that the influence of study time on GPA is about 1.5 times greater than the influence of SAT scores ($.56/.36 = 1.55$).

The standardized partial regression coefficients are related to the partial correlation coefficients $r_{y1.2}$ and $r_{y2.1}$. Recall that in Chapter 12 we showed that the Pearson product-moment correlation r is identical to the slope of the standardized least-squares prediction equation. Although the partial slopes of the multiple regression equation are not identical to the partial correlations $r_{y1.2}$ and $r_{y2.1}$, they are closely related.

RELATIONSHIP BETWEEN PARTIAL CORRELATION COEFFICIENTS
AND STANDARDIZED SLOPES FOR THE THREE-VARIABLE
REGRESSION EQUATION

$$r_{y1.2} = b_{s_1} \sqrt{\frac{1 - r_{12}^2}{1 - r_{y2}^2}}$$

$$r_{y2.1} = b_{s_2} \sqrt{\frac{1 - r_{12}^2}{1 - r_{y1}^2}}$$

We have shown that one advantage of using the standardized regression
equation is that we can meaningfully compare the relative influence of
independent variables on the dependent variable by examining the partial
slopes of the equation. Another advantage is that we can easily compute the
coefficient of determination R^2, which measures the proportion of the total
variability among the Y values that is accounted for by the independent
variables X_1 and X_2. We now turn our attention to R^2 and its relationship to
the standardized regression equation.

13.6   COEFFICIENT OF DETERMINATION R^2

You will recall from Chapter 12 on bivariate regression that when we are
dealing with only one independent variable, the coefficient of determination
r^2 is

$$r^2 = \frac{\text{explained variation}}{\text{total variation}} = \frac{S_{yy} - \text{SSE}}{S_{yy}}$$

where $S_{yy} - \text{SSE}$ reflects the reduction in the sum of squares for error
obtained by using the information on the independent variable. The proportional reduction in the error sum of squares is thus equal to r^2. In other
words, r^2 represents the amount of variance in the Y values that is explained
by X.

We can use the same formulation for multiple regression to determine
how much variation X_1 and X_2 can explain in the Y values. That is, with more
than one independent variable, the coefficient of determination is the square
of the **multiple correlation coefficient R**. We can compute R^2 for one
dependent and for two independent variables by using the following formula.

(handwritten margin notes): R^2 adjusted = depends on # of observations & variables ✳

COMPUTATION OF THE COEFFICIENT OF DETERMINATION R^2 FOR THE REGRESSION EQUATION $\hat{Y} = a + b_1X_1 + b_2X_2$

$$R^2 = b_{s1}r_{y1} + b_{s2}r_{y2}$$

where b_{s1} and b_{s2} are partial slopes calculated for the regression equation using standard deviation units of measurement (z-scores).

EXAMPLE 13.4

Using the data of Example 13.3, fit the standardized regression equation

$$\hat{z}_y = b_{s1}z_{x1} + b_{s2}z_{x2}$$

Use these results to obtain R^2, the coefficient of determination. Interpret your findings.

SOLUTION

For the data of Example 13.3, $r_{y1} = .65$, $r_{y2} = .50$, and $r_{12} = .25$. Using these correlation coefficients, we calculate $b_{s1} = .56$ and $b_{s2} = .36$. Substituting these values into the equation for R^2, we have

$$R^2 = (.56)(.65) + (.36)(.50) = .544$$

Thus the independent variables X_1 and X_2 account for 54.4% of the variability in the Y values. In other words, study time and SAT scores together explain 54.4% of the variance of GPA for students who have completed their first year of college.

It is useful to examine the relationship between the squared partial correlation coefficient and the coefficient of determination. Whereas the squared partial correlation coefficient represents the amount of variance in Y that is explained when the other independent variable is controlled, R^2 represents the proportional reduction in error we obtain in using knowledge of two independent variables to predict the dependent variable. As we noted previously, we cannot add squared partial correlations to obtain R^2. If independent variables are correlated, each would contribute some of the same information for the prediction of Y. We illustrate with an example.

EXAMPLE 13.5

Recall that in Example 13.2 we computed $r_{y1.2}$ equal to .63 and $r_{y2.1}$ equal to .46. That is, the strength of the relationship between study time and GPA is .63 when SAT scores are controlled, and the strength of the association between SAT scores and GPA is .46 when study time is controlled. If we square these coefficients and add them, will we find that their sum is equal to R^2? (Recall that we calculated R^2 to be .544 in Example 13.4.)

SOLUTION

If we square $r_{y1.2}$ and $r_{y2.1}$ and then add them, we find that

$$(.63)^2 + (.46)^2 = .3969 + .2116 = .6085$$

It is obvious that this obtained value of .6085 is larger than the R^2 value of .544 that we computed in Example 13.4. This is because study time and SAT scores are correlated ($r_{12} = .25$), so each variable contributes some of the same information in predicting GPA. If r_{12} were larger than .25, it is likely that the difference between the sum of the squared partial correlation coefficients and R^2 would be even larger than what we have just shown.

It is useful at this point to review our discussion of multiple regression and correlation. We have demonstrated how to obtain least-squares coefficients for the multiple regression prediction equation $\hat{Y} = a + b_1 X_1 + b_2 X_2$, how to interpret these coefficients, how to measure the strength of the relationship between a dependent and an independent variable while controlling for a second independent variable by using a partial correlation coefficient, how to relate these partial correlation coefficients to the slopes of a standardized multiple regression prediction equation, and, finally, how to calculate and interpret the coefficient of determination R^2.

Although the concepts for developing multiple regression prediction equations, partial correlations, and R^2 extend very easily to situations where we are dealing with more than two independent variables, the formulas we have presented in this chapter apply only for the case in which there is one dependent variable and two independent variables and the prediction equation is of the form $Y = a + b_1 X_1 + b_2 X_2$. Rather than presenting the more complicated formulas necessary to apply our results to any general multivariate situation, we recommend using a computer to solve such complicated problems. Your knowledge of multiple regression, partial correlations, and R^2 should give you a basic understanding of the results, even though you do not know how the computations are performed.

EXERCISES

4. Define a partial correlation coefficient.

5. How does b_1 differ from b_{s1}?

6. A medical researcher selects a random sample of 300 adult males and for each one determines weight (Y), the number of minutes exercised each week (X_1), and father's weight (X_2). The Pearson product-moment correlation coefficients for the sample are $r_{y1} = .71$, $r_{y2} = .53$, and $r_{12} = .24$. Calculate $r_{y1.2}$ and $r_{y2.1}$. Interpret your answers. Calculate $r_{y1.2}^2$ and $r_{y2.1}^2$. Interpret your answers.

7. Refer to Exercise 6. Calculate b_{s1} and b_{s2}. Interpret your answers. Is amount of exercise or father's weight more important in determining a man's weight?

8. Refer to Exercise 6. Calculate R^2. Interpret your answer. Add $r_{y1.2}^2$ and $r_{y2.1}^2$, which you obtained in Exercise 6. Is this value different from R^2? Explain your answer.

13.7   APPLYING THE ASSUMPTIONS OF REGRESSION AND CORRELATION

In Chapter 12 we examined several important assumptions that must apply in order to use bivariate regression and correlation sample results to make inferences about the population. These assumptions also apply to multiple regression and correlation. In this section we explore the application of these assumptions to the three-variable multiple regression equation. Since we illustrate the application of the assumptions with data used in Section 13.2, we repeat the data here as Table 13.4.

TABLE 13.4

Three demographic characteristics of ten nations

Nation	Life Expectancy (in years)	Level of Technology Development (0–100)	Percentage of Population that is Urban
Algeria	60	17	43
Bolivia	53	10	49
Chile	71	22	84
Colombia	66	15	68
Egypt	60	13	45
Ireland	74	48	56
Japan	79	53	77
Malawi	49	12	14
Peru	65	12	69
Romania	71	33	61

Source: Population Reference Bureau, *1990 World Population Data Sheet* (Washington, D.C.: Population Reference Bureau, Inc., 1990).

One of the most important assumptions underlying bivariate regression is that the theoretical model represented by the prediction equation is valid. For this assumption to be met, all important independent variables must be included in the equation. We illustrate with an example.

Suppose we hypothesize that level of technology (X) predicts life expectancy (Y) for the sample of ten nations in Table 13.4. Our prediction equation is

$$\hat{Y} = a + bX$$

If we calculated values for the regression estimates a and b, we would find that $a = 53.189$ and $b = .494$. Thus the bivariate prediction equation would be

$$\hat{Y} = 53.189 + .494X$$

If we calculated the coefficient of determination r^2, we would find that $r^2 = .682$. Thus level of technology explains 68.2% of the variance in life expectancy for our sample of ten nations.

At this point, the thoughtful social scientist should know that factors other than level of technology influence a nation's life expectancy. Thus the theoretical relationship between life expectancy and technology is not accurately represented by a simple bivariate prediction equation; relevant independent variables have been excluded from the equation. Based on previous research, we know that the percentage of the nation's population that is urban should be included in the prediction equation along with the level of technology. Our prediction equation for life expectancy is thus

$$\hat{Y} = a + b_1 X_1 + b_2 X_2$$

where X_1 is the nation's level of technology and X_2 is the percentage of the nation's population that is urban.

When we use the data of Table 13.4 to calculate a, b_1 and b_2, the resulting prediction equation for life expectancy is

$$\hat{Y} = 41.388 + .358X_1 + .265X_2$$

You will recall that this equation is identical to the prediction equation we obtained in Section 13.2. If we then calculate the coefficient of determination R^2, we find that $R^2 = .951$. Thus level of technology and percentage that is urban together explain 95.1% of the variance in life expectancy for our sample of ten nations. We summarize the values obtained from the bivariate and multivariate prediction equations of life expectancy in Table 13.5.

To determine which equation best predicts life expectancy, we compare the coefficients of determination in Table 13.5. It is clear that the multivariate prediction equation predicts life expectancy more accurately for these nations than the bivariate equation. Level of technology and percentage that is urban together explain 95.1% of the variance in life expectancy, whereas level of

TABLE 13.5

Bivariate and multivariate prediction equations of life expectancy obtained from data in Table 13.4

Y: life expectancy	
X_1: level of technology	
X_2: percentage that is urban	
$\hat{Y} = a + bX$	$\hat{Y} = a + b_1X_1 + b_2X_2$
$a = 53.189$	$a = 41.388$
$b = .494$	$b_1 = .358$
$r^2 = .682$	$b_2 = .265$
	$R^2 = .951$

technology alone explains only 68.2% of the variance in life expectancy. In other words, the multivariate prediction equation explains nearly 1.4 times more of the variance in life expectancy than does the simple bivariate equation (95.1/68.2 = 1.394).

The information in Table 13.5 can also be used to examine another important assumption of regression — namely, that an independent variable is not correlated with the error that results from using the variable to predict Y. If the error in the bivariate prediction equation for life expectancy is related to the level of technology, this could mean that other important variables related to level of technology are missing from the prediction equation. For example, if technology is related to the percentage of the population that is urban, and the latter variable is not included in the prediction equation, the regression slope b will be a biased estimate of the slope for the population. In other words, b will over- or underestimate the size of the slope for the population. Recall from our discussion in Chapters 1 and 12 that the importance of statistics to the social sciences is to enable us to make inferences about the population by analyzing a sample that was drawn from the population. That is, we use statistics to measure the goodness of an inference (e.g., partial regression slope) that is obtained from sample data.

In our present example level of technology (X_1) may appear to account for some of the variance in life expectancy that is actually due to percentage that is urban (X_2), and the two independent variables might also be related. In this case the slope b for the variable technology will be too large if percentage that is urban is not included in the prediction equation. In other words, b will overestimate the size of the slope for the population.

To determine whether this assumption has been met for our prediction of life expectancy, we compare the regression coefficient b to the partial regression coefficient b_1. We can see from Table 13.5 that the value for b (.494) is considerably larger than b_1 (.358). Thus we will obtain an overestimated value of the regression coefficient b if percentage that is urban is excluded from the prediction equation.

The information in Table 13.5 shows that although the magnitude of the relationship between level of technology and life expectancy becomes somewhat smaller when percentage that is urban is held constant, level of technology is still very important in the prediction of life expectancy for our sample of nations. However, there are other possible outcomes for a bivariate relationship when a third variable is controlled. In the following section we explore some of these outcomes.

EXERCISES

9. One of the most important assumptions underlying bivariate regression is that the theoretical model represented by the prediction equation is valid. What is one necessary condition for this assumption to be met?

10. What are two ways that we can determine whether a two-variable or a three-variable prediction equation best predicts the dependent variable?

11. Refer to Table 13.5. Suppose that both r^2 and R^2 are equal to .682. What would this suggest about the two prediction equations?

12. Refer to the data of Table 13.4 and the accompanying computer output.
   a. Locate the bivariate and multiple regression equations $\hat{Y} = a + bX_1$ and $\hat{Y} = a + b_1X_1 + b_2X_2$.
   b. Compare these results to those shown in Table 13.5.
   c. Compare the R^2 values for the two prediction equations.

EXERCISE 12

```
MTB > REGRESS 'LIFE' 1 'TECH'

The regression equation is
LIFE = 53.2 + 0.494 TECH

Predictor       Coef       Stdev     t-ratio          p
Constant      53.189       3.321       16.02      0.000
TECH          0.4941      0.1192        4.14      0.003

s = 5.636       R-sq = 68.2%      R-sq(adj) = 64.2%

Analysis of Variance

SOURCE        DF          SS          MS         F          p
Regression     1      545.45      545.45     17.17     0.003
Error          8      254.15       31.77
Total          9      799.60
```

```
MTB > REGRESS 'LIFE' 2 'TECH' 'URBAN'

The regression equation is
LIFE = 41.4 + 0.358 TECH + 0.265 URBAN

Predictor       Coef       Stdev     t-ratio        p
Constant       41.411       2.353      17.60     0.000
TECH           0.35772    0.05459       6.55     0.000
URBAN          0.26471    0.04264       6.21     0.000

s = 2.362       R-sq = 95.1%      R-sq(adj) = 93.7%

Analysis of Variance

SOURCE         DF          SS          MS         F         p
Regression      2      760.54      380.27     68.14     0.000
Error           7       39.06        5.58
Total           9      799.60

SOURCE         DF      SEQ SS
TECH            1      545.45
URBAN           1      215.08

Unusual Observations
Obs.    TECH       LIFE         Fit  Stdev.Fit   Residual   St.Resid
  2     10.0     53.000      57.959      1.007     -4.959      -2.32R

R denotes an obs. with a large st. resid.
```

13.8   OUTCOMES FOR A BIVARIATE RELATIONSHIP WHEN CONTROLLING FOR A THIRD VARIABLE

In Chapter 11 we presented several possible outcomes for a bivariate relationship when a third variable is controlled, involving variables measured on nominal and ordinal scales. Multiple regression and correlation can be used to examine these outcomes when variables are measured on interval and ratio scales. We illustrate with an example.

A study of 250 college students who have completed their first year of college shows a fairly strong correlation between GPA for the year and study time; the Pearson product-moment correlation coefficient for the two variables is .65.

Now suppose an educational researcher argues that this relationship is *spurious* when controlling for a third variable, SAT scores. Recall from Chapter 11 that **spuriousness** means that the relationship is not true because a third variable is affecting both the independent variable and the dependent variable. In other words, a bivariate relationship appears to exist only because both variables are influenced by a third variable. Thus, when the relevant third variable is controlled, the bivariate association disappears.

The educational researcher is suggesting, then, that there is no real relationship between study time (X_1) and GPA for the first year (Y), because both variables are influenced by students' SAT scores (X_2). How would we determine whether the relationship between GPA and study time is spurious because of SAT scores?

Multiple regression and correlation allow us to test this hypothesis of spuriousness by controlling for (holding constant) SAT scores. If the relationship between study time and GPA then disappears, we conclude that the association is indeed spurious. To test the hypothesis of spuriousness, we calculate the partial correlation coefficient between GPA and study time, controlling for SAT scores, and compare it to the Pearson correlation coefficient.

Our research example was previously discussed in Example 13.2. In that example, we calculated the partial coefficient for the relationship between GPA and study time to be .64 when SAT scores are controlled. Since the value of the partial correlation coefficient is nearly identical to the Pearson product-moment correlation coefficient (.65), we would reject the hypothesis of spuriousness.

Another way to assess whether a relationship is spurious is to examine the bivariate correlation coefficients. If the correlation between the independent variable and the third variable is of about the same magnitude as the correlation between the dependent variable and the third variable, the third variable may be influencing both the independent and the dependent variables. In this case the bivariate association would be spurious. However, the partial correlation coefficients should be calculated to be certain that the relationship is in fact spurious.

We showed in Example 13.2 that the correlation between study time and SAT scores was only .25, compared to the correlation between GPA and SAT scores of .50. These correlational values indicate that the relationship between study time and GPA is not spurious because of SAT scores. However, the relationship could still be spurious because of some other variable that was not included.

From our examination of bivariate correlations and partial correlations in Example 13.2, we would probably conclude that the association between study time (X_1) and GPA (Y) was *replicated* when SAT scores (X_2) were held constant. Recall from Chapter 11 that **replication** occurs when a bivariate association does not change appreciably when a third variable is controlled. That the partial correlation (.63) is nearly identical to the bivariate correlation (.65) shows that the relationship between study time and GPA is replicated when SAT scores are controlled.

EXAMPLE 13.6   A sociologist is hired by a consortium of higher educational institutions in the South to determine which factors influence the amount of money that college alumni contribute to the alumni fund. The sociologist hypothesizes that both annual income and the number of yearly contacts by the college for money will predict the amount of money contributed to the fund. The researcher then obtains a random sample of 400 individuals who were previously students at one of the colleges in the consortium and asks them their annual income and how often they have been contacted by their college in the past year. The data obtained from the study appear in Table 13.6.

TABLE 13.6

Variables and regression and correlation estimates from a sample of alumni of Southern colleges

| Y: amount former student contributed last year |
| X_1: number of times contacted by college last year |
| X_2: annual income of former student |

$r_{y1} = .40$	$r_{y1.2} = .403$
$r_{y2} = .65$	$r_{y2.1} = .651$
$r_{12} = .15$	

Based on the correlation coefficients, is the relationship between alumni contacts and alumni contributions spurious because of annual income, or is the relationship replicated? Explain your answer.

SOLUTION

Because the bivariate correlations in Table 13.6 show that $r_{12} = .15$, a low correlation, it would appear that the relationship between alumni contacts and alumni contributions is not spurious because of annual income. The partial correlation coefficient $r_{y1.2}$ is further proof that the relationship is not spurious, since $r_{y1.2}$ is nearly identical to r_{y1}. In other words, the strength of the relationship between alumni contacts and alumni contributions does not change when annual income is controlled. These findings suggest that the relationship between alumni contacts and alumni contributions is replicated when annual income is held constant.

Another possible outcome for a bivariate relationship when controlling for a third variable is *interpretation*. You will recall that the statistical outcomes for both a spurious relationship and an interpreted relationship are identical; that is, the bivariate association disappears when the third variable is held constant. However, the theoretical meaning of interpretation is very different from that of spuriousness. **Interpretation** occurs when the control variable interprets or mediates the relationship between an independent variable and a dependent variable. In other words, the control variable connects the independent variable to the dependent variable. Thus it is the researcher's knowledge of theory and/or prior research that determines if a bivariate association is spurious because of the third variable or if the association is mediated by the third variable.

EXAMPLE 13.7	Refer to the data in Example 13.6. Suppose that the bivariate association between alumni contacts (X_1) and alumni contributions (Y) disappears when annual income (X_2) is controlled. Is it likely that annual income mediates or interprets the relationship between alumni contacts and alumni contributions? Explain your answer.
SOLUTION	It is doubtful that the relationship between alumni contacts and alumni contributions is mediated by annual income. It would make little sense to hypothesize that the number of alumni contacts will influence or cause a former student's annual income.

It is frequently the case that a control variable does interpret a bivariate relationship. We illustrate with an example.

EXAMPLE 13.8	Suppose that the sociologist who conducted the study of alumni for the consortium of educational institutions (Example 13.6) hypothesized that age and annual income of former students would most likely influence the amount of money that these students contributed annually to the alumni fund. Furthermore, suppose that the sociologist obtained the regression and correlation estimates shown in Table 13.7.

TABLE 13.7

Variables and regression and correlation estimates from a sample of alumni of Southern colleges

Y: **amount former student contributed last year**

X_1: **age of former student**

X_2: **annual income of former student**

$$r_{y1} = .40 \qquad r_{y1.2} = .067$$
$$r_{y2} = .65 \qquad r_{y2.1} = .562$$
$$r_{12} = .55$$

What happens to the relationship between age and alumni contributions when annual income is controlled? Is the relationship between age and alumni contributions spurious because of annual income, or does annual income mediate the relationship?

SOLUTION

The relationship between age and alumni contributions nearly disappears when annual income is controlled: r_{y1} is .40, and $r_{y1.2}$ is only .067. This suggests that either spuriousness or interpretation characterizes the association between age and alumni contributions. It is likely that annual income mediates the bivariate relationship, since we know that age does influence annual income; individuals tend to earn more the longer they are employed. In turn, annual income affects alumni contributions. It is doubtful that the bivariate association is spurious because of income. Although annual income influences alumni contributions, it is not reasonable to conclude that income influences how old a person is.

In Chapter 11 we discussed one additional outcome, *specification* or *interaction*, for a bivariate association when a third variable is controlled. For nominal and ordinal variables, **specification** or **interaction** occurs when the bivariate association is of a different magnitude or sign for each category of the control variable. When this outcome is present, we say that the control variable *interacts with* the independent variable to influence the dependent variable.

Testing for interaction effects is much more complex when variables are measured on interval and ratio scales. For example, if a social scientist hypothesizes that age (X_1) interacts with education (X_2) to influence annual income (Y), the resulting multiple regression prediction equation is

$$\hat{Y} = a + b_1 X_1 + b_2 X_2 + b_3 X_3$$

where X_3 is the interaction of age and education. The variable X_3 is created by multiplying corresponding values of X_1 and X_2. Thus for an individual who is 40 years old and who has completed 13 years of formal schooling, the value of X_3 is 520. Many social researchers and statisticians think it is problematic to test for interaction effects when variables are measured on interval or ratio scales. The discussion of the statistical problems with this form of variable interaction is beyond the scope of this text.

Most social scientists who examine the interaction of variables in a multiple regression framework test for the interaction of nominal or ordinal variables with interval or ratio variables. For instance, a sociologist might hypothesize that gender interacts with education to influence annual income. That is, the influence of education on income is hypothesized to depend on the gender of the employee. Although the inclusion of nominal or ordinal variables in a multiple regression analysis creates no statistical problem, the treatment of this topic is also beyond the scope of this text (see Bohrnstedt and Knoke, 1982).

In this section we have compared Pearson product-moment correlation coefficients with partial correlation coefficients to determine whether and how a third variable affects a bivariate relationship. We used these comparisons because they are most analogous to the measures used in Chapter 11 to explore the influence of a third variable when variables are measured on nominal or ordinal scales. However, since interval and ratio data enable us to derive prediction equations to describe the relationships between variables, we could also have compared regression coefficients with partial regression coefficients or compared standardized slopes with standardized partial slopes. The interpretation of these comparisons is identical to the interpretation of the comparisons of correlation coefficients. For example, if b_1 is similar in magnitude to b, we would conclude that the relationship between the independent and dependent variables is replicated when we control for a third variable.

EXERCISES

13. What are two ways that a social researcher might use to determine whether a third variable is influencing a bivariate relationship if the variables are measured on interval or ratio scales?

14.. Refer to Table 13.6. If $r_{y1} = .55$ and $r_{y1.2} = .04$, what would you conclude about the relationship between alumni contacts and contributions to the alumni fund? Explain your answer.

15. A sociologist hypothesizes that the number of years that a male worker has been employed (X_1) influences the worker's annual income (Y). The sociologist decides to control for the worker's age (X_2). After surveying a random sample of 250 male workers and analyzing the data, the researcher finds that $r_{y1} = .68$, $r_{12} = .59$, and $r_{y1.2} = .05$. Does the third variable, age, influence the relationship between years previously employed and annual income for this sample of male workers? Explain your answer.

16. Refer to Exercise 15. Is the relationship between years previously employed and income likely to be spurious because of age, or is the relationship likely to be interpreted or mediated by age? Explain your answer.

13.9   THE PROBLEM OF MULTICOLLINEARITY IN MULTIPLE REGRESSION

In Section 13.7 we examined some of the assumptions of regression and correlation. One important assumption is that an independent variable is not correlated with the error that results from using the variable to predict Y. If there is such a correlation, it could mean that other important variables are missing from the regression prediction equation, and the regression coefficient will then be biased. In Table 13.5 we showed the regression and correlation estimates when level of technology is used alone to predict life expectancy for a sample of ten nations, and the estimates when both level of technology (X_1) and percentage that is urban (X_2) are used to predict life expectancy (Y). Recall that our comparison of b and b_1 showed that b overestimates the size of the population slope because level of technology and percentage that is urban are correlated (.402).

The correlation between independent variables is not a serious problem in multiple regression if the correlation is relatively small. However, when the correlation of independent variables is relatively high (say, .70 or above), the results of a multiple regression analysis become increasingly unreliable. In this situation the problem of **multicollinearity** exists in the regression analysis. We illustrate with an example.

Table 13.8 shows data on life expectancy, per capita gross national product (GNP) in hundreds of U.S. dollars, and level of technology for the sample of ten nations we have discussed throughout this chapter.

TABLE 13.8

Three demographic
characteristics of ten
nations

Nation	Y Life Expectancy (in years)	X_1 Per Capita GNP (in US $100s)	X_2 Level of Technology Development (0–100)
Algeria	60	24.50	17
Bolivia	53	5.70	10
Chile	71	15.10	22
Colombia	66	12.40	15
Egypt	60	6.50	13
Ireland	74	74.80	48
Japan	79	201.40	53
Malawi	49	1.60	12
Peru	65	14.40	12
Romania	71	54.00	33

Source: Population Reference Bureau, *1990 World Population Data Sheet* (Washington, D.C.: Population Reference Bureau, Inc. 1990).

Suppose that we are interested in the effect of per capita GNP on life expectancy for the ten nations, and we use the prediction equation

$$\hat{Y} = a + bX_1$$

where Y = life expectancy and X_1 = per capita GNP.

In calculating values of a and b, we find that $a = 60.202$ and $b = .112$. Thus our bivariate prediction equation for life expectancy is

$$\hat{Y} = 60.202 + .112X_1$$

The value of b shows that for each \$100 increase in a nation's per capita GNP, the life expectancy of the nation increases by .112 years, on average. Thus the predicted life expectancy for Egypt, for example, is

$$\hat{Y} = 60.202 + .112(6.50) = 60.935$$

Now suppose we decide that level of technology should be included in the prediction equation as the independent variable X_2. Here X_2 is measured on an interval scale. Our prediction equation thus becomes

$$\hat{Y} = a + b_1X_1 + b_2X_2$$

In calculating values for the multiple regression estimates, we find that $a = 52.987$, $b_1 = -.005$, and $b_2 = .511$, so our multivariate prediction equation for life expectancy is

$$\hat{Y} = 52.987 - .005X_1 + .511X_2$$

You will note that b is positive but b_1 is negative. Thus the interpretation of b_1 is that an increase in per capita GNP tends to lower a nation's life expectancy when technology is held constant. The thoughtful researcher would probably conclude that a negative relationship between per capita GNP and life expectancy is highly unreasonable, regardless of what other variables might be included in the prediction equation. The important issue, then, is to determine why the relationship between per capita GNP and life expectancy changes drastically when level of technology is included in the prediction equation.

When the magnitude and/or sign of a partial regression coefficient is highly unreasonable, this is a clue that multicollinearity might be present in the data. Multicollinearity can cause large changes in the values and changes in the signs of multiple regression estimates that result in an unreliable prediction equation. However, the presence of changes in the magnitude or sign of regression estimates does not actually establish that multicollinearity is present.

To determine whether multicollinearity exists, we must look at the Pearson product-moment correlation coefficients of the independent variables. For our sample of ten nations, the correlation between per capita GNP and level of technology is .719. Thus we would conclude that multicollinearity does exist in our data.

EXAMPLE 13.9

An industrial sociologist is hired by the COMSAC Corporation to design a skill-level test that will help predict the job performance of employees. The COMSAC Corporation then requests that the sociologist establish which factors are most important in determining how well employees are doing their jobs. The corporation is particularly interested in finding out whether the skill-level test or a standard IQ test is the better predictor of workers' job performance. Variables and regression and correlation estimates obtained for a sample of 150 employees of the corporation are shown in Table 13.9. Can the sociologist conclude that one of the tests for workers is relatively more important in predicting job performance?

TABLE 13.9

Variables and regression and correlation estimates from a sample of 150 workers

Y: job performance (0–100)	
X_1: skill-level test scores (0–100)	
X_2: IQ test scores (50–200)	
$r_{y1} = .682$	$b_s = .682$
$r_{y2} = .55$	$b_{s1} = -.042$
$r_{12} = .75$	$b_{s2} = .314$

SOLUTION

To answer this question, we would first compare b_s and b_{s1}, the standardized partial regression slopes. Recall from Section 13.5 that partial regression estimates must be converted to z-scores to determine the relative influence that an independent variable has on a dependent variable, if independent variables in the prediction equation are measured in different units.

We might expect the relative influence of the skill-level test to decrease in value when we control for IQ if the two variables are correlated. However, the value of b_{s1} is unreasonably small, and its sign is negative. These differences between b_s and b_{s1} suggest that there is multicollinearity between skill-level test scores and IQ test scores. If we examine the Pearson product-moment correlation for the two variables, we see that $r_{12} = .75$. The high value of the correlation suggests that multicollinearity is indeed present. Thus the sociologist cannot conclude that one of these tests is the better predictor of job performance, because the variables are too highly correlated.

Besides examining the correlation coefficients, there are other ways to test for the presence of multicollinearity in a multiple regression analysis, but these are beyond the scope of this text (see Lewis-Beck, 1990). Techniques for correcting multicollinearity in the data also exist, including dropping one or more of the independent variables from the multiple regression prediction equation. However, these techniques are also beyond the scope of an introductory text.

EXERCISES

17. Define multicollinearity.

18. In performing a multiple regression analysis, how might you first notice that there could be a problem with multicollinearity?

19. Refer to Exercise 14. How would you determine if multicollinearity exists in the data?

20. A statistical software package was used to fit two regression equations to the data of Table 13.8. (See the accompanying output.)

    a. Identify the two regression equations and compare these results to those shown in the text.

    b. Do these results also point toward a multicollinearity problem? Explain what additional data, if any, would be helpful in reaching this conclusion.

EXERCISE 20

```
MTB > REGRESS 'LIFE' 1 'GNP'

The regression equation is
LIFE = 60.2 + 0.112 GNP

Predictor        Coef       Stdev    t-ratio        p
Constant       60.202       2.669      22.56    0.000
GNP           0.11204     0.03761       2.98    0.018

s = 6.884       R-sq = 52.6%     R-sq(adj) = 46.7%

Analysis of Variance

SOURCE          DF          SS          MS         F         p
Regression       1      420.46      420.46      8.87     0.018
Error            8      379.14       47.39
Total            9      799.60

Unusual Observations
Obs.      GNP       LIFE      Fit Stdev.Fit  Residual   St.Resid
  7       201      79.00     82.77     6.41     -3.77      -1.50 X

X denotes an obs. whose X value gives it large influence.
MTB > REGRESS 'LIFE' 2 'GNP' 'TECH'


The regression equation is
LIFE = 53.0 - 0.0051 GNP + 0.512 TECH

Predictor        Coef       Stdev    t-ratio        p
Constant       52.986       4.533      11.69    0.000
GNP          -0.00514     0.07115      -0.07    0.944
TECH           0.5117      0.2755       1.86    0.106

s = 6.023       R-sq = 68.2%     R-sq(adj) = 59.2%
```

```
Analysis of Variance

SOURCE         DF          SS          MS         F        p
Regression      2      545.64      272.82      7.52    0.018
Error           7      253.96       36.28
Total           9      799.60

SOURCE         DF      SEQ SS
GNP             1      420.46
TECH            1      125.18


Unusual Observations
Obs.      GNP       LIFE       Fit  Stdev.Fit  Residual   St.Resid
   7      201      79.00     79.07       5.95     -0.07      -0.08 X

X denotes an obs. whose X value gives it large influence.

MTB > CORRELATION 'GNP' 'TECH'

Correlation of GNP and TECH = 0.887
```

SUMMARY

This chapter is concerned with multivariate relationships between interval and ratio variables. It is a natural extension of Chapter 12, where we examined the bivariate regression prediction equation, measures of association between an independent variable and a dependent variable, and the coefficient of determination.

We use the relationship between one dependent variable and two independent variables to illustrate the basic concepts of multiple regression and correlation. We demonstrate how to obtain least-squares coefficients for the multiple regression prediction equation and how to interpret these coefficients. A partial correlation coefficient measures the strength of the relationship between a dependent and an independent variable while controlling for a second independent variable. We also relate partial correlation coefficients to the slopes of a standardized multiple regression prediction equation. We then show how to calculate and interpret the coefficient of determination R^2.

Two important assumptions underlying bivariate regression and correlation, discussed in Chapter 12, are applied to multivariate data. Some possible outcomes for a bivariate association when controlling for a third variable are also explored by comparing bivariate correlations and partial correlation coefficients. Finally, we consider the potential problem of multicollinearity in multiple regression analysis when two independent variables are highly correlated.

KEY WORDS

Coefficient of determination   The proportion of the total variance in a dependent variable that is explained by the independent variables.

Interpretation   An outcome for a relationship between an independent and a dependent variable when a third variable is controlled. The association disappears, because the third variable connects the independent variable to the dependent variable.

Multicollinearity   A problem in multiple regression in which two independent variables are highly correlated. Results in a highly unreliable multiple regression prediction equation.

Multiple correlation coefficient   The measure of dependence among three or more variables measured on an interval or ratio scale, which equals the square root of the coefficient of determination.

Multiple regression   A statistical technique for analyzing multivariate data measured on interval or ratio scales. The dependent variable is predicted by two or more independent variables.

Partial correlation coefficient   The measure of linear dependence between two variables while controlling for one or more other variables.

Regression plane   A three-dimensional plot of data in which each dot represents a trio of values on a plane: one for the dependent variable and one for each of the two independent variables.

Replication   An outcome for a relationship between an independent and a dependent variable when a third variable is controlled. For variables measured on interval or ratio scales, the bivariate correlation is of the same magnitude and sign as the partial correlation coefficient. The third variable has no effect.

Specification (interaction)   An outcome for a relationship between an independent and a dependent variable when a third variable is controlled. The effect of the independent variable on the dependent variable varies with (depends on) the values of another independent variable.

Spuriousness   An outcome for a relationship between an independent and a dependent variable when a third variable is controlled. The bivariate relationship disappears, because the third variable is the cause of both the independent and dependent variables.

KEY FORMULAS

Coefficient of determination, R^2

$$R^2 = b_{s1}r_{y1} + b_{s2}r_{y2}$$

Least-squares estimates for multiple regression equation, $\hat{Y} = a + b_1X_1 + b_2X_2$

$$b_1 = \frac{s_y}{s_1}\left(\frac{r_{y1} - r_{y2}r_{12}}{1 - r_{12}^2}\right)$$

$$b_2 = \frac{s_y}{s_2}\left(\frac{r_{y2} - r_{y1}r_{12}}{1 - r_{12}^2}\right)$$

$$a = \bar{Y} - b_1\bar{X}_1 - b_2\bar{X}_2$$

Partial correlation coefficients

$$r_{y1.2} = \frac{r_{y1} - r_{y2}r_{12}}{\sqrt{(1 - r_{y2}^2)(1 - r_{12}^2)}}$$

$$r_{y2.1} = \frac{r_{y2} - r_{y1}r_{12}}{\sqrt{(1 - r_{y1}^2)(1 - r_{12}^2)}}$$

SUPPLEMENTARY EXERCISES FOR CHAPTER 13

21. Refer to Table 13.1, where Y = annual income, X_1 = education, and X_2 = number of children. For these data, $r_{y1} = .736$, $r_{y2} = -.768$, and $r_{12} = -.145$. Determine the least-squares prediction equation that best predicts Y and interpret the values of a, b_1, and b_2. (*Hint*: First calculate s_y, s_1, and s_2.) What is the predicted annual income for a wife who has 13 years of education and 3 children?

22. Refer to Exercise 21. The value of b for education when number of children is *not* held constant is 2957.32. Explain why b is different from b_1.

23. Refer to Exercise 21. Calculate the magnitude of the relationship between education and income when the number of children is held constant, and interpret your answer. How much of the variability in annual income is explained by education when number of children is held constant?

24. Refer to Exercise 21. Calculate the coefficient of determination. Interpret your answer.

25. Refer to Exercise 21. Is multicollinearity evident in these data? Explain your answer.

26. Refer to Table 13.6. Toogaloo University contacts former students twice a year, and Henshaw State contacts former students seven times a year. If a former student of each of these universities has an annual income of $30,000, how much more would Henshaw State be predicted to receive from its alumni than Toogaloo University would receive from its alumni?

27. What advantages does multiple regression have compared to bivariate regression?

28. Can you draw a freehand regression line for a trivariate multiple regression prediction equation? Explain.

29. Two criminologists were interested in the relationships among age, poverty, and property crime. They sampled 45 metropolitan areas of 100,000 or more population and used percentage of the population age 15 to 24 (X_1) and percentage of the population below the poverty level (X_2) to predict the property crime rate (Y) per 10,000 population. Their multiple regression prediction equation was

$$\hat{Y} = 19.424 + 1.873X_1 + 1.526X_2$$

  a. Interpret the value of the intercept.
  b. Interpret the values for b_1 and b_2.
  c. Calculate the predicted property crime rate for a metropolitan area in which X_1 is 23% and X_2 is 16%.

30. Refer to Table 13.1. Use the data to derive a multiple regression prediction equation for annual income, and interpret a, b_1, and b_2.

31. Refer to Table 13.1.
  a. Calculate $r_{y1.2}$ and $r_{y2.1}$, and interpret your answers.
  b. Square each partial correlation coefficient and interpret your answers.

32. Refer to part a of Exercise 31. Derive the standardized multiple regression prediction equation and interpret b_{s1} and b_{s2}.

33. Refer to Exercise 29. Can you calculate a standardized multiple regression prediction equation based on the data given here? Explain.

34. Refer to Exercise 30. Can the magnitudes of b_1 and b_2 be compared to determine the relative importance of the independent variables as predictors of Y? Explain.

35. Refer to Exercise 81 in Chapter 12. Assume that Y is the number of births per unmarried woman, X_1 is the poverty rate, and X_2 is population density.
  a. Calculate b_{s1} and b_{s2} and interpret your answers.
  b. Calculate $r_{y1.2}$ and $r_{y2.1}$ and interpret your answers.
  c. Calculate the coefficient of determination and interpret your answer.

36. John Olson (1990) studied the relationship between crime and religion for nearly 1600 counties in the Northeast, Midwest, and West. He reported that counties with higher levels of urbanization and education had higher crime rates. You replicate the study for 400 counties in the Southeastern United States and report the following information:
- Y = crime rate
- X_1 = percentage of persons living in urban areas
- X_2 = percentage of persons graduating from high school
- $r_{y1} = .61$
- $r_{y2} = .33$
- $r_{12} = .41$

  a. Calculate $r_{y1.2}$ and $r_{y2.1}$ and interpret your answers.
  b. Calculate the coefficient of determination and interpret your answer.

37. Refer to Exercise 36.

 a. Square $r_{y1.2}$ and $r_{y2.1}$ and interpret your answers.

 b. Add the squared values in part a. Is this value the same as the coefficient of determination in part b of Exercise 32? Explain.

38. Refer to Exercise 29. In using X_1 to predict Y, the researchers' bivariate regression prediction equation was

$$\hat{Y} = 24.367 + 2.691X_1$$

 a. Compare the values of b and b_1.

 b. What important assumption underlying regression and correlation applies to part a? Explain.

39. Refer to Exercise 35. Does population density influence the relationship between number of births to unmarried women and poverty rate? Explain.

40. Refer to Exercise 36.

 a. Compare r_{y2} and $r_{y2.1}$.

 b. Does percentage that is urban influence the relationship between crime rate and education? Explain.

41. What is one indication that multicollinearity is present in your data?

42. Refer to Exercise 29. Does multicollinearity appear to be present? Explain.

43. Refer to Exercise 29. Suppose that b_2 was $-.023$. What would this suggest about the presence of multicollinearity? Explain.

44. Refer to Database B, Appendix Table 8. Select countries with a level of technology of 50 or higher. Assume that Y is freedoms, X_1 is level of technology, and X_2 is percentage of the population that is urban.

 a. Derive the multiple regression prediction equation and interpret b_1 and b_2.

 b. What is the predicted value of freedoms when level of technology is 65 and percentage that is urban is 78?

45. Refer to Exercise 44.

 a. Calculate r_{y1}, r_{y2}, and r_{12}.

 b. Calculate $r_{y1.2}$ and compare to r_{y1}.

 c. Calculate R^2 and interpret your answer.

46. Refer to Exercise 45. Does percentage that is urban influence the relationship between freedoms and level of technology? Explain.

47. A social researcher reanalyzed 1985 demographic data for ten nations. Use the accompanying computer output for the data in Table 13.10 to do the following:

 a. Determine the least-square regression line

$$\hat{Y} = a + b_1X_1 + b_2X_2 + b_3X_3 + b_4X_4$$

 b. Predict Y (population increase) for birth rate, $X_1 = 30$; death rate, $X_2 = 15$; life expectancy, $X_3 = 65$; and per capita gross national product, $X_4 = \$1100$.

 c. Does the regression seem to fit the data?

	Percent Projected Population Increase for 2000	Birth Rate	Death Rate	Life Expectancy (yr)	Per Capita Gross National Product
Nation	Y	X_1	X_2	X_3	X_4
Bolivia	53.2	42	16	51	$ 510
Cuba	14.9	17	6	73	1050
Cyprus	14.3	29	9	74	3720
Egypt	39.3	37	10	57	700
Ghana	60.1	47	15	52	320
Jamaica	21.7	28	6	70	1300
Nigeria	71.6	48	17	50	760
South Africa	40.1	35	14	54	2450
South Korea	21.1	23	6	66	2010
Turkey	36.9	35	10	63	1230

TABLE 13.10 Demographic characteristics of ten nations

Source: Population Reference Bureau, *1985 World Population Data Sheet* (Washington, D.C.: Population Reference Bureau, Inc., 1985).

EXERCISE 47

```
MTB > REGRESS 'POPUL' 4 'BIRTH' 'DEATH' 'LIFE' 'GNP';
SUBC> PREDICT 30 15 65 1100.

The regression equation is
POPUL = 27.7 + 0.738 BIRTH + 1.46 DEATH - 0.422 LIFE - 0.00406 GNP

Predictor       Coef        Stdev      t-ratio         p
Constant       27.73       40.59         0.68     0.525
BIRTH         0.7384      0.4275         1.73     0.145
DEATH          1.457       1.202         1.21     0.280
LIFE         -0.4224      0.5055        -0.84     0.441
GNP        -0.004056    0.002120        -1.91     0.114

s = 4.910       R-sq = 96.6%     R-sq(adj) = 93.8%

Analysis of Variance

SOURCE          DF          SS          MS         F         p
Regression       4     3377.16      844.29     35.02     0.001
Error            5      120.54       24.11
Total            9     3497.70

SOURCE          DF      SEQ SS
BIRTH            1     3097.66
DEATH            1       72.67
LIFE             1      118.56
GNP              1       88.26


      Fit   Stdev.Fit        95% C.I.            95% P.I.
    39.81        7.80   (  19.75,  59.87)  (  16.11,  63.51) XX

X  denotes a row with X values away from the center
XX denotes a row with very extreme X values
```

48. Refer to the data in Table 13.10. Use the accompanying Minitab output.

a. Use the computer output to find the following least-squares regression equations:

$$\hat{Y} = a + b_1 X_1$$
$$\hat{Y} = a + b_1 X_1 + b_2 X_2$$
$$\hat{Y} = a + b_1 X_1 + b_2 X_2 + b_3 X_3$$

b. Refer to Exercise 47 and the output below. Does it appear that all four variables are needed to predict Y? The variables X_1, X_2, and X_3? The variables X_1 and X_2? Or might knowledge of X_1 (birth rate) be sufficient? Explain.

EXERCISE 48

```
MTB > REGRESS 'POPUL' 1 'BIRTH'

The regression equation is
POPUL = - 25.6 + 1.84 BIRTH

Predictor       Coef        Stdev       t-ratio        p
Constant      -25.563       8.297        -3.08      0.015
BIRTH           1.8441      0.2343        7.87      0.000

s = 7.071       R-sq = 88.6%      R-sq(adj) = 87.1%

Analysis of Variance

SOURCE         DF          SS           MS          F         p
Regression      1        3097.7       3097.7      61.95     0.000
Error           8         400.0         50.0
Total           9        3497.7

Unusual Observations
Obs.    BIRTH       POPUL       Fit Stdev.Fit   Residual   St.Resid
  3      29.0       14.30      27.92     2.54     -13.62      -2.06R

R denotes an obs. with a large st. resid.

MTB > REGRESS 'POPUL' 2 'BIRTH' 'DEATH'

The regression equation is
POPUL = - 21.7 + 1.22 BIRTH + 1.60 DEATH

Predictor       Coef        Stdev       t-ratio        p
Constant      -21.740       8.590        -2.53      0.039
BIRTH           1.2213      0.5486        2.23      0.061
DEATH           1.598       1.282         1.25      0.253

s = 6.839       R-sq = 90.6%      R-sq(adj) = 88.0%

Analysis of Variance

SOURCE         DF          SS           MS          F         p
Regression      2        3170.3       1585.2      33.90     0.000
Error           7         327.4         46.8
Total           9        3497.7

SOURCE         DF        SEQ SS
BIRTH           1        3097.7
DEATH           1          72.7
```

```
Unusual Observations
Obs.   BIRTH     POPUL     Fit  Stdev.Fit  Residual   St.Resid
 3     29.0      14.30     28.06    2.45     -13.76     -2.16R

R denotes an obs. with a large st. resid.

MTB > REGRESS 'POPUL' 3 'BIRTH' 'DEATH' 'LIFE'

The regression equation is
POPUL = 59.3 + 0.916 BIRTH + 0.40 DEATH - 0.944 LIFE

Predictor      Coef      Stdev    t-ratio        p
Constant      59.33      44.54       1.33    0.231
BIRTH        0.9159     0.5013       1.83    0.117
DEATH         0.398      1.283       0.31    0.767
LIFE        -0.9439     0.5114      -1.85    0.114

s = 5.899      R-sq = 94.0%     R-sq(adj) = 91.0%

Analysis of Variance

SOURCE        DF          SS         MS        F        p
Regression     3      3288.9     1096.3    31.50    0.000
Error          6       208.8       34.8
Total          9      3497.7

SOURCE        DF      SEQ SS
BIRTH          1      3097.7
DEATH          1        72.7
LIFE           1       118.6
```

49. Use the data in the following table and the accompanying Minitab printout.
   a. Locate the regression line and predict average state and local taxes paid for an average personal income of $12,000 and $13,500.
   b. Does the least-squares line seem to fit the data? (See Figure 13.2 and the computer printout.)
   c. Locate r^2 and interpret its value.

EXERCISE 49

Average personal income and average state and local taxes paid in 10 states

State	Average Personal Income	Average State and Local Taxes Paid per Capita
Arkansas	$ 9,724	$ 771
California	14,344	1337
Connecticut	16,369	1434
Illinois	13,728	1255
Louisiana	10,850	1051
Mississippi	8857	769
New Jersey	15,282	1457
North Dakota	12,461	1110
Oregon	11,582	1229
Oklahoma	11,745	1123

EXERCISE 49

```
MTB > REGRESS 'TAXES' 1 'INCOME';
SUBC> PREDICT 12000;
SUBC> PREDICT 13500.

The regression equation is
TAXES = - 26 + 0.0944 INCOME

Predictor        Coef        Stdev      t-ratio        p
Constant        -26.3        148.5        -0.18      0.864
INCOME         0.09444      0.01169        8.08      0.000

s = 84.91       R-sq = 89.1%       R-sq(adj) = 87.7%

Analysis of Variance

SOURCE         DF          SS           MS          F          p
Regression      1        470263       470263      65.22      0.000
Error           8         57679         7210
Total           9        527942

Unusual Observations
Obs.   INCOME      TAXES       Fit Stdev.Fit   Residual   St.Resid
  9    11582      1229.0     1067.5     28.9      161.5       2.02R

R denotes an obs. with a large st. resid.

   Fit  Stdev.Fit        95% C.I.            95% P.I.
 1106.9      27.5    ( 1043.6, 1170.3)   (  901.1, 1312.8)

 1248.6      29.3    ( 1181.0, 1316.2)   ( 1041.4, 1455.8)
```

FIGURE 13.2

Computer-generated
graph and least-
squares line for the
data from Exercise 49

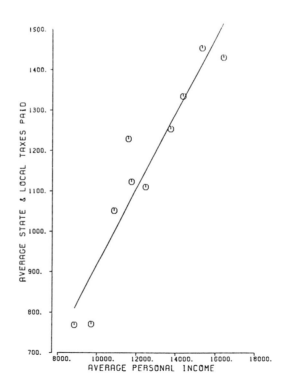

50. English, mathematics, and social studies achievement test scores (labeled ENGLACT, MATHACT, and SOCSACT, respectively) are displayed for 20 grade school children in the accompanying Minitab output. Determine pairwise correlation coefficients for ENGLACT, MATHACT, and SOCSACT.

EXERCISE 50

```
MTB > CORRELATE 'ENGLACT' 'MATHACT' 'SOCSACT'

         ENGLACT   MATHACT
MATHACT   0.595
SOCSACT   0.668     0.567

MTB > REGRESS 'SOCSACT' 1 'ENGLACT'

The regression equation is
SOCSACT = - 2.41 + 1.07 ENGLACT

Predictor      Coef      Stdev    t-ratio        p
Constant     -2.405      5.049      -0.48    0.640
ENGLACT      1.0689     0.2803       3.81    0.001

s = 5.341       R-sq = 44.7%      R-sq(adj) = 41.6%

Analysis of Variance

SOURCE        DF         SS         MS         F        p
Regression     1     414.72     414.72     14.54    0.001
Error         18     513.48      28.53
Total         19     928.20

Unusual Observations
Obs. ENGLACT    SOCSACT       Fit Stdev.Fit  Residual   St.Resid
  2    15.0      24.00      13.63      1.38     10.37      2.01R

R denotes an obs. with a large st. resid.

MTB > REGRESS 'SOCSACT' 2 'ENGLACT' 'MATHACT'

The regression equation is
SOCSACT = - 2.77 + 0.820 ENGLACT + 0.274 MATHACT

Predictor      Coef      Stdev    t-ratio        p
Constant     -2.766      4.992      -0.55    0.587
ENGLACT      0.8196     0.3443       2.38    0.029
MATHACT      0.2737     0.2250       1.22    0.240

s = 5.271       R-sq = 49.1%      R-sq(adj) = 43.1%

Analysis of Variance

SOURCE        DF         SS         MS         F        p
Regression     2     455.85     227.92      8.20    0.003
Error         17     472.35      27.79
Total         19     928.20

SOURCE        DF     SEQ SS
ENGLACT        1     414.72
MATHACT        1      41.13

Unusual Observations
Obs. ENGLACT    SOCSACT       Fit Stdev.Fit  Residual   St.Resid
  8    17.0      23.00      13.36      2.31      9.64      2.03R

R denotes an obs. with a large st. resid.
```

51. Refer to the computer output of Exercise 50.

    a. Identify the least-squares prediction equations

$$\hat{Y} = a + bX_1$$
$$\hat{Y} = a + b_1X_1 + b_2X_2$$

where

$$Y = \text{SOCSACT} \qquad X_1 = \text{ENGLACT} \qquad X_2 = \text{MATHACT}$$

    b. Which regression equation seems to predict Y better? Explain.

52. A sample of 15 students was drawn from Database A, Appendix Table 7; information on number of crimes (Y), year in college (X_1), age (X_2), and income of parents (X_3) is recorded in the accompanying table.

EXERCISE 52

Sample of 15 students drawn randomly from the data bank

Student ID	# of Crimes Y	Year in College X_1	Age X_2	Income of Parents X_3
004	18	3 (junior)	30	2 (middle)
011	18	4 (senior)	21	3 (upper)
015	15	3	20	2
016	22	2	29	3
056	18	4	24	3
060	13	1	18	3
063	12	3	28	1 (low)
067	17	3	22	3
081	18	4	22	3
112	18	4	21	2
134	20	3	22	3
144	16	3	27	2
146	21	4	26	3
150	13	4	20	3
161	20	3	33	1

Use the accompanying computer output to answer the following questions:

a. What are the means and standard deviations for the variables Y, X_1, X_2, and X_3?

b. Determine the least-squares regression equations for the following:

    1. $\hat{Y} = a + b_1X_1$

    2. $\hat{Y} = a + b_1X_1 + b_2X_2$

    3. $\hat{Y} = a + b_1X_1 + b_2X_2 + b_3X_3$

c. Based on the output, which model appears to fit the data best?

EXERCISE 52   MTB > DESCRIBE 'CRIMES' 'COLLEGE' 'AGE' 'INCOME'

	N	MEAN	MEDIAN	TRMEAN	STDEV	SEMEAN
CRIMES	15	17.267	18.000	17.308	2.987	0.771
COLLEGE	15	3.200	3.000	3.308	0.862	0.223
AGE	15	24.20	22.00	24.00	4.38	1.13
INCOME	15	2.467	3.000	2.538	0.743	0.192

	MIN	MAX	Q1	Q3
CRIMES	12.000	22.000	15.000	20.000
COLLEGE	1.000	4.000	3.000	4.000
AGE	18.00	33.00	21.00	28.00
INCOME	1.000	3.000	2.000	3.000

MTB > REGRESS 'CRIMES' 1 'COLLEGE'

The regression equation is
CRIMES = 15.4 + 0.596 COLLEGE

Predictor	Coef	Stdev	t-ratio	p
Constant	15.359	3.131	4.91	0.000
COLLEGE	0.5962	0.9470	0.63	0.540

s = 3.054   R-sq = 3.0%   R-sq(adj) = 0.0%

Analysis of Variance

SOURCE	DF	SS	MS	F	p
Regression	1	3.696	3.696	0.40	0.540
Error	13	121.237	9.326		
Total	14	124.933			

Unusual Observations

Obs.	COLLEGE	CRIMES	Fit	Stdev.Fit	Residual	St.Resid
4	2.00	22.000	16.551	1.383	5.449	2.00R
6	1.00	13.000	15.955	2.228	-2.955	-1.41 X

R denotes an obs. with a large st. resid.
X denotes an obs. whose X value gives it large influence.

MTB > REGRESS 'CRIMES' 2 'COLLEGE' 'AGE'

The regression equation is
CRIMES = 7.94 + 0.698 COLLEGE + 0.293 AGE

Predictor	Coef	Stdev	t-ratio	p
Constant	7.937	5.314	1.49	0.161
COLLEGE	0.6977	0.8894	0.78	0.448
AGE	0.2933	0.1751	1.68	0.120

s = 2.862   R-sq = 21.3%   R-sq(adj) = 8.2%

Analysis of Variance

SOURCE	DF	SS	MS	F	p
Regression	2	26.672	13.336	1.63	0.237
Error	12	98.261	8.188		
Total	14	124.933			

SOURCE	DF	SEQ SS
COLLEGE	1	3.696
AGE	1	22.976

```
Unusual Observations
Obs. COLLEGE    CRIMES       Fit Stdev.Fit  Residual   St.Resid
  6    1.00    13.000     13.914    2.417    -0.914    -0.60 X
  7    3.00    12.000     18.242    1.002    -6.242    -2.33R
```

R denotes an obs. with a large st. resid.
X denotes an obs. whose X value gives it large influence.

MTB > REGRESS 'CRIMES' 3 'COLLEGE' 'AGE' 'INCOME'

The regression equation is
CRIMES = - 5.48 + 0.631 COLLEGE + 0.570 AGE + 2.82 INCOME

```
Predictor       Coef        Stdev     t-ratio         p
Constant       -5.484       6.416      -0.85       0.411
COLLEGE         0.6307      0.7112      0.89       0.394
AGE             0.5695      0.1714      3.32       0.007
INCOME          2.818       1.010       2.79       0.018
```

s = 2.287   R-sq = 54.0%   R-sq(adj) = 41.4%

Analysis of Variance

```
SOURCE        DF           SS          MS        F         p
Regression     3        67.407     22.469      4.30     0.031
Error         11        57.526      5.230
Total         14       124.933
```

```
SOURCE        DF        SEQ SS
COLLEGE        1         3.696
AGE            1        22.976
INCOME         1        40.735
```

CHAPTER 14

DIFFERENCES AMONG MORE THAN TWO POPULATION MEANS

GENERAL OBJECTIVES

In practical social research designs, investigators often focus on a whole series of independent and dependent variables. This chapter looks at differences involving more than two population means. We hope that as you study the materials in this chapter, you will see the need for more advanced work and also see that statistical techniques are built on rather straightforward assumptions. If you grasp the fundamentals of statistics, you can readily appreciate research findings presented in more complex forms.

SPECIFIC OBJECTIVES

1. To extend your knowledge of differences between two means to differences among several means. To this end, we present a major statistical technique: analysis of variance.
2. To show how to test and interpret specific hypotheses involving more than two means.
3. To provide a nonparametric counterpart to analysis of variance when the data are measured at the ordinal level or when parametric assumptions cannot be met.

14.1   INTRODUCTION

The methods we routinely use to compare two population means based on random samples of interval or ratio data were presented in Chapter 8. Very often, however, the two-sample problem is just a simplification of what is encountered in social research. Frequently we wish to compare more than two population means.

For example, suppose we wish to compare the mean incomes of steelworkers for three different ethnic groups (say, black, white, and Spanish-American) in a certain steel city. We would select independent random samples of steelworkers from each of the three ethnic groups (the three populations). Then we would consult the personnel files of the steel companies in the city, list steelworkers in each ethnic group, and select a random sample from each list. On the basis of the three sample means, we wish to know whether the population mean incomes differ and, if so, by how much. Note that the sample means most likely will differ, but this does not imply a difference in mean income for the three ethnic groups. Even if the population mean incomes were identical, the sample means would most probably differ. How do we decide whether the differences among the sample means are large enough to imply a difference among the corresponding population means? We will answer this question by using a technique known as an **analysis of variance**.

14.2   THE LOGIC BEHIND AN ANALYSIS OF VARIANCE

The reason for calling the method an *analysis of variance* can be demonstrated with an example. Assume that we wish to compare three population means based on samples of five observations, each selected from their respective populations. Although a sample of size 5 seems rather small, it will allow us to illustrate the basic ideas. Suppose the data for the three samples appear as shown in Table 14.1. Do the data present sufficient evidence to indicate differences among the three population means? A brief visual analysis of the data in Table 14.1 might lead us to a rapid, intuitive yes. A glance at each of the three samples indicates very little variation within the samples, while the spread or variation among the sample means appears to be larger. Since the variability among the sample means is so large relative to the within-sample variation, we might conclude intuitively that a real difference exists among the population means.

How our intuition works when a larger within-sample variation is present can be illustrated by viewing the data in Table 14.2. Now the

TABLE 14.1

Comparison of three sample means (small amount of within-sample variation)

Population 1	Population 2	Population 3
29.0	25.1	20.1
29.2	25.0	20.0
29.1	25.0	19.9
28.9	24.9	19.8
28.8	25.0	20.2
$\bar{X}_1 = 29.0$	$\bar{X}_2 = 25.0$	$\bar{X}_3 = 20.0$
$s_1 = .16$	$s_2 = .07$	$s_3 = .16$

TABLE 14.2

Comparison of three sample means (large amount of within-sample variation)

Population 1	Population 2	Population 3
29.0	33.1	15.2
14.2	5.4	39.3
45.1	17.3	14.8
48.9	42.0	25.5
7.8	27.2	5.2
$\bar{X}_1 = 29.0$	$\bar{X}_2 = 25.0$	$\bar{X}_3 = 20.0$
$s_1 = 18.19$	$s_2 = 14.17$	$s_3 = 12.96$

variation within samples is quite large, and the spread or variation among the sample means is not so great that it could not be due to chance.

The variations in the two sets of data in Tables 14.1 and 14.2 are shown graphically in Figure 14.1. The strong evidence to indicate a difference in the population means for the data of Table 14.1 is apparent in Figure 14.1a. The

FIGURE 14.1

Dot diagrams for the data in Tables 14.1 and 14.2

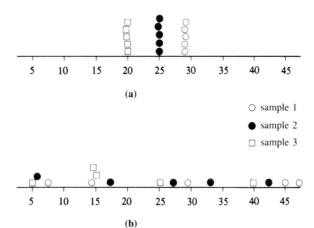

lack of such evidence for the data of Table 14.2 is indicated by the overlapping of data points for the samples in Figure 14.1b.

The data of Tables 14.1 and 14.2 (and Figure 14.1) should indicate very clearly what we mean by an analysis of variance. **All differences in sample means are judged for statistical significance by comparing them with a measure of the random variation within the sample data.**

14.3   A TEST OF A HYPOTHESIS ABOUT MORE THAN TWO POPULATION MEANS

In Chapter 8 we presented a method for testing the equality of two population means. We hypothesized two normal populations (1 and 2) with means denoted by μ_1 and μ_2, respectively. To test the null hypothesis that $\mu_1 = \mu_2$, independent random samples of size n_1 and n_2 were drawn from the two populations. The sample data were then used to compute the value of the test statistic t:

$$t = \frac{\bar{X}_1 - \bar{X}_2}{s\sqrt{\dfrac{1}{n_1} + \dfrac{1}{n_2}}}$$

where

$$s^2 = \frac{(n_1 - 1)s_1^2 + (n_2 - 1)s_2^2}{n_1 + n_2 - 2}$$

is a pooled estimate of the common population variance σ^2. The rejection region for a specified value of the probability α of a type I error was then found by using Appendix Table 2.

Suppose now that we wish to extend this method to test the equality of more than two population means. The test procedure described previously applies only to two means and is therefore inappropriate. Hence we will employ a more general method of data analysis known as the *analysis of variance*. We will illustrate its use with the following example.

Local unions from five different industries throughout the country were surveyed to determine the average salary of their members. Each local union sampled was asked to provide the necessary salary information. Suppose that nine local unions were selected in each of the five industries and that we wish to examine the average worker's salary in each of the five industries.

We label the set of all salaries that could have been obtained from industry 1 as population 1 and assume that this population possesses a mean μ_1. A random sample of nine measurements (salaries) is obtained from this population. The set of all salaries (scores) that could have been obtained from local unions in industry 2 will be labeled population 2 (which has a mean μ_2). The data from a random sample of nine scores are obtained from this population. Similarly, μ_3, μ_4, and μ_5 represent the means of the populations for salaries in industries 3, 4, and 5, respectively. We also obtain random samples of nine local unions and their average salaries from these populations.

From each of these five samples we calculate a sample mean and variance. The sample results can then be summarized as shown in Table 14.3.

If we are interested in testing the equality of the population means (i.e., $\mu_1 = \mu_2 = \mu_3 = \mu_4 = \mu_5$), we might be tempted to run all possible pairwise comparisons of two population means. Hence, if we assume that the five distributions are approximately normal with a common variance σ^2, we could run the ten t-tests by comparing two means, as listed in Table 14.4 (see also Section 8.4).

TABLE 14.3

Summary of the sample results for five industries

Characteristic	Industry 1	Industry 2	Industry 3	Industry 4	Industry 5
sample mean	$\bar{X}_1$	$\bar{X}_2$	$\bar{X}_3$	$\bar{X}_4$	$\bar{X}_5$
sample variance	s_1^2	s_2^2	s_3^2	s_4^2	s_5^2

TABLE 14.4

All possible null hypotheses for comparing two means from five populations

$\mu_1 = \mu_2$	$\mu_2 = \mu_3$	$\mu_3 = \mu_4$
$\mu_1 = \mu_3$	$\mu_2 = \mu_4$	$\mu_3 = \mu_5$
$\mu_1 = \mu_4$	$\mu_2 = \mu_5$	$\mu_4 = \mu_5$
$\mu_1 = \mu_5$		

One obvious disadvantage to this test procedure is that it is tedious and time-consuming. **However, the more important and less apparent disadvantage of running multiple t-tests to compare means is that the probability of falsely rejecting at least one of the hypotheses increases as the number of t-tests increases.** Thus, although we may have the probability of a type I error fixed at $\alpha = .05$ for each individual test, the probability of falsely rejecting at least one of these tests is larger than .05. In other words, the combined probability of a type I error for the set of ten hypotheses is larger than the value .05 set for each individual test. Indeed, it could be as large as .40.

What we need is a single test of the hypothesis "all five population means are equal" that will be less tedious than the individual t-tests and that can be performed with a specified probability of a type I error (say, .05). For this single test we first assume that the five sets of measurements are normally distributed with means given by $\mu_1, \mu_2, \mu_3, \mu_4,$ and μ_5 and a common variance σ^2. Consider the quantity

$$s_w^2 = \frac{(n_1-1)s_1^2 + (n_2-1)s_2^2 + (n_3-1)s_3^2 + (n_4-1)s_4^2 + (n_5-1)s_5^2}{(n_1-1)+(n_2-1)+(n_3-1)+(n_4-1)+(n_5-1)}$$

$$= \frac{(n_1-1)s_1^2 + (n_2-1)s_2^2 + (n_3-1)s_3^2 + (n_4-1)s_4^2 + (n_5-1)s_5^2}{n_1+n_2+n_3+n_4+n_5-5}$$

Note that this quantity is merely an extension of

$$s^2 = \frac{(n_1-1)s_1^2 + (n_2-1)s_2^2}{n_1+n_2-2}$$

which is used to estimate the common variance for two populations in a test of the hypothesis $\mu_1 = \mu_2$ (Section 8.4). Thus s_w^2 represents a combined estimate of the common variance σ^2 and measures the variability of the observations within each of the five populations. (The subscript w refers to the within-population variability.)

Next we consider a quantity that measures the variability between (or among) the sample means. If the null hypothesis $\mu_1 = \mu_2 = \mu_3 = \mu_4 = \mu_5$ is true, the populations are identical, with mean μ and variance σ^2. Drawing single samples from the five populations is then equivalent to drawing five different samples from the same population. What kind of variation might be expected for these sample means? If the variation is too great, we would then reject the hypothesis that $\mu_1 = \mu_2 = \mu_3 = \mu_4 = \mu_5$.

To assess the variation from sample mean to sample mean, we need to know the distribution of the mean of a sample of nine observations in repeated sampling. The sampling distribution for sample means based on nine measurements will have the same mean μ and variance $\sigma^2/9$. Since we have drawn five different samples of nine observations each, we can estimate the variance $\sigma^2/9$ of the distribution of sample means by computing the sample variance of the five sample means:

$$\text{sample variance (of the means)} = \frac{\Sigma \bar{X}^2 - (\Sigma \bar{X})^2/5}{5-1}$$

Note that we merely consider the $\bar{X}$s as a sample of five observations and calculate their variance. This quantity estimates $\sigma^2/9$, so 9 times the sample variance of the mean estimates σ^2. We designate the estimate of σ^2 by s_B^2, where the subscript B denotes the variability among the sample means for the five populations (between-population variability).

Under the null hypothesis that all five population means are identical, we have two estimates of σ^2: s_w^2 and s_B^2. Suppose that the ratio

$$\frac{s_B^2}{s_w^2}$$

is used as a test statistic to test the hypothesis that $\mu_1 = \mu_2 = \mu_3 = \mu_4 = \mu_5$. What is the distribution of this quantity if we repeat the experiment over and over again, each time calculating s_B^2 and s_w^2?

When independent random samples are drawn in repeated sampling from normal populations with equal variances, the quantity s_B^2/s_w^2 possesses a probability distribution that is known as an *F distribution*. The equation for this probability distribution is omitted here, but we note several of its important properties, as follows.

PROPERTIES OF THE *F* DISTRIBUTION

1. The *F* distribution, unlike the normal distribution or *t* distribution, is unsymmetrical (see Figure 14.2).
2. There are many *F* distributions (and hence many shapes). We can specify a particular one by designating the degrees of freedom associated with s_B^2 and s_w^2. We designate these quantities as d.f._1 and d.f._2, respectively.
3. Tail-end values for the *F* distributions are tabulated and appear in Appendix Tables 4 and 5.

FIGURE 14.2

Distribution of s_B^2/s_w^2, the *F* distribution

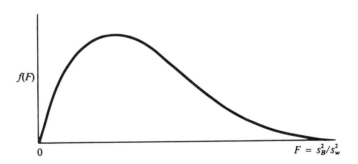

$f(F)$

0 $F = s_B^2/s_w^2$

Appendix Table 4 records the upper-tail value of *F* that has an area of .05 to its right (see Figure 14.3). The degrees of freedom for s_B^2, designated by d.f._1, are indicated across the top of the table, and the degrees of freedom for s_w^2, designated by d.f._2, appear in the first column on the left. For $\text{d.f.}_1 = 8$ and $\text{d.f.}_2 = 10$, the tabulated value is 3.07; that is, only 5% of the measurements for s_B^2/s_w^2 in repeated sampling from an *F* distribution with $\text{d.f.}_1 = 8$ and $\text{d.f.}_2 = 10$ will exceed 3.07 (see Figure 14.3). Similarly, an entry in Appendix Table 5 records an upper-tail value of the *F* distribution that has an area of .01 to its right. The .01 tail-end value of the *F* distribution with $\text{d.f.}_1 = 5$ and $\text{d.f.}_2 = 3$ is 28.24.

FIGURE 14.3

Critical value for the F distribution with d.f.$_1$ = 8, d.f.$_2$ = 10, and an area of .05 to its right

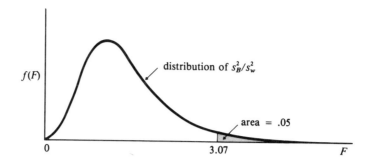

For our example, s_B^2/s_w^2 follows an F distribution with degrees of freedom that can be shown to be d.f.$_1$ = 4 (for s_B^2) and d.f.$_2$ = 40 (for s_w^2). The proof of these remarks is beyond the scope of this text. However, we make use of this result for testing the null hypothesis that $\mu_1 = \mu_2 = \mu_3 = \mu_4 = \mu_5$.

The test statistic used to test equality of the population means is

$$F = \frac{s_B^2}{s_w^2}$$

When the null hypothesis is true, both s_B^2 and s_w^2 estimate σ^2, and F assumes a value near $F = 1$. When the hypothesis of equality is false, s_B^2 tends to be larger than s_w^2 due to the differences among the population means. Hence we will reject the null hypothesis in the upper tail of the distribution of $F = s_B^2/s_w^2$. For the probability of a type I error equal to .05 or .01, we can locate the rejection region for this one-tailed test by using Appendix Tables 4 or 5, respectively, with d.f.$_1$ = 4 and d.f.$_2$ = 40. For α = .05, the critical value of $F = s_B^2/s_w^2$ is 2.61 (see Figure 14.4). If the calculated value of F falls in the rejection region, we conclude that not all five population means are identical.

This procedure can be generalized with only slight modifications in the formulas to test the equality of k (where k is an integer equal to or greater than 2) population means from normal populations with a common variance σ^2. Random samples of size $n_1, n_2, \ldots, n_k$ would be drawn from the respective populations. We would then compute the sample means and variances. The null hypothesis $\mu_1 = \mu_2 = \cdots = \mu_k$ would be tested against the alternative

FIGURE 14.4

Critical value of F for α = .05, d.f.$_1$ = 4, and d.f.$_2$ = 40

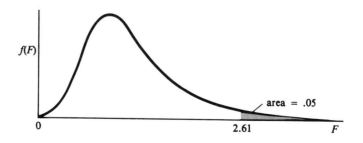

that at least one of the population means is different from the others. The test procedure is given next.

ANALYSIS OF VARIANCE FOR TESTING THE EQUALITY OF k POPULATION MEANS

Research hypothesis H_1: At least one of the population means is different from the others.

Null hypothesis H_0: $\mu_1 = \mu_2 = \cdots = \mu_k$

Test statistic $F = \dfrac{s_B^2}{s_w^2} \Rightarrow \left(\dfrac{(BSS \div df1)}{(WSS \div df2)} \right)$

where

$$s_w^2 = \frac{(n_1 - 1)s_1^2 + (n_2 - 1)s_2^2 + \cdots + (n_k - 1)s_k^2}{n_1 + n_2 + \cdots + n_k - k}$$

# of obs w/in ea group minus 1 then added

$$s_B^2 = \frac{\Sigma n_i \bar{X}_i^2 - (\Sigma n_i \bar{X}_i)^2 / n}{k - 1}$$

Number of Groups

Rejection region   R.R.: Reject H_0 if F is greater than the tabulated value for $a = \alpha$, d.f.$_1 = k - 1$, and d.f.$_2 = n_1 + n_2 + \cdots + n_k - k$. See Appendix Tables 4 and 5 for F-values corresponding to $a = .05$ and $a = .01$, respectively. (*Note*: $n = n_1 + n_2 + \cdots + n_k$.)

EXAMPLE 14.1

A group of social psychologists was interested in studying the effect of anxiety on learning as measured by student performance on a series of tests. Using a prestudy test, 27 students were classified into one of three anxiety groups. Group I students scored extremely low on the anxiety scale. Students placed in group III were students who scored extremely high on the anxiety scale. The remaining students were placed in group II. The results of the prestudy anxiety test indicated that 6 students were in group I, 12 in group II, and 9 in group III. Following the assignment of students to groups, the same battery of tests was given to each of the 27 students. The sample means and variances of the battery test scores (based on a total of 100 points) have been summarized for each group in Table 14.5. Use the sample data to test the hypothesis that the average test score for low-, medium-, and high-anxiety students is identical (i.e., that anxiety has no effect on a student's performance on this battery of tests).

TABLE 14.5

Summary of battery
test scores

Characteristic	Group I (Low Anxiety)	Group II (Medium Anxiety)	Group III (High Anxiety)
sample size	6	12	9
sample mean	88	82	78
sample variance	10.1	14.8	13.9

SOLUTION

We first hypothesize a population for each anxiety group corresponding to all possible battery test scores for students who could have been included in the study. We will assume that the measurements in each population are approximately normally distributed, with the mean of population I equal to μ_1, the mean of II, μ_2, and the mean of III, μ_3. In addition, we will assume that the populations have a common variance σ^2. From these populations, random samples of size $n_1 = 6$, $n_2 = 12$, and $n_3 = 9$ students were obtained and assigned to the respective groups.

To test the null hypothesis of equality of the population means, $\mu_1 = \mu_2 = \mu_3$, we must first compute s_w^2 and s_B^2. We can calculate s_w^2 directly from the sample data:

$$s_w^2 = \frac{(n_1 - 1)s_1^2 + (n_2 - 1)s_2^2 + (n_3 - 1)s_3^2}{n_1 + n_2 + n_3 - 3}$$

$$= \frac{5(10.1) + 11(14.8) + 8(13.9)}{6 + 12 + 9 - 3}$$

$$= \frac{324.5}{24}$$

$$= 13.52$$

Before obtaining s_B^2, we must compute $\Sigma\, n_i \bar{X}_i$ and $\Sigma\, n_i \bar{X}_i^2$. From Table 14.5 we can calculate the following quantities:

$$\Sigma\, n_i \bar{X}_i = 6(88) + 12(82) + 9(78) = 2214$$

$$\Sigma\, n_i \bar{X}_i^2 = 6(88)^2 + 12(82)^2 + 9(78)^2 = 181,908$$

Hence for $k = 3$ and $n = n_1 + n_2 + n_3 = 27$, we have

$$s_B^2 = \frac{\Sigma\, n_i \bar{X}_i^2 - (\Sigma\, n_i \bar{X}_i)^2/n}{k - 1}$$

$$= \frac{181,908 - (2214)^2/27}{2}$$

$$= \frac{181,908 - 181,548}{2}$$

$$= 180$$

The test statistic for the null hypothesis $\mu_1 = \mu_2 = \mu_3$ is

$$F = \frac{s_B^2}{s_w^2} = \frac{180.0}{13.52} = 13.31$$

Using $\alpha = .01$ as the probability of a type I error, we can locate the upper-tail rejection region for this one-tailed test by using Appendix Table 5, with

$$\text{d.f.}_1 = k - 1 = 2$$

and

$$\text{d.f.}_2 = n_1 + n_2 + n_3 - 3 = 24$$

This table value is 5.61. Since the observed value of F is greater than 5.61, we reject the hypothesis of equality of the population means (i.e., at least one of the means is different from the rest). Although the F-test does not indicate where the differences lie—only that there are differences—the sample data indicate that anxiety has a detrimental effect on a student's performance in the battery of tests.

EXERCISES

1. State the assumptions underlying an analysis-of-variance test about k population means.
2. Distinguish between s_w^2 and s_B^2 in testing the equality of k population means.
3. What is the F ratio and how does it function in an analysis of variance?
4. Six small groups were randomly selected from each of three populations. Group tension was measured, and the results are shown in the accompanying table. Perform an analysis of variance for the experiment to determine if there are differences in the mean group tension scores among the three populations. (Use $\alpha = .05$.)

EXERCISE 4

Results of tension measurements

Group A	Group B	Group C
4.2	5.6	3.2
1.1	5.1	2.5
3.7	4.4	2.9
2.6	4.2	3.6
2.1	4.2	3.2
3.7	5.1	4.1

5. The duration of fights between grade school children was studied at five different schools. A sample of nine fights at each school was selected. A summary of the resulting data for each of the five schools is shown in the accompanying table. Run an analysis of variance to test the hypothesis that the mean duration of fights at the five schools, $\mu_1, \mu_2 \ldots, \mu_5$, is equal. (Use $\alpha = .05$.)

EXERCISE 5

Duration of fights between grade school children at five schools

Characteristic	School 1	School 2	School 3	School 4	School 5
sample size	9	9	9	9	9
sample mean	3.2	3.8	4.1	4.0	3.7
sample variance	.46	.51	.45	.20	.28

6. The accompanying data are based on four random samples of SMSAs. Researchers determined the percentage of adults for each SMSA who had at least completed high school. Run an analysis of variance to test the hypothesis that the four samples come from identical populations. (Use $\alpha = .05$.)

EXERCISE 6

Percentage of adults completing at least high school in four SMSAs

Characteristic	Sample 1	Sample 2	Sample 3	Sample 4
sample size	10	10	10	10
sample mean	54	50	48	42
sample variance	49.7	31.4	43.1	30.4

7. Refer to Exercise 6. Use only samples 2, 3, and 4 and run an analysis of variance to test the hypothesis that these three samples come from a common population. (Use $\alpha = .05$.)

14.4 KRUSKAL-WALLIS ONE-WAY ANALYSIS OF VARIANCE BY RANK

In this section we will present the **Kruskal-Wallis one-way analysis of variance by rank,** a procedure for use on data measured on an ordinal scale. **In contrast to the procedure of Section 14.3, we do not require that the data for each of the samples be drawn from a normal population with common variance σ^2. We merely assume that the sample data are obtained from a population with a continuous frequency distribution.** Although the Kruskal-Wallis procedure was developed for use with ordinal data, it also provides a useful alternative to the analysis-of-variance procedure of Section 14.3 when the normality assumption or the equality-of-variances assumption (often called the *assumption of homoscedasticity*) does not hold. In such situations the data from an interval or ratio scale can be converted to ordinal data and then analyzed by using the Kruskal-Wallis procedure.

Under the null hypothesis, we assume that each of k samples was drawn from identical populations. The observations from all k samples are then combined and jointly ranked, with the largest observation receiving the rank n. If a tie occurs between two or more measurements, each measurement is assigned a rank equal to the mean of the occupied ranks.

Having jointly ranked the measurements from the k samples, we compute the sum of the ranks for each sample. The Kruskal-Wallis test procedure then asks the question: Are the differences among the sums of ranks for the k samples too large for the samples to have been drawn from identical populations? To answer this question, we utilize the following notation:

S_1: sum of ranks for n_1 observations in sample 1
S_2: sum of ranks for n_2 observations in sample 2
.
.
.
S_k: sum of ranks for n_k observations in sample k

Then our test statistic is

$$H = \frac{12}{n(n+1)} \left(\frac{S_1^2}{n_1} + \frac{S_2^2}{n_2} + \cdots + \frac{S_k^2}{n_k} \right) - 3(n+1)$$

Under the null hypothesis that the k samples were drawn from identical populations, the statistic H has a distribution that can be approximated by a chi-square distribution with d.f. $= k - 1$. This approximation should be reasonably good, provided the sample sizes $n_1, n_2, \ldots, n_k$ are all greater than 5.

We summarize the Kruskal-Wallis analysis of variance by rank as follows.

SUMMARY OF THE KRUSKAL-WALLIS ONE-WAY ANALYSIS OF VARIANCE BY RANK

Research hypothesis H_1: At least one of the k samples was drawn from a population that is not identical to the other populations.

Null hypothesis H_0: All k samples were drawn from identical populations.

Test statistic $H = \dfrac{12}{n(n+1)} \left(\dfrac{S_1^2}{n_1} + \dfrac{S_2^2}{n_2} + \cdots + \dfrac{S_k^2}{n_k} \right) - 3(n+1)$

where $S_1, S_2, \ldots, S_k$ are the sums of the ranks and $n_1, n_2, \ldots, n_k$ are the sample sizes for populations $1, 2, \ldots, k$, respectively.

Rejection region   R.R.: For a specified value of α, reject the null hypothesis if H exceeds the critical value of chi-square for $a = \alpha$ and d.f. $= k - 1$.

EXAMPLE 14.2

Three random samples of clergy were drawn, one containing ten Methodist ministers, the second containing ten Catholic priests, and the third containing ten Pentecostal ministers. Each member of the clergy was then administered a test to measure knowledge about the causes of mental illness. These test scores are listed in Table 14.6. Use the data in the table to determine if the three groups of clergy differ in their knowledge about the causes of mental illness. (Use $\alpha = .05$.)

TABLE 14.6

Scores for knowledge of mental illness for the clergy

Methodist	Catholic	Pentecostal
32	32	28
30	32	21
30	26	15
29	26	15
26	22	14
23	20	14
20	19	14
19	16	11
18	14	9
12	14	8

SOLUTION

The research and null hypotheses for this example can be stated as follows:

H_1: At least one of the three groups of clergy differs from the others with respect to knowledge about causes of mental illness.

H_0: There is no difference among the three groups with respect to knowledge about the causes of mental illness (i.e., the samples of scores were drawn from identical populations).

Before computing H (not to be confused with H_1 and H_0), we must jointly rank the 30 test scores from highest to lowest. From Table 14.6 we see that 32 is the highest test score, and three individuals achieved this score. These three occupy the ranks 1, 2, and 3. Each is assigned the average of the first three ranks, namely 2. The second highest score, 30, was obtained by two individuals. Each of these scores is assigned the rank 4.5, the average of the fourth and fifth ranks occupied by these scores. In a similar way we can assign the remaining ranks to test scores. Table 14.7 lists the 30 test scores and associated ranks (in parentheses). Note from the table that the sums of the ranks for the three groups are 113, 132, and 220, respectively. Hence the computed value of H is

$$H = \frac{12}{30(30+1)}\left[\frac{(113)^2}{10} + \frac{(132)^2}{10} + \frac{(220)^2}{10}\right] - 3(30+1)$$

$$= \frac{12}{930}(1276.9 + 1742.4 + 4840.0) - 93 = 8.4$$

TABLE 14.7

Test scores and ranks for the clergy study

Methodist	Catholic	Pentecostal
32 (2)	32 (2)	28 (7)
30 (4.5)	32 (2)	21 (13)
30 (4.5)	26 (9)	15 (20.5)
29 (6)	26 (9)	15 (20.5)
26 (9)	22 (12)	14 (24)
23 (11)	20 (14.5)	14 (24)
20 (14.5)	19 (16.5)	14 (24)
19 (16.5)	16 (19)	11 (28)
18 (18)	14 (24)	9 (29)
12 (27)	14 (24)	8 (30)
$n_1 = 10$	$n_2 = 10$	$n_3 = 10$
$S_1 = 113$	$S_2 = 132$	$S_3 = 220$

The critical value of chi-square with $a = .05$ and d.f. $= k - 1 = 2$ can be found in Appendix Table 3. This value is 5.99. Since the observed value of H is greater than 5.99, we reject the null hypothesis and conclude that at least one of the clergy groups has more knowledge about causes of mental illness than the other two groups. In fact, the data suggest that Pentecostal ministers are less knowledgeable in this area.

EXERCISES

8. Why would a social scientist be particularly interested in the Kruskal-Wallis one-way analysis of variance by ranks? Explain in detail.

9. Treat the data in Exercise 4 at the ordinal level and compute the one-way analysis of variance by ranks. (Use $\alpha = .05$.)

10. Random samples of six people were selected from four ethnic minority groups and asked to score, on a 0-to-30 scale, how well they have been socially accepted in their community. Run an analysis of variance — a one-way analysis of variance by rank — on the data in the accompanying table. (Use $\alpha = .05$.)

EXERCISE 10

Social acceptance scores for four ethnic minority groups

Group A	Group B	Group C	Group D
10	18	15	22
9	16	13	24
14	14	12	21
11	15	14	23
12	16	13	22
8	19	11	26

11. Refer to Exercise 10. Another researcher had undertaken a similar study but selected random samples of eight people from three ethnic minorities. Rank the data and run a Kruskal-Wallis one-way analysis of variance by rank. Explain your results.

EXERCISE 11

Social acceptance scores for three ethnic minority groups

Group A	Group B	Group C
14	16	18
10	13	22
9	15	24
14	12	21
15	16	19
11	14	23
12	13	22
8	17	26

SUMMARY

In this chapter we considered the problem of comparing more than two population means based on independent random samples of interval (or ratio) data from each population. To test the hypothesis of no difference in population means, we employ an analysis of variance. That is, we compare the variation between sample means with the variability within samples by using an F statistic. If the F statistic is larger than expected (by comparing it with the critical value of the F tables), we have evidence that indicates a difference in population means. Note that though an analysis of variance is usually applied when comparing three or more population means, it is also appropriate for the special two-sample case.

An analysis of variance is appropriate when the data for each population are normally distributed when the populations have the same variability. We will not usually know whether these assumptions hold, but this is not a major drawback if the variation is similar for the populations. When we have doubts that this is true, or when the data are measured only at an ordinal level of measurement, we must adopt an alternative method. Then a suitable test statistic is the Kruskal-Wallis H.

KEY WORDS

Analysis of variance   A method of data analysis useful in testing the equality of k population means.
Kruskal-Wallis one-way analysis of variance by rank   A one-way analysis of variance when dealing with ordinal data and k populations. Can also be used with interval and ratio data.

KEY FORMULAS

Analysis of variance

$$F = \frac{s_B^2}{s_w^2}$$

where

$$s_w^2 = \frac{(n_1 - 1)s_1^2 + (n_2 - 1)s_2^2 + \cdots + (n_k - 1)s_k^2}{n_1 + n_2 + \cdots + n_k - k}$$

$$s_B^2 = \frac{\Sigma\, n_i \overline{X}_i^2 - (\Sigma\, n_i \overline{X}_i)^2/n}{k - 1}$$

Kruskal-Wallis one-way analysis of variance by rank

$$H = \frac{12}{n(n + 1)}\left(\frac{S_1^2}{n_1} + \frac{S_2^2}{n_2} + \cdots + \frac{S_k^2}{n_k}\right) - 3(n + 1)$$

where $S_1, S_2, \ldots, S_k$ are the sums of the ranks and $n_1, n_2, \ldots, n_k$ are the sample sizes for populations $1, 2, \ldots, k$, respectively.

SUPPLEMENTARY EXERCISES FOR CHAPTER 14

12. Refer to Exercise 5. Suppose that we eliminate three fights from schools 1 and 2, two from school 3, and one each from 4 and 5 because they were staged. The sample means remain the same, but all the sample sizes change, as do the standard deviations. Run an analysis of variance to test the equality of means, using the revised data given in the accompanying table. (Use $\alpha = .05$.)

EXERCISE 12

Modified data from table in Exercise 5

Characteristic	School 1	School 2	School 3	School 4	School 5
sample size	6	6	7	8	8
sample mean	3.2	3.8	4.1	4.0	3.7
sample variance	.36	.53	.40	.31	.37

13. A clinical psychologist wished to compare three methods for reducing hostility levels in university students. A certain psychological test (HLT) was used to measure the degree of hostility. High scores on this test indicate great hostility. Twenty-one students obtaining high and nearly equal scores were used in the experiment. Eight were selected at random from among the 21 problem cases and treated by method A. Seven were taken at random from the remaining 13 students and treated by method B. The other 6 students were treated by method C. All treatments continued throughout a semester. Each student was given the HLT test at the end of the semester, with the results shown. Do these data present sufficient evidence to indicate a difference in mean student response for the three methods after treatment? (Use $\alpha = .01$.)

EXERCISE 13

Three methods for reducing hostility levels in university students

Method A	Method B	Method C
95	78	74
80	70	63
92	81	76
87	74	70
83	73	71
78	72	72
89	75	
86		

14. Refer to Exercise 13. Use the Kruskal-Wallis one-way analysis of variance. Do you obtain the same conclusions? (Use $\alpha = .05$.)

15. Three methods of instruction in group encounter techniques were to be compared with respect to the mean level of group interaction. A total of 19 group leaders participated in the study; 6 were randomly assigned to method 1, 6 to method 2, and 7 to method 3. After a one-week training period, all leaders were assigned to an encounter group and, after a four-hour session, were scored on their ability to achieve meaningful group interaction. Use the data in the table and run an analysis of variance to test the hypothesis that all three instructional methods result in the same average level of group interaction. (Use $\alpha = .05$.)

EXERCISE 15

Comparison among three methods of instruction in group encounter techniques

Method 1	Method 2	Method 3
82	71	91
80	29	93
81	78	84
83	74	90
84	75	88
79	36	96
		92

16. Repeat Exercise 15 but use the Kruskal-Wallis one-way analysis of variance. (Use $\alpha = .05$.)

17. When would the Kruskal-Wallis one-way analysis of variance be more appropriate than the analysis of variance presented in Section 14.3?

18. Set up a study in which an analysis of variance would be the appropriate statistical method of analysis.

19. Would a researcher with ratio data ever consider using the Kruskal-Wallis one-way analysis of variance on these data? Explain.

20. A sociologist randomly draws five samples of six cities each from regional areas. Within each city he computes an index of consumer confidence concerning the government's ability to curb inflation. Considering the data in the accompanying table, carry out an analysis-of-variance test among the five sample means. (Use $\alpha = .05$.)

EXERCISE 20

Comparison among cities in 5 regions concerning consumer confidence

West	Southwest	North Central	East	South
12.3	19.2	34.8	19.2	31.9
15.9	20.5	29.3	21.8	42.5
11.7	18.4	31.4	17.5	29.6
14.8	9.7	18.4	24.3	37.1
25.7	21.5	26.3	18.7	33.3
16.2	22.6	30.5	25.3	38.8

21. Using the same data in Exercise 20, carry out the Kruskal-Wallis analysis of variance by rank. How do these results compare with those in Exercise 20?

22. Using the information in Database A, Appendix Table 7, draw four random samples of $n = 10$, one sample from each category of major (social sciences, humanities, natural sciences, and business). Use the Kruskal-Wallis one-way analysis of variance by rank and test the hypothesis that the four samples come from identical populations with respect to the number of acts thought to be crimes.

23. Refer to Exercise 22 and Database A, Appendix Table 7. Repeat the exercise and analyze the data by an analysis of variance. Are your conclusions the same?

24. Refer to Exercise 22 and Database A, Appendix Table 7. Do the four samples differ with respect to age? Use the Kruskal-Wallis one-way analysis of variance by rank. Also use $\alpha = .05$.

25. Refer to Exercise 24 and Database A, Appendix Table 7. Assume that these data are interval data. Answer the same question using an analysis of variance.

26. Use Database B, Appendix Table 8, and draw three random samples of $n = 5$. Test the hypothesis that the three samples come from identical populations in terms of the average score on level of technology. Use the Kruskal-Wallis one-way analysis of variance by rank. Also use $\alpha = .05$.

27. Refer to Exercise 26 and Database B, Appendix Table 8. Now test the same hypothesis by using an analysis of variance. Comment.

28. Refer to Database C, Appendix Table 9, and randomly draw four samples, $n = 5$, from each of the treatment groups. Do the four groups differ in terms of their HOPKINS OBRIST scores? Use an analysis-of-variance test.

29. Refer to Exercise 28 and Database C, Appendix Table 9. Now answer the same question using Kruskal-Wallis one-way analysis of variance by rank.

30. Refer to Exercise 28 and Database C, Appendix Table 9. Use the same four samples and test the hypothesis that these samples come from identical populations with respect to age.

APPENDIX

Index to Useful Mathematical Notation and Algebraic Topics

Table 1	Normal Curve Areas
Table 2	Percentage Points of the t Distribution
Table 3	Percentage Points of the Chi-square Distribution
Table 4	Percentage Points of the F Distribution, $a = .05$
Table 5	Percentage Points of the F Distribution, $a = .01$
Table 6	Random Numbers
Table 7	Database A
Table 8	Database B
Table 9	Database C
Table 10	Database D

INDEX TO USEFUL MATHEMATICAL NOTATION
AND ALGEBRAIC TOPICS

This textbook has been written so that anyone with a limited mathematical background can understand our discussion of statistics and use some of the techniques presented. We do assume that addition, subtraction, multiplication, and division with numbers containing decimals have been mastered. The mathematical notation and algebraic topics beyond this fundamental level that are used in the text are thoroughly discussed where the topic or notation is first introduced.

Some people recommended that we provide an index for a review of the necessary topics. We have found, however, that mastery of the necessary skills in mathematics and algebra is best achieved by an orderly progression through the chapters of this text. By integrating the new notation and algebraic topics into the body of the text and by pausing to provide the necessary discussion, we hope to show the utility of the topics and avoid the sterile presentation that is so common when review sections are presented in appendices.

The list that follows provides an index to useful mathematical notation and algebraic topics presented in the text. Included for each topic is the page number where the explanation appears. No supplemental reading in these areas beyond the discussion presented in the text should be required for adequate understanding of the topics.

Mathematical Notation or Algebraic Topic	Page Reference for Text Discussion
constants and variables	19
scales of measurement	23
ratios	33
proportions	34
percentages	34
rates	35
rounding of measurements	39
constructing graphs	51
summation notation	118
use of subscripts	118
coding to simplify calculations	123
functional notation (algebraic formulas)	129
percentage comparisons	337

TABLE 1 Normal
curve areas

Z-score

Area of Shaded region

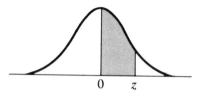

z	.00	.01	.02	.03	.04	.05	.06	.07	.08	.09
0.0	.0000	.0040	.0080	.0120	.0160	.0199	.0239	.0279	.0319	.0359
0.1	.0398	.0438	.0478	.0517	.0557	.0596	.0636	.0675	.0714	.0753
0.2	.0793	.0832	.0871	.0910	.0948	.0987	.1026	.1064	.1103	.1141
0.3	.1179	.1217	.1255	.1293	.1331	.1368	.1406	.1443	.1480	.1517
0.4	.1554	.1591	.1628	.1664	.1700	.1736	.1772	.1808	.1844	.1879
0.5	.1915	.1950	.1985	.2019	.2054	.2088	.2123	.2157	.2190	.2224
0.6	.2257	.2291	.2324	.2357	.2389	.2422	.2454	.2486	.2517	.2549
0.7	.2580	.2611	.2642	.2673	.2704	.2734	.2764	.2794	.2823	.2852
0.8	.2881	.2910	.2939	.2967	.2995	.3023	.3051	.3078	.3106	.3133
0.9	.3159	.3186	.3212	.3238	.3264	.3289	.3315	.3340	.3365	.3389
1.0	.3413	.3438	.3461	.3485	.3508	.3531	.3554	.3577	.3599	.3621
1.1	.3643	.3665	.3686	.3708	.3729	.3749	.3770	.3790	.3810	.3830
1.2	.3849	.3869	.3888	.3907	.3925	.3944	.3962	.3980	.3997	.4015
1.3	.4032	.4049	.4066	.4082	.4099	.4115	.4131	.4147	.4162	.4177
1.4	.4192	.4207	.4222	.4236	.4251	.4265	.4279	.4292	.4306	.4319
1.5	.4332	.4345	.4357	.4370	.4382	.4394	.4406	.4418	.4429	.4441
1.6	.4452	.4463	.4474	.4484	.4495	.4505	.4515	.4525	.4535	.4545
1.7	.4554	.4564	.4573	.4582	.4591	.4599	.4608	.4616	.4625	.4633
1.8	.4641	.4649	.4656	.4664	.4671	.4678	.4686	.4693	.4699	.4706
1.9	.4713	.4719	.4726	.4732	.4738	.4744	.4750	.4756	.4761	.4767
2.0	.4772	.4778	.4783	.4788	.4793	.4798	.4803	.4808	.4812	.4817
2.1	.4821	.4826	.4830	.4834	.4838	.4842	.4846	.4850	.4854	.4857
2.2	.4861	.4864	.4868	.4871	.4875	.4878	.4881	.4884	.4887	.4890
2.3	.4893	.4896	.4898	.4901	.4904	.4906	.4909	.4911	.4913	.4916
2.4	.4918	.4920	.4922	.4925	.4927	.4929	.4931	.4932	.4934	.4936
2.5	.4938	.4940	.4941	.4943	.4945	.4946	.4948	.4949	.4951	.4952
2.6	.4953	.4955	.4956	.4957	.4959	.4960	.4961	.4962	.4963	.4964
2.7	.4965	.4966	.4967	.4968	.4969	.4970	.4971	.4972	.4973	.4974
2.8	.4974	.4975	.4976	.4977	.4977	.4978	.4979	.4979	.4980	.4981
2.9	.4981	.4982	.4982	.4983	.4984	.4984	.4985	.4985	.4986	.4986
3.0	.4987	.4987	.4987	.4988	.4988	.4989	.4989	.4989	.4990	.4990

This table is abridged from Table I of *Statistical Tables and Formulas*, by A. Hald (New York: John Wiley & Sons, Inc., 1952). Reproduced by permission of A. Hald and the publishers, John Wiley & Sons, Inc.

TABLE 2 Percentage
points of the t distri-
bution

degrees of freedom $= n-1$ (handwritten)

Area of Shaded region (handwritten)

$0 \quad t_a$

d.f.	$a = .10$	$a = .05$	$a = .025$	$a = .010$	$a = .005$
1	3.078	6.314	12.706	31.821	63.657
2	1.886	2.920	4.303	6.965	9.925
3	1.638	2.353	3.182	4.541	5.841
4	1.533	2.132	2.776	3.747	4.604
5	1.476	2.015	2.571	3.365	4.032
6	1.440	1.943	2.447	3.143	3.707
7	1.415	1.895	2.365	2.998	3.499
8	1.397	1.860	2.306	2.896	3.355
9	1.383	1.833	2.262	2.821	3.250
10	1.372	1.812	2.228	2.764	3.169
11	1.363	1.796	2.201	2.718	3.106
12	1.356	1.782	2.179	2.681	3.055
13	1.350	1.771	2.160	2.650	3.012
14	1.345	1.761	2.145	2.624	2.977
15	1.341	1.753	2.131	2.602	2.947
16	1.337	1.746	2.120	2.583	2.921
17	1.333	1.740	2.110	2.567	2.898
18	1.330	1.734	2.101	2.552	2.878
19	1.328	1.729	2.093	2.539	2.861
20	1.325	1.725	2.086	2.528	2.845
21	1.323	1.721	2.080	2.518	2.831
22	1.321	1.717	2.074	2.508	2.819
23	1.319	1.714	2.069	2.500	2.807
24	1.318	1.711	2.064	2.492	2.797
25	1.316	1.708	2.060	2.485	2.787
26	1.315	1.706	2.056	2.479	2.779
27	1.314	1.703	2.052	2.473	2.771
28	1.313	1.701	2.048	2.467	2.763
29	1.311	1.699	2.045	2.462	2.756
∞	1.282	1.645	1.960	2.326	2.576

From "Table of Percentage Points of the t-distribution," computed by Maxine Merrington, *Biometrika*, Vol. 32 (1941), p. 300. Reproduced by permission of the *Biometrika* Trustees.

t-score (handwritten)

TABLE 3 Percentage points of the chi-square distribution

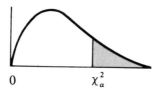

d.f.	a = .995	a = .990	a = .975	a = .950	a = .900
1	0.0000393	0.0001571	0.0009821	0.0039321	0.0157908
2	0.0100251	0.0201007	0.0506356	0.102587	0.210720
3	0.0717212	0.114832	0.215795	0.351846	0.584375
4	0.206990	0.297110	0.484419	0.710721	1.063623
5	0.411740	0.554300	0.831211	1.145476	1.61031
6	0.675727	0.872085	1.237347	1.63539	2.20413
7	0.989265	1.239043	1.68987	2.16735	2.83311
8	1.344419	1.646482	2.17973	2.73264	3.48954
9	1.734926	2.087912	2.70039	3.32511	4.16816
10	2.15585	2.55821	3.24697	3.94030	4.86518
11	2.60321	3.05347	3.81575	4.57481	5.57779
12	3.07382	3.57056	4.40379	5.22603	6.30380
13	3.56503	4.10691	5.00874	5.89186	7.04150
14	4.07468	4.66043	5.62872	6.57063	7.78953
15	4.60094	5.22935	6.26214	7.26094	8.54675
16	5.14224	5.81221	6.90766	7.96164	9.31223
17	5.69724	6.40776	7.56418	8.67176	10.0852
18	6.26481	7.01491	8.23075	9.39046	10.8649
19	6.84398	7.63273	8.90655	10.1170	11.6509
20	7.43386	8.26040	9.59083	10.8508	12.4426
21	8.03366	8.89720	10.28293	11.5913	13.2396
22	8.64272	9.54249	10.9823	12.3380	14.0415
23	9.26042	10.19567	11.6885	13.0905	14.8479
24	9.88623	10.8564	12.4011	13.8484	15.6587
25	10.5197	11.5240	13.1197	14.6114	16.4734
26	11.1603	12.1981	13.8439	15.3791	17.2919
27	11.8076	12.8786	14.5733	16.1513	18.1138
28	12.4613	13.5648	15.3079	16.9279	18.9392
29	13.1211	14.2565	16.0471	17.7083	19.7677
30	13.7867	14.9535	16.7908	18.4926	20.5992
40	20.7065	22.1643	24.4331	26.5093	29.0505
50	27.9907	29.7067	32.3574	34.7642	37.6886
60	35.5346	37.4848	40.4817	43.1879	46.4589
70	43.2752	45.4418	48.7576	51.7393	55.3290
80	51.1720	53.5400	57.1532	60.3915	64.2778
90	59.1963	61.7541	65.6466	69.1260	73.2912
100	67.3276	70.0648	74.2219	77.9295	82.3581

TABLE 3 *(continued)*

$a = .10$	$a = .05$	$a = .025$	$a = .010$	$a = .005$	d.f.
2.70554	3.84146	5.02389	6.63490	7.87944	1
4.60517	5.99147	7.37776	9.21034	10.5966	2
6.25139	7.81473	9.34840	11.3449	12.8381	3
7.77944	9.48773	11.1433	13.2767	14.8602	4
9.23635	11.0705	12.8325	15.0863	16.7496	5
10.6446	12.5916	14.4494	16.8119	18.5476	6
12.0170	14.0671	16.0128	18.4753	20.2777	7
13.3616	15.5073	17.5346	20.0902	21.9550	8
14.6837	16.9190	19.0228	21.6660	23.5893	9
15.9871	18.3070	20.4831	23.2093	25.1882	10
17.2750	19.6751	21.9200	24.7250	26.7569	11
18.5494	21.0261	23.3367	26.2170	28.2995	12
19.8119	22.3621	24.7356	27.6883	29.8194	13
21.0642	23.6848	26.1190	29.1413	31.3193	14
22.3072	24.9958	27.4884	30.5779	32.8013	15
23.5418	26.2962	28.8454	31.9999	34.2672	16
24.7690	27.5871	30.1910	33.4087	35.7185	17
25.9894	28.8693	31.5264	34.8053	37.1564	18
27.2036	30.1435	32.8523	36.1908	38.5822	19
28.4120	31.4104	34.1696	37.5662	39.9968	20
29.6151	32.6705	35.4789	38.9321	41.4010	21
30.8133	33.9244	36.7807	40.2894	42.7956	22
32.0069	35.1725	38.0757	41.6384	44.1813	23
33.1963	36.4151	39.3641	42.9798	45.5585	24
34.3816	37.6525	40.6465	44.3141	46.9278	25
35.5631	38.8852	41.9232	45.6417	48.2899	26
36.7412	40.1133	43.1944	46.9630	49.6449	27
37.9159	41.3372	44.4607	48.2782	50.9933	28
39.0875	42.5569	45.7222	49.5879	52.3356	29
40.2560	43.7729	46.9792	50.8922	53.6720	30
51.8050	55.7585	59.3417	63.6907	66.7659	40
63.1671	67.5048	71.4202	76.1539	79.4900	50
74.3970	79.0819	83.2976	88.3794	91.9517	60
85.5271	90.5312	95.0231	100.425	104.215	70
96.5782	101.879	106.629	112.329	116.321	80
107.565	113.145	118.136	124.116	128.299	90
118.498	124.342	129.561	135.807	140.169	100

From "Tables of the Percentage Points of the χ^2-Distribution," *Biometrika*, Vol. 32 (1941), pp. 188–189, by Catherine M. Thompson. Reproduced by permission of the *Biometrika* Trustees.

TABLE 4 Percentage
points of the F distri-
bution, $a = .05$

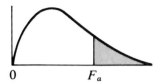

d.f.$_1$ d.f.$_2$	1	2	3	4	5	6	7	8	9
1	161.4	199.5	215.7	224.6	230.2	234.0	236.8	238.9	240.5
2	18.51	19.00	19.16	19.25	19.30	19.33	19.35	19.37	19.38
3	10.13	9.55	9.28	9.12	9.01	8.94	8.89	8.85	8.81
4	7.71	6.94	6.59	6.39	6.26	6.16	6.09	6.04	6.00
5	6.61	5.79	5.41	5.19	5.05	4.95	4.88	4.82	4.77
6	5.99	5.14	4.76	4.53	4.39	4.28	4.21	4.15	4.10
7	5.59	4.74	4.35	4.12	3.97	3.87	3.79	3.73	3.68
8	5.32	4.46	4.07	3.84	3.69	3.58	3.50	3.44	3.39
9	5.12	4.26	3.86	3.63	3.48	3.37	3.29	3.23	3.18
10	4.96	4.10	3.71	3.48	3.33	3.22	3.14	3.07	3.02
11	4.84	3.98	3.59	3.36	3.20	3.09	3.01	2.95	2.90
12	4.75	3.89	3.49	3.26	3.11	3.00	2.91	2.85	2.80
13	4.67	3.81	3.41	3.18	3.03	2.92	2.83	2.77	2.71
14	4.60	3.74	3.34	3.11	2.96	2.85	2.76	2.70	2.65
15	4.54	3.68	3.29	3.06	2.90	2.79	2.71	2.64	2.59
16	4.49	3.63	3.24	3.01	2.85	2.74	2.66	2.59	2.54
17	4.45	3.59	3.20	2.96	2.81	2.70	2.61	2.55	2.49
18	4.41	3.55	3.16	2.93	2.77	2.66	2.58	2.51	2.46
19	4.38	3.52	3.13	2.90	2.74	2.63	2.54	2.48	2.42
20	4.35	3.49	3.10	2.87	2.71	2.60	2.51	2.45	2.39
21	4.32	3.47	3.07	2.84	2.68	2.57	2.49	2.42	2.37
22	4.30	3.44	3.05	2.82	2.66	2.55	2.46	2.40	2.34
23	4.28	3.42	3.03	2.80	2.64	2.53	2.44	2.37	2.32
24	4.26	3.40	3.01	2.78	2.62	2.51	2.42	2.36	2.30
25	4.24	3.39	2.99	2.76	2.60	2.49	2.40	2.34	2.28
26	4.23	3.37	2.98	2.74	2.59	2.47	2.39	2.32	2.27
27	4.21	3.35	2.96	2.73	2.57	2.46	2.37	2.31	2.25
28	4.20	3.34	2.95	2.71	2.56	2.45	2.36	2.29	2.24
29	4.18	3.33	2.93	2.70	2.55	2.43	2.35	2.28	2.22
30	4.17	3.32	2.92	2.69	2.53	2.42	2.33	2.27	2.21
40	4.08	3.23	2.84	2.61	2.45	2.34	2.25	2.18	2.12
60	4.00	3.15	2.76	2.53	2.37	2.25	2.17	2.10	2.04
120	3.92	3.07	2.68	2.45	2.29	2.17	2.09	2.02	1.96
∞	3.84	3.00	2.60	2.37	2.21	2.10	2.01	1.94	1.88

TABLE 4 *(continued)*

10	12	15	20	24	30	40	60	120	∞	d.f.$_1$ / d.f.$_2$
241.9	243.9	245.9	248.0	249.1	250.1	251.1	252.2	253.3	254.3	1
19.40	19.41	19.43	19.45	19.45	19.46	19.47	19.48	19.49	19.50	2
8.79	8.74	8.70	8.66	8.64	8.62	8.59	8.57	8.55	8.53	3
5.96	5.91	5.86	5.80	5.77	5.75	5.72	5.69	5.66	5.63	4
4.74	4.68	4.62	4.56	4.53	4.50	4.46	4.43	4.40	4.36	5
4.06	4.00	3.94	3.87	3.84	3.81	3.77	3.74	3.70	3.67	6
3.64	3.57	3.51	3.44	3.41	3.38	3.34	3.30	3.27	3.23	7
3.35	3.28	3.22	3.15	3.12	3.08	3.04	3.01	2.97	2.93	8
3.14	3.07	3.01	2.94	2.90	2.86	2.83	2.79	2.75	2.71	9
2.98	2.91	2.85	2.77	2.74	2.70	2.66	2.62	2.58	2.54	10
2.85	2.79	2.72	2.65	2.61	2.57	2.53	2.49	2.45	2.40	11
2.75	2.69	2.62	2.54	2.51	2.47	2.43	2.38	2.34	2.30	12
2.67	2.60	2.53	2.46	2.42	2.38	2.34	2.30	2.25	2.21	13
2.60	2.53	2.46	2.39	2.35	2.31	2.27	2.22	2.18	2.13	14
2.54	2.48	2.40	2.33	2.29	2.25	2.20	2.16	2.11	2.07	15
2.49	2.42	2.35	2.28	2.24	2.19	2.15	2.11	2.06	2.01	16
2.45	2.38	2.31	2.23	2.19	2.15	2.10	2.06	2.01	1.96	17
2.41	2.34	2.27	2.19	2.15	2.11	2.06	2.02	1.97	1.92	18
2.38	2.31	2.23	2.16	2.11	2.07	2.03	1.98	1.93	1.88	19
2.35	2.28	2.20	2.12	2.08	2.04	1.99	1.95	1.90	1.84	20
2.32	2.25	2.18	2.10	2.05	2.01	1.96	1.92	1.87	1.81	21
2.30	2.23	2.15	2.07	2.03	1.98	1.94	1.89	1.84	1.78	22
2.27	2.20	2.13	2.05	2.01	1.96	1.91	1.86	1.81	1.76	23
2.25	2.18	2.11	2.03	1.98	1.94	1.89	1.84	1.79	1.73	24
2.24	2.16	2.09	2.01	1.96	1.92	1.87	1.82	1.77	1.71	25
2.22	2.15	2.07	1.99	1.95	1.90	1.85	1.80	1.75	1.69	26
2.20	2.13	2.06	1.97	1.93	1.88	1.84	1.79	1.73	1.67	27
2.19	2.12	2.04	1.96	1.91	1.87	1.82	1.77	1.71	1.65	28
2.18	2.10	2.03	1.94	1.90	1.85	1.81	1.75	1.70	1.64	29
2.16	2.09	2.01	1.93	1.89	1.84	1.79	1.74	1.68	1.62	30
2.08	2.00	1.92	1.84	1.79	1.74	1.69	1.64	1.58	1.51	40
1.99	1.92	1.84	1.75	1.70	1.65	1.59	1.53	1.47	1.39	60
1.91	1.83	1.75	1.66	1.61	1.55	1.50	1.43	1.35	1.25	120
1.83	1.75	1.67	1.57	1.52	1.46	1.39	1.32	1.22	1.00	∞

From "Tables of Percentage Points of the Inverted Beta (*F*)-Distribution," *Biometrika*, Vol. 33 (1943), pp. 73–88, by Maxine Merrington and Catherine M. Thompson. Reproduced by permission of the *Biometrika* Trustees.

TABLE 5 Percentage
points of the F distri-
bution, $a = .01$.

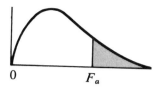

$0 \qquad F_a$

d.f.$_1$									
d.f.$_2$	1	2	3	4	5	6	7	8	9
1	4052	4999.5	5403	5625	5764	5859	5928	5982	6022
2	98.50	99.00	99.17	99.25	99.30	99.33	99.36	99.37	99.39
3	34.12	30.82	29.46	28.71	28.24	27.91	27.67	27.49	27.35
4	21.20	18.00	16.69	15.98	15.52	15.21	14.98	14.80	14.66
5	16.26	13.27	12.06	11.39	10.97	10.67	10.46	10.29	10.16
6	13.75	10.92	9.78	9.15	8.75	8.47	8.26	8.10	7.98
7	12.25	9.55	8.45	7.85	7.46	7.19	6.99	6.84	6.72
8	11.26	8.65	7.59	7.01	6.63	6.37	6.18	6.03	5.91
9	10.56	8.02	6.99	6.42	6.06	5.80	5.61	5.47	5.35
10	10.04	7.56	6.55	5.99	5.64	5.39	5.20	5.06	4.94
11	9.65	7.21	6.22	5.67	5.32	5.07	4.89	4.74	4.63
12	9.33	6.93	5.95	5.41	5.06	4.82	4.64	4.50	4.39
13	9.07	6.70	5.74	5.21	4.86	4.62	4.44	4.30	4.19
14	8.86	6.51	5.56	5.04	4.69	4.46	4.28	4.14	4.03
15	8.68	6.36	5.42	4.89	4.56	4.32	4.14	4.00	3.89
16	8.53	6.23	5.29	4.77	4.44	4.20	4.03	3.89	3.78
17	8.40	6.11	5.18	4.67	4.34	4.10	3.93	3.79	3.68
18	8.29	6.01	5.09	4.58	4.25	4.01	3.84	3.71	3.60
19	8.18	5.93	5.01	4.50	4.17	3.94	3.77	3.63	3.52
20	8.10	5.85	4.94	4.43	4.10	3.87	3.70	3.56	3.46
21	8.02	5.78	4.87	4.37	4.04	3.81	3.64	3.51	3.40
22	7.95	5.72	4.82	4.31	3.99	3.76	3.59	3.45	3.35
23	7.88	5.66	4.76	4.26	3.94	3.71	3.54	3.41	3.30
24	7.82	5.61	4.72	4.22	3.90	3.67	3.50	3.36	3.26
25	7.77	5.57	4.68	4.18	3.85	3.63	3.46	3.32	3.22
26	7.72	5.53	4.64	4.14	3.82	3.59	3.42	3.29	3.18
27	7.68	5.49	4.60	4.11	3.78	3.56	3.39	3.26	3.15
28	7.64	5.45	4.57	4.07	3.75	3.53	3.36	3.23	3.12
29	7.60	5.42	4.54	4.04	3.73	3.50	3.33	3.20	3.09
30	7.56	5.39	4.51	4.02	3.70	3.47	3.30	3.17	3.07
40	7.31	5.18	4.31	3.83	3.51	3.29	3.12	2.99	2.89
60	7.08	4.98	4.13	3.65	3.34	3.12	2.95	2.82	2.72
120	6.85	4.79	3.95	3.48	3.17	2.96	2.79	2.66	2.56
∞	6.63	4.61	3.78	3.32	3.02	2.80	2.64	2.51	2.41

TABLE 5 *(continued)*

10	12	15	20	24	30	40	60	120	∞	d.f.$_1$ / d.f.$_2$
6056	6106	6157	6209	6235	6261	6287	6313	6339	6366	1
99.40	99.42	99.43	99.45	99.46	99.47	99.47	99.48	99.49	99.50	2
27.23	27.05	26.87	26.69	26.60	26.50	26.41	26.32	26.22	26.13	3
14.55	14.37	14.20	14.02	13.93	13.84	13.75	13.65	13.56	13.46	4
10.05	9.89	9.72	9.55	9.47	9.38	9.29	9.20	9.11	9.02	5
7.87	7.72	7.56	7.40	7.31	7.23	7.14	7.06	6.97	6.88	6
6.62	6.47	6.31	6.16	6.07	5.99	5.91	5.82	5.74	5.65	7
5.81	5.67	5.52	5.36	5.28	5.20	5.12	5.03	4.95	4.86	8
5.26	5.11	4.96	4.81	4.73	4.65	4.57	4.48	4.40	4.31	9
4.85	4.71	4.56	4.41	4.33	4.25	4.17	4.08	4.00	3.91	10
4.54	4.40	4.25	4.10	4.02	3.94	3.86	3.78	3.69	3.60	11
4.30	4.16	4.01	3.86	3.78	3.70	3.62	3.54	3.45	3.36	12
4.10	3.96	3.82	3.66	3.59	3.51	3.43	3.34	3.25	3.17	13
3.94	3.80	3.66	3.51	3.43	3.35	3.27	3.18	3.09	3.00	14
3.80	3.67	3.52	3.37	3.29	3.21	3.13	3.05	2.96	2.87	15
3.69	3.55	3.41	3.26	3.18	3.10	3.02	2.93	2.84	2.75	16
3.59	3.46	3.31	3.16	3.08	3.00	2.92	2.83	2.75	2.65	17
3.51	3.37	3.23	3.08	3.00	2.92	2.84	2.75	2.66	2.57	18
3.43	3.30	3.15	3.00	2.92	2.84	2.76	2.67	2.58	2.49	19
3.37	3.23	3.09	2.94	2.86	2.78	2.69	2.61	2.52	2.42	20
3.31	3.17	3.03	2.88	2.80	2.72	2.64	2.55	2.46	2.36	21
3.26	3.12	2.98	2.83	2.75	2.67	2.58	2.50	2.40	2.31	22
3.21	3.07	2.93	2.78	2.70	2.62	2.54	2.45	2.35	2.26	23
3.17	3.03	2.89	2.74	2.66	2.58	2.49	2.40	2.31	2.21	24
3.13	2.99	2.85	2.70	2.62	2.54	2.45	2.36	2.27	2.17	25
3.09	2.96	2.81	2.66	2.58	2.50	2.42	2.33	2.23	2.13	26
3.06	2.93	2.78	2.63	2.55	2.47	2.38	2.29	2.20	2.10	27
3.03	2.90	2.75	2.60	2.52	2.44	2.35	2.26	2.17	2.06	28
3.00	2.87	2.73	2.57	2.49	2.41	2.33	2.23	2.14	2.03	29
2.98	2.84	2.70	2.55	2.47	2.39	2.30	2.21	2.11	2.01	30
2.80	2.66	2.52	2.37	2.29	2.20	2.11	2.02	1.92	1.80	40
2.63	2.50	2.35	2.20	2.12	2.03	1.94	1.84	1.73	1.60	60
2.47	2.34	2.19	2.03	1.95	1.86	1.76	1.66	1.53	1.38	120
2.32	2.18	2.04	1.88	1.79	1.70	1.59	1.47	1.32	1.00	∞

TABLE 6

Random numbers

Col. Line	1	2	3	4	5	6	7	8	9	10	11	12	13	14
1	10480	15011	01536	−02011	81647	91646	69179	14194	62590	36207	20969	99570	91291	90700
2	22368	46573	25595	85393	30995	89198	27982	53402	93965	34095	52666	19174	39615	99505
3	24130	48360	22527	97265	76393	64809	15179	24830	49340	32081	30680	19655	63348	58629
4	42167	93093	06243	61680	07856	16376	39440	53537	71341	57004	00849	74917	97758	16379
5	37570	39975	81837	16656	06121	91782	60468	81305	49684	60672	14110	06927	01263	54613
6	77921	06907	11008	42751	27756	53498	18602	70659	90655	15053	21916	81825	44394	42880
7	99562	72905	56420	69994	98872	31016	71194	18738	44013	48840	63213	21069	10634	12952
8	96301	91977	05463	07972	18876	20922	94595	56869	69014	60045	18425	84903	42508	32307
9	89579	14342	63661	10281	17453	18103	57740	84378	25331	12566	58678	44947	05585	56941
10	85475	36857	53342	53988	53060	59533	38867	62300	08158	17983	16439	11458	18593	64952
11	28918	69578	88231	33276	70997	79936	56865	05859	90106	31595	01547	85590	91610	78188
12	63553	40961	48235	03427	49626	69445	18663	72695	52180	20847	12234	90511	33703	90322
13	09429	93969	52636	92737	88974	33488	36320	17617	30015	08272	84115	27156	30613	74952
14	10365	61129	87529	85689	48237	52267	67689	93394	01511	26358	85104	20285	29975	89868
15	07119	97336	71048	08178	77233	13916	47564	81056	97735	85977	29372	74461	28551	90707
16	51085	12765	51821	51259	77452	16308	60756	92144	49442	53900	70960	63990	75601	40719
17	02368	21382	52404	60268	89368	19885	55322	44819	01188	65255	64835	44919	05944	55157
18	01011	54092	33362	94904	31273	04146	18594	29852	71585	85030	51132	01915	92747	64951
19	52162	53916	46369	58586	23216	14513	83149	98736	23495	64350	94738	17752	35156	35749
20	07056	97628	33787	09998	42698	06691	76988	13602	51851	46104	88916	19509	25625	58104
21	48663	91245	85828	14346	09172	30168	90229	04734	59193	22178	30421	61666	99904	32812
22	54164	58492	22421	74103	47070	25306	76468	26384	58151	06646	21524	15227	96909	44592
23	32639	32363	05597	24200	13363	38005	94342	28728	35806	06912	17012	64161	18296	22851
24	29334	27001	87637	87308	58731	00256	45834	15398	46557	41135	10367	07684	36188	18510
25	02488	33062	28834	07351	19731	92420	60952	61280	50001	67658	32586	86679	50720	94953

Abridged from *Handbook of Tables for Probability and Statistics*, Second Edition, edited by William H. Beyer, © The Chemical Rubber Co., 1968. Used by permission of CRC Press, Inc.

TABLE 7
Database A

Students at a West Coast state university were asked: "Which of the following acts do you personally think should be publicly regarded as crimes?" The acts presented were: aggravated assault, armed robbery, arson, atheism, automobile theft, burglary, civil disobedience, communism, drug addiction, embezzlement, forcible rape, gambling, homosexuality, land fraud, masturbation, Nazism, payola (kickbacks), price fixing, prostitution, sexual abuse of children, sexual discrimination, shoplifting, strip mining, treason, and vandalism.

Each student is identified with a number. Descriptions for the variables measured are as follows.

VARIABLE DESCRIPTIONS

STUDENT: student number
CRIMES: number of acts regarded as a crime
COLLEGE: year in college (freshman, sophomore, junior, or senior)
SEX: sex (M or F)
AGE: age (years)
MAR_STAT: marital status (single or married)
RELIGION: religious preference (Protestant, Catholic, Jewish, other, or none)
RACE: race (black, white, or other)
INCOME: income of parents (low, medium, or high)
MAJOR: major in college (business, humanities, natural sciences, social sciences)

STUDENT	CRIMES	COLLEGE	SEX	AGE	MAR–STAT	RELIGION	RACE	INCOME	MAJOR
001	25	Junior	F	26	Single	Protestant	Other	High	SocSciences
002	09	Sophomore	F	20	Single	Other	Other	High	SocSciences
003	18	Sophomore	F	21	Single	Catholic	Other	Medium	SocSciences
004	18	Junior	M	30	Married	Catholic	White	Medium	SocSciences
005	18	Freshman	F	31	Married	None	White	Low	SocSciences
006	20	Junior	M	20	Single	Catholic	Other	High	SocSciences
007	17	Senior	M	28	Married	Other	White	Medium	SocSciences
008	16	Junior	F	26	Married	Other	White	Medium	SocSciences

STUDENT	CRIMES	COLLEGE	SEX	AGE	MAR—STAT	RELIGION	RACE	INCOME	MAJOR
009	17	Senior	F	21	Single	Other	White	Medium	SocSciences
010	16	Freshman	M	24	Single	Protestant	White	Medium	SocSciences
011	18	Senior	M	21	Single	Jewish	White	Medium	SocSciences
012	12	Senior	M	27	Married	Protestant	White	High	SocSciences
013	18	Sophomore	M	27	Married	Protestant	Black	High	SocSciences
014	17	Junior	F	26	Married	None	White	Medium	SocSciences
015	15	Junior	M	20	Single	None	White	Medium	SocSciences
016	22	Sophomore	F	29	Single	None	Black	High	SocSciences
017	18	Junior	F	32	Single	None	Black	Low	SocSciences
018	17	Junior	F	19	Single	Protestant	Black	Medium	SocSciences
019	11	Sophomore	F	30	Single	None	Other	Low	SocSciences
020	18	Junior	F	21	Single	None	Black	Medium	SocSciences
021	16	Junior	M	24	Married	None	White	High	SocSciences
022	17	Junior	F	31	Married	None	White	High	SocSciences
023	15	Senior	M	32	Single	None	White	High	SocSciences
024	18	Junior	M	20	Single	None	White	Low	SocSciences
025	14	Freshman	F	18	Single	Protestant	White	Medium	SocSciences
026	17	Junior	F	21	Married	Protestant	White	High	SocSciences
027	17	Senior	M	29	Single	None	Black	High	SocSciences
028	19	Senior	F	19	Single	Protestant	White	Medium	SocSciences
029	16	Senior	F	33	Married	Protestant	White	High	SocSciences
030	21	Junior	F	21	Single	Catholic	Black	High	SocSciences
031	16	Senior	M	32	Married	Protestant	White	Low	SocSciences
032	14	Senior	F	23	Single	None	White	High	SocSciences
033	20	Senior	M	26	Single	Jewish	White	High	SocSciences
034	16	Senior	M	23	Single	Catholic	White	High	SocSciences
035	12	Senior	F	22	Single	None	White	High	SocSciences
036	16	Senior	M	25	Married	Protestant	White	Medium	SocSciences
037	15	Junior	M	19	Single	Other	White	High	SocSciences
038	16	Senior	F	35	Married	Other	Black	Medium	SocSciences
039	19	Junior	F	21	Single	Protestant	Black	Medium	SocSciences
040	21	Senior	F	34	Married	Catholic	Black	Medium	SocSciences
041	18	Senior	F	22	Married	Catholic	Other	Medium	SocSciences
042	12	Junior	M	33	Married	Protestant	Black	Medium	Humanities
043	19	Sophomore	F	18	Single	None	White	Medium	Humanities
044	18	Senior	F	32	Married	None	White	Low	Humanities
045	14	Senior	M	25	Single	None	White	Medium	Humanities
046	20	Senior	F	30	Married	Catholic	White	Medium	Humanities
047	16	Senior	F	22	Single	Other	White	High	Humanities
048	12	Sophomore	F	18	Single	Protestant	Other	High	Humanities

STUDENT	CRIMES	COLLEGE	SEX	AGE	MAR—STAT	RELIGION	RACE	INCOME	MAJOR
049	18	Senior	F	20	Single	Catholic	White	Medium	Humanities
050	21	Sophomore	F	21	Single	Catholic	White	Medium	Humanities
051	16	Senior	F	22	Single	Protestant	White	High	Humanities
052	12	Junior	F	23	Single	Other	Black	Low	Humanities
053	19	Senior	F	32	Married	Protestant	White	High	Humanities
054	21	Junior	F	22	Married	Other	White	Medium	Humanities
055	15	Junior	M	31	Married	None	Other	Low	Humanities
056	18	Senior	F	24	Married	Jewish	White	High	Humanities
057	18	Senior	F	33	Married	Protestant	White	High	Humanities
058	20	Sophomore	M	31	Married	Protestant	White	Medium	Humanities
059	16	Junior	F	32	Married	None	White	High	Humanities
060	13	Freshman	F	18	Single	None	White	High	Humanities
061	16	Senior	F	30	Married	Catholic	Other	High	Humanities
062	20	Senior	F	27	Married	Protestant	Black	Medium	Humanities
063	12	Junior	M	28	Married	None	White	Low	Humanities
064	20	Senior	F	24	Single	Jewish	White	High	Humanities
065	17	Junior	M	37	Married	Protestant	White	Low	Humanities
066	21	Senior	M	35	Married	Other	White	High	Humanities
067	17	Junior	M	22	Single	None	White	High	Humanities
068	18	Sophomore	M	19	Single	None	White	Low	Humanities
069	17	Junior	M	21	Single	None	White	High	Humanities
070	18	Junior	F	21	Single	Other	White	Medium	Humanities
071	17	Senior	M	23	Single	None	White	High	Humanities
072	18	Junior	F	24	Single	Protestant	Other	Low	Humanities
073	13	Junior	M	22	Married	None	White	Medium	Humanities
074	25	Senior	F	32	Married	Protestant	Other	Medium	Humanities
075	20	Junior	F	20	Single	Protestant	White	High	Humanities
076	20	Senior	F	21	Single	None	White	Medium	Humanities
077	17	Senior	F	25	Single	Catholic	Other	Medium	Humanities
078	15	Junior	F	24	Married	Catholic	Other	Medium	Humanities
079	14	Senior	M	23	Single	Other	Other	High	NatSciences
080	16	Senior	F	26	Married	None	White	Low	NatSciences
081	18	Senior	F	22	Married	None	White	High	NatSciences
082	09	Sophomore	F	18	Single	Other	Other	Medium	NatSciences
083	18	Sophomore	F	20	Single	None	Black	Medium	NatSciences
084	17	Sophomore	M	18	Single	None	Other	Medium	NatSciences
085	15	Senior	M	27	Married	Catholic	Other	Low	NatSciences
086	19	Senior	F	35	Single	None	White	Medium	NatSciences
087	14	Junior	F	20	Single	None	White	Medium	NatSciences

S T U D E N T	C R I M E S	C O L L E G E	S E X	A G E	M A R — S T A T	R E L I G I O N	R A C E	I N C O M E	M A J O R
088	15	Sophomore	F	19	Single	None	White	High	NatSciences
089	20	Sophomore	F	26	Single	Catholic	White	Medium	NatSciences
090	15	Senior	F	24	Married	Catholic	Other	Medium	NatSciences
091	17	Junior	F	20	Single	None	White	Medium	NatSciences
092	24	Junior	M	27	Single	Protestant	White	Low	NatSciences
093	15	Junior	F	20	Single	Protestant	White	Medium	NatSciences
094	19	Senior	M	23	Single	Catholic	White	Medium	NatSciences
095	18	Junior	F	19	Single	None	Other	High	NatSciences
096	16	Junior	F	23	Single	Other	White	High	NatSciences
097	19	Senior	M	24	Married	Other	Other	Medium	NatSciences
098	15	Senior	F	29	Single	None	White	High	NatSciences
099	17	Senior	F	20	Single	Catholic	Black	Medium	NatSciences
100	21	Senior	M	38	Married	Protestant	White	High	NatSciences
101	14	Junior	M	22	Married	None	White	High	NatSciences
102	11	Senior	M	26	Married	None	White	Medium	NatSciences
103	20	Senior	F	27	Married	Protestant	White	Medium	NatSciences
104	15	Senior	M	23	Single	Protestant	White	High	NatSciences
105	11	Senior	F	28	Single	Other	Black	Medium	NatSciences
106	11	Senior	M	29	Married	None	Black	Medium	NatSciences
107	17	Junior	M	21	Single	Other	Other	Medium	NatSciences
108	16	Junior	F	19	Single	Protestant	White	High	NatSciences
109	15	Sophomore	M	17	Single	Protestant	Other	High	NatSciences
110	16	Senior	M	29	Married	None	White	High	NatSciences
111	15	Senior	M	28	Married	None	Other	High	NatSciences
112	18	Senior	F	21	Single	Catholic	White	Medium	NatSciences
113	18	Junior	F	20	Single	Other	Other	High	NatSciences
114	15	Senior	F	20	Single	Catholic	Black	High	NatSciences
115	15	Senior	F	23	Single	Other	Other	Low	NatSciences
116	19	Senior	M	22	Single	Catholic	Other	Medium	Business
117	12	Senior	M	20	Single	Protestant	White	Medium	Business
118	22	Senior	F	23	Married	Catholic	White	High	Business
119	23	Senior	M	22	Single	Catholic	White	Medium	Business
120	18	Freshman	F	18	Single	Catholic	Black	High	Business
121	21	Junior	M	20	Single	Other	White	Medium	Business
122	16	Sophomore	M	21	Single	None	White	High	Business
123	23	Sophomore	F	19	Single	Other	Black	High	Business
124	16	Senior	F	22	Single	Catholic	White	Low	Business
125	13	Sophomore	M	20	Single	Catholic	Other	Medium	Business
126	18	Senior	M	34	Married	None	White	High	Business

S T U D E N T	C R I M E S	C O L L E G E	S E X	A G E	M A R — S T A T	R E L I G I O N	R A C E	I N C O M E	M A J O R
127	14	Junior	F	20	Single	Other	Black	Low	Business
128	15	Sophomore	M	19	Single	Catholic	Other	Low	Business
129	16	Senior	M	28	Married	None	White	High	Business
130	16	Freshman	F	18	Single	None	White	High	Business
131	17	Junior	M	29	Married	Protestant	White	High	Business
132	23	Junior	M	34	Married	Protestant	White	Medium	Business
133	15	Senior	F	33	Married	Protestant	White	Medium	Business
134	20	Junior	F	22	Married	Other	White	High	Business
135	15	Senior	F	38	Married	None	White	Medium	Business
136	20	Senior	M	20	Single	Protestant	White	Low	Business
137	19	Sophomore	M	18	Single	Protestant	Other	High	Business
138	13	Senior	M	21	Married	None	White	High	Business
139	14	Senior	F	28	Married	None	White	Medium	Business
140	16	Senior	M	20	Single	None	White	Medium	Business
141	22	Senior	M	21	Single	Protestant	White	Medium	Business
142	17	Senior	F	23	Single	None	White	Medium	Business
143	17	Senior	F	30	Married	Protestant	White	High	Business
144	16	Junior	M	27	Married	None	Black	Medium	Business
145	16	Senior	M	23	Single	Other	White	High	Business
146	21	Senior	M	26	Single	Catholic	White	High	Business
147	23	Senior	F	22	Single	Other	White	Medium	Business
148	11	Junior	M	20	Single	None	White	High	Business
149	17	Junior	F	21	Single	None	White	Medium	Business
150	13	Senior	F	20	Single	Catholic	White	High	Business
151	15	Senior	F	21	Single	None	Other	Medium	Business
152	16	Senior	M	23	Single	Protestant	Other	High	Business
153	17	Senior	M	27	Married	Catholic	White	High	Business
154	20	Senior	M	21	Single	None	White	Medium	Business
155	24	Senior	M	25	Single	Catholic	White	Medium	Business
156	19	Junior	F	20	Single	Catholic	White	Medium	Business
157	18	Junior	M	37	Married	Catholic	White	Medium	Business
158	17	Junior	F	20	Single	None	White	Medium	Business
159	15	Junior	M	22	Single	None	White	High	Business
160	19	Senior	F	34	Married	Protestant	White	Medium	Business
161	20	Junior	M	33	Married	None	White	Low	Business
162	23	Junior	M	37	Married	Protestant	White	Low	Business
163	18	Junior	M	20	Single	Catholic	White	High	Business
164	18	Senior	F	35	Married	Protestant	Black	Medium	Business
165	19	Senior	M	28	Married	None	White	Medium	Business

S T U D E N T	C R I M E S	C O L L E G E	S E X	A G E	M A R — S T A T	R E L I G I O N	R A C E	I N C O M E	M A J O R
166	17	Junior	M	31	Married	Catholic	Other	Medium	Business
167	16	Senior	M	29	Single	Protestant	White	High	Business
168	16	Junior	M	23	Married	Catholic	White	High	Business
169	17	Senior	M	22	Single	Protestant	White	High	Business
170	15	Senior	M	29	Single	None	White	Medium	Business
171	24	Senior	M	22	Single	Protestant	White	High	Business
172	18	Senior	M	27	Single	None	White	High	Business
173	17	Senior	F	20	Single	None	White	High	Business
174	21	Senior	M	23	Single	Other	Other	High	Business
175	17	Senior	M	38	Single	None	White	Low	Business
176	21	Junior	F	24	Single	Catholic	Other	Medium	Business
177	17	Senior	M	23	Single	None	White	Low	Business
178	24	Junior	F	20	Married	Protestant	White	Medium	Business
179	18	Junior	M	27	Married	Catholic	White	Medium	Business
180	18	Junior	F	25	Married	Catholic	White	Medium	Business
181	23	Sophomore	F	22	Married	Protestant	White	High	Business
182	18	Senior	M	24	Married	Catholic	White	Medium	Business
183	15	Senior	M	33	Married	None	White	High	Business
184	15	Junior	F	20	Single	Catholic	White	Medium	Business
185	21	Junior	F	21	Single	Catholic	White	High	Business
186	16	Junior	M	23	Single	Catholic	White	High	Business
187	18	Senior	M	19	Married	Other	White	High	Business
188	16	Junior	M	22	Single	Protestant	White	Medium	Business
189	13	Junior	M	25	Married	None	White	Medium	Business
190	12	Junior	M	33	Married	Jewish	White	High	Business
191	17	Junior	M	36	Married	Catholic	White	High	Business
192	16	Junior	M	22	Single	Catholic	White	High	Business
193	16	Junior	F	24	Single	Protestant	Other	Medium	Business
194	17	Junior	F	30	Married	Other	White	High	Business
195	17	Junior	M	24	Single	Protestant	White	High	Business
196	16	Senior	M	23	Single	Catholic	White	Medium	Business
197	17	Sophomore	M	18	Single	Protestant	White	High	Business
198	16	Junior	F	20	Single	Catholic	White	High	Business
199	15	Junior	M	20	Single	Protestant	White	High	Business
200	18	Junior	F	36	Single	Protestant	White	High	Business

TABLE 8

Database B

International, national, and local agencies routinely collect social and demographic information of special interest to social researchers. Some of this information describes changes in the population structures of nations. From this extensive body of information, we have culled data on a sample of 60 different nations. For each nation we have information on the following variables: crude birth rate, crude death rate, infant mortality rate, life expectancy in years, percentage of the population living in urban areas, per capita gross national product (GNP) in U.S. dollars, level of technological development (where 100 is the maximum as of this date), and degree to which civil liberties are denied (where 2 is minimal denial of civil liberties and 14 is maximal denial).

There is a body of literature dealing with modernization. One of the themes in this body of literature is that modernization (elaborate technology) reduces both the crude birth rate and crude death rate as well as enhances the quality of life, including civil liberties.

Our database will allow us to examine some of these relationships, including the influence that technology has upon birth and death rates as well as upon civil liberties. Description for the variables measured are as follows.

VARIABLE DESCRIPTIONS

COUNTRY:	country
BIRTHRAT:	crude birth rate
DEATHRAT:	crude death rate
INF_MORT:	infant mortality rate
LIFE_EXP:	life expectancy
PERURBAN:	percentage of population in urban areas
PERC_GNP:	per capita GNP in U.S. dollars
LEV_TECH:	level of technology (100 highest)
FREEDOMS:	measure of freedom (2 greatest)

COUNTRY	BIRTHRAT	DEATHRAT	INF—MORT	LIFE—EXP	PERURBAN	PERC—GNP	LEV—TECH	FREEDOMS
Algeria	40	9	74	60	43	2,450	17	10
Argentina	21	9	32	71	85	2,640	23	3
Australia	15	7	9	76	86	12,390	71	2
Austria	12	11	8	75	55	15,560	50	2
Bolivia	38	12	110	53	49	570	10	5
Brazil	27	8	63	65	74	2,280	15	4
Bulgaria	13	12	14	72	67	6,440	44	14
Canada	14	7	7	77	77	16,760	75	2
Chile	22	6	19	71	84	1,510	22	7
Colombia	28	7	46	66	68	1,240	15	7
Czechoslovakia	14	11	12	71	75	8,750	72	12
Denmark	12	12	8	76	84	18,470	71	2
Egypt	38	9	90	60	45	650	13	9
Finland	13	10	6	75	62	18,610	57	2
France	14	9	8	77	73	16,080	62	3
Ghana	44	13	86	55	32	400	10	11
Greece	11	9	11	77	58	4,790	23	3
Hungary	12	13	16	70	60	7,504	49	7
India	32	11	95	57	26	330	6	5
Ireland	15	9	10	74	56	7,480	48	2
Israel	23	7	10	75	89	8,650	33	4
Italy	10	9	10	75	72	13,320	41	2
Ivory Coast	51	14	96	53	43	740	9	11
Japan	10	6	5	79	77	21,040	53	2
Kenya	46	7	62	63	20	360	11	12
Madagascar	46	14	120	54	22	180	12	9
Malawi	52	18	130	49	14	160	12	13
Malaysia	30	5	30	68	35	1,870	14	9
Morocco	35	10	82	61	43	750	12	8
Netherlands	13	8	8	77	89	14,530	68	2
New Zealand	17	8	10	74	85	9,620	66	2
Nigeria	46	17	121	48	31	290	8	11
Norway	14	11	8	76	71	20,020	63	2
Pakistan	44	13	110	56	28	350	8	6
Peru	32	8	76	65	69	1,440	12	6
Philippines	33	7	48	64	42	630	15	5
Poland	16	10	16	71	61	1,850	53	7
Portugal	12	10	15	74	30	3,670	22	3
Romania	16	11	26	71	61	5,400	33	14
Senegal	46	19	128	46	36	630	11	7

TABLE 8 (*continued*)

COUNTRY	BIRTHRAT	DEATHRAT	INF—MORT	LIFE——EXP	PERURBAN	PERCGNP	LEV—TECH	FREEDOMS
South Africa	35	8	55	63	56	2,290	33	11
South Korea	16	6	30	68	70	3,530	12	5
Spain	11	8	9	77	91	7,740	28	2
Sri Lanka	21	6	23	70	22	420	9	9
Sweden	14	11	6	76	83	19,150	81	2
Switzerland	12	9	7	77	61	27,260	57	2
Syria	45	7	48	65	50	1,670	16	14
Thailand	22	7	39	66	18	1,000	12	5
Togo	50	14	114	55	22	370	15	12
Tunisia	28	7	59	65	53	1,230	15	8
Turkey	29	8	74	64	53	1,280	14	5
United Kingdom	14	12	10	75	90	12,800	61	2
United States	16	9	10	75	74	19,780	100	2
Uruguay	18	10	22	71	87	2,470	20	5
USSR	19	10	29	69	66	7,480	59	11
Venezuela	28	5	33	70	83	3,170	25	4
West Germany	11	11	8	76	94	18,530	66	2
Yugoslavia	15	9	25	71	46	2,680	23	9
Zaire	47	14	108	53	40	170	10	13
Zambia	51	14	80	53	45	290	12	11

(Source: Adapted from Population Reference Bureau, *1990 World Population Data Sheet* (Washington, D.C.: Population Reference Bureau, Inc., 1990); and R. Bruce McColm, "The Comparative Survey of Freedom: 1990," *Freedom at Issue*, January/February 1990, pp. 18–19.)

TABLE 9

Database C

The data presented here are from a clinical trial that was conducted to compare the safety and efficacy of three different compounds (A, B, and C) and a placebo (D) in the treatment of patients who exhibited characteristic signs and symptoms of depression. Certain predrug (baseline) determinations were made on each of the 100 patients to determine their suitability for the study. Each patient who qualified for the study was assigned at random to one of the four treatment groups and was dispensed medication for the duration of the study. Neither the investigator nor the patient knew which medication had been assigned.

At the end of the study, scores on numerous anxiety and depression scales were made. Descriptions of the variables measured and their codes are as follows.

VARIABLE DESCRIPTIONS

PATIENT: patient number

AGE: age (years)

MAR_STAT: marital status

      1 = single

      2 = married

      3 = separated or divorced

      4 = widowed

COFF_TEA: coffee/tea consumption (cups/day)

TOBACCO: tobacco consumption

      0 = none

      1 = <1 pack daily

      2 = 1 pack daily

      3 = >1 pack daily

ALCOHOL: alcohol consumption

      0 = none

      1 = social drinker (<1 drink weekly)

      2 = social drinker (1 to 2 drinks weekly)

      3 = 1 to 2 drinks most days

      4 = 3 or more drinks most days

TRT_EMOT: previous treatment for emotional problems

      1 = psychiatrist

      2 = nonpsychiatrist physician

      3 = both

      4 = other

HOSPITAL: hospitalization for emotional problems

      0 = no

      1 = yes

PSY_DIAG: psychiatrist diagnosis

      1 = major depressive disorder, single episode

      2 = major depressive disorder, recurrent episode

      3 = bipolar affective disorder

      4 = chronic depressive disorder

      5 = atypical depressive disorder

      6 = adjustment disorder with depressed mood

ANXIETY:	HAM-D anxiety score
RETARDTN:	HAM-D retardation score
SLEEP:	HAM-D sleep disturbance score
TOTAL:	HAM-D total score
OBRIST:	HOPKINS OBRIST cluster total
APPETITE:	appetite disturbance score
CHANGED:	how much the patient has changed

                    1 = very much improved
                    2 = much improved
                    3 = minimally improved
                    4 = no change
                    5 = minimally worse
                    6 = much worse
                    7 = very much worse

THER_EFF: therapeutic effect
                    1 = marked
                    2 = moderate
                    3 = minimal
                    4 = unchanged
                    5 = worse

ADV_EFF: adverse effects
                    1 = none
                    2 = does not significantly interfere with patient's functioning
                    3 = significantly interferes with patient's functioning
                    4 = nullifies therapeutic effect

TREATMNT: drug treatment group
                    A
                    B
                    C
                    D—placebo (control) group

PATIENT	AGE	MAR—STAT	COFF—TE	TOBACCO	ALCOHOL	TRT—EMOT	HOSPITAL	PSY—DIAG	ANXIETY	RETARDTN	SLEEP	TOTAL	OBRIST	APPETITE	CHANGED	THER—EFF	ADV—EFF	TREATMNT
1	23	2	3	1	0	0	0	1	0.33	0.75	0.00	16	56	91.0	4	4	1	D
2	18	1	0	2	0	1	0	2	0.33	1.25	0.33	12	57	42.5	3	3	1	A
3	36	2	2	2	2	1	0	2	0.50	0.25	0.33	6	40	91.0	1	1	2	B
4	51	4	5	3	0	0	0	1	0.17	0.75	0.67	6	39	61.0	2	1	1	A
5	24	1	6	2	1	1	0	2	1.00	1.00	1.00	13	49	1.5	3	3	1	B
6	59	4	3	1	0	1	0	4	0.33	1.50	0.00	11	40	72.0	2	2	1	A
7	56	1	2	0	0	1	1	4	1.67	1.75	0.00	21	44	7.5	2	2	1	B
8	70	4	1	0	0	1	0	2	0.50	1.75	0.00	12	39	92.5	2	2	2	A
9	30	3	4	3	2	1	0	2	0.83	1.00	0.67	15	49	2.0	2	2	4	D
10	55	4	2	0	2	0	0	1	0.33	1.00	1.00	11	44	31.0	2	2	1	D
11	40	2	4	2	0	1	0	2	0.83	1.50	1.33	23	79	92.0	4	4	1	C
12	61	2	2	0	1	1	1	2	0.50	0.75	0.00	8	30	1.0	2	2	2	C
13	64	2	3	2	0	1	0	2	0.33	1.50	0.00	9	48	11.5	2	2	3	A
14	19	1	10	2	2	1	0	1	0.50	0.75	0.00	7	42	91.5	2	2	1	B
15	46	3	2	0	1	1	0	1	0.17	0.25	0.00	4	35	92.0	1	1	1	A
16	36	2	10	3	0	1	0	2	0.50	1.50	0.00	9	42	72.0	2	2	1	C
17	30	2	2	0	2	0	0	1	0.00	0.50	0.67	4	35	41.0	2	1	1	B
18	34	2	8	3	1	1	0	1	0.50	1.00	0.33	14	56	91.5	3	3	1	D
19	28	1	2	0	1	0	0	1	0.67	1.00	0.33	12	43	72.5	1	2	2	B
20	33	3	3	2	1	1	0	2	0.67	0.75	0.33	8	39	93.0	2	2	2	C
21	51	3	7	3	2	1	1	5	0.83	2.00	0.00	21	99	42.5	4	4	2	A
22	51	2	0	0	0	1	0	4	0.83	1.00	0.00	12	68	61.0	3	3	3	C
23	54	2	3	0	0	0	1	2	0.83	1.00	1.00	16	49	11.0	3	3	2	B
24	35	3	5	0	2	1	0	4	0.67	1.50	0.00	11	42	61.0	2	2	3	A
25	46	2	3	0	1	0	1	2	0.67	2.00	1.33	17	63	61.5	4	4	1	D
26	34	2	7	0	0	1	1	2	0.33	0.25	0.33	6	51	12.5	2	2	2	C
27	27	3	2	1	2	1	0	5	0.83	0.75	0.00	11	58	11.0	2	2	2	A
28	23	2	0	1	0	0	0	1	0.33	0.75	0.00	6	47	91.5	2	2	2	C
29	35	3	6	0	3	1	0	5	0.33	0.50	0.00	9	68	1.0	3	2	2	B
30	19	1	2	0	0	0	0	4	0.67	0.50	0.00	11	47	2.5	3	3	2	B
31	40	3	3	0	3	0	0	1	1.00	1.75	0.00	17	71	62.0	4	4	1	D
32	52	2	5	0	0	1	1	2	0.83	1.75	0.67	19	41	91.5	3	3	2	B
33	51	3	6	0	0	1	0	2	0.83	1.00	1.67	20	63	11.0	3	4	2	D
34	34	3	0	0	2	1	0	4	0.17	0.50	0.33	5	37	13.0	2	2	1	C
35	59	2	4	2	0	1	0	1	0.67	2.50	0.00	17	54	62.5	3	3	2	C

P A T I E N T	A G E	M A R — S T A T	C O F F — F — T E A	T O B A C C O L	A L C O H O L	T R T — E M O T	H O S P I T A L	P S Y — D I A G	A N X I E T Y	R E T A R D T N	S L E E P	T O T A L	O B R I S T	A P P E T I T E	C H A N G E D	T H E R — E F F	A D V — E F F	T R E A T M N T
36	31	3	2	0	1	1	1	5	0.50	1.75	0.33	12	51	11.5	3	2	2	C
37	54	2	10	0	2	1	0	2	1.17	1.25	1.33	22	96	92.5	5	5	1	A
38	63	4	2	0	2	1	0	1	0.33	0.25	0.33	7	58	32.5	2	2	2	B
39	34	2	1	2	2	0	1	1	0.50	0.25	0.33	27	90	92.0	5	5	1	D
40	30	1	1	0	1	1	0	1	1.00	0.50	0.67	13	59	33.0	2	2	1	A
41	32	3	2	3	1	1	0	2	0.67	1.25	0.67	14	58	61.0	2	2	2	C
42	21	1	2	0	3	1	0	2	0.83	1.00	1.00	20	60	41.5	3	3	2	B
43	42	2	1	2	1	1	1	2	1.00	1.50	1.00	24	85	62.0	3	2	1	B
44	60	2	0	3	0	1	0	4	0.17	0.75	0.33	5	39	1.5	1	1	1	A
45	53	2	2	0	1	1	0	2	0.67	1.00	0.67	10	38	31.0	2	2	2	B
46	54	4	4	0	1	1	0	4	1.50	1.75	0.00	14	42	93.5	2	2	1	C
47	38	2	2	1	0	1	0	2	1.50	1.75	1.00	24	85	15.0	3	4	2	D
48	41	2	4	0	0	1	1	2	0.33	0.75	0.00	11	47	2.5	2	2	1	A
49	32	3	0	0	1	1	0	4	1.00	1.00	1.00	20	35	42.5	3	2	2	B
50	43	2	4	0	0	1	0	4	0.83	1.25	1.33	21	44	31.5	4	4	1	B
51	51	2	1	0	1	1	0	2	0.83	2.25	0.00	20	80	61.0	5	5	1	A
52	23	2	0	1	3	1	0	2	1.33	1.25	0.67	20	39	31.5	3	3	1	A
53	55	2	2	0	0	1	0	1	0.83	1.25	0.00	16	52	12.5	3	3	1	C
54	45	1	3	3	0	1	0	2	0.33	1.25	0.00	14	46	41.5	2	2	1	C
55	30	2	1	0	0	0	0	1	1.17	1.75	0.00	17	64	2.0	3	3	2	C
56	53	4	1	3	4	0	0	1	0.83	0.50	0.00	19	82	62.0	3	4	2	D
57	45	1	3	1	3	0	0	4	0.83	0.50	0.00	8	40	2.0	1	2	1	A
58	48	2	10	1	2	1	0	4	0.33	1.00	0.00	8	32	41.0	2	2	2	B
59	49	1	4	0	3	1	0	5	0.67	1.75	0.33	16	68	12.0	2	2	2	A
60	55	2	6	0	2	0	1	4	0.50	1.00	0.00	9	42	91.0	2	2	2	A
61	33	2	1	0	1	1	0	2	1.17	2.25	2.00	32	112	42.0	4	4	1	D
62	27	1	1	2	3	1	0	5	0.17	0.00	0.00	3	34	72.5	1	1	2	C
63	30	1	2	1	3	1	0	4	0.67	0.00	0.00	6	37	73.5	1	1	2	A
64	35	2	4	3	0	1	0	2	0.50	1.50	0.33	16	43	11.0	3	3	1	A
65	55	2	4	0	0	1	0	2	1.00	2.00	0.33	24	37	92.0	3	3	1	B
66	22	3	0	1	1	1	0	2	1.00	1.50	0.33	20	46	11.5	3	3	1	D
67	37	3	1	2	0	1	0	2	0.50	0.75	0.00	11	32	41.5	2	2	1	C
68	49	2	6	3	0	1	0	2	0.50	0.75	0.00	13	54	2.5	2	1	1	C
69	21	1	0	1	0	1	0	2	1.17	2.50	2.00	34	74	11.5	5	5	1	A
70	33	3	1	3	2	1	0	1	0.17	0.50	0.00	8	34	42.5	1	1	1	C

P A T I E N T	A G E	M A R — S T A T	C O F F — T T E A	T O B A C C O	A L C O H O L	T R T — E M T	H O S P I T A L	P S Y — D I A G	A N X I E T Y	R E T A R D T N	S L E E P	T O T A L	O B R I S T	A P P E T I T E	C H A N G E D	T H E R — E F F	A D V — E F F	T R E A T M N T
71	35	3	10	2	0	1	0	2	1.17	2.50	0.00	24	39	92.5	4	4	2	B
72	39	3	0	0	0	1	0	2	0.50	1.25	0.00	22	66	41.0	2	3	1	D
73	34	1	0	0	0	1	0	2	0.33	0.75	0.00	14	48	71.0	2	2	1	C
74	53	3	3	1	0	1	0	2	0.50	1.00	0.00	12	39	43.5	2	2	1	A
75	34	2	0	0	0	1	0	2	0.33	0.50	0.00	10	36	3.0	2	2	1	A
76	35	2	2	0	1	1	0	2	0.83	1.00	0.33	14	35	92.0	2	2	1	B
77	32	2	0	0	0	1	0	2	0.50	1.00	0.00	12	39	91.0	2	2	1	B
78	43	2	2	2	0	1	0	2	0.17	0.50	0.67	5	57	41.5	2	2	1	C
79	64	2	3	0	0	0	1	1	1.33	1.50	1.67	26	42	72.5	5	5	1	D
80	31	3	2	2	0	1	0	2	0.17	0.00	0.00	2	35	43.0	2	1	1	B
81	41	2	2	2	1	0	0	1	0.83	1.25	0.00	16	66	41.5	3	3	1	C
82	53	2	2	0	0	1	0	2	1.67	1.50	1.67	23	47	32.0	6	5	4	D
83	61	2	3	2	1	1	0	2	0.83	1.25	0.00	15	43	31.0	3	2	1	C
84	36	2	2	2	0	1	0	4	1.00	1.75	0.00	16	63	42.0	3	3	1	C
85	29	1	0	0	0	0	1	1	0.33	0.25	0.00	5	53	12.0	1	1	1	A
86	25	2	8	3	2	1	0	1	1.17	1.25	0.00	14	80	91.0	4	4	4	A
87	55	2	1	0	0	1	0	2	0.67	0.50	2.00	16	68	31.0	2	2	2	D
88	34	2	3	0	0	0	0	1	0.67	0.00	0.00	5	31	1.0	1	1	2	C
89	20	1	0	0	0	1	0	2	0.50	0.75	1.67	15	36	43.0	3	2	1	B
90	33	2	1	2	2	1	1	2	0.83	1.25	0.67	16	63	61.5	2	2	1	B
91	44	2	0	0	0	1	0	2	0.33	1.75	1.00	16	55	42.5	4	4	1	B
92	58	2	3	0	0	1	1	2	1.17	1.75	1.00	21	75	11.5	3	4	1	D
93	46	4	3	0	2	1	0	1	0.83	1.25	1.00	16	83	13.5	3	3	2	D
94	31	2	2	0	1	1	0	4	1.17	1.50	0.00	21	65	61.5	4	4	2	D
95	29	3	2	2	2	0	0	1	0.50	1.00	0.67	20	92	32.5	4	4	2	D
96	50	3	3	0	2	1	0	1	0.83	0.25	0.67	18	50	91.0	2	1	2	D
97	27	2	0	0	0	1	0	2	0.67	1.00	2.00	17	64	62.5	3	3	2	D
98	31	3	5	0	1	1	0	2	0.50	0.75	0.67	19	74	61.5	3	3	1	D
99	69	4	4	1	2	1	0	1	1.67	2.25	1.33	26	87	63.5	5	5	3	D
100	41	2	0	0	0	1	0	2	0.00	0.50	0.00	3	37	92.5	2	2	1	D

TABLE 10
Database D

The federal government routinely collects and summarizes incidents of social behavior. Data are often available by state. The data shown here come from 30 states and involve abortion, births to unmarried women, forcible rape, murder, population density, poverty, and suicide. The abortion rate is based on the number of abortions per 1000 women age 15–44; other rates are per total 100,000 population.

VARIABLE DESCRIPTIONS

STATE:	state
ABORTION:	number of abortions per 1000 women age 15–44
BIRT_UNM:	births to unmarried women, percentage of total
FOR_RAPE:	number of forcible rapes per 100,000 people
MURDER:	number of recorded murders per 100,000 people
POP_DENS:	average number of people per square mile
POVERTY:	percentage of people living below the poverty level
SUICIDE:	number of suicides per 100,000 deaths

STATE	ABORTION	BIRT_UNM	FOR_RAPE	MURDER	POP_DENS	POVERTY	SUICIDE
Alabama	27.3	26.8	29.8	9.9	81	18.9	12.4
Arizona	28.8	27.2	38.8	8.5	31	13.2	19.3
California	45.9	27.2	41.8	10.4	181	11.4	14.7
Connecticut	31.2	23.5	26.2	5.4	664	8.0	9.6
Florida	31.5	27.5	49.7	11.4	228	13.5	16.0
Hawaii	43.0	21.3	32.5	4.0	171	9.9	10.0
Illinois	26.4	28.1	38.5	8.6	209	11.0	11.0
Iowa	14.6	16.2	15.7	1.7	51	10.1	12.9
Maine	16.2	19.8	18.6	3.3	39	13.0	10.1
Massachusetts	30.2	20.9	32.0	3.5	753	9.6	9.3
Minnesota	18.2	17.1	31.0	2.9	54	9.5	12.8
Missouri	16.4	23.7	29.3	8.0	75	10.4	14.2
Nebraska	17.7	16.8	24.0	3.6	21	10.7	14.3

STATE	ABORTION	BIRTH—UNM	FOR—RAPE	MURDER	POP—DENS	POVERTY	SUICIDE
New Hampshire	17.5	14.7	25.2	2.3	121	8.5	13.0
New Mexico	19.1	29.6	38.4	11.5	12	17.6	19.4
New York	43.3	29.7	30.6	12.5	380	13.4	7.6
North Carolina	25.4	24.9	28.1	7.8	133	14.8	12.2
North Dakota	14.9	13.9	11.2	1.8	10	12.6	10.8
Ohio	21.0	24.9	42.6	5.4	265	10.3	11.6
Oregon	23.9	22.4	40.5	5.1	29	10.7	16.7
Pennsylvania	18.9	25.3	24.9	5.5	267	10.5	12.2
Rhode Island	30.6	21.8	30.5	4.1	940	10.3	10.2
South Carolina	16.7	29.0	42.7	9.3	115	16.6	11.4
South Dakota	5.7	19.4	26.7	3.1	9	16.9	14.3
Tennessee	18.9	26.3	44.7	9.4	119	16.5	12.9
Texas	24.8	19.0	48.4	12.1	64	14.7	13.6
Vermont	25.8	18.0	23.0	2.0	60	12.1	14.0
Virginia	23.7	22.8	27.1	7.8	152	11.8	14.1
Washington	27.6	20.8	56.5	5.7	70	9.8	15.3
Wisconsin	16.0	20.7	19.9	3.0	89	8.7	12.5

(Source: Bureau of the Census, *Statistical Abstract of the United States*, and Department of Justice, *Crime in the United States*.)

REFERENCES

Andrews, B., and Brewin, C. R. "Attributions of Blame for Marital Violence: A study of Antecedents and Consequences." *Journal of Marriage and the Family* 52 (1990): 757–767.

Berardo, F. M. *Internal Migrants and Extended Family Relations—A Study of Newcomer Adaptation.* Tallahassee: Florida State University, 1965.

Beyer, W. H. *Handbook of Tales for Probability and Statistics*, 2nd ed. Cleveland: CRC Press, 1968.

Bohrnstedt, G. W., and Knoke, D. *Statistics for Social Data Analysis.* Itasca, Ill.: F. E. Peacock, 1982.

Bumpass, L., Sweet, J., and Martin, T. C. "Changing Patterns of Remarriage." *Journal of Marriage and the Family* 52 (1990): 747–756.

Burg, M. A., Lane, D. S., and Polednak, A. P. "Age Group Differences in Breast Cancer Screening Tests: The Effects of Health Care Utilization and Socioeconomic Variables." *Journal of Aging and Health* (1990): 514–530.

Cochran, W. G. "Some Methods for Strengthening the Common χ^2 Tests." *Biometrics* 10 (1954): 417–451.

Danziger, S. K., and Radin, N. "Absent Does Not Equal Uninvolved: Predictors of Father in Teen Mother Families." *Journal of Marriage and the Family* 52 (1990): 636–642.

Demos, V. "Black Family Studies in the *Journal of Marriage and the Family* and the Issue of Distortion: A Trend Analysis." *Journal of Marriage and the Family* 52 (1990): 603–620.

Deutsch, M., and Collins, M. E. *Interracial Housing: A Psychological Evaluation of a Social Experiment.* Minneapolis: University of Minnesota Press, 1951.

Dillman, D. A., et al. "Reducing Refusal Rates for Telephone Interviews." *Public Opinion Quarterly* 40 (1976): 67–68.

Eichler, M. "Power and Sexual Fear in Primitive Societies." *Journal of Marriage and the Family* 57 (1975): 917–926.

Eisinga, R., Felling, A., and Peters, J. "Religious Belief, Church Involvement, and Ethnocentrism in the Netherlands." *Journal for the Scientific Study of Religion* 29 (1990): 54–75.

Farber, N. "The Significance of Race and Class in Marital Decisions among Unmarried Adolescent Mothers." *Social Forces* 37 (1990): 51–63.

Form, W. H. "The Social Construction of Anomie: A Four-Nation Study of Industrial Workers." *American Journal of Sociology* 80 (1975): 1165–1191.

Frisbie, W. P., and Clark, C. J. "An Index of Technology." In *Readings for Introducing Sociology* (edited by Larson, R. F., and Knapp, R J.). New York: Oxford University Press, 1982.

Hald, A. *Statistical Tables and Formulas.* New York: Wiley, 1952.

Hathaway, W. L., and Pargament, K. I. "Intrinsic Relgiousness, Religious Coping, and Psychosocial Competence: A Covariance Structure Analysis." *Journal for the Scientific Study of Religion* 29 (1990): 423–441.

Hughes, M., and Hertel, B. R. "The Significance of Color Remains: A Study of Life Chances, Mate Selection, and Ethnic Consciousness Among Black Americans." *Social Forces* 68 (1990): 1105–1120.

Lewis-Beck, M. S. *Applied Regression.* Beverly Hills, Calif.: Sage, 1990.

McColm, R. B. "The Comparative Survey of Freedom: 1990." *Freedom at Issue,* January–February (1990): 18–19.

Mendenhall, W., Reinmuth, J. E., and Beaver, R. *Statistics for Management and Economics,* 6th ed. Boston: PWS-Kent, 1989.

Merrington, M. "Table of Percentage Points of the *t*-distribution." *Biometrika* 32 (1941): 300.

Merrington, M., and Thompson, C. M. "Tables of Percentage Points of the Inverted Beta (*F*)-Distribution." *Biometrika* 33 (1943): 73–88.

Meyer, M. H., and Quadango, J. "Ending a Career in a Declining Industry: The Retirement Experience of Male Auto Workers." *Sociological Perspectives* 33 (1990): 51–62.

Mueller, J. H., Schuessler, K. F., and Costner, H. L. *Statistical Reasoning in Sociology,* 3rd ed. Boston: Houghton Mifflin, 1977.

Neal, A. G., and Seeman, M. "Organizations and Powerlessness: A Test of the Mediation Hypothesis." *American Sociological Review* 29 (1964): 216–226.

Nelsen, H. M. "The Religious Identification of Children of Interfaith Marriages." *Review of Religious Research* 32 (1900): 122-134.

Nelson, L. D., and Henry, N. W. "Simultaneous Control and Cross-tabular Presentation with Polytomous Variables: The Case of Religion Predictors." *Journal for the Scientific Study of Religion* 29 (1990): 255-263.

Olson, J. K. "Crime and Religion: A Denominational and Community Analysis." *Journal for the Scientific Study of Religion* 29 (1990): 395-403.

Popkin, S. J. "Welfare: Views from the Bottom." *Social Forces* 37 (1990): 64-79.

Rosenfeld, R. A., and Kalleberg, A. L. "A Cross-national Comparison of the Gender Gap in Income." *American Journal of Sociology* 96 (1990): 69-106.

Siegel, S. *Nonparametric Statistics for the Behavioral Sciences.* New York: McGraw-Hill, 1956.

Stafford, L., and Reske, J. R. "Idealization and Communication in Long-Distance Premarital Relationships." *Family Relations* 39 (1990): 274-279.

Thompson, C. M. "Tables of the Percentage Points of the χ^2 Distribution." *Biometrika* 32 (1941): 188-189.

Walsh, A. "Twice Labeled: The Effect of Psychiatric Labeling on the Sentencing of Sex Offenders." *Social Problems* 37 (1990): 375-389.

Weiss, A. S., and Mendoza, R. H. "Effects of Acculturation into the Hare Krishna Movement on Mental Health and Personality." *Journal for the Scientific Study of Religion* 29 (1989): 173-184.

Wong, M. G. "The Education of White, Chinese, Filipino, and Japanese Students: A Look at 'High School and Beyond'." *Sociological Perspectives* 33 (1990): 355-374.

ANSWER SECTION

This section includes answers to all odd-numbered exercises except for those that relate to the database, have more than one answer, or require essay-type answers.

CHAPTER 2

1. quantitative:measurable according to the degree of sexism, thus can be ordered

3. type of economy, social institutions, caste systems, marriage forms

5. An infant mortality rate is calculated by first counting the number of infant deaths over a long period of time and then dividing this number by the total number of infants born during this same period.

7. discrete: voter concern, income tax bracket
continuous: campaign contributions, assessed valuation of homes

9. nationality, religious preference

11. A ratio scale preserves the distance between scores as well as defining where the origin of the scale lies. Interval scale preserves only distance.

15. A ratio is the number of elements in one group relative to the number of elements in a second group. A rate is the number of actual occurrences of a particular outcome divided by the number of possible times the outcome could have occurred.

17. 31.25%

19. a) 0.375   b) 0.814   c) 0.103

21. a) 4.727   b) 0.825   c) 49.6%

23. Yes. For example, the number of students enrolled in universities could be rounded to the nearest 100.

25. 0.0, 0.7, 1.2, 1.6, 139.8, 17.4

27. 20, 30, 10, 10, 20, 20, 10, 20, 10, 10

29. A quantitative variable is one whose observations vary in magnitude. A qualitative variable is one whose observations vary in kind but not magnitude.

31. NOMINAL: primitive tribes; sex; employment status; religious affiliation
ORDINAL: alienation; religiosity; social status
RATIO: population of Sacramento; suicide rate

33. a) 1.308   b) 0.765   c) 0.567   d) 0.433

35.
80.2	80	80
49.7	50	50
65.3	65	70
67.4	67	70
72.9	73	70
75.1	75	80
73.0	73	70
63.3	63	60
60.0	60	60
70.6	71	70
80.7	81	80
74.7	75	70
68.3	68	70
50.5	50	50
69.6	70	70
64.1	64	60
84.8	85	80
72.8	73	70
56.1	56	60
81.8	82	80

39. 2.5–3.5
11.5–12.5
15.5–16.5
8.5–9.5
5.5–6.5
19.5–20.5
7.5–8.5
2.5–3.5
10.5–11.5
3.5–4.5

41. Rates enable researchers to compare occurrences between two different groups or populations. Since ratios are used to compare some occurrences in one set with the number of occurrences in another set, ratios can't be used to compare 2 groups when the groups differ in makeup.

43. 60, 70, 40, 60, 50, 30, 30, 30

45. 0.6085–0.6095
0.7235–0.7245
0.4285–0.4295
0.6255–0.6265
0.4585–0.4595
0.3325–0.3335
0.2925–0.2935

47.

$74 = 70$	65–75
$32 = 30$	25–35
$9 = 10$	5–15
$8 = 10$	5–15
$110 = 110$	105–115
$63 = 60$	55–65
$14 = 10$	5–15
$7 = 10$	5–15
$19 = 20$	15–25
$46 = 50$	45–55
$12 = 10$	5–15
$8 = 10$	5–15
$90 = 90$	85–95
$6 = 10$	5–15
$8 = 10$	5–15
$86 = 90$	85–95
$11 = 10$	5–15
$16 = 20$	15–25
$95 = 100$	95–105
$10 = 10$	5–15

49. sex, marital status, religion, race, major

51. 12, 19, 15, 10, 16, 10, 11, 13, 10, 9, 13, 14, 14, 13, 19, 8, 12, 11, 12, 17, 12, 10, 11, 14, 13, 14, 14, 14, 15, 12
 a) $21/9 = 2.33$
 b) $6/30 = 0.20$
 C) $21/30 = 0.70$

CHAPTER 3

3. Exclusiveness is violated. Inclusiveness is followed.

5. Graphic procedure for describing qualitative data. Too many categories would likely lead pie chart to lose its clarity.

7.

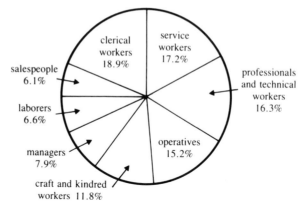

9.

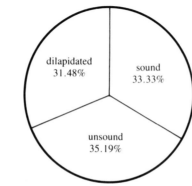

11.

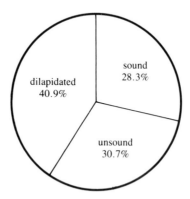

13.

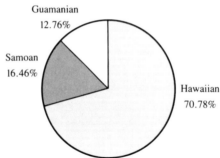

15.

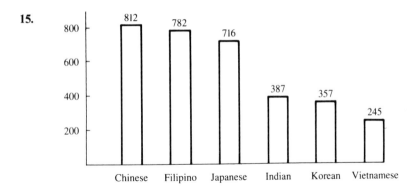

19.

Age	Frequency	Relative Frequency
8–9	1	.0032
10–11	5	.0161
12–13	42	.1350
14–15	68	.2186
16–17	64	.2058
18–19	72	.2315
20–21	29	.0932
22–23	13	.0418
24–25	13	.0418
26–27	2	.0064
28–29	0	.0000
30–31	2	.0064

21. Class interval width is 3.

23. a. The real class limits for the ten intervals are:

Size of Campus	Real Class Limits
0– 2,499	−0.5– 2,499.5
2,500– 4,999	2,499.5– 4,999.5
5,000– 7,499	4,999.5– 7,499.5
7,500– 9,999	7,499.5– 9,999.5
10,000–12,499	9,999.5–12,499.5
12,500–14,999	12,499.5–14,999.5
15,000–17,499	14,999.5–17,499.5
17,500–19,999	17,499.5–19,999.5
20,000–22,499	19,999.5–22,499.5
22,500–24,999	22,499.5–24,999.5

b. The frequency histogram for this data would be as follows.

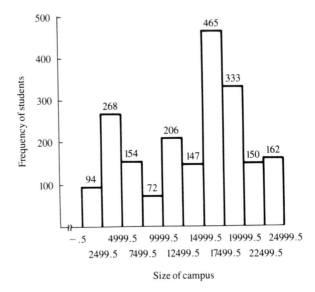

25.

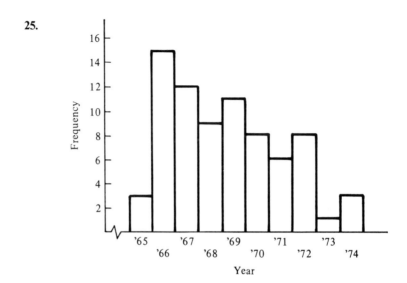

27.

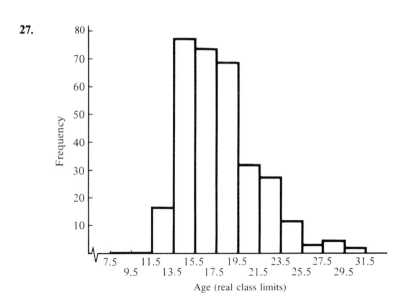

29. If drawn to scale, the relative frequency histogram and the frequency histogram have essentially the same shape. The only difference exists along the vertical axis, where the units are different.

31. You would use 370.5 to 385.5. Real class limits are used to avoid the possibility of an observation actually lying between the boundaries of two adjacent apparent class intervals.

33.
```
   8      1 : 55788889
 (38)     2 : 0000111222222333333344444455556666778899
   5      3 : 06
   3      4 : 23
   0      5 :
   0      6 :
   0      7 :
   0      8 :
   0      9 :
   0     10 :
   0     11 :
   0     12 :
   0     13 :
   1     14 : 0
```

35.

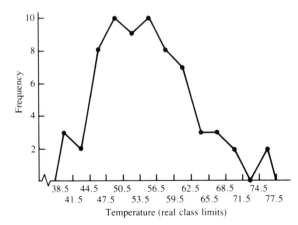

39.

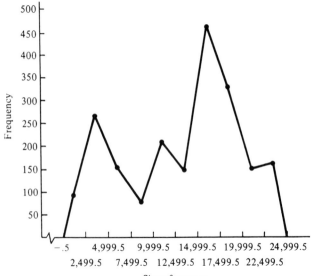

41.

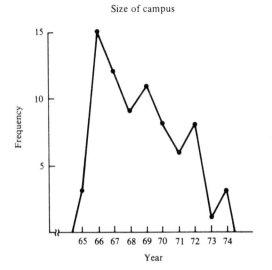

43.

Age	Frequency	Relative Frequency	Cumulative Relative Frequency
8–9	0	.0000	.0000
10–11	0	.0000	.0000
12–13	16	.0502	.0502
14–15	77	.2414	.2916
16–17	74	.2320	.5236
18–19	70	.2194	.7430
20–21	32	.1003	.8433
22–23	28	.0878	.9311
24–25	12	.0376	.9687
26–27	3	.0094	.9781
28–29	5	.0157	.9938
30–31	2	.0063	1.0001

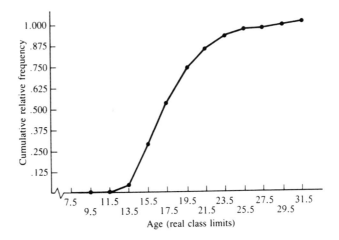

45.

Score	Percentage	Relative Frequency	Cumulative Relative Frequency
0–2	7.9	.079	.079
3–5	18.4	.184	.263
6–8	28.1	.281	.544
9–11	22.2	.222	.766
12–14	14.1	.141	.907
15–17	5.3	.053	.960
18–20	2.5	.025	.985
21–23	.7	.007	.992
24–26	.5	.005	.997
27–29	.2	.002	.999
30–32	.1	.001	1.000

47.

Expenditure	Frequency	Relative Frequency	Cumulative Relative Frequency
371–385	1	0.0213	1.0000
356–370	1	0.0213	0.9787
341–355	1	0.0213	0.9574
326–340	3	0.0638	0.9361
311–325	1	0.0213	0.8723
296–310	4	0.0851	0.8510
281–295	1	0.0213	0.7659
266–280	4	0.0851	0.7446
251–265	3	0.0638	0.6595
236–250	7	0.1489	0.5957
221–235	2	0.0426	0.4468
206–220	5	0.1064	0.4042
191–205	7	0.1489	0.2978
176–190	4	0.0851	0.1489
161–175	3	0.0638	0.0638

49. Graphic display of the numerical values of a quantitative or qualitative variable at various points in time. More timepoints show a more complete picture of changes in a variable over time.

51.

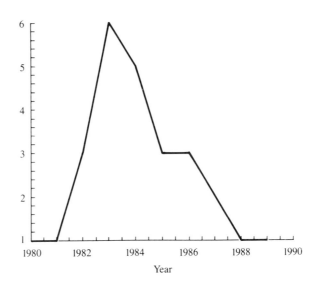

57.

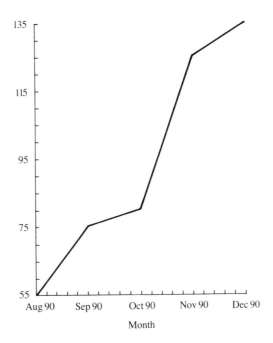

61.

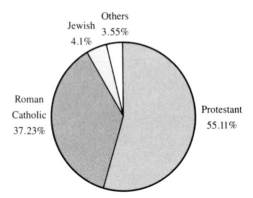

67.

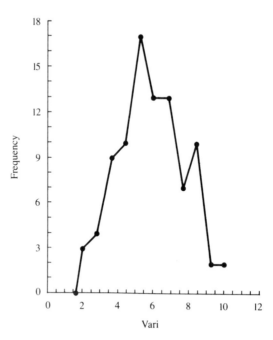

71.

Score	Relative Frequency	Cumulative Relative Frequency
0–4	.050	.050
5–9	.213	.263
10–14	.214	.477
15–19	.201	.678
20–24	.130	.808
25–29	.089	.897
30–34	.049	.946
35–39	.027	.973
40–44	.016	.989
45–49	.005	.994
50–54	.004	.998
55–59	.001	.999
60–64	.001	1.000

73. a. The youngest inaugural age is 42 (T. Roosevelt); the oldest is 68 (W.H. Harrison). The range is $68 - 42 = 26$; 7 intervals of width 4 is one way to group the data.

Class Boundaries	Frequency
41.5–45.5	2
45.5–49.5	5
49.5–53.5	7
53.5–57.5	13
57.5–61.5	4
61.5–65.5	3
65.6–69.5	1

b.

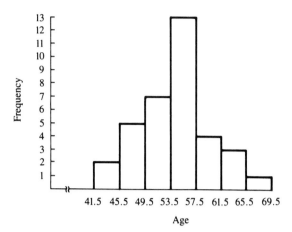

75. a.

% Change	Frequency	Relative Frequency
−2	1	.02
−1	0	.00
0	0	.00
+1	4	.08
2	3	.06
3	3	.06
4	2	.04
5	5	.10
6	8	.16
7	9	.18
8	6	.12
9	2	.04
10	4	.08
11	2	.04
12	0	.00
13	1	.02

b.

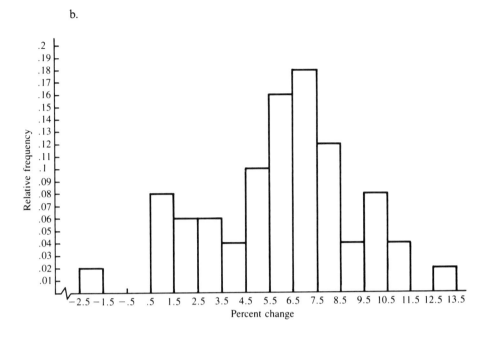

c.

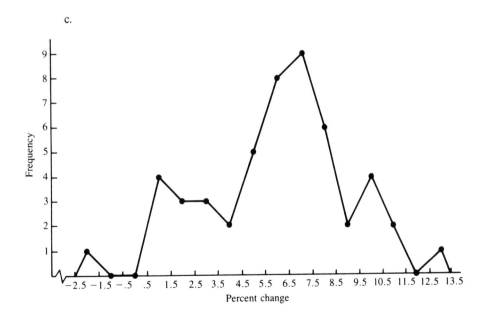

77. a.

% Increase	Frequency	Relative Frequency
0	1	.02
1	0	.00
2	0	.00
3	1	.02
4	0	.00
5	2	.04
6	3	.06
7	6	.12
8	13	.26
9	10	.20
10	9	.18
11	2	.04
12	2	.04
13	1	.02

b.

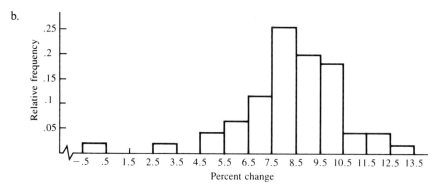

c.

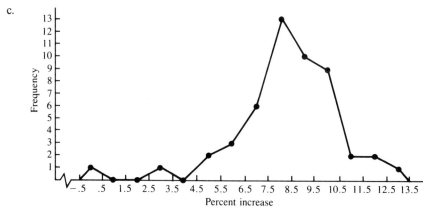

79. a.

% Change		Frequency	Relative Frequency
−5−	−1	2	.04
0−	4	11	.22
5−	9	10	.20
10−	14	5	.10
15−	19	8	.16
20−	24	6	.12
25−	29	3	.06
30−	34	2	.04
35−	39	2	.04
40−	44	0	.00
45−	49	1	.02

b.

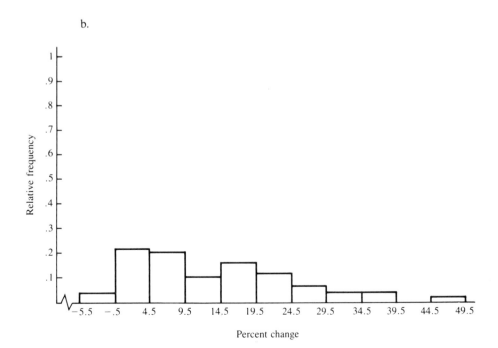

c.

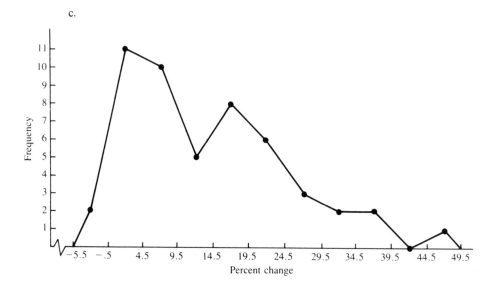

81.

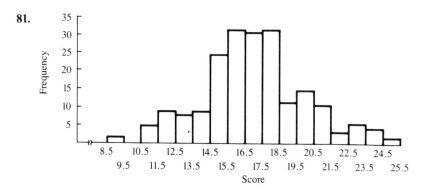

83.

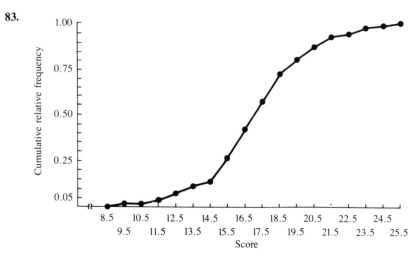

CHAPTER 4

1. 45

3. 12

5. 16,249.5

7. 4.5

9. 129.05   ~~wrong~~ ≈ 6

11. 16.73

13. 53.95

15. 4.9

17. 247.15

19. 16.9759

21. 54.60

23. 247.15

25. 16,556.49

27. 200.68

29. 240.86

31. $P_{50} = 8.0357$

33. 635.05

35. 87.9%

37. 68.3%

39. 4.604

41. 268.12

43. 21.22

45. 8.626

47. 3.4834

49. 8.1391

51. 6591.25

53. 55.95

55. 12.68

57. 6249.75

59. lower inner fence: 13.5
    upper inner fence: 33.5
    lower outer fence: 6
    upper outer fence: 41

61. lower inner fence: -2.475
upper inner fence: 32.525
lower outer fence: -15.6
upper outer fence: 45.65

65. 7.86

69. $62.27; $138.73

71. Yes, data mound-shaped

73. 1.965; 2.706

75. no

77. 14.5

79. 14.4; 15; 16

81. Since $\overline{X}$ is almost 3 standard deviations away from 25, conclude this class differs from previous students.

83. 14.87; 15; 16

85.

1	05	11	12	13	14	20	20	21	22	22	24	25	26	28	28	30	30	30	36	38
	39	40	41	44	45	46	46													
1	50	51	53	54	63	63	64	64	68	71	71	73	73	75	75	76	80	82	85	87
	89	98																		
2	06	07	13	19	24	25	27	31	34											
2	55																			
3																				
3	51																			

87. $s \approx 3.5$; $s = 3.98$

89. a) 11.2   b) 10.307   c) 10.35   d) 1.718   e) 2.11

91. a) 32; 6; 19   b) No, it does not appear to be mound-shaped.

CHAPTER 5

1. yes

7. 120, 1

9. yes

11. 0.729; 0.972

13. 0.1875; yes

15. yes

17. a) 0.1538   b) 0.6916   c) 0.1359   d) 0.0215

19. a) 0.8537   b) 0.0267   c) 0.7488   d) 0.6181

21. Between 0.95 and 0.96

23. 5.42

25. 0.1191

27. 0.1736; 0.0301

29. $np; \sqrt{npq}$

31. The workers are not selected at random from the city, but the employer is not necessarily biased against women.

33. yes, yes

35. A random sample of n measurements from a population is one that gives every different sample of size n from the population an equal probability of selection.

39. Proportion of times the outcome will occur in a long series of observations of the phenomenon.

41. 10

45. $z = (X - \mu)/\sigma$

47. a) 0.4938   b) 0.4332

49. a) 0.9500   b) 0.9902

51. 0.524

53. 1.96

55. 0.75

57. $\mu = 20; \sigma = 3.46$

59. -0.583

61. $\mu = 30; \sigma = 4.58$

63. No; 2600 lies approximately 28 standard deviations below the mean.

65. 1.28

67. 0.0475

69. approximately 0

71. a) 0.0060   b) 0.02508   c) 0.6331   d) 0.0001

73. a) 0.205   b) 0.39   c) 0.445

75. a) 12   b) 24   c) 20

CHAPTER 6

1. Set of all registered democrats in a specified large voting district.

3. Set of all registered democrats and the set of all registered republicans in a specified large voting district. The proportion favoring capital punishment within each party.

5. σ is the population standard deviation. $\sigma/\sqrt{n}$ is the standard deviation of $\bar{X}$ where repeated samples of size n are obtained from the population with standard deviation σ.

7. $0.6623 to $0.8377

9. 3121.08 to 3478.92 ml

11. from 3300 ± 150.17 to 3300 ± 235.92; the interval increases in size

13. 0.464 to 0.736

15. 0.6395 to 0.7305

17. 0.2224 to 0.2936

19. 0.0371 to 0.1163

21. 212.07

23. Difference of 136 cases. Estimating s by using the range versus using the actual s from prior experience.

25. 486.2025

29. 24.15 to 27.05

31. 3.82 to 4.58

33. 0.21 to 0.34

35. No.

37. 0.074 to 0.126

39. 118.584 to 121.416

41. 0.4095 to 0.4905

43. 361.456

45. $n = 368.79$; A change of only 16

47. Mothers: 0.422 to 0.618; 0.229 to 0.411
Fathers: 0.148 to 0.312; 0.402 to 0.598

CHAPTER 7

1. insufficient evidence to reject; rejection region is greater than 730.11 and less than 669.89

3. sufficient evidence to reject; rejection region is greater than 8.143

5. sufficient evidence to reject; rejection region is less than 64.7

7. a. Do not reject H_0; $\bar{X} < 550.9$ or $\bar{X} > 1149.1$
b. Do not reject H_0; $\bar{X} < 466.9$ or $\bar{X} > 1065.1$

9. use sample deviation, s.

11. 0.10

15. a) Do not reject H_0; $z = -4.31$
   b) Do not reject H_0; $z = 6.98$
   c) Do not reject H_0; $z = -4.26$

17. The research hypothesis places the rejection region in one tail of the distribution.

19. a) H_0: $p = 0.30$ b) $z = (\hat{p} - p_0)/\sigma_p$ c) $z = -2.18$
   d) no; $-2.18 < -1.96$

21. H_0: $p = 0.45$; H_1: $p < 0.45$

23. a) H_0: $p = 0.45$ b) $z = 1.4$ c) Do not reject H_0 since $1.4 < 1.645$

25. s is not as good an approximation of σ when n is small; thus $(\bar{X} - \mu)/s/\sqrt{n}$ does not approximate the standard normal

27. Reject H_0 if:
   a) $t < -1.761$ b) $|t| > 2.074$ c) $t > 2.015$

29. 90% interval: 4.317 to 5.743; 95% interval: 4.150 to 5.910; 99% interval: 3.766 to 6.294

31. no, $t = 2.00$

33. Have frequency data and wish to compare a distribution of frequencies against a theoretical distribution.

35. d.f. $= k - 1$

37. Observed frequencies differ significantly from the expected frequencies

39. $\chi^2 = 96.23$; reject H_0

41. $\chi^2 = 91.025$; reject H_0

43. Type I: Reject H_0 when it is true; Type II: Do not reject H_0 when it is false

45. α and β decrease

47. Do not reject H_0; rejection region is greater than 372.11 and less than 347.89

49. $\chi^2 = 10$; reject H_0

51. Reject H_0; rejection region is greater than 0.4473 and less than 0.3127

53. yes; $z = 4.66$

55. Reject H_0; $z = -5.67$; $\alpha = 0.01$; one-tail test

63. Reject H_0; $\chi^2 = 93.15$

65. Reject H_0; $\chi^2 = 24.10$

CHAPTER 8

1. a) approximately normal with mean $= 250$ and standard error $= 6$
   b) approximately normal with mean $= 200$ and standard error $= 8$
   c) approximately normal with mean $= 50$ and standard error $= 10$

3. a) approximately normal with mean $= 0.2$ and standard error $= 0.063$
   b) approximately normal with mean $= 0.1$ and standard error $= 0.061$
   c) approximately normal with mean $= -0.15$ and standard error $= 0.078$

5. reject H_0; $z = -4.21$

7. $\bar{X}_1 = 16.976$; $s_1 = 3.483$; $n_1 = 311$
   $\bar{X}_2 = 17.854$; $s_2 = 3.528$; $n_2 = 319$
   reject H_0; $z = -3.143$

9. reject H_0; $z = -3.83$

11. a) reject H_0; $z = -2.7$
   b) reject H_0; $z = -2.42$
   c) reject H_0; $z = -5.97$

13. insufficient evidence to reject H_0; $t = 1.7117$

15. insufficient evidence to reject H_0; $t = -1.48$

17. reject H_0; $z = -5.01$

19. insufficient evidence to reject H_0; $t = 1.19$

23. (1) independent samples   (2) data at least ordinal

25. insufficient evidence to reject H_0; $z = -1.65$

27. Reject H_0

29. insufficient evidence to reject H_0; $z = 1.67$

31. reject H_0; $z = 3.962$

33. -0.126 to -0.054

35. 90% interval: 0.001 to 0.159
   99% interval: -0.044 to 0.204

37. No

41. insufficient evidence to reject H_0; $t = 2.20$

43. yes; $z = -7.258$; reject H_0

45. reject H_0; $z = 7.987$

47. 95% interval: 0.732 to 9.268

49. reject H_0; $z = 2.62$; conclude, yes there is a difference

51. (1) using only ordinal level data
   (2) assumptions for z or t tests fail to hold

55. insufficient evidence to reject H_0; $t = -1.86$

65. reject H_0; $z = 3.69$

67. a) reject H_0
   b) reject H_0
   c) reject H_0

69. reject H_0; $z = 5.27$

71. a) $z = -2.56$; reject H_0
   b) $z = -2.845$; reject H_0

CHAPTER 9

3.

Per Capita State and Local Taxes	Per Capita Spending on Education		
	Under $650	$650 to $775	More Than $775
over $1200	11.8	47.0	50.0
$1000 to $1200	11.8	41.2	43.8
under $1200	76.5	11.8	6.2
Total %	100.1	100.0	100.0
Sample size	17	17	16

5. a) 112 males of medium skin color who have medium job mobility orientation
   b) 70 males of light skin color who have medium job mobility orientation
   c) There are 215 men out of 500 with medium job mobility orientation

7. If you take percentages based on marginals of dependent variable, conclusions can be questionable. If you are unable to specify independent or dependent variable, it makes little difference in the way percentages are calculated.

9. reject H_0; $\chi^2 = 6.08$

11. level of significance is between 0.025 and 0.05; $\chi^2 = 6.14$

13. when one wishes to compare two population proportions where sample sizes are less than 30

15. when one wishes to analyze whether a change has occurred between two different time periods

19. $\chi^2 = 8.84$; level of significance < 0.005

23. 0.0862; we cannot reject the null hypothesis

25. Yes; the expected cell count is less than 5 in more than 20% of the cells.

27. yes; $\chi^2 = 18.52$

29. reject H_0; $\chi^2 = 74.38$; level of significance < 0.005

31. 2; reject H_0; $\chi^2 = 19.5$

33. reject H_0; $x_M^2 = 30$

35. reject H_0; $\chi^2 = 44$

37. reject H_0; $\chi^2 = 25.88$

39. reject H_0; $\chi^2 = 23.55$; level of significance < 0.005

41. insufficient evidence to reject H_0; $\chi^2 = 0.004$

47. reject H_0; $\chi^2 = 130.21$

49. reject H_0; $\chi^2 = 16.29$

51. reject H_0; $\chi^2 = 11.41$

CHAPTER 10

1. $C = 0.2104$; $C_{adj} = 0.2976$

3. yes; 0.3260

5. 0.5592

7. C_{adj} should always be used instead of C for square two-way tables

9. independent variable contributes no information toward predicting the dependent variable

13. 0.4

15. 0.45

17. 0.12

19. 0.4

21. 0.286

25. 0.4871

27. a) 0.47   b) insufficient evidence to reject $H_0(\hat{\gamma} = 1.53)$

29. reject $H_0(\hat{\gamma} = -0.506; z = -3.36)$

31. n items ranked; few ties; $n \geq 10$

33. Assign each observation of the dependent variable a rank of $(n + 1)/2$, the average of the ranks for n pairs.

35. $\hat{\rho} = -0.982$; reject $H_0(t = -13.89)$

37. $Q = 0.385$; no($z = 1.57$ with significance level of 0.1164)

41. has a PRE interpretation

43. amount of error in prediction of one variable that is reduced by knowing another variable

49. reject $H_0(t = 4.469)$; yes

51. yes; $t = -2.3$

53. reject H_0; $z = 5.1$

55. no; need a 2×2 table

57. $Q = 0.516$; yes($z = 6.45$)

67. $Q = -0.806$; reject H_0

69. $Q = 0.52$; reject H_0

71. $\lambda_r = 0.1$; $\hat{\gamma} = 0.516$

CHAPTER 11

12. a) $\chi^2 = 193.239$
   b) $\chi_p^2 = 189.9929$

13. $\lambda_p = 0$

15. $\lambda_{male} = 0$; $\lambda_{female} = -0.04$; replication

17. a) $\gamma_{personal} = 0.07$; $\gamma_{blind} = -0.44$
   b) $\gamma_p = -0.173$

23. a) $Q = 0.714$
   b) no

25. a) $Q = 0.43$
   b) yes

27. a) 37.6%
   b) $Q = 0.36$
   c) yes

33. $\chi^2 = 26.105$; reject H_0
   $\chi^2 = 0.539$; do not reject H_0

37. a) 'age at first birth' independent variable; 'living arrangements' dependent
   variable
   b) $x_p^2 = 40.629$

39. $\lambda_r = 0.07$

41. a) $\lambda_r = 0$
   b) not an influence

43. a) $Q = -0.355$
   b) yes

47. a) $\gamma_{whites} = 0.426$; $\gamma_{blacks} = 0.210$; $\gamma_{other} = 0.377$
   b) $\gamma_p = 0.355$
   c) $\gamma = 0.328$

CHAPTER 12

5. b) $a = 3.5$; $b = 1.5$ c) 33.5

7. y value when $x = 0$

13. $\hat{Y} = 0.5 + 1.70X$

17. $a = 51.11$; $b = 0.00896$

19. $a = 0.257$; $b = 0.728$

23. $\hat{Y} = a + bX$; i.e., X and Y are linearly related

25. 0.792

27. 0.99

29. 0.993

31. a) 4.29   b) 0.46   c) 0.924

33. yes; $t = 13.199$

35. yes; $t = 4.84$

39. 0.70; reject $H_0 (t = 2.94)$

41. 0.924; reject H_0; $t = 7.16$

49. $b = 0.89$

59. $r = 0.988$; $r^2 = 0.976$

63. $\hat{Y} = -265 + 3.7X$

65. 0.961

69. a) strong positive linear relationship
     b) little or no relationship
     c) perfect negative relationship

79. yes; each is significantly different from 0

CHAPTER 13

7. $b_{s1} = 0.77$ $b_{s2} = 0.47$

9. All important independent variables must be included in the equation.

11. X_2 adds no significant information to predicting life expectancy.

13. Compare bivariate correlations and partial correlation coefficients.

15. Yes

17. two independent variables are highly correlated

19. Examine $r_{12} = 0.15$. Since it is close to 0, we would conclude we do not have a problem of multicollinearity

21. $\hat{Y} = 2875 + 2066X_1 - 2256X_2$; $22,791

23. 0.985

25. $r_{12} = -0.415$; multicollinearity not evident

27. Multiple regression may be able to more accurately predict Y than the bivariate regression by including more variables

29. a) average property crime rate when X_1 and X_2 are equal to 0
   b) b_1: one point increase in X_1 is associated with an average increase in property crime rate of 1.873 when X_2 is held constant
   b_2: one point increase in X_2 is associated with average increase in property crime rate of 1.526 when X_1 is held constant
   c) $\hat{Y} = 20.1$

31. a) $r_{y1.2} = 0.98$ $r_{y2.1} = -0.976$
   b) 0.9604; 0.9526

37. a) $r^2_{y1.2} = 0.305$; $r^2_{y2.1} = 0.012$
   b) 0.317; no

41. r_{12} is close to 1 or -1, i.e., correlation between independent variables is relatively high

43. Might be a clue that multicollinearity exists since it seems unreasonable that the sign for the partial coefficient of the percentage below poverty level would be negative—expect it to be positive.

CHAPTER 14

1. k populations are normally distributed; common σ^2

5. $F = 2.913$, d.f.$_1 = 4$, d.f.$_2 = 40$; reject H_0

7. $F = 14.25$, d.f.$_1 = 2$, d.f.$_2 = 27$; reject H_0

9. $H = 10.75$; reject H_0

11. $H = 17.36$; reject H_0

13. $F = 19.64$, d.f.$_1 = 2$, d.f.$_2 = 18$; reject H_0

15. $F = 9.626$, d.f.$_1 = 2$, d.f.$_2 = 16$; reject H_0

21. $H = 20.19$; reject H_0

INDEX

Alpha, choice of, 256–259
Alternative hypothesis. *See* Research hypothesis.
Ames, R. G., 75
Analysis of variance, 548–588, 559–560, 563
   Kruskal-Wallis one-way analysis of variance by ranks, 558–562, 563
Andrews, B., 373, 595
Apparent class limits, 66, 68
Arithmetic mean. *See* Mean.
Assumption of homoscedasticity, 558
Average. *See* Mean.

Bar graph, 57–59, 96
Basu, A., 75
Beaver, R., 596
Bell-shaped normal curve, 87–88, 569
Berardo, F. M., 377, 595
Between-population variability, 552–554
Beyer, W. H., 577, 595
Binomial, 175–183
   normal approximation to, 197–201
Binomial experiment, 177–185, 209
Binomial parameter, 228–231
   comparison of two, 315–320
   confidence interval for, 228–

231, 316–321
   point estimate of, 228–229
   sample size for, 200, 231–235
   sampling distribution of the difference between two, 291–295
   test about, 259–263
Binomial probability, P(X), 209
Binomial probability distribution, 179–185, 197
Binomial variable, 197–201, 209
   means of a, 197, 209
   standard deviation of a, 197, 209
Bivariate data. *See* Measures of association.
   chi-square test of independence for, 346–358, 365
   percentage comparisons for, 337–345
Bivariate frequency table, 339, 365
Bohrnstedt, G. W., 528, 595
Box plot, 109, 148–154, 155
   extreme outlier, 151, 155
   mild outlier, 151, 155
Brewin, C. R., 373, 595
Bumpass, L., 287, 595
Burg, M. A., 457, 595

Categorical data, 23–24. *See also* Pie chart.
Chi-square
   distribution, 350–351, 571–572

goodness-of-fit, 274–281, 283
   of independence, 346–358, 365
   pooled, 444
Clark, C. J., 15, 596
Class frequency, 69, 96
Class interval, 65–70, 96
Class limits, 66–69, 96
   apparent, 66
   real, 66, 97
Class width, 65–66, 68–69
Classical interpretation of probability, 168–169, 209
Cochran, W. G., 352, 595
Coding
   for mean, 123–125
   for standard deviation, 143–145
   for variance, 143–145
Coefficient of determination, 475–479, 495, 535
Coefficient of relative variation (CRV), 143, 155
Collins, M. E., 281, 595
Comparison of measurements. *See* Percentage; Proportion; Rate; Ratio.
Concordant pairs, 391
Confidence interval, 223, 236
   for binomial parameter, 229–230, 316–317
   for comparison of population means, 296, 306
   for large samples, 224–225
   lower limit, 223

Confidence interval (*cont.*)
  for μ, 219–228
  for *p,* 228–231
  for population mean, 220–228
  for small samples, 272–273, 306
  for small-sample difference between two means, 306
  upper limit, 225
Confidence limit, 223–224, 236
Constant, 19–20, 45
Contingency coefficient, 375–378, 411
Contingency table, 337, 365
Continuous variable, 21, 45, 172, 209
  normal probability distribution as, 188–189
  probability distribution for, 185–187, 209
Control variable, 422–423, 425, 454
Controlling for the effect of a third variable
  and interpretation, 429–434, 454, 535
  nominal, with only two categories, 420–424
  nominal, with three or more categories, 439–448
  ordinal, with three or more categories, 448–454
  and partial gamma, 448–454, 455
  with ratio data, 523–529
  and replication, 424–426, 455, 525–526, 535
  and specification (interaction), 434–439, 455, 528, 535
  and spuriousness, 426–429, 432, 455, 535
Correlation coefficient
  assumptions underlying, 489–494, 520–523
  multiple, 517–520, 545
  partial, 512–514, 545
  Pearson product-moment, 479–484, 484–487, 487–489, 496
  Spearman's rho, 400–405, 412
Costner, H. L., 403, 596
Cramer's V., 379, 412
Cross-classification data. *See* Bivariate data.
Cumulative relative frequency
  for a class, 85–87, 96
  for a polygon, 85–86, 96

Cumulative relative frequency for a class, 85–87, 96

Danziger, S. K., 281, 373, 458, 595
Data, 217. *See also* Grouped data; Qualitative data; Quantitative data.
  collection, 3–6
  cross-classification of. *See* Bivariate data.
  distortion of, 92–93
  social, 28–30
  validity and reliability of, 42–44
  variation, 129. *Also see* Measures of variability.
Data bank, 578–593
Degrees of freedom (d.f.), 268, 351, 365
Demos, V., 309, 595
Dependent variable, 338, 365, 381
Descriptive statistics, 6–11, 12, 15
Deutsch, D. A., 281, 595
Dichotmous variable, 405, 412
Dillman, D. A., 596
Discordant pairs, 391
Discrete variable, 20–21, 45, 172, 209. *See also* Binomial.
  probability distribution for, 172–185, 209
  properties of, 173
Distortion, graphical, 92–93
Dot diagram, 136

Eichler, M., 38, 367, 596
Eisinga, R., 502, 595
Empirical rule, 141, 155, 190
Equality of variances assumption, 559
Error. *See* Proportional reduction in error; Standard error; Sum of squares for error.
Estimate, 217–219, 236. *See also* Interval estimate; Point estimate.
Event, 168, 209
Exclusiveness, principle of, 52–53, 65, 96
Expected cell counts, 348–349, 365
Experiment, 275–276, 283
  binomial, 177, 209
  multinomial, 275–276, 283
Explained variation, 476–477, 495

Exploratory data analysis (EDA), 7, 80
  stem-and-leaf plot of, 80–83, 97
Extreme outlier, 151, 155
"Eyeball fit." *See* Freehand regression line.

F distribution, 553–554, 573–574, 575–576
Face validity, 43
Fail to reject, 242–245, 245–247
Farber, N., 263, 596
Felling, A., 502, 596
First-order correlation. *See* Partial correlation coefficient.
Fisher's exact test, 358–362, 365
Form, W. H., 449, 596
Freehand regression line, 467–468, 495
Frequency distribution, 69, 96
Frequency histogram, 71–73, 76–80, 96
Frequency polygon, 83–85, 87–88, 96
  cumulative relative, 85–87, 96
Frequency table
  bivariate, 339
  univariate, 339
Frisbie, W. P., 15, 596

Gallup polls, 8–9
Gamma, 389–400, 412
  partial gamma, 448–454, 455
Goodness-of-fit, chi-square, 274–281, 283
Gosset, W. S., 267
Graeven, D. B., 75, 278
Graphical descriptive techniques,
  bar graph, 57–59, 96
  cumulative relative frequency polygon, 85–87, 96
  distortions, 92–93
  frequency histogram, 71–73, 76–80, 96
  frequency polygon, 87–88, 96
  pie chart, 54–57, 96
  relative frequency histogram, 71–73, 76–80, 97
  scatter diagram, 464–470, 496
  statistical map, 59–61, 97
  stem-and-leaf plot, 80–83, 97
Graphical distortions, 92–93
Grouped data, 112, 115–117, 119–121, 123–126, 155

Hald, A., 569, 596
Hathaway, W. L., 334, 596
Henry, N. W., 373, 597
Hertel, B. R., 345, 596
Heteroscedasticity, 489–490, 495
Histogram, 71–73, 76–80, 96
    frequency, 71, 76–80
    population, 76–80
    relative frequency, 69–70, 76–80, 97
Homoscedasticity, 489–490, 495
Hughes, M., 345, 596
Hypothesis testing, *See also* Null hypothesis; Research hypothesis

Inclusiveness, principle of, 52–53, 65, 97
Independence, chi-square test of, 346–358, 365
Independent variable, 338–342, 365, 381
Index of qualitative variation (IQV), 130–133, 155
Inference, 6, 217–218. *See also* Inferential statistics.
Inferential statistics, 5–11, 12, 15, 217–218. *See also* Estimate; Probability; Statistical tests.
Interaction. *See* Specification.
Interpretation, 429–434, 454–455, 526, 535
Interquartile range, 135, 155
Interval estimate, 219, 236
    for binomial parameter, 228–231, 316–317
    for population mean, 219–228
Interval measure of association. *See* Measures of association, interval and ratio.
Interval scale, 24–25, 27–28, 45
Interval width, 69–70
Intervening variable, 430, 455

Jackman, N. R., 75
Jones, A., 278
J-shaped curve, 87–88

Kalleberg, A. L., 334, 597
Knapp, R. J., 596
Knoke, D., 528, 595
Kruskal-Wallis one-way analysis of variance by ranks, 558–562, 563

Lambda, 385–389, 412
Lane, D. C., 595
Larson, R. F., 596
Least squares. *See* Method of least squares.
    multicollinearity in multiple regression, 529–534
    multiple regression assumptions, 520–523
    multiple regression estimates, 509–511
    regression line, 471, 496
    regression plane, 507–509
    relative importance of independent variables, 514–517
Level of significance, of a statistical test, 263–266, 283
Levels, of the scale, 23–28
Lewis-Beck, M. S., 490, 532, 596
Linear relationship, 466, 495
Literary Digest, 8, 17
Lower confidence limit, 223, 236
Lower quartile, 127, 150, 155
Lower true limit, 41

Mann, P. H., 309
Mann-Whitney *U*-test, 309–315, 326
Marginals, 338–339
Martin, T. C., 287, 595
McColm, R. B., 586, 596
McNemar test, 362–364, 365
Mean, 117–126, 155. *See also* Population mean; Sample mean.
    of a binomial variable, 197, 209
    of the differences between two proportions, 228
    of grouped data, 119–121
    of sample, 118
    of sampling distribution of binomial parameter, 228
    for the sampling distribution of $\overline{X}$, 220
    of universe, 118
Mean, standard error of the, 206, 209, 220, 236
Measure of association, multivariate extension of ordinal partial gamma, 448–454, 455
Measure of location, percentile ranks, 126–129, 155
Measurement of location. *See* Percentile.

Measurements,
    comparisons of, 31–39. *See also* Percentage; Proportion; Rate; Ratio.
    scales of. *See* Scales of measurement.
Measures of association, interval and ratio
    multiple correlation assumptions, 520–523
    multiple correlation coefficient, 517–520
    multivariate extensions of interval and ratio, 504–534
    partial correlation coefficient, 512–514
    partial regression coefficients, 510–511
    Pearson's product-movement correlation coefficient, 479–484, 484–487, 487–489, 496
Measures of association, nominal, 375–380, 385–389. *See also* Proportional reduction in error.
    contingency coefficient, C, 375–378, 411
    Cramer's V, 379, 412
    lambda, 385–389, 412
    standardized (normed), 375
    type A, 375, 376, 379, 412
    type B, 375, 376, 412
    Yule's Q, 405–411, 412
Measures of association, ordinal
    gamma, 389–400, 412
    Spearman's rho, 400–405, 412
    Yule's Q, 405–411, 412
Measures of central tendency, 110–123
    mean, 117–123, 155
    median, 91, 113–117, 122–123, 155
    mode, 110–113, 122, 155
Measures of variability
    interquartile range, 135, 155
    qualitative variation, 130–133, 155
    range, 133–135, 155
    variance, 136–143
Median, 91, 113–117, 122–123, 155
Mendenhall, W., 596
Mendoza, R. H., 335, 597
Merrington, M., 570, 574, 576, 596
Method of least squares, 470–475,

496
multicollinearity in multiple regression, 529–534
multiple regression assumptions, 520–523
for multiple regression prediction equation, 505–507
relative importance of independent variables, 514–517
Meyer, M. H., 287, 596
Mild outlier, 151, 155
Minitab, 13, 16
Mode, 110–113, 155
Monsees, D. M., 73, 300, 301
Mueller, J. H., 403, 596
Multicollinearity in multiple regression, 529–534, 535
Multinomial experiment, 275–276, 283
Multiple correlation coefficient, 517–520, 535
Multiple regression, 504–509, 535
assumptions, 520–523
interpretation, 509–511, 535
multicollinearity in, 529–534
plane, 506
prediction equation, 505–507
relative importance of independent variables, 514–517
Multiple *t*-tests, 551
Multivariate analysis, 419–462
Multivariate extension of measures of association. *See* Measures of association, multivariate extension of ordinal.
interpretation, 429–434, 454–455, 526, 535
replication, 424–426, 455, 525–526, 535
spuriousness, 426–429, 432, 455, 535
specification (interaction), 434–439, 455, 528, 535

Neal, A. G., 29, 596
Negative association, 376, 395, 480
Nelsen, H. M., 334, 597
Nelson, L. D., 373, 597
No association rule, 381, 385
gamma and, 391
lambda and, 386–387
Spearman's rho, 403

No association tests. *See also* Statistical tests.
Nominal measures of association. *See* Measures of association, nominal.
Nominal scale, 23, 26–28, 45
Nonparametric statistical techniques, 309, 326
Normal curve, 188–189, 209. *See also* Bell-shaped normal curve.
areas under, 189–196, 569
Normal probability distribution, 188–189
Normed measures of association, 375
Null hypothesis, 241–243, 283. *See also* Statistical tests.
for binomial parameter, 259–263
selecting, 254–256
Numerical descriptive measures, 109
Numerical outcome, 168–169

Objective of inferential statistics, 7–11, 12, 15
Objectivity, 3
Olson, J., 537, 597
One-tailed test, 250, 283
One-way analysis of variance, Kruskal-Wallis, 558–562
One-way table. *See* Frequency table.
Ordinal measures of association. *See* Measures of association, ordinal.
Ordinal scale, 24, 26–28, 45
Outcome, 168, 170, 209
numerical, 172–173
probability of an, 168–169

Paired *t*-test, 321–325, 326
Parameter, 110, 155
Parametric tests, 309
Pargament, K. I., 334, 596
Partial correlation coefficient, 512–514, 535
Partial gamma, 448–454, 455
Partial regression coefficients, 510–511, 514–515
Partial table, 423, 449, 455
Pearson, Karl, 276

Pearson product-moment correlation coefficient, 479–484, 496
interpretations of r, 487–489
test of significance of r, 484–487
Percentage, 34–35, 45
Percentage comparison, for bivariate data, 337–344
Percentage table, 337–345
Percentile, 126–129, 155
Percentile rank, 126–129, 155
Perfect association rule, 381, 385
gamma and, 394–395
lambda and, 386–387
Spearman's rho, 403
Personal probability, 169, 209
Peters, J., 502, 596
Pie chart, 54–57, 96
Point estimate, 219, 228, 236
of binomial parameter, 228–229
Polednak, A. P., 595
Polls, 8–9, 175–177
Pooled chi-square test, 443–444
Pooled estimate, 304
Popkin, S. J., 287, 597
Population, 11, 16. *See also* Universe.
Population correlation coefficient statistical test for, 484–487
Population histogram, 76–80, 96
Population mean. *See also* Analysis of variance.
confidence interval for, 223–225, 296, 306
interval estimate of, 219–228
large-sample comparison of two, 295–302
paired *t*-test, 321–325, 326
sample size for estimating, 231–235
small-sample comparison of two, 302–309
small-sample test for a mean, 266–274
statistical test about, 247–254
Population parameter, 217. *See also* Mean; Standard deviation.
Population standard deviation, 139
Population variance, 138
Positive association, 376, 394, 480
Prediction, 3–4

Principle of exclusiveness, 52–53, 65, 96
Principle of inclusiveness, 52–53, 65, 97
Probability, 167–169, 209
  classical interpretation of, 168–169, 209
  in inferences, 174–175
  of an outcome, 168–169
  personal, 169, 209
  relative frequency concept of, 169, 209
Probability distribution of, 172–204, 209
  binomial, 179–183, 197
  for continuous variables, 185–187, 209
  for discrete variables, 172–185, 209
  normal, 188–189
Proportion, 33–34, 45
  sample. See Binomial parameter.
Proportional reduction in error (PRE), 380–385, 386, 389–400, 412
  gamma, 389–400
  lambda, 385–389
  Pearson's product-moment correlation coefficient, 479–484, 484–487, 487–489
  Spearman's rho, 403

Quadango, J., 287, 596
Qualitative data
  bar graph for, 57–59, 96
  measures of variability for, 130–133
  pie chart for, 54–57, 96
  statistical map for, 59–61, 97
Qualitative variable, 22, 45
Quantitative data
  cumulative relative frequency polygon for, 85–87, 96
  frequency polygon for, 83–85, 96
  histogram for, 71–73, 77–79, 96
  measures of variability for, 133–143
  organizing, 65–70
  stem-and-leaf plot for, 80–83, 97
  variance, 136–143, 156

Quantitative variable, 20–21, 45
Quotient, 33. See also Ratio scale.

Radin, N., 281, 373, 458, 595
Random numbers tables, 202–204, 577
Random sample, 7–8, 201–204, 209
Randomized-block design, 324
Range, 66, 97, 133, 155
Rank-order correlation coefficient, Spearman's rho, 400–405, 412
Rate, 35–37
Rate of occurrence, 35, 45
Ratio, 32–33, 45
Ratio scale, 25–26, 27–28, 45
Real class limits, 66, 97
Reduction in error, 379. See also Proportional reduction in error.
Regression line, 470–475, 489–494, 496
  assumptions underlying bivariate, 489–494
  freehand, 467–468, 495
Regression plane, 535
Reinmuth, J. E., 596
Rejection region, 242–243, 283. See also Statistical tests.
Relative frequency for a class, 69–70, 97
Relative frequency concept of probability, 169, 209
Relative frequency histogram, 71–73, 76–80, 97
Reliability, 43–44, 45
  test-retest, 43
Replication, 424–426, 455, 525–526, 535
Research hypothesis, 241–242, 260, 283. See also Statistical test.
  selecting, 254–256
Reske, J. R., 254, 301, 302, 597
Rosenfeld, R. A., 334, 597
Rounding, 39–42
Rounding error, 39

Sample, 12, 16
  random, 201–204, 209
  sampling distribution for $\overline{X}$, 204–207, 209
Sample mean

for grouped data, 123–125
  for ungrouped data, 117
  sampling distribution for, 220–223, 236
  sampling distribution for difference between two, 291–295, 295–309
  z-score for, 256–259
Sample proportion. See Binomial parameter.
Sample size, 69, 97
  for binomial, 200, 232–233
  for estimating population mean or proportion, 231–235
Sample standard deviation, 139, 155
Sample variance, 138
  for grouped data, 140
  for ungrouped data, 140
Sampling, 9–11
Sampling distribution
  for binomial parameter, 228, 236
  of difference between two population means, 295–309
  of difference between two sample statistics, 291–295
  of sample mean, 204–207, 209, 220–223, 226
  for $\overline{X}$, 209
Scales of measurement, 23–31
  interval, 24–25, 27–28, 45
  nominal, 23, 26–28, 45
  ordinal, 24, 26–28, 45
  ratio, 25–26, 27–28, 45
Scatter diagram, 464–470, 496
  shapes of, 488, 489
Scedasticity, 489
Schuessler, K. F., 403, 596
Seeman, N., 29, 596
Siegel, S., 352, 361, 597
Significance, level of, 263–266, 283
Slopes, 510, 514–517
Social data, examples of, 27–31
Social science research, 3–5
  prediction for, 3–4
  statistics used in, 5–6
  understanding in, 3–4
Software, 13–14, 16
Spearman's rho, 400–405, 412
Specification, 434–439, 455, 528, 535
SPSS^x, 13, 16

Spuriousness, 426–429, 432, 455, 535

Stafford, L., 254, 301, 302, 597

Standard deviation, 139, 155
  of a binomial variable, 197, 209
  how to guess, 146–148
  of sampling distribution, 292

Standard error, 315
  of the mean, 206, 209, 220, 236
  of sampling distribution, 292
  for the sampling distribution for $_p$, 236
  for the sampling distribution for $\overline{X}$, 236

Standardized (normed) means of association, 375

Standardized units, 481–482

Statistic, 12, 16, 100, 110, 155

Statistical map, 59–61, 97

Statistical software systems, 13–14, 16

Statistical tests, 218–219, 241–245. *See also* Null hypothesis; Rejection region; Research hypothesis; Test statistic.
  for analysis of variance of, 555
  for a binomial parameter, 259–263, 315–321
  chi-square goodness-of-fit, 274–281, 279
  chi-square test of independence, 346–358
  choice of alpha, 256–259
  Fisher's exact test, 358–362
  for gamma, 398–399
  large-sample comparison of two population means, 295–302
  large-sample test for identical population, 310–311
  level of significance of, 263–266
  Mann-Whitney U-test, 309–315
  McNemar test, 362–364
  nonparametric, 310–315
  one-tailed, 250, 283
  paired t-test, 321–325
  parametric, 309
  Pearson product-moment correlation coefficient, r, 484–487
  for population correlation coefficient r, 484–487

for population mean, 247–254
small-sample comparison of population mean, 266–274
small-sample comparison of two population means, 302–309
for Spearman's rho, 403–404
with Student's t, 270–271
two-tailed, 250, 283
type I error of, 245–247, 283
type II error of, 245–247, 283
Yates's correction, 356
for Yule's Q, 408–409

Statistics
  descriptive, 6–11, 12, 15
  inferential, 6–11, 12, 15
  reasons for studying, 2–3
  social science research using, 5–6

Stem-and-leaf plot of, 80–83, 97

Student's t, 266–274, 283, 551, 570
  small sample for comparing two means and, 302–309

Subjective probability, 169

Subtraction, 32. *See also* Interval scale; Ratio scale.

Sum of squares for error (SSE), 471, 496

Sweet, J., 287, 595

t distribution 570. *See also* Student's t.

Test statistic, 241–245, 283. *See also* Statistical tests.

Thompson, C. M., 572, 574, 576, 596, 597

Time trend, 88–92

Trend line, 88–92, 97, 496. *See also* Regression line.

True limits, 41, 45

t-test, 267–274, 283, 303, 550–551

t-test, paired, 321–325

Two-tailed test, 250, 283

Two-way table. *See* Contingency table.

Type A measure of association, 375, 376, 379, 386, 412

Type B measure of association, 375, 376, 395, 412

Type I error, 245–247, 283

Type II error, 245–247, 283

Understanding, 3–4

Understanding, in social science research, 3–4

Unexplained variation, 476–477, 496

Univariate frequency table, 339, 365

Universe, 11, 16. *See also* Population.

Upper confidence limit, 225, 236

Upper quartile, 127, 150, 156

Upper true limit, 41

U-shaped curve, 87–88

U-test, Mann-Whitney, 309–315, 326

Validity, 43–44, 45
  face, 43

Variability. *See* Measures of variability.

Variable, 20, 45. *See also* Categorical data; Continuous variable; Discrete variable.
  continuous, 21, 45, 185–187
  dependent, 338, 365
  discrete, 20, 45, 172–175
  independent, 338, 338–342, 365
  qualitative, 22, 45
  quantitative, 20–21, 45

Variance, 136–143, 156

Walsh, A., 287, 333, 460, 597

Ward, D. A., 413

Warheit, G. J., 74, 99

Weiss, A. S., 335

Whitney, 309

Within-population variability, 552–554

Wong, M. G., 334, 372, 373, 460, 597

Yates, R. C., 356

Yates's correction, 356, 366

Y-intercept, 467

Yule's Q, 405–411, 412
  and gamma, 408
  test of significance for, 409

Zero-order correlation. *See* Pearson product-moment correlation coefficient.

z-score, 190–196, 209, 256–259, 266, 283, 481–483